TAKE A CHANCE

SARAH WEBB

ISIS
LARGE PRINT
Oxford

First published in Great Britain 2005
by
Macmillan,
an imprint of Pan Macmillan Ltd.

Published in Large Print 2006 by ISIS Publishing Ltd.,
7 Centremead, Osney Mead, Oxford OX2 0ES
by arrangement with
Pan Macmillan Ltd.

British Library Cataloguing in Publication Data
Webb, Sarah
    Take a chance. – Large print ed.
    1. Women singers – Fiction
    2. Sisters – Fiction
    3. Large type books
    I. Title
    823.9'2 [F]

ISBN 0–7531–7606–8 (hb)
ISBN 0–7531–7607–6 (pb)

Printed and bound in Great Britain by
T. J. International Ltd., Padstow, Cornwall

TAKE A CHANCE

To Ali Gunn and Imogen Taylor
for pointing me in the right general direction.
One day I might just get there.

"If you cannot get rid of the family skeleton,
you may as well make it dance"

GEORGE BERNARD SHAW, 1856–1950

This book is about being a sister, and I'm blessed to have two fantastic sisters of my own, Kate and Emma. Thank you both for being not only my sisters, but also my best friends. And to Mum, Dad and Richard for putting up with me.

To my own family, Ben, Sam and Amy Rose for all the love and support. And to the Cookes.

To my dear friends Andrew, Nicky and Tanya — for being there no matter what.

To Denise, best wishes on your new "voyage", and to Carolyn, a strong woman and much loved friend.

To Anne Christine Ronvel and Katarina Zemkova for looking after Amy so well. There would have been no book without your help.

To Ali Gunn, my agent, for all her hard work on my behalf. And also to Stephanie.

To all in Macmillan for making the whole book process such a pleasure, especially my editor, Imogen Taylor, a real lady and a pleasure to work with; the two Davids — North and Adamson; Trisha Jackson, Rebecca Lewis and Cormac Kinsella.

To all the Irish Girls, my partners in (writing) crime, especially Martina Devlin, for all the hand-holding and physical sustenance.

To all the booksellers who have taken a chance on me — a million thanks! I won't name you all, as I know

I'll leave someone out. Thank you for making me so welcome in your shops. A special mention to my local bookshops — the Exchange in Dalkey, and Eason and Dubray Books in Dun Laoghaire. And to the gang in Eason, shops and wholesale, for your ongoing support and kindness. And all my new friends in Dubray.

And a special mention for Maria Dickenson, a woman with impeccable taste in books, among other things.

To all my supporters in Dalkey village — Country Bake, Senso Studio and Dalkey Arts in particular.

To all in Abbasolutely, the best Abba tribute band ever, especially Eoin and the Moussoulides family — the book wouldn't have been half as authentic without your help and inspiration. All mistakes are entirely my own!

And to Abba, thank you for the music. It never fails to make me smile.

To all the readers I've met on my bookshop tours and through my website — thanks for all the encouragement, emails and kind letters. And a special thanks to Oonagh for her dedicated reading.

And to Pauline and all the girls of 6th class in St Kevin's in Kilnamanagh. Keep reading, girls!

And finally to you, the reader. I hope you enjoy *Take a Chance* as much as I enjoyed writing it. If you'd like to contact me, my email address is sarah@sarahwebb.info

CHAPTER
ONE

Waterloo

"Gemma!" Wendy Redden watched in horror as her sister lurched forward at the end of their feisty rendition of "Waterloo", ripping the seat of her snug-fitting blue satin jumpsuit in the process. Gemma landed awkwardly on her ankle, her long blonde Agnetha wig slipping down and obscuring her eyes.

"Are you all right?" Wendy asked her over the wolf whistles and applause. "What happened?"

"I'm not sure," Gemma said from her prone position, straightening her wig so she could see. "I think someone must have spilt a drink on the stage, it's wet."

"Probably champagne," Wendy muttered. "Bloody rich hooligans."

AbbaFab were singing at Saffron Wolfe-Remington's twenty-first. Saffron was a spoilt, if rather beautiful girl whose parents had more money than sense and whose "closest friends" (all three hundred of them) left a lot to be desired. The Wolfe-Remingtons' stately pile, Wolfe Castle, was in the wilds of County Wicklow.

"I'll help you." Wendy held out her hand, but when Gemma tried to move her right leg she felt a searing pain.

"I think I've done something to my ankle," Gemma said. "Can you get Ronan to lift me up?"

"I'll manage." Wendy put her hands under Gemma's armpits, took the weight in her strong arms and hoiked Gemma's body up off the wooden stage floor. Gemma put her uninjured foot down, Wendy supporting her, and straightened her knee. Then she stood upright on her left leg with Wendy's help. Her right leg was bent at the knee, her foot inches off the floor.

"Try putting some weight on it." Wendy nodded down at Gemma's rogue ankle.

Gemma put down her right foot, but winced the moment she tried to shift her balance. "Not good," she managed, her face turning pale even under the heavy stage make-up. She felt nauseous with pain. "I think it may be sprained or broken. I'd better get my boot off before it swells up."

"We'll sit you down first. Don't want you losing your balance again."

"What's happening?" Ronan asked, coming out from behind his keyboard. He was dripping with sweat and

2

his blond Benny beard glistened under the strong stage lights.

"Gemma's in trouble," Wendy said. "It's her ankle. Can you keep the audience distracted? I'll help her off the stage."

Luke, the other member of AbbaFab, came over to see what was going on. "Everything all right?" he asked.

"Keep playing," Ronan told him. "Gemma's hurt. Wendy's sorting her out."

Luke nodded and went back to strumming his electric guitar. Ronan jumped behind the keyboard and launched into playing the opening bars of "Does Your Mother Know?" with his feet and his bum, always a crowd-pleaser with that kind of audience.

"Wendy, it's fine!" Gemma protested. "I'll stay up here and sing. We only have a few more numbers to go. Put me on a chair behind the keyboard, beside Ronan, pull my boot off and hand me a microphone. I think the seam's gone in the bum of my costume again, so it's probably just as well to have me seated. Although this lot wouldn't even notice," she said, gesturing with her free hand at the audience, "they're all half cut."

"Are you serious?" Wendy said. "You want to stay on stage?"

Gemma nodded. "I'll be OK. Really. You sang through labour contractions, remember? In Bray?"

Wendy winced. "Don't remind me. We nearly didn't make it to the hospital in time. But are you sure?"

The young crowd started clapping at the end of Ronan and Luke's song, stamping their feet and shouting.

3

Gemma attempted a reassuring smile. "Yes. The show must go on and all that. Better hurry, the natives are getting restless." Luke and Ronan were now playing an ad-libbed instrumental which wasn't going down too well.

"We want more!" someone in the audience yelled out. "We want more," several voices joined in. Followed by a loud "Spit on me, Frida!"

Wendy sighed. "OK, if you're positive, Gemma. But we're never playing at a twenty-first like this again, trust me."

"Too right," Gemma said. "They're animals!"

As Wendy pulled a chair for Gemma on to the stage her mind raced. They'd played some rough gigs in their time, but this party was something else. They'd already had cold sausages thrown at them, and a leering boy with a face full of spots had grabbed her leg a few minutes earlier. She'd given him a swift kick with her white platform boot for his trouble, but he'd just laughed. She should never have agreed to let the band play. Baroness Wolfe-Remington, the matriarch who had booked AbbaFab, was just plain rude and for all the family's old money, Wolfe Castle was a rundown shambles. The young guests had been fed sandwiches and sausages instead of a proper meal, and now they were all careering around the large ballroom as the result of an excess of cheap champagne and a lack of soakage.

But there's no time for regrets, Wendy told herself, there's work to be done. She settled Gemma on to the chair, pulled her boot off carefully (Gemma had to bite on her thumb with the pain), and then took centre stage again as Ronan and Luke played the opening bars of "Super Trouper".

As Wendy waited to sing, swaying to the intro music, she suddenly realized that if Gemma really had broken her ankle — and it looked pretty likely from the swelling — AbbaFab was in serious trouble.

But what Wendy didn't realize was that her life was about to change forever.

After the gig, Baroness Wolfe-Remington tried to get Ronan and Luke to help the bouncers dismantle the stage, but Wendy was having none of it.

"Are you mad?" she exploded. "We have to get my sister to hospital. She fell on your stupid stage and I think her ankle's broken. We should sue you for personal injury."

"Sue?" The Baroness recoiled and wrinkled her nose as if "sue" was a dirty word. "It was hardly my fault."

"No? The stage was wet, Baroness."

Ronan put his hand on Wendy's arm. "We're ready. You go with Luke and Gemma. I'll travel in the van with Pat. He loaded up the lights and sound equipment with Luke and the bouncers while we were packing the costumes."

"Bless him," Wendy said. Pat was their loyal and hardworking roadie, a good man to have around in a fix. She turned back to the Baroness. "Baroness Wolfe-Remington," she said, giving the woman her

5

ridiculous full title, "I don't have time for this. We're leaving now. Please excuse me."

"You won't really sue, will you, dear?" the Baroness called after her.

Wendy ignored her. Stupid cow hadn't even asked about Gemma.

"How's Gemma?" Wendy asked Ronan as they walked out of the castle.

"She's coping. We've put her across the back seat of Luke's car. But the sooner we get her to hospital the better. I'll follow you in the van with Pat."

Wendy got into the front of Luke's car and turned her body right around to face Gemma, her knees on the seat. Gemma was still in her blue satin jumpsuit, sitting sideways across the rear passenger seat. Luke and Ronan had placed coats behind her back and had propped her right leg up with bags and rolled-up costumes. Her face looked white and drawn.

"Ready to go?" Luke asked.

"Yes," said Wendy. "How are you doing?" she asked Gemma as he started up the car.

"OK," Gemma replied.

"I still think we should have taken an ambulance." Wendy had rung St John's Hospital and they'd offered to send an ambulance, but Gemma had refused it. At least the hospital was expecting her now, though. Plus St John's had the best orthopaedic department in the country, with surgeons who worked at the weekends, which was why Wendy had chosen it and not the small, local hospital.

"It would have taken them ages to get down here," Gemma said. "It's quicker this way. And I'm OK, really I am. Stop worrying."

"I can't help it, you know what I'm like."

Gemma smiled at her sister. Wendy was a born worrier.

They went over a bump and Gemma gasped.

"Sorry, Gemma," Luke said. "I'll go a little slower. The surface of this drive is in bits."

"Thanks," Gemma said. "And Wendy, put your seat belt on, please. You're making me nervous."

"OK, OK." Wendy clicked herself in and then extended the belt so that she could still turn round. She looked at Gemma again.

"Stop staring at me!" Gemma said. The pain was starting to make her a little edgy.

"Sorry," said Wendy.

"No, I'm sorry, I didn't mean to snap."

"That's all right. I understand."

After a few minutes Gemma asked, "Do you think we should ring Mia?"

Wendy looked at her watch. "It's after one. Maybe we should leave it till the morning. Or till later in the morning — you know what I mean. There's no point waking her up. I'll ring her first thing."

"OK," Gemma said. Personally she thought Wendy was wrong — their younger sister Mia hated being left out of the loop and would be livid that they hadn't rung her. But Gemma didn't have the energy to argue. Her ankle was swelling up like a balloon and had started to throb ominously. She wished it wasn't such a long drive to the hospital.

"I'm heading on to the main Wicklow road now," Luke said, turning left. "It should be a lot smoother. We'll have you there in no time."

"Thanks," Gemma said. She lay back against the coats, staring out of the passenger window at the darkness, trying not to think about the pain.

Wendy, Luke and Ronan sat in the Accident and Emergency waiting room. They hadn't had time to change, and their Abba costumes, even with their jackets thrown over the top, had raised a few eyebrows, but they were all too tired to care. Gemma was on a trolley in one of the cubicles, waiting for a bed. A doctor had already seen her and, as she'd suspected, her ankle was badly broken. The surgeon would see her in the morning to decide what was to be done. The nurses had been amused by Gemma's blue jumpsuit, and when she'd explained had asked for a song.

"Go on, love," one of them cajoled. "Give us a few bars of 'Dancing Queen'. It's my favourite."

"Later," Gemma joked, feeling a little better due to the strong painkillers she'd been given. "Fix my ankle and then I'll give you a song."

Wendy's head was resting on Ronan's shoulder, her eyes closed. She'd gone past exhaustion at this stage.

"Are you OK, Wendy?" Ronan asked, taking one of her hands in his.

"Humm," she murmured.

Luke yawned and stretched his long white satin-covered legs out in front of him. Pat had left after dropping Ronan off, but Luke had insisted on staying to drive Ronan and Wendy home. One of the nurses had already warned them that due to the serious nature of Gemma's break, she'd have to stay in hospital for at least a couple of nights.

A nurse approached them. Ronan nudged Wendy gently and she opened her eyes and sat up. "We've found her a bed," the nurse said. "In St Patrick's Ward. We'll bring her up now. The other patients are asleep so . . ."

"We'll come back later on," Ronan said. "We don't want to disturb anyone."

"Can I just say goodbye to my sister?" Wendy asked.

"Of course," the nurse said.

"I'll go and get the car," Luke said. "I'll pick you both up outside the door."

As Wendy and Ronan walked down the brightly lit corridor after saying goodbye to Gemma, Wendy said, "Frida's mother died in a hospital, you know," referring to the dark-haired Frida Lyngstad from Abba.

"Um," Ronan grunted non-committally. He was well used to his wife's Abba obsession. And he knew better than to show any interest in what she'd just said or he'd get a ten-minute diatribe on everything from the nature of the woman's death to the colour Frida wore at the funeral. Wendy had an encyclopaedic knowledge of everything Abba had ever done, especially her idol, Frida. She'd been consumed by the band for as long as

9

he'd known her. It was sad really but, Ronan reasoned, everyone had their strange obsessions and an Abba fixation probably wasn't as bad as most.

"She was only twenty-one when she died, poor woman," Wendy continued, undaunted.

"Really?" Ronan asked, forgetting himself.

"Yes. Have I ever told you about Anni-Frid's mother and the German soldier? Tragic story. It was during the Second World War when Norway was invaded by Germany. Her mother . . ."

"There's Luke," Ronan said as they walked out the door, glad of the distraction. He'd heard the German soldier story many, many times. "Let's go home and get some sleep."

At eight o'clock that morning, after a few hours' sleep, Wendy dialled Mia's home number. As she waited for a reply, she tapped her nails on the desk in front of her. Even though it was Saturday, she'd been up since just after seven doing accounts and dealing with the email bookings, and she was already exhausted. Most of their bookings came through their impressive website www.abbafab.ie (which Wendy had designed herself) and she fielded several hundred AbbaFab emails a week.

Wendy had been managing AbbaFab and singing as Frida from the band's inception almost seven years ago. It had been Ronan who'd had the idea initially, after spotting Wendy and Gemma singing "Dancing Queen" at a karaoke pub in Blackrock called the Singing Tree. They had real stage presence and their voices meshed together perfectly. He'd been toying with the idea of putting a tribute band together and as soon as he heard the girls he knew exactly which band to replicate.

Mia wasn't answering, which wasn't unusual — it was the weekend, after all, and she wasn't exactly a morning person. She didn't own a mobile either and often let her house phone ring out, much to her sisters' annoyance. Deciding she'd try again later, Wendy clicked off the phone, rose from her chair and walked into the kitchen. Her two young sons were sitting at the table. The boys were worlds apart in both temperament and looks — Steve was a blond and stocky six-year-old with a strong personality and a fiery temper, and everyone said he was the spitting image of Wendy. Greg, a year older, had a slimmer build and dark hair and was placid by nature, more like his father.

"Hiya, Mum!" Steve said enthusiastically, his mouth crammed with cornflakes.

"Steve," she said. "What have I told you about speaking with your mouth full?"

He closed his mouth and grinned. "Oops," he said, opening it again. A stray cornflake fell on to the table.

Wendy stifled a smile. She clicked her tongue against the back of her teeth.

Steve swallowed and said, "Sorry, Mum."

She ruffled his blond head. "Try to remember." Steve nodded and resumed eating.

"And how are my two fine boys this morning? Don't answer that, Steve."

Greg looked up at her and swallowed down his own mouthful. "Mum, will you be at home this afternoon?"

11

he asked. "Can we go to the park? I want to ride my bike."

"No, sorry. But I'll get Nadia to take you instead. I have to visit Gemma. She'll be in St John's Hospital for a few days and I promised."

"Hospital, cool!" Steve said. "Can we come too?"

"No."

"What's wrong with her?" Greg asked.

"She broke her ankle last night. Someone spilt a drink on the stage and she slipped. Like that time you spilt milk all over the floor and I slipped and hurt my elbow, remember, Steve?"

"Was Gemma's leg covered in blood?" Steve asked, his eyes widening, relishing the thought. He ignored his mother's cautionary tale.

"No!" Wendy said forcefully, eager to nip Steve's morbid visualizations in the bud. He had such a well-developed blood fixation that she wondered if her firstborn had been a vampire in a former life.

Wendy looked around the kitchen. She liked to keep the house looking nice and this required constant vigilance. There was orange juice spilled on one of the kitchen counters and the fridge hadn't been closed properly. She nudged it shut with her elbow, tore a piece of kitchen paper off the roll and mopped up the juice. "Where's Nadia?" she asked.

The au pair agency still hadn't found Wendy a new girl and she was losing patience with their current "help", Nadia — a flaky nineteen-year-old from Paris who was in the habit of pursing her lips and "pahing" at the slightest provocation. Nadia hadn't quite decided whether she was staying in Ireland for two more weeks or two more years, which was most annoying and made it difficult for Wendy to plan ahead. The boys loved Nadia, of course, as she was quite happy to roll around on the floor wrestling with them, getting them all excited and out of breath.

"Dunno," Steve said with a shrug.

"She's tidying our room," Greg said.

Wendy shook her head. "She shouldn't have to do that, boys. What have I told you time and time again?"

"But she doesn't mind," Steve insisted. "She likes it."

"Unlikely," Wendy murmured, an image of their hastily discarded dirty Simpsons' socks and Man United underpants flashing through her mind. But she had too much to do this morning to worry about it.

Less than an hour later Wendy was racing around south County Dublin, trying to get all her errands run before visiting Gemma in hospital. There were two house viewings pencilled into her diary for that afternoon — a special treat: a Victorian villa in Dalkey that used to belong to a well-known Irish artist, and a three-storey red brick in Sandycove. But there was no way she'd get to them now. And it was the very last viewing of the Dalkey villa before it went to auction — damn! She did so want to see it. She had no intention of buying the properties she visited, even if she could afford any of their hefty price tags — she and Ronan were quite happy with their modern semi in Monkstown. But she was strangely addicted to viewing houses, especially period properties, picking up tips for the interior of her own home and seeing how the other half lived.

She also had to phone all her music contacts to find a short-term replacement for Gemma. Ronan was ringing round the agencies while she was out. Luckily most of them worked on Saturdays. She had already collected her new Frida wig from the costume store in Blackrock, and bought a new school jumper for Steve in Dun Laoghaire. Steve was always leaving his jumpers and coats behind him and she spent her life chasing his clothes and sewing name tags on to new ones. Now she was in the Credit Union waiting to deposit last week's payments.

As she waited in line, the tanned, blond male teller behind the counter caught her eye. He looked strangely familiar. Bert, she thought with a start. That's who he looks like, Bert from the cruise ship. Wendy put her hand on the counter beside her to steady herself. Lord, she was tired. She closed her eyes.

In a matter of seconds she was back on the *Emerald Star*, dressed in all her finery — dark pink feathered and sequinned headdress, gold-sequinned leotard that plunged rather indecently at both the back and the front, tan tights and gold high-heeled sandals — and high-kicking her way across the stage while belting out "Shall We Dance?", accompanied by four other backing dancers dressed in similar costumes but without the headdress. The feathers marked Wendy out as the principal, and on the *Emerald Star* she was *the* star of the highly regarded cabaret show, *Broadway on Board*, with its repertoire of popular songs from musicals such

14

as *South Pacific, The King and I* and *My Fair Lady* to the more modern *Grease* and *West Side Story*. The average age of the holidaymakers was sixty-seven, and their tastes tended towards the conservative. To them, *Grease* was very risqué.

Wendy had been living in London for several years, singing and dancing in various musicals, always in the chorus. When she was offered the chance to star in a show, even if it was only on a cruise ship, she jumped at the chance. At twenty-three, she already had six solid years of experience behind her and she was eager to use it.

Wendy was treated like a princess on board, eating at the captain's table and socializing with the crème de la crème, and she lapped up the attention. She worked hard — there were three shows a day for starters, not to mention the dance and singing classes she organized and taught for the on-board Active Retirement Fitness Programme. And as the star of *Broadway on Board*, she also had her pick of the co-stars, a motley crew of ex-ballet dancers, wannabe entertainers and even the odd Eurovision singer. Like Bert from Norway who had represented his country twice. At least, Bert was what everyone called him, his real name being something traditionally Nordic and completely unpronounceable. He first attracted Wendy's attention when he'd told her that his father (who worked on the oil rigs) had known Anni-Frid from Abba when they were both children. This impressed Wendy, a huge Abba fan even in her twenties, no end. Bert was an attractive man in his early thirties, a little cleaner-cut than the Irishmen she was

15

used to, with his full head of wavy blond hair and perfect rows of pearly-white teeth, honed from gnawing on raw fish in his native Norway, no doubt. He was a generous and adventurous lover, gently encouraging Wendy's burgeoning sexual confidence and delighting in her increasingly excitable libido. He'd always heard that Irish girls were shy and nervous when it came to sex, but not his Wendy. After six weeks together, they'd made love all over the boat: in her tiny cabin; in his even tinier cabin; in the cramped dressing rooms in the middle of a show; on stage, behind the curtain in the small hours of the morning — the more risky the location the better, as far as Wendy was concerned. In fact, they'd once made love on deck, Wendy conveniently "forgetting" to put any underwear on under her chiffon skirt. Late one evening they'd climbed to the deserted top deck, and while Wendy held the ship's rail and gazed out to sea, Bert had lifted her skirt above her waist, unbuttoned his jeans and entered her, making her gasp. It was all the more exciting knowing that at any second someone could happen upon them. They were almost caught — only once — when they'd shut themselves into the small cinema mid-afternoon and were interrupted by a cleaner. Luckily it was gloomy in there as the cleaner hadn't flicked all the lights on and they'd had time to scramble into their discarded clothes before she happened upon them.

Of course, the ship's entire staff and crew were well aware of Wendy and Bert's antics, but as they hadn't been caught by any of the holidaymakers they'd all turned a blind eye to their behaviour. Many of them were impressed and more than a little envious, to tell the truth, especially the men. Wendy was one popular lady. And no one was surprised when she broke up with the rather boring Bert and set her sights on the far more glamorous Captain, a fit and attractive divorced man in his early forties. Except for Bert, that was. He left the cast of the show in disgust several weeks after Wendy and the Captain had been caught in flagrante in the ship's kitchen late one night by a retired couple from the Home Counties who were looking for some milk for their cocoa. The Captain promised the couple seats at his table if they overlooked his little, ahem, indiscretion, so no harm was done.

As for the Captain, Noel Stone, there was a man . . .

Wendy heard a loud cough. "Excuse me, I think you're next," the woman behind her in the queue said kindly.

"Um, thanks." Still a little caught up in her daydream, Wendy moved forward and smiled at the young blond bank teller. "Hi," she said with a flirtatious smile.

"Good morning," he replied rather formally.

The smile dropped off Wendy's face and she came back down to earth with a bump. She passed the cheques under the glass partition. "I'd like to lodge these. Thanks."

On Wendy's way home, Gemma rang.

"Wendy, I saw the surgeon this morning and I have news."

17

"One second, I'm driving." Wendy pulled the car in. "OK, fire ahead."

"I'm going to be out of action for ages, my ankle's pretty badly broken according to the surgeon. They're operating on it late this afternoon or this evening."

"But it's June!" Wendy said in a panic. "We're wall-to-wall with weddings and summer festivals. I haven't found a replacement yet."

"I know, and I'm so sorry. I'll be in plaster up to my knee. There'll be no 'Waterlooing' for me for quite some time."

"How long exactly?"

"A couple of months at least."

"A couple of months! Poor you." Wendy's heart sank. Finding someone to replace Gemma for a week or two was one thing, but for several months . . .

"Have you tried any of the agencies yet?" Gemma asked, aware of the pressure she'd put Wendy under.

"Ronan's at home doing just that. And I haven't tried all my contacts yet. But don't you worry, we'll find someone."

"I was thinking about it this morning and I had an idea," Gemma said.

"Yes?"

"What about Mia?" There was silence on the other end of the phone. "Wendy, are you there?"

"Sorry, yes. But — Mia? Are you serious?"

"Why not? She's got a great voice. And from the sound of things, the music school's about to be sold to a developer." Mia taught the piano at the Dublin Academy of Music.

18

"I don't think she's ready for that kind of pressure," Wendy said. "She's so young."

"She's twenty-four," Gemma pointed out.

"But a very young twenty-four, you have to admit. She's not emotionally ready."

"I'm not so sure," Gemma said. "Besides, it might be good for her. It would give her confidence, stretch her a bit."

"Hum," Wendy murmured. She wasn't convinced. "I'll try the rest of my contacts and then we'll see."

"It was just a suggestion."

"I know, thanks. But you just concentrate on getting better, do you hear me?"

"I will."

Gemma said goodbye to Wendy and clicked her mobile off. Her ankle was hurting badly and she felt tired and irritable. It was broken in several places and the surgeon who'd been in to see her earlier said he was so busy he couldn't operate until after five. He warned her the moderately lengthy surgery would involve inserting a metal plate and two pins under her skin and muscle to hold the ankle joint together as the bones were badly fractured, and to tell the truth she was very nervous.

She'd had a horrid morning all in all and she felt lonely and weepy, which wasn't surprising seeing as she'd had enough painkillers pumped into her to tranquillize a baby elephant. But at least Wendy would be in later, and Mia too. And if anyone could cheer her up, her baby sister could.

CHAPTER
TWO

I Have a Dream

Mia Redden had the strangest feeling that something momentous was about to happen. She was lying on the sofa in the living room of her Monkstown flat in her pyjamas, her legs thrown over one of the sofa arms, when her body suddenly chilled and she gave an involuntary shudder. It was the very same feeling she'd had just before her mum had died. When Mia was only five, her dad, Seamus, a sales rep for a printing company, had been killed in a horrific car crash. She had only vague memories of him, mostly gleaned from old family photographs and the stories Wendy, Gemma and her mum, Miriam, had told her over the years. But she'd been a feisty fifteen when her mum had died after a second, fatal heart attack, only two days after the first.

Soon after Miriam's death, Wendy, at the tender age of twenty-nine, became Mia's legal guardian.

Miriam had never quite got around to telling her eldest daughter about her will, although she had of course meant to, and the new role had come as quite a shock to Wendy, not to mention Mia. Wendy moved back to Dublin, leaving her life on the cruise ship reluctantly behind her, and took to her new "job" with the impeccable organizational skills that she brought to everything. She threw herself into looking after Mia's practical needs from day one. It helped deaden the pain of losing Miriam. And after Wendy and Ronan's marriage, Mia had lived with them for several years until she moved into the Monkstown flat two years ago.

The phone began to ring shrilly in the hall. I was right! Mia thought. She swung her legs down and sat up poker-straight. Something *is* about to happen. She listened and waited, willing the phone to ring out. She chewed on the inside of her lip and fixed her eyes on the fireplace in front of her. Who would be ringing on a Saturday morning? It must be one of her sisters, she surmised. Something was wrong, she just knew it. The phone rang out.

What seemed like seconds later, it started to ring again. This time Mia walked into the hall, took a deep breath and picked it up.

"Yes?" she answered nervously.

"Mia, thank goodness," said Gemma. "I rang a few minutes ago, why didn't you answer?"

21

"Where are you?" Mia asked, ignoring her sister's question. She could hear voices and something rattling in the background.

"In St John's Hospital."

Mia sat down on the chair beside the hall table, her heart pounding. "I knew there was something wrong. What are you doing there? Are you OK? Has something happened to Wendy?"

"I'm fine and Wendy's fine. There's nothing to worry about, honestly," Gemma soothed, hearing the anxiety in her sister's voice. "I've broken my ankle and I'm going to be in here for a few days. They have to put a pin in it later."

Mia winced. She hated anything to do with hospitals or surgery. "That's terrible. How did it happen?"

Gemma told her the story.

"I'll come in straight away," said Mia. "You should have rung me last night."

"It was late, Mia, and we didn't want to disturb you. I'm sorry, you're right, we should have. I wasn't really thinking straight. And Wendy said it was better not to worry you."

Mia said nothing.

"Wendy tried to get you several times already this morning," Gemma continued, "but you weren't answering."

"It's Saturday morning," Mia said. "I've just got out of bed."

"Sorry. Of course. I hope I didn't wake you up."

"No, it's fine. I was up."

"Listen, Wendy's coming in early this afternoon, how about visiting later on instead, say at four? It'll be a bit less manic then and we can have a proper chat. I'd love the company to tell the truth. I'm really nervous about the operation — it's supposed to be at five but I'm sure it will be delayed. You could help take my mind off it. Any news about the music school?"

"No. Not yet. I'm expecting a phone call from the director today or tomorrow." Mia picked up a pencil from the hall table and started to doodle on the notepad beside the phone. "I was in yesterday but lots of my classes had been cancelled. I think it's a lost cause at this stage. The owners of the building are determined to develop the site. And we can't afford to relocate."

"Surely the building is listed?" Gemma exclaimed. "It's Georgian, isn't it?"

"Yes, but there are so many alterations and extensions tacked on to it that it has no architectural value any more apparently."

"So it really is closing for good?"

"It certainly looks like it."

"Oh, Mia, I'm sorry to hear that. But you'll find something else, won't you?"

"Yes, I suppose so. But I've been working there since college." Mia sighed. "It's just a bit of a shock to the system, I guess."

"I understand. Will you be OK? If you need money . . ."

"Thanks, but I'll manage. I'll find some other job to tide me over. Maybe in a café or something, I wouldn't mind that. Anyway, enough about me. Is there anything *you* need?"

"No, I'm fine. But thanks for asking."

"Are you in pain?"

"No, they're giving me something for it. I'm a little spaced out but I can't feel a thing. Listen, I'd better go, the battery on my phone's running low."

"Ring Wendy," Mia suggested. "She could bring in a recharger for you. I'm sure she has one or two lying around the house in case of emergencies. In fact, she probably has a whole rake of them carefully filed away in a box under the stairs."

Gemma laughed. "You're probably right." Her phone beeped ominously. "I really must go now. We'll talk this evening. See you later, alligator."

"In a while, crocodile."

Mia sat in the hall for several minutes, allowing her heart rate to return to normal. Gemma had given her quite a fright when she'd mentioned St John's. Mia didn't know what she'd do without Gemma and Wendy, and even the mere thought of losing either of them made her decidedly anxious. At a pinch, there was always Alva, although you never quite knew where you were with her. Alva was Mia's oldest friend; they'd been inseparable since childhood and were as close as sisters, but Alva could be a little self-absorbed at times, to put it kindly.

Eventually Mia got to her feet and walked up the three steps into her kitchen, situated at the rear of the old house, overlooking the back yard. Mia loved its lofty fourth-floor perch, from which she could see into a whole area of neighbours' back gardens. The house, divided up into four smallish flats in the Seventies, was in a slightly rundown Victorian square, and many of the other old houses, despite the paint cracking off the window frames and flaking off the exteriors, still had large, meticulously kept gardens. She flicked the red switch on the kettle and gazed out of the window at the gardens directly beneath her.

As Mia watched, a white-haired woman pulled off her gardening gloves, ran her fingers through a small green shrub and placed her hands over her face, taking in the scent. Mia smiled. Her mum used to do that. She looked away. That was twice she'd been reminded of her mum today. She concentrated on spooning instant coffee into her favourite chipped Beatrix Potter mug, poured boiling water over the granules and sat down at the table to read yesterday's copy of the *Irish Times*.

Later that day, Mia made her way along the seafront towards Monkstown train station. It was a fine evening and as she walked at a brisk pace her red leather satchel swayed jauntily from side to side on her back. Mia loved walking, which was just as well as she didn't own a car and relied on the haphazard Irish public transport system to get her around the city.

She'd found some "homemade real lemonade" in the local deli, which she happened to know was Gemma's favourite, and although the large glass bottle was rather heavy, she was lugging it, together with a new hardback crime novel, into the hospital for her sister. Gemma was an avid reader and was always complaining that her busy life didn't leave her nearly enough time to devour all the books she'd like. Gemma will have plenty of time to read now, Mia mused. Gemma liked to be busy, however much she bemoaned her time-poor lifestyle, in fact, she positively thrived on work and activity-packed days. Unlike Wendy, who was a born worrywart, she took problems and setbacks in her stride. Perhaps not ones that literally stopped her in her tracks, however. Mia wondered how her sister would cope with her ankle-imposed rest. She had a feeling that ankles took a considerable time to heal.

Mia reached the station and bought a ticket from the young (and dishevelled-looking) stationmaster, whose eyes didn't leave the soccer game playing on the portable television screen once while he served her, a feat in itself. As she clicked down the metal steps to the platform she thought about Italian policemen, dressed in their crisp white uniforms, their snug-fitting trousers ironed to perfection, a sharp, precise crease cutting down the centre of each leg, and sighed. She'd visited Rome on a school trip in fifth year and had fallen in love with the bustling, bubbling romantic city, not to mention the dark-skinned and tantalizingly (to a teenager escorted around by her teachers) out-of-reach men. There wasn't much fear of coveting the young Irish stationmaster, that was for sure, or the local Gardai, the Irish police force. Most of them seemed to be female these days, for a start.

After a few minutes a green DART train pulled into the station and Mia hopped on. The carriage was deliciously empty and she swung her rucksack off her back and sat down on a vacant seat beside the window, the bag resting on her knee. As she stared out of the window, she noticed a family on Sandymount strand. A young mother with long dark hair streaming behind her in the wind was holding a toddler by the hand, both splashing in their wellies in a puddle of seawater. A tall blond man, the dad Mia presumed, was standing beside a little boy, watching him draw on the sand with a stick. Mia looked away and stuck her head into her dog-eared paperback copy of *The Secret Garden*. She'd read it countless times, but it was one of her favourites. The words swam a little in front of her eyes at first, but she persevered and soon she was engrossed in the story.

"Gemma." Mia leaned over and gave her a kiss on the cheek. "How are you feeling? How's the ankle?"

Gemma pulled herself up in the bed and smiled warmly at her little sister. "Not too bad, thanks. I'm dreading the operation though. The surgeon has put it off until tomorrow morning as he's swamped with operations. Which gives me lots of time with you."

"Lucky me." Mia winked and smiled.

Gemma smiled back. "Less of that, Madam."

Mia sat down on the chair beside Gemma's bed. The ward was quiet, with only the gentle hum of conversation and the odd clink of water glass against vase on a bedside table breaking the silence.

"I feel like I should be whispering in here," Mia said looking around. "It's as quiet as a church." Most of the other beds were occupied by older women, many of whom were asleep.

"I know what you mean," Gemma agreed. "It's mostly hips. I feel like the baby of the ward."

"Hips?"

"The other women — hip operations."

Mia nodded. "Ah, I see. So Wendy and her gang were in earlier?"

"Just Wendy. She said the boys would be too much for the ward so she left them at home with Ronan."

Mia smiled. "She was probably right. They're not exactly shy and retiring, are they?" She pulled the book and the bottle of lemonade out of her bag. "I brought you a book, it's a new one, I hope you haven't read it. And I found this lemonade in a local shop, I know you love it."

"You are an angel." Gemma grinned at her. "Wendy brought me in some interiors magazines but they're frightfully boring." She picked up the book and studied the cover. "No, haven't read it. Excellent! Thanks."

"Let me pour you some lemonade."

"You're a star. I've run out of 7-Up — the water in here is lukewarm and tastes of plastic."

Mia handed the full glass to Gemma, who downed the tart liquid in one. "You're thirsty." Mia laughed and poured her another.

"It's always so bloody hot in hospitals. Makes you dehydrated."

"So how was Wendy?" Mia asked, putting the bottle down on the bedside table with a sharp clink and settling herself on the edge of Gemma's bed.

"Fine. As hectic as ever. She brought me a huge box of chocolates. She's trying to find a replacement for me at the moment. We have another big gig at the weekend."

Mia whistled softly. "That's not going to be easy. Has she had any luck yet?"

"No. It's a really busy time of the year for everyone." Gemma decided to bite on the bullet. "Mia, I've been thinking," she said as casually as she could manage. "*You* could take my place in the band while I'm in plaster. Actually it's quite good timing, what with the music school closing and everything. What do you think?"

Mia stared at her incredulously. "You're joking, right?"

"You'd be well able for it, Mia. You have a fantastic voice, you know you do."

Mia blew out her breath in a noisy rush. "Yeah, right."

"You do. You sang the lead in all the school musicals, remember? *Calamity Jane* and *Grease.*"

"That's different. It was a long time ago. I haven't sung in years."

"Will you just think about it?"

"Gemma, there's no way I'm singing with AbbaFab." Mia narrowed her eyes. "Anyway, what about Wendy?"

"What about her?"

"What does she think? I presume you both talked about it earlier. Does *she* want me in the band?"

Gemma hesitated for a second. A second too long.

"Wendy doesn't think I'm good enough, does she?" Mia asked astutely.

"No, it's not that," Gemma began. "She's just worried . . ."

"You're far too nice for your own good." Mia combed her long blonde hair off her face with her fingers and lifted it away from the nape of her neck. "Wendy's right, I'd be terrible. And anyway, she'll find someone to replace you eventually. She has loads of contacts in the business and she won't give up until she's found someone good."

"Mia, let me finish. Wendy's just worried that singing with AbbaFab might be too much pressure for you. Being on stage and everything. But she'll come round. I think you'd be great. Really I do. I wouldn't have suggested it otherwise. Why don't you think about it, please? Maybe the music school is closing for a reason, have you considered that? Maybe AbbaFab is your destiny."

Mia laughed. "And maybe you're out of your tiny little mind, Gemma! I think those drugs are getting to you. Now, you mentioned chocolates. Hand them over."

Gemma looked at Mia. Mia met her gaze for a moment and then looked away. Gemma sensed confusion and understood that the subject of AbbaFab was firmly closed, for the moment at least. "They're in the locker," she said instead. "Help yourself. But lay off the toffees, they're mine."

Later that evening Mia pottered around her flat, making sure everything was in its place. She moved the square red rug so that it lay against the hearthstone of the original black marble fireplace. She lifted the silver-framed photograph of AbbaFab off the mantelpiece and ran a yellow duster over the glossy stone surface. She looked at the picture as she dusted it. The group were dressed in their "Arrival" outfits — snug-fitting white flight jumpsuits — and Ronan was holding a tiny toy helicopter in the palm of his hand. She put the frame back in its place and, still staring at the photo, sat down on the sofa opposite the fireplace.

AbbaFab. The band had played such a huge part in her life for years now. When AbbaFab first formed Mia was only sixteen and still in school, her whole life stretched out before her, a blank page. At that age, joining the band was the last thing on her mind. A long time ago, before her mum died, she had dreamt of being a professional singer like Wendy. But things had changed. Now she was a music teacher and she enjoyed it most of the time. She had an ordinary life, a quiet life, unlike Gemma and Wendy. And mostly she was satisfied with her lot. So why, at this precise moment, did she feel like life was passing her by? Mia sighed. Wendy had Ronan and the boys, Gemma always had plenty of admirers and it was only a matter of time before she settled down with one of them. Where would that leave her? The spinster of the family. She winced at the word. Spinster. It sounded hopelessly old-fashioned and out of date. But that's what she would be — a spinster living all alone in a flat with her cats. She'd die alone and her cats would eat her. She shuddered. Stop being so morbid, Mia, she told herself.

She looked at the photograph again. What if she did take Gemma's place? What would happen then? For a fleeting moment she saw herself up on a stage in a white karate suit, white PVC boots up to her knees, dancing and singing "Take a Chance", her favourite Abba song, with Wendy by her side. Then she came back down to earth. She wasn't good enough, Wendy had as good as said so. There was no point even thinking about it. AbbaFab wasn't for her. Not now, not ever.

A little later that evening, Mia's phone rang.

"Mia, I've had a fight with Sean," Alva said in a rush. "Can I sleep on your sofa, just for a night or two? Please? It's an emergency."

Mia groaned inwardly. "Alva, not again. Can't you just talk to him? I'm sure it's not all that bad." Alva had a terrible temper that often whipped up out of nowhere like a desert sandstorm, and she and her long-term boyfriend, Sean, had regular fights triggered by anything from Sean's devotion to his job as an electrician, to his obsession with restoring his Victorian cottage, which had been sadly neglected by its previous owners. Alva hated spending their weekends sanding floors, filling holes and grouting tiles, but Sean loved fixing the place up, tinkering with his toolbox and making weekly visits to the local DIY store.

It was all a bit awkward for Mia, as she and Sean were also old friends; they'd been in school together and it was Mia who'd introduced Alva to Sean all those years ago. But at the end of the day, Mia's loyalty lay with Alva, although she wasn't naive enough to think that she was easy to live with, far from it. Mia didn't know how Sean put up with her at times.

Mia was quite used to her friend's frantic phone calls after an argument with Sean, so she took Alva's request with a large pinch of salt.

"It's serious this time!" Alva protested.

"I'm sure it is," Mia said calmly. It always was.

"Sean walked out yesterday morning and he hasn't come home yet."

"What?" Mia was taken aback. Sean had never stayed out all night before. "Have you tried ringing him?"

"Yes, he's not answering his mobile. I think he's switched it off."

"I see." Now Mia *was* shocked. That wasn't like Sean at all. He rarely turned his mobile phone off — to him, it was like another limb. Alva and Mia often teased him about his devotion to it. "What happened?"

"Oh, I don't know. I lost my temper with him, I guess. He's always leaving his dirty work boots in the hall, so I left them outside the back door overnight to teach him a lesson. It rained and they got wet." Alva sniffed. "It was his own fault for leaving them in the hall in the first place. And then he said he couldn't live with me any more, that I was selfish and impossible. I threw his keys at him and told him to get out if he felt like that, and so he did. But he didn't come back. What am I going to do?"

Mia could hear the anguish in her friend's voice. And then Alva began to sob. "Oh, Mia. He's gone. He's really gone. When I got home from work last night, he'd left me a note. It said to leave the house and take all my belongings with me. That it was over. Mia, how could he be so cruel?"

Mia took a deep breath. "Alva, he's just annoyed, he doesn't mean it. Pack some things and come over here. Of course you can stay."

She sighed inwardly. All in all, it was shaping up to be quite a week.

CHAPTER
THREE

Super Trouper

"Hi, Mia." Wendy was standing on Mia's doorstep at nine on the button on Monday morning. "Lovely day, isn't it?" She lifted her oversized sunglasses from her eyes and settled them on the top of her head. Even at this hour, she was perfectly made-up, her lips red and glossy, the gently blushered pink apples of her cheeks sparkling in the light.

"Wendy." Mia faltered as she opened the front door and blinked in the bright morning sunlight. "Is anything wrong? It's pretty early."

Wendy seemed a little nervous, hopping from one foot to the other as if she needed to go to the bathroom. "No, no, not at all. Can I come in?"

"Of course." Mia was still in her pyjamas. The directors of the music school had finally admitted defeat and vacated the premises after weeks of speculation: she'd received the official phone call yesterday evening. There was no question of any redundancy payments; the school had always run on a shoe-string budget, leaving its entire staff, Mia included, high and dry. Regardless of this, Mia had decided to postpone worrying about her jobless state and to make the most of her newly acquired free time by having a lazy morning, reading all the parts of the Sunday newspapers that she normally didn't have time to get round to, even the travel and sports sections.

She had promised herself that she'd start looking for a new job first thing the following morning. There were several Dublin secondary schools with well-developed music departments, she'd ring around and see if any of them needed a new music teacher. It was a long shot but it was better than doing nothing. At least it would stop her thinking about her jobless state and worrying about Alva and Sean. And it would show Wendy and Gemma that she was actively looking for work. At the end of the day, Mia knew that both her sisters were good for a loan (Gemma had already offered, after all) and this made her rather more relaxed about her precarious financial state. Alva had offered to pay rent, but Mia had refused this. After all, Alva's tenancy was only temporary, she hoped.

Mia hadn't realized quite how difficult living with someone could be, especially when that someone was Alva. She had taken over the living room with her clothes and toiletries, not to mention her shoes. It was only a fraction of her wardrobe, for which Mia was grateful, but it still took up a lot of space. Alva was incredibly messy, and quite frankly Mia had no idea how Sean had put up with it for so long. Alva never thought of tidying up after herself and was genuinely surprised when Mia pointed out that she'd dirtied every coffee mug Mia owned and hadn't once rinsed one out in the sink, let alone washed one properly. It hadn't occurred to Alva to bother — Sean always did that kind of thing in their house.

"I'm not interrupting anything, am I? Were you asleep?" Wendy said, taking in Mia's pyjamas.

Mia blushed and crossed her arms self-consciously over her chest. Her blue cotton Snoopy pyjamas had seen better days. In fact she'd owned them since she was in her early teens and it was a wonder that the threads still held together.

"Of course not, I've been up for ages. I was just about to get dressed. Come on in." She stood back from the door and led the way up the stairs and into her flat, holding her pyjama bottoms up with one hand as the elastic was shot and they had a habit of sniggling down her waist. She really would have to invest in new ones and throw these away, even if they were her favourites. As they walked into the living room she winced. "Sorry about the mess," she said. "Alva's staying with me at the moment. Sit down. Would you like some coffee?"

"No thanks, I'm fine." Wendy lifted a pair of black lacy pants off the sofa, held them up gingerly between two fingers and smiled. "Alva's, I presume."

"Just throw them on top of that pile." Mia pointed at the mound of clothes to one side of the sofa.

Wendy did as suggested, then moved the overflowing and rancid-smelling ashtray, which had been balanced dangerously on the sofa cushions, on to the floor, swatted the velvet covering with her hand to remove the stray ash and finally sat down. Mia sat opposite her on the small armchair.

"Why is she staying here?" Wendy asked. "Is Sean pulling down walls in the cottage again?"

"Something like that." Mia didn't really want to get into it at this hour of the morning. Wendy would probably try to help the rowing couple, and Mia didn't think either Alva or Sean needed any outside interference, however well intended. Besides, hopefully they'd be back together again by this evening, if they weren't already. "Can I get you anything, some coffee, a glass of water?" she asked.

"No, really. I've just had breakfast. I'm fine." Wendy smiled at her sister again, a little too brightly, Mia thought, immediately becoming suspicious. It was quite obvious that Wendy wanted something. The last time she'd arrived on the doorstep at such an early hour (with Steve and Greg in tow) she'd asked Mia to babysit the boys while she had her roots touched up in the salon in Sandycove. She was talking about AbbaFab on a daytime chat show and was convinced that the strong studio lights would illuminate the slightly darker blonde slash of her parting. The irony was that Wendy, like Mia, was a natural blonde. A slightly darker blonde than Mia, whose hair was an almost Nordic white, yet a blonde none the less. But Wendy had been highlighting it for so many years that she now felt powerless to stop the chemical enhancement.

"I was sorry to hear about the music school finally closing," she said. "There was something about it in the arts section of Saturday's *Irish Times*. I did try to ring you as soon as I read it but you weren't home." Wendy knew better than to implore Mia yet again to get a mobile phone. Mia was adamant that she didn't need one.

Mia nodded. "I was out with Alva. But thanks for trying. As you know, it's been on the cards for a while. One of the directors rang last night. They're moving out this morning. So I'm now officially out of a job."

"Will you be all right?" Wendy asked gently. "I know you'd been half expecting it, but it still must have come as a bit of a shock."

"I'll be fine. Hopefully I'll find another teaching job at a school or something. I'm going to start looking tomorrow. Otherwise . . . well, I'll just have to wait and see what comes up." She shrugged.

"If you need any money to tide you over, you only have to ask," Wendy said.

"Thanks. I appreciate that. But I'm all right for the moment." Mia paused for a moment. "But I might have to take you up on that next week if I still haven't found anything."

"Sure." Wendy seemed distracted. "Let me know how much you need."

Mia stared at her. "You're being a little odd, Wendy. What's up?"

"I guess you're wondering why I'm here so early in the morning?"

Mia nodded.

"There is something."

"You mean you didn't call in to check if I was OK about the music school business?" Mia raised her eyebrows and stifled a grin.

"Of course I did," Wendy assured her. "But there's something else."

"Yes?" Mia stared at Wendy. Surely her über-confident sister wasn't finding it difficult to ask a simple question? Mia noticed that she was clutching her hands together in her lap.

Wendy looked around the room and her eyes settled on the AbbaFab photograph on the mantelpiece. "I want to ask you a favour." She took off her wedding ring and jiggled it around in the palm of her right hand.

"Go on." Mia was more than a little curious now. It really wasn't like Wendy to be so on edge.

"I've been mulling it over and I think Gemma's right, you'd make a great Agnetha." Wendy put up her hand as Mia opened her mouth to protest. "I know Gemma already said something to you about it in the hospital, but she suggested I should talk to you about it myself."

"But . . ." Mia protested.

"Please, hear me out before you say anything. When Gemma first suggested you, I have to admit I wasn't convinced. You haven't been on stage for so long, I was worried it would all be too stressful for you. It's pretty exhausting work, to be honest, and I know you love the teaching. But I thought it over and Gemma's right, you'd be brilliant. You have an amazing voice, you know you do, and we could work on your confidence and your stage presence. With a bit of practice you'd be perfect. And it's only for a few months. You might even enjoy it, Mia. What do you say?"

"*No!* No way." Mia stared at her wide-eyed.

"Mia, please?"

"Wendy, I can't. I'm sorry. I know you're pretty desperate and you've tried all the agencies but . . ."

"Is it because I didn't ask you first," Wendy cut in, "before I tried the agencies?"

"No," Mia said. "Well, maybe a little. And maybe you're just desperate, maybe you don't *really* think I'm good enough."

"That's ridiculous, Mia. You're the best singer of the three of us, you know you are. You've got an amazing voice. I've been thinking about it a lot, Mia, and I think you're ready to perform again. And more importantly, I think you need AbbaFab as much as we need you."

"What are you talking about? I don't need AbbaFab, I'm perfectly happy without all of that glitzy stage stuff. Just because you and Gemma feel the need to be the centre of attention all the time doesn't mean that I do too. It's not genetic, you know, that need to be important, to be . . ." Mia looked at her sister's stricken face. "Ah, Wendy, I didn't mean to upset you."

"Is that what you think, that me and Gemma sing to make ourselves feel important?" Wendy asked. "Do you really believe that?"

"No, of course I don't. I don't know why I said it. I'm sorry."

"Mia, we sing because that's our job. And it pays well, far better than working in an office or singing in a chorus line, which is probably what I'd be doing otherwise. Gemma's OK, she has her Leaving Cert, but I don't even have that. I left school at seventeen to sing in that show in London, remember, *Cats*? It's not as if I'm exactly qualified to do anything else. And it means I can be around my family and not stuck on some godforsaken cruise ship half-way around the world."

Mia was taken aback. Wendy rarely lost her temper. "Wendy? Are you all right?"

"Yes, sorry, I didn't mean to raise my voice."

"And I'm sorry I said . . . you know . . . about you and Gemma. I just wasn't thinking."

"That's OK." Wendy stood up, walked towards the window and stared out at the park across the road. The wind was whipping the trees around and stray litter was swirling in the gusts. "And I'm sorry for bothering you so early in the morning." She turned back and faced Mia. "But I'm going to ask you one last time. Please, fill in for Gemma, be Agnetha. It'll only be for a few weeks and I wouldn't ask unless I really thought you could do it, Mia. And however much you protest, I think it would be the making of you. And we need you. *I* need you. Please, do it for *me*. I'm begging you."

"Wendy, you don't understand, even if I want to, I can't. I just can't physically do it. I'd freeze on stage or something and let you all down. I'm terrified of singing

42

in public now, you know I am. I haven't stepped foot on a stage since . . . you know."

"You weren't always terrified. Your confidence just took a bit of a knock when Mum died, that's all," Wendy said gently. "But you're a different person now. I'd be there to help you. And Gemma has promised to train you in herself. Plus Ronan would prompt you if you forgot any of the words. And Luke's such a gentleman, he'd take care of you too. It would be so much fun, you and me together. Please?"

"I can't. Leave it, won't you?" Mia was almost in tears. "You'll find someone else. Someone better than me."

Wendy decided to give it one last shot. "We really do need you, Mia, I'm not exaggerating. The band's in trouble otherwise. I've tried all the agencies and all my contacts, believe me. Unless we find someone by this weekend, I'll have to start cancelling gigs, word will get out and no one will book us ever again, especially not for weddings. I've already had to cancel a slot in the Olympia Theatre this week. Please? For the sake of the band. For your sisters' future?"

Mia sighed. She'd never forgive herself if AbbaFab had to break up when there was some way she could help save it. It was Wendy and Gemma's life, not to mention their livelihood, and she owed it to them. Maybe she could give it a try. She *was* out of work now, after all.

"I'll think about it," she said tentatively. "But only until Gemma gets better," she added.

Wendy jumped up and gave her a huge hug. "Oh, thank you, Mia. You've saved my life. What a relief!"

"I only said I'd think about it," Mia insisted as Wendy pulled back and kissed her on both cheeks. There were tears in her eyes.

Wendy smiled. "There's no time for thinking, Mia. First practice is tomorrow morning. Ten o'clock at my house. I'll tell Gemma — she'll be over the moon. We'll lick you into shape in no time."

"I'm not sure . . ." Mia began.

Wendy ploughed on. "And Ronan. He can accompany us and teach you some of the lyrics and routines. And I wonder if Luke's free? Actually, maybe we'll go hen at the first rehearsal, it might be less intimidating for you, Mia."

"But Wendy . . ."

"Mia," Wendy beamed, "welcome to AbbaFab. You've made me one happy sister."

That evening when Mia got back from a walk along the west pier in Dun Laoghaire, she found Alva slumped on the sofa digging a large spoon into a carton of chocolate ice cream.

"Dinner?" Mia asked, raising an eyebrow. Alva was a junk-food addict — it was amazing she maintained such a slim figure with the amount of ice cream, biscuits, cakes, hamburgers, chips and chocolate she threw into her system. Alva had some metabolism, lucky thing. She didn't believe in the gym and drove everywhere, even to the local shops. She reminded Mia of a sloth with her long, spindly limbs and her general distaste for anything that involved moving off the sofa, especially anything that smacked of healthy living or fitness. Ironically, she worked as an account manager for an Australian sportswear company called Bluewater. But for all her faults, Mia adored Alva. She had been there for her when Mia's mum died, distracting her and making her leave her room when all she wanted to do was to curl up in a ball and weep her little heart out.

Alva looked up at her. "Just a snack." She licked the spoon and put it and the empty carton down on the sofa beside her.

Mia leaned over and picked them both up wordlessly. "Do you want anything in the kitchen?" she asked.

"Just a glass of orange juice. With ice if you have it. Thanks."

"OK." Mia walked into the kitchen, rinsed the spoon in the sink, tossed it on to the draining board and put the empty ice-cream carton in the bin. She was getting a little fed up with Alva treating her like a servant. She opened the fridge. She could have sworn she'd left some lasagne on the top shelf.

"Have you seen the lasagne?" she shouted into the living room. "It was in a dish in the fridge."

"Sorry, I think I may have eaten it earlier," Alva shouted back over the excited hype of a supermarket ad on the television. "Hope you don't mind," she added.

"No, it's fine," Mia replied before sighing deeply and noisily, not that Alva could hear her over the blare of the television. She was dog-tired and Alva's company was beginning to grate on her nerves. Alva had brought her own portable television with her, knowing that

Mia's house was goggle box-free, which in Alva's humble opinion was simply unnatural. She was a big television fan and claimed she'd suffer terrible withdrawal symptoms without her daily fix of the soaps, especially *Coronation Street* and its Irish counterpart, *Fair City*. Mia also missed silence. Alva rarely turned the television off, even when having a conversation. And if she played music or the radio, it was always at top volume. At least the small kitchen was quiet, except for the gentle hum of the elderly fridge and the soft constant drip, drip of the cold tap, which no one except Ronan could ever fully turn off. Indeed the last time he'd turned it off for her he'd closed it so tightly Mia had had to borrow a wrench from one of her neighbours to turn it back on again.

"Either you ate it or you didn't," she muttered, peering into the murky depths of the fridge. If they weren't such good friends Mia would have said something, but instead she bit her tongue. She'd just have some cheese on toast instead. She searched for the lump of red Cheddar that she knew had been there last night as she'd hacked off a slice to eat with an apple, but it had disappeared, along with the entire sliced loaf. All that was left in the slightly frosty interior was a bag of decidedly brown-around-the-edges iceberg lettuce, some squashy tomatoes and a chunk of cucumber that had also seen better days. "Salad and crackers again," she murmured. "And the fridge needs to be defrosted," she added with irritation. She hated defrosting the fridge — it was such a thankless task and she always managed to get water all over the kitchen floor, no matter how carefully she covered the tiles with newspaper and kitchen roll. She looked over at the fruit bowl on the table. It hadn't been touched. "And fruit." Not that she needed to diet. Mia was blessed with great skin and a good figure — she had never dieted in her life, much to her sisters' chagrin. She seemed to be able to eat what she wanted without putting on weight, assisted by the fact that she didn't have much of a sweet tooth, unlike Gemma, or a body that constantly craved carbohydrates, like Wendy's did. Mia's favourite treat was a bowl of cashew nuts or sea-salted peanuts, a large bag of cheese and onion crisps, or if she was feeling really decadent, a tube of Pringles. None of which, however calorific, seemed to put an ounce on her.

Alva's eating habits were just plain weird. She grazed in the evenings but never seemed to eat a proper meal during the day. She also smoked like a chimney, much to Mia's annoyance. She tried to make her go outside to smoke, but Alva paid no attention to her. "You don't mind really, Mia, do you?" She'd smile and light up yet another. "Sure, didn't you used to smoke yourself?"

"Alva, I smoked for two days when I was fourteen. That hardly counts, does it?"

"Reformed smokers are always the worst," Alva replied with a smile.

Mia said nothing. Sometimes there was no talking to Alva.

Mia poured the last of the orange juice into a glass and added some ice. She'd have to go shopping again tomorrow — thanks to Alva she was out of practically everything.

She walked back into the living room and handed the glass over. Alva was watching an awful Irish teenage soap, set in a strict Catholic boys' school, called *Paddy's Place* — a peculiar hybrid of *Dawson's Creek* and *Father Ted* — and had lit up again, the blue-grey smoke wafting up towards Mia's face.

"I'm going to the supermarket tomorrow," Mia said, stepping back to avoid the fumes. "Is there anything you'd like in particular?"

Alva peeled her eyes off the screen and looked up at her. "I'll give you a list," she said. "That's what I do with Sean. I think I'm out of cleanser. Do they have Nivea in your supermarket? And I need some razors. Oh, and some shampoo."

"I meant food, Alva," Mia said, trying to remain calm.

"Sorry," Alva murmured. She fished out the remote control from the side of the sofa where it had become lodged, flicked the television off and turned her full attention to Mia. "I'm not the easiest house guest, am I?"

"You're not that bad," Mia said. Yes, you're terrible and you're driving me mad, she felt like saying but bit her lip.

"I really appreciate you letting me stay," Alva said. "I don't know what I'd do without you, Mia. I'm lucky to have you. I know that. You're so patient with me. I know I'm not the best at housework or shopping and that kind of thing. But I'll try and be more helpful. I've just been a little . . ." She shrugged and gave Mia a half-smile.

"Down?" Mia suggested kindly.

Alva nodded. After a moment she said, "I'll take you out for lunch next weekend to make up for it. What about Guilbauds?" Guilbauds was one of the most exclusive (and expensive) restaurants in Dublin and one of the few establishments in Ireland with two Michelin stars.

"It's fine, you don't need to do that," Mia protested.

"I'd like to," Alva insisted. "We could get all dolled up and drink champagne. Sean took me there for lunch on Valentine's Day last year — the food's delicious."

"It would be fun," Mia said hesitantly. "Are you sure?"

"Yes. It's a date." Alva gave what sounded like a cross between a hiccup and a sob. Tears began to well up in her eyes.

"Oh, Alva, what's wrong?"

Alva looked at Mia, large drops spilling from her eyes. "Mia, what have I done? I miss Sean so much and he hates me."

Mia sat down on the sofa beside her friend and put her arms around her. There was nothing to be said. There was no point in giving Alva false hope, after all. That would only make things worse in the long run. She knew that she had been ringing Sean several times a day, to no avail — he steadfastly refused to answer her calls. When Alva had tried ringing from different numbers he'd hung up as soon as he realized who it was. She had even called by the cottage, but Sean had left her standing on the doorstep like an idiot, ignoring her increasingly frantic raps of the doorknocker. She'd been so embarrassed when one of the neighbours had come out to see what the commotion was. Alva had murmured something about a misunderstanding and had run back to her car in mortification, tears streaming down her face.

Mia stroked Alva's hair. "You'll be OK," she soothed. "And you can stay here as long as you need to."

"Thanks, Mia," Alva sniffed. "You're so good to me. I do appreciate it. You're the best."

Mia's heart softened. What were a few dirty coffee cups between friends, after all?

Just after ten the following morning Mia found herself opening Wendy's gate and crunching up the short gravel drive. Unusually, she'd woken before six and had been unable to get back to sleep as her mind started to race with conflicting thoughts about the band. AbbaFab had played such a huge part in her life for so many years now and her secret childhood daydream of joining Wendy on stage was about to come true. But now the dream had become reality, she was terrified. Singing on a stage again — the very thought made her nauseous. Could she really do it?

Mia took in the new duo of bay trees on either side of the front door, standing straight and proud in their square terracotta pots, slightly incongruous against the white pebble-dash of the modest semi. Delusions of grandeur, Mia smiled to herself as she stroked one of the leaves between her fingers, holding her hand up to her nose and inhaling the strong, distinctive smell.

She lingered on the doorstep, dithering. Should she ring the doorbell, thus sealing her fate, or should she walk away? It was her last chance; once she'd stepped inside Wendy's house she knew there'd be no going back. She heard the crunch of gravel behind her and whipped her head around, catching a nerve in her neck in the process. "Ouch," she exclaimed, raising her hand and massaging the tender area she'd tweaked.

"Are you all right?" asked Wendy. She was standing in front of Mia, a two-litre container of milk cradled against her body like a plastic baby. She was wearing a snow-white velour tracksuit, matching white runners and her obligatory sunglasses, and she was panting a little.

"It's just my neck," Mia said. "I caught a nerve, I think. I'll be fine in a minute." She looked at Wendy. "Where were you?"

Wendy gestured at the carton. "I ran down to the shop. The boys used up all the milk making hot chocolate last night with Ronan. Made one hell of a mess too. I've told them a thousand times not to put empty cartons back in the fridge, but do they ever listen? Honestly, I'll swing for those three one of these days. Now, are you coming in?"

"Um, of course," Mia murmured. "I was just . . ."

"Good," Wendy said firmly. She pulled her keys out of a pocket and opened the door. "We have one hell of a lot of work to do if you're to be ready for the Blackrock Music Festival tomorrow evening."

"Tomorrow!" Mia's stomach lurched. "You never said anything about that yesterday. I thought the next gig was at the weekend."

"Must have forgotten," Wendy said mildly. "Sorry, I have a lot on my mind. But it's only a short set — six songs at the most. It'll be a doddle."

"Wendy!" Mia said, following her sister into the kitchen. Gemma was sitting at the kitchen table, a mug of coffee in front of her.

Gemma looked up at Mia. "Hi, Mia. How are you this morning?"

"OK," Mia said and then added, "but a little nervous."

"You'll be fine," Gemma said with a warm smile.

Mia opened her mouth to continue but Wendy leaned over her, put the carton down on the table, opened it and handed it to Gemma. Wendy was in one of her slightly manic, let's-get-everything-done-nice-and-quickly moods.

"Now you can drink your coffee," Wendy said. "If it hasn't gone cold, that is."

"You really didn't have to go out for milk, I could have had it black. It's a little lukewarm all right, but if you throw my mug into the microwave for a second it'll be fine," Gemma said.

"I most certainly will not!" Wendy protested. "It'll taste awful." She took the mug from Gemma's hand and sloshed the coffee down the sink.

"Wendy!" Gemma said, a little shocked at the waste. "There was no need for that. I wouldn't have minded, honestly."

52

Wendy made her fresh coffee in the cafetière and handed a mug to her. "I know you don't like it black. And I needed milk anyway so it was no trouble. This should be perfect."

"Thanks." Gemma sloshed milk into her mug. "What were you saying, Mia?"

"Nothing," Mia mumbled.

"Go on, tell me. What's up?" Gemma cajoled.

"Wendy's just told me about the Blackrock gig and I'm not sure about any of this, Gemma. I'll never be ready by tomorrow and I'll be useless." Mia bit her lower lip. "Can't you find someone else? Please?" She looked at Gemma beseechingly.

"You *can* do it, Mia," Gemma reassured her. "You have a great voice and once you're in costume you'll be the mighty Agnetha, not Mia at all. And Wendy will be there with you, and Ronan and Luke."

"But," Mia began. "I don't think . . ."

"Let's get started then," Wendy said firmly. She winked at Gemma who smiled back at her. They both knew that sometimes it was best to jolly Mia along. "We're wasting time, girls. You can drink your coffee in the garage, Gemma. I'll carry it in for you. Come on, Mia. We have work to do."

Wendy opened the door at one side of the kitchen and led Mia and Gemma into the garage, which was fitted out as a practice room for the band. Gemma sat down on the old, well-worn sofa, demoted years ago from Wendy's sitting room, which slouched in all its flowery finery against one of the walls. She put her crutches on the floor in front of her.

"Come on, let's get started," Wendy said, picking up two microphones and switching on the large black amplifier. She clicked the small switches on the base of each microphone and tested them both with a flick of her nail. They gave a metallic "thunk". Satisfied they were working, she lifted one to her mouth and began to sing the opening bars of "Thank You for the Music". '*I'm nothing special, in fact I'm a bit of a bore.*'"

Gemma joined in, singing loudly to compensate for the lack of amplification. "'*If I tell a joke, you've probably heard it before.*'"

"Come on Mia, next line," Wendy encouraged, handing her the other mic. "'*But I've got a talent . . .*' — go on!"

Mia took a deep breath, put her mouth up to the mic and began to sing. "'*But I've got a talent, a wonderful thing, everyone listens when I start to sing, I'm so grateful and proud. And I want to sing it out loud.*'"

Wendy and Mia sang the chorus together, Gemma dropping out this time to listen. It didn't sound half bad. As soon as they'd finished, Wendy put her arm around Mia's shoulders. "That's it, you see, you *can* do this," she whispered into Mia's hair. "You're my Little Star, don't forget that. You're going to be great." Wendy kissed the top of Mia's head tenderly. Mia felt tears prick her eyes. Her mum used to call her that — "Little Star". Wendy gave her a tight squeeze and then let go. "We're going to start with 'Waterloo', Mia, are you OK with that? Do you know the words?"

"I'd want to," Mia said, "I grew up with you and your Abba obsession, Wendy. It's part of our family's history. You told me how you used to make Abba costumes for your Sindy dolls and dress them all up as band members. You made Gemma be Bjorn and Benny, and you were Agnetha *and* Frida. And you made Mum choreograph a special dance for 'Nina, Pretty Ballerina'. And when I was three, just before you left for London you dressed me up in your old tutu and taught me the dance, remember?"

"Ah, yes." Wendy grinned. "That was a great dance. Hey, that's an idea. We could resurrect that dance. It was a mini-ballet, wasn't it?" She looked at Mia. "What do you think?"

"No." Mia frowned. "Definitely not. I refuse to wear a tutu, Wendy. It would look ridiculous."

"Quite right too," Gemma said, dragging the conversation back to safer territory. "No tutus. Speaking of costumes, what are you thinking of wearing tomorrow night?"

"The cats. The karate suits are in the dry-cleaner's until Thursday. And your blue jumpsuit will need to be, um, altered a little to fit Mia. No offence."

Gemma smiled. "None taken. I can't help it if I'm more voluptuous than my little sis, can I?" Gemma was a curvy size fourteen and proud of it.

"Cats?" Mia asked. "You mean the white dresses with the matching skirts that come off? Aren't they a bit Bucks Fizz?"

Wendy snorted. "Not at all! Abba had the idea back in 1975. They had these amazing Swedish costume designers called Owe Sandstorm and Lars . . ."

Gemma nipped Wendy in the bud. They didn't have time for her Abba stories today. "I'll pop on the Blackrock backing track," she said, crutching herself over to the stereo in the corner. "Ronan prepared it for you last night, Mia. It has the music for all six songs on it. He also printed out all the corresponding lyrics, just in case. Here." She handed Mia a sheaf of paper.

"Thanks." Mia took the pages and began flicking through them. She felt slightly better when she realized that most of the words were more than familiar to her. She just hoped she'd remember them all on stage.

Gemma pressed play on the stereo and the room was flooded with the opening bars of "Waterloo". "Wendy, you go through the movements with Mia. I'd suggest you keep them simple. Cut out the twirling bit at the middle, just do the swaying and the singing to each other. I'll watch and advise."

"OK," Wendy said, slightly miffed. She was used to giving directions, but she knew it made more sense for Gemma to watch them both and to give Mia feedback.

Mia stifled a smile and winked at Gemma. "Ready when you are, Gemma," she said. Wendy coughed. "And Wendy, of course."

By lunchtime Mia and Wendy had practised four out of the six songs, with Gemma looking on and making suggestions, and all three were ready for a break. Mia and Gemma flopped down on chairs in Wendy's kitchen and leaned over the table.

"I'm exhausted," Mia moaned. "I haven't done so much exercise in years. My legs are killing me."

"It's the dancing," Gemma commiserated. "It'll take a while to get used to it."

"I'm just popping out," Wendy said, still on her feet and glancing at her watch. "I won't be long. Make yourself something to eat, you know where everything is. We'll get going again at two if that's all right."

"Where are you off to?" Gemma asked, sitting up. "Are you collecting the boys from school?"

"No, Nadia's collecting them and taking them to the park to give us some peace," Wendy replied. "I've just got an errand to run."

"What kind of errand?" Gemma asked, her curiosity tweaked.

"I have to buy some stamps," Wendy said. "And, um, send a parcel."

"But Wendy," Mia began. "I think we need to talk about the costumes, I don't think . . ."

"Sorry, have to dash." Wendy had grabbed her bag and flown out of the house before Mia had had a chance to finish her sentence. Seconds later, they heard the sound of Wendy's car screeching away. She'd left the handbrake on again.

"Is the post office in Monkstown even open now?" Mia asked. "I thought it closed for lunch."

Gemma shrugged. "I have no idea. Who knows where she's really going?"

"What do you mean?" Mia asked.

"Nothing."

"Tell me."

Gemma lowered her voice and leaned towards Mia. "Maybe she's having an affair."

Mia's eyes widened and she gave a surprised little squeak. "You don't really think . . ."

Gemma hooted with laughter. "Of course not. I'm only joking, Mia. This *is* Wendy we're talking about. I bet she's off to some interior design shop, to order some hideously expensive curtains or cushions or something. You know Wendy. Now, let's get some lunch. I'm starving." Gemma stood up. "Wendy's fridge is usually groaning with nice things from that deli in Dalkey." She opened the tall, baby-pink Smeg fridge, which didn't exactly match the stainless-steel kitchen cupboards but was very "cutting edge" according to Wendy. Besides, it made her smile every time she looked at it, and that was enough to earn its place in her kitchen. Keeping the cupboard doors clean and smear-free, not to mention little boys' greasy fingerprints-free was a chore, but Wendy loved the lustre and gleam of the metal. Personally, Gemma thought it looked cold and uninviting. Give me good old natural wood any day, she thought to herself. But she did like the fridge.

Gemma was right, the fridge was crammed full of food. She took out some delicious-looking pâté, a generously full cheese box and some ready-made cartons of potato and pasta salad. Then she took a loaf out of the bread bin and placed it all on the table.

"Here we go," she said, placing everything on the kitchen table. "Why don't you set the table?"

"Sure," Mia said. "Will Wendy be joining us, do you think?"

"I shouldn't think so. But put a place out for her anyway, just in case."

Funny, Mia thought as she clinked the heavy, gleaming knives and forks out of the perfectly ordered cutlery drawer, I'm actually quite enjoying myself.

"What are you smiling at?" Gemma asked her.

"Nothing really," Mia said. "I'm starving too, let's eat."

"You're a funny one," Gemma said affectionately and smiled back. "Always were."

The estate agent was standing at the door of number 7 Eagle Terrace as Wendy dashed up the path. "Sorry I'm late," she said to the dark-suited woman. "The traffic was brutal."

"Not to worry," the woman said pleasantly, handing her a brochure. "It's guiding at seven hundred thousand; I'll let you have a look around at your leisure and if you have any questions just ask. The auction's on Thursday week. There's another couple here as well and two more are expected."

"Thanks." Wendy took the brochure and flicked through it. Nice big colour pictures of the newly renovated living room — excellent. She walked into the white, wooden-floored hallway. It smelt of fresh paint and there were framed prints of shells on the walls. Nice, Wendy thought, but a little bland. As she walked into the kitchen she winced as a whole rail of chrome halogen spotlights struck her in the face. She located the light switch and flicked them off. The room was immediately thrown into shadow, daylight struggling to illuminate the large open plan space. "Very little natural light, shame really," she murmured, looking around and admiring the cream cabinets and Belfast sink. There was a huge vase of lilies on the round kitchen table and a door led to a wooden-decked patio area to the left. She flicked the light switch back on and continued her rounds.

After a perfunctory look at the tasteful but safe cream bedrooms and white, fully tiled bathroom Wendy found what she'd been looking for — the living room. The room that had been featured in last week's property supplement of the *Irish Times*. It was a generously proportioned rectangular room painted an unusual shade of green; the walls had been professionally dappled with a highly specialized paint-on-damp-plaster technique that Wendy recognized from one of her interiors magazines. Must have cost them a pretty penny, she thought as she ran her finger down one of the tactile surfaces. The room was full of dark wood furniture and the two small sofas were upholstered in purple velvet and artfully finished with lime-green and raspberry-pink scatter cushions in various shapes and sizes. Those are nice, Wendy noted, picking up one of the smaller cushions and turning it over in her hands, looking for a label. There wasn't one — how disappointing. She replaced it and turned her attention to the green velvet drapes, complete with elaborate swathed pelmet. Personally I would have kept the window dressing much simpler, Wendy thought as she peered at their immaculately piped tiebacks. The curtains are just a little too much. The room had clearly been put together by an over-enthusiastic interior designer. Still, the sofas with their contrasting cushions certainly worked.

"What do you think?" the estate agent asked eagerly, as she walked through the doorway. "Need any help?"

"No," said Wendy politely. "I've seen everything I need to see. It's not quite what I'm looking for. But thank you anyway."

CHAPTER
FOUR

Summer Night City

Mia was woken on Wednesday morning by the sound of the phone ringing. "No, no, no!" she muttered, opening her eyes and sitting up quickly. She looked at the clock on her bedside table: it was just after eight and her alarm was set for a quarter past. But she resented being woken up early all the same. "Who's ringing at this hour?" She staggered to her feet, walked into the hall and whipped the phone off its cradle.

"Yes?" she answered irritably.

"Mia?"

"Hi, Sean," she said, recognizing his voice instantly. "What's up?" She didn't have time to mess around; Wendy and Gemma were expecting her at nine for a costume fitting and final rehearsal before the music festival that evening.

"You sound a bit groggy," Sean commented.

Not surprising as I've just been woken up by the bloody phone, Mia felt like snapping, but it wasn't Sean's fault that she'd had such a bad night's sleep, and it wasn't all *that* early after all. "To be honest, I didn't sleep very well," she admitted. "I have to sing with AbbaFab later and I'm a little nervous. Actually I'm terrified. I had this really bad nightmare last night — a taxi driver had locked me into his cab and he wouldn't let me out until I'd recited all the lyrics to 'Knowing Me, Knowing You' backwards. It was very scary."

"Sounds it. But what's all this about AbbaFab? It's news to me. When did you join?"

"Only yesterday. Did Alva not tell you about Gemma's accident?" Mia asked without thinking.

There was a deathly silence on the other end of the line.

"Sorry," Mia said, berating herself. "I forgot. But while I have you on the phone, what *are* you thinking of? Alva's in bits, Sean. Why won't you talk to her? It's not like you."

"Ah, Mia, I don't know what's going on in my head to tell the truth. I'm not proud of my behaviour, but I don't know what else to do. Listen, I really need to talk to you. Are you free for lunch?"

"Oh, Sean, I'm hideously busy today. I'm sorry, but lunch is out. How about sometime tomorrow? I'm supposed to be at Wendy's in half an hour so I can't really talk now. But I do think you should ring Alva."

"Tomorrow is fine," he said, ignoring her comment about Alva. "I'll survive until then. I'll give you a ring in the morning to arrange a time."

"And how are *you*?" Mia asked, feeling a little guilty for being so abrupt with him.

"Not too bad in the circumstances," he said.

This annoyed Mia. He *had* walked out on Alva after all. "Sean, I don't want to take sides or anything and I know you're probably upset too, but Alva is *very* upset. Please, return her calls; at least let her know you're all right. She cried herself to sleep last night." Mia bit her lip. Damn, she thought, I shouldn't have said that. Alva will kill me.

Another deathly silence.

"Sean?" Mia asked. "Are you still there?"

"Yes," Sean answered tightly. "And you're right — I should talk to Alva, I know. I just don't know what to say to her. It's all such a mess."

"Are you sure you're all right?" Mia asked gently. He sounded very despondent.

"I miss her so much," he said in a rush. "I love her, Mia, really I do — I just can't live with her. She's impossible at times."

"I know what you mean," Mia said before she could help herself.

Sean snorted. "Helping around the house, is she?"

"She's not the worst," Mia insisted, back-pedalling furiously. "She's taking me out at the weekend. To Guilbauds no less. *And* she went to the supermarket with me yesterday."

"Really? Food shopping?"

"Yes."

"Well, there's a first."

"Alva has a good heart," Mia said. "Can't you just talk to each other? Work things out?"

"But, Mia, I've met someone else," Sean blurted out.

"*What?*" Mia demanded incredulously. "Already? You're joking?"

"No. She's called Sadie. I rewired her house a few months back and we kept in touch. Nothing's happened yet, but we have a date on Saturday night."

"A date? Sean, are you mad? What about Alva?"

"I don't know, Mia. I'm just trying to get on with my life. Sadie thinks . . ."

"Please don't tell me you've been talking to *her* about all of this?"

"But she's been very helpful."

"I'm sure she has," Mia muttered darkly. Any woman who muscled in on another woman's territory was bad news in her book, very bad news. Mia glanced at her watch. She wanted to hear more about this Sadie woman, but she really had to go or she'd be very late and Wendy was a stickler for punctuality. "Sean, I'll talk to you about this tomorrow. I'm sorry, I must dash or I'll be late for band practice."

"Just one last thing," Sean added. "Please don't tell Alva about Sadie."

"What do you take me for? Of course I won't! I'll leave that to you. I'll see you tomorrow, we can talk more then."

"Thanks, Mia. See you tomorrow."

"Damn, damn, damn," Mia swore as she ran into the bathroom and turned on the shower. She didn't have time for one, but she needed to freshen up as she'd be trying on costumes this morning. She stepped into the shower cubicle and winced as she felt something cold and slimy under her left foot. She looked down. A soapy, matted loop of dark hair peeped out from under her toes. "Yuck!" She reached down, picked it up between her fingers, opened the shower door and threw it into the sink. "Oh, Alva!" she sighed.

Wendy and Gemma stood back and looked Mia up and down.

"The skirt needs to come in a good bit," Gemma commented. "It's practically a hipster at the moment."

"And I might put a couple of tucks into the top," Wendy mused. She walked towards Mia and took a clump of white satin in her hands, pulling in the back of the top.

"That's better," Gemma said. "Shows off her figure."

"Hello," Mia said, waving both her hands in the air. "I am here, you know."

"Sorry, Mia." Wendy took her hands away and lifted a white-blonde wig off the sofa. "It seems a shame to cover up your own hair, it's the perfect colour for Agnetha. But if you don't wear this, the rest of us will look wrong. It'll look like our heads are much bigger than yours." She handed Mia the wig. "Try it on for size."

Mia put the wig down for a moment, twisted her own hair into a roll and then slipped the wig over her head. Wendy tucked some stray strands of Mia's real hair under the wig and then smiled. "It suits you. What do you think, Gemma?"

Before she had a chance to answer, Ronan and Luke crashed through the door carrying a large silver flight box, which held the heavy stage spotlights.

"Sorry, ladies," Luke said with a grin. "Hope we're not interrupting anything?"

"Mia's just trying on her costume for tonight," Wendy said. "What do you think?"

Luke wolf-whistled. "Looking good, Mia. The skirt's a bit long though, you can't see the boots properly. We need to see more leg."

Mia blushed, then pulled the wig off her head and handed it to Wendy. "I'll just go and change," she mumbled, brushing past Luke and Ronan.

"Was it something I said?" Luke asked Wendy.

"She's just nervous," Wendy said, putting the wig down on the sofa. "I'll go after her. You guys stay here."

"I'm sorry," Luke said, "I didn't mean anything by it, really I didn't."

"Don't worry, Luke," Gemma said. "Mia's just a little sensitive sometimes."

"Luke, stop standing around gabbing and put the box down," Ronan said, puffing under the weight.

"Sorry, boss," Luke said. He turned towards Gemma again. "Was it the leg thing — saying we needed to see more leg? Did she think I was, you know, flirting with her?"

Gemma gave a laugh. "Luke, stop worrying. Mia's fine. Wendy's right, she's nervous."

"So what's the plan for the afternoon?" Ronan asked. "Wendy asked us to meet her here."

"Confidence building," Gemma said glancing at the doorway to make sure Mia wasn't on her way back in.

"Got it," Ronan said. "We're all yours."

"Mia has no reason to worry. She looks a million dollars in that costume," Luke said. "As far as the audience is concerned she doesn't even have to sing a note. She could mime all night and they'd be perfectly happy. Actually that's not a bad idea. Why don't we get Mia to mime the songs?"

"The men might be happy with that," Gemma said dryly. "But the women might not be so amused. Abba songs are sacrosanct to women, you must know that by now. And delivery is everything. Miming just won't cut it."

"But can Mia actually sing?" he asked.

Gemma winced and shook her head. Luke followed her gaze to the doorway. Mia was standing there, fixed to the spot. She felt their eyes resting on her and she turned on her heels and ran straight into Wendy.

"Mia!" Wendy said. "You nearly winded me. What's wrong?"

"I can't do this!" Mia cried. She ran past Wendy up the stairs and locked herself in the bathroom.

"What happened?" Wendy asked, looking at Ronan. "Did you go and say something?"

"Don't look at me like that," Ronan said. "I didn't say a word."

"It was me," Luke said sheepishly. "I was just asking Gemma if Mia could actually sing, and Mia overheard me. I'm sorry. I should have kept my big mouth shut."

Wendy strode towards the tape recorder in the corner and pressed rewind and then play. She turned the volume up. "Listen!" she commanded. "I was taping her earlier."

Mia's voice rang out clear and sweet.

"I asked her to sing 'Dancing Queen' on her own so that I could listen. She had no idea I was taping her."

"Wow, that's some voice," Luke said. "I feel like such an idiot."

Wendy said nothing. She was annoyed with him for upsetting Mia, but there was no point in making him feel any worse than he already did.

"Can I borrow the tape recorder?" Luke said. "I have an idea." He turned it off and unplugged it before Wendy had a chance to protest. "Back in a second," he said. He strode out of the practice room through the kitchen into the hall, then popped his head around the living-room door.

Greg and Steve looked up from the table against the window where they had been doing their homework under Nadia's supervision.

"Have you seen Mia, lads?" Luke asked.

"No," Steve said. "But I heard someone go upstairs. Will I help you look for her?" he asked eagerly.

"Not at all, you stay there and do your homework like a good chap," Luke said.

Steve groaned. "Great."

Nadia shushed him.

Luke walked out of the door and bounded up the stairs. Seeing the bathroom door closed in front of him, he rapped on it with his knuckle. "Mia, are you in there?"

No answer.

He rapped again and tried the door. It was locked.

"Mia, listen, I'm sorry about all that business downstairs. I'm always putting my foot in it. I know you're probably feeling a little nervous right now and I'm sure I didn't help matters. But you have an amazing voice. Really. And I'm not just saying that. Every bit as good as your sisters'." He thought it better not to say "Even better than your sisters" just in case he was overheard again.

"How can you say that?" Mia said through the door, incised by his audacity. "You've never even heard me sing."

"Oh yes I have." Luke found a socket and plugged in the tape recorder. He pressed play and sat down on the carpet outside the door. Mia's voice rang out, pitch perfect.

After a few minutes Mia unbolted the door, opened it and stepped out. Her eyes were a little red but there was a shy smile lingering on her lips. "Is that me?" she asked.

Luke nodded. "Agnetha Faltskog, eat your heart out. Are you coming back downstairs?"

Mia looked down at him. "Yes," she said in a small voice.

He jumped to his feet and grinned at her. "Great."

Mia noticed the tiny wrinkles fanning the outer edges of his eyes when he smiled. She looked away quickly, embarrassed to be caught staring at him. But he didn't seem to notice.

The rest of the afternoon passed in a whirlwind of "Mamma Mias", "Super Troupers" and "Fernandos", and Mia was quite worn out by the end of it; worn out but excited. It was as if someone had discovered the loose end of the little ball of hope she'd kept buried in her heart for all this time, had given it a gentle tug and was slowly unravelling it. A scary feeling, Mia thought, scary yet exhilarating, and she felt more alive than she'd felt in a long, long time.

After a swift bite to eat in Wendy's kitchen, Ronan and Luke left in Luke's car. The three sisters piled into Wendy's car and, after screeching off the driveway ("Handbrake, Wendy!"), arrived in Blackrock just after five.

"What time are we on stage again?" Mia asked nervously.

"Seven," Wendy said. It was the third time Mia had asked her in the last hour. "I know we're a bit early, but we're on first and I want to make sure that everything's in order. The stage, lights, sound, that kind of thing," she added for Mia's benefit.

"And it usually takes at least an hour to wangle a cheque out of the organizers," Gemma said with a grin. "Money up front is the only way to go, isn't it, Wendy? Wendy's great at getting them to pay up."

"Years of practice." Wendy laughed. "Debt collection isn't exactly one of my favourite jobs. But as Gemma so rightly pointed out, it's always best to get paid up front. Here we are."

Wendy pulled into the Frascati Centre car park and drove the car head first into a parking space (she found manoeuvring into the tight spaces in the Blackrock Shopping Centre car park difficult and had scraped her car on the huge concrete pillars more than once). The music festival was being held in a large marquee in Blackrock Park, and Mia's hands had been shaking through the entire car journey at the mere thought of it.

Mia stepped out of the car and held her hand out to Gemma. "Here you go, Gemma," she said, pulling her sister out of the car. Gemma rested her body against it while Mia retrieved her crutches. "Here," Mia said, handing them over. "I'll hold them while you put your arms in."

"Thanks." Gemma smiled gratefully. "I feel like such an invalid these days." When she was sorted, she leaned over towards Mia. "Do you think we'd have time to have a quick look around the shops?"

Mia looked at Wendy who was pulling bags out of the boot and muttering to herself. Wendy seemed a little frazzled.

"I wouldn't say so," Mia said.

"What was that?" Wendy asked, looking over at Mia. "Did you say something to me?"

"Nothing," Mia said. "Can I give you a hand, Wendy?"

"Please." Wendy lifted the plastic-covered costumes out and placed them on the top of the car. The edges of the thin, clear plastic fluttered in the breeze and Mia shivered as she surveyed the cat outfits underneath their flimsy see-through coverings. Suddenly she felt her face blanch and she felt terribly queasy, as if her stomach was turning elaborate somersaults.

"Are you all right, Mia?" Gemma asked with concern. "You've gone very pale."

Mia gulped. "Um, I'm fine. I just feel a little . . ."

At that moment she felt her blood rushing to her head with all the force of a tidal wave and her legs went from under her. "Mia!" she heard Gemma cry out. "Wendy, Wendy, help!" and then — nothing.

Moments later Mia opened her eyes. She was lying on the tarmac beside Wendy's car and her left arm hurt dreadfully. Wendy and Gemma were crouched over her, Wendy holding Mia's head gently in her cupped hands.

"Mia?" Wendy asked with concern. "Can you talk?"

"Where am I?" Mia said. "What happened?" She felt extremely cold and her whole body was shaking.

"You fainted, Mia," Gemma explained. "Wendy managed to catch you, but you landed a little awkwardly on your arm."

"I'm sorry, I should have moved quicker," Wendy said.

"Wendy, Flo Jo herself couldn't have moved any faster," Gemma insisted. "You did brilliantly. I was no help. Bloody cast."

"I need to . . ." Mia pushed her upper body up with her hands.

"You should stay lying down," Wendy said firmly. "You need to get the blood back to your head, that's what you need." Mia put her head down again and allowed it to rest in Wendy's warm, firm hands.

"You used to faint a lot when you were younger." Gemma smiled down at her. "Remember that time in school? You passed out in Assembly and they let Alva bring you home in a taxi as Mum was in Wexford at a funeral."

"And we spent the whole day watching really bad daytime television," Mia said. "And Alva made me drink a whole bottle of Lucozade. She said it would be good for my blood-sugar levels." She laughed. "That was a really good day. And no, we didn't feel a bit guilty about missing school, before you ask, Wendy."

"I wasn't going to," Wendy said, although the thought had crossed her mind. "Gemma, do you think you could pass me something soft for Mia's head? I'd better ring Ronan and let him know what's happened. He'll be wondering where we've got to."

"And you should ring the organizer of the festival, Wendy," Gemma suggested.

Wendy looked at her. "Why?"

"To cancel."

Wendy said nothing for a moment. "Cancel? Do you think?"

Gemma stared at her. "Of course. Mia was unconscious a few minutes ago. What are you thinking of, Wendy?"

74

"I'm starting to feel a lot better," Mia protested from her supine position. "I can do it. There's really no need to cancel on my account."

"We're cancelling and that's that," Gemma said firmly.

"Now wait a second," Wendy snapped. "I make the decisions around here when it comes to the band, Gemma. Or have you forgotten that?"

Gemma glared at Wendy. "But Mia's still my sister. You can't be serious about making her sing."

Mia sat up and leaned back against the car.

"Mia!" Wendy said, but her sister ignored her.

"No one's making me do anything," Mia said. "I'm singing and that's final. I'm all psyched up, so I may as well get it over with. Now, I'd like some water, please. Is there any in the car, Wendy?"

"No. Sorry, I'll go and buy some," Wendy said. "Wait here." She flashed Gemma a look and then strode off in search of a shop.

"You shouldn't let Wendy bully you like that," Gemma said as soon as Wendy was out of earshot.

"She wasn't bullying me."

"Yes she was and you know it."

"I don't want to argue with you, Gemma. I *have* to sing this evening, don't you see? If I don't, I'll be even more nervous by Saturday for the wedding. And besides, I can't let everyone down."

"Let Wendy down, you mean?" Gemma said gently.

"I suppose so."

Gemma sighed. "Mia, are you sure you're up to it?"

"Positive. I fainted, that's all. And my arm seems OK." She moved it gingerly. "It's just bruised, I think. Please, no more arguing with Wendy, OK?"

"OK. And Mia?"

"Yes?"

"You really have nothing to worry about, you'll be great."

"Thanks."

"And I'll be right there in the wings, watching your every move. If you feel in the least bit faint or queasy just wave at me and I'll make sure Wendy stops the show. Understand?"

Mia nodded. "Thanks, Gemma," she said. "But I hope I won't need to."

"But I'll be there for you, just in case."

Mia smiled. "Thanks. Now, here's Wendy, and it looks like, yes, an entire fridgeload of water."

Gemma looked over at Wendy who was fast approaching, cradling five bottles of water in her arms, and began to laugh. "Hey, Wendy," she said loudly. "Expecting a drought?"

"Ha, bloody ha," Wendy replied. She dumped her load into the boot of the car. The bottles rolled towards the back of the almost empty boot, following the natural slope. "I'm sorry for snapping at you, Gemma, I'm just tired. I don't know what came over me. And you're right, what was I thinking? Mia's not well. I'll cancel the gig immediately."

"You'll do no such thing," Mia said. "Now, stop it, the pair of you, I'm fine. I'd just like some water. What have you got there, Wendy?"

"Sparkling, still, oxygen-enhanced, lemon-flavoured and orange-flavoured. What would you like?"

"Just plain still," Mia said. "Sparkling gives me hiccups."

Wendy fished out a bottle, opened the cap and handed it to her sister. "Take your time, Mia. Don't bolt it down."

Mia took a long swig of the deliciously cool liquid, droplets escaping from her mouth and running down the sides of her face like two tiny streams.

"Mia!" Wendy exclaimed. "Take it easy."

"What?" Mia said. "I'm thirsty."

"She's grand, Wendy," Gemma said. "I think we should both stop fussing over her. Is that Ronan?" She pointed to the far side of the road.

"Yes." Wendy began to wave at him frantically to catch his attention. "Cooee!" she called. "Over here!"

Ronan looked over, waved back, and crossed the road, jaywalking rather dangerously between the cars. Luke followed closely behind.

"Are you all right, Mia?" Ronan asked as soon as he reached them. Mia was still sitting on the ground, her back against Wendy's car.

"Fine," Mia insisted. "It's nothing to worry about, really. I just fainted."

"Wendy rang me a minute ago. She was really worried about you," Ronan said, looking at Wendy. "She blames herself for pushing you so hard at practice this afternoon. She's feeling very guilty."

Gemma and Mia looked at each other and then at Wendy. "Really?" Gemma asked. Wendy was always a worrier, but today she seemed to be even more stressed out than usual. "It's not your fault, Wendy," Mia said. "Honestly. There's no need to feel bad. Like Gemma said, I'm prone to fainting. I just haven't done it for a while."

"I suppose you're right," Wendy said. "But I still shouldn't have pushed you so hard."

"As I keep telling you," Mia said, "I'm fine."

"If you're sure," Wendy said, "I guess we'd better start getting organized. Ronan, can you help Mia up and keep an eye on her? And, Luke, would you mind carrying our costumes and bags over to the changing area? I believe there's a caravan in the park for us to use as a changing room."

"A caravan?" Luke whistled. "A whole caravan for the four of us? How posh can you get!"

"Don't be so sarcastic!" Wendy said, trying not to laugh. "It's better than a tent."

"Or the back of the van," Ronan pointed out.

"True." Luke smiled. "Such a glamorous life we all lead, eh?"

"Too right, mate!" Ronan snorted.

At half past six, Mia was still sitting in the caravan staring at her rather paler than usual face in Wendy's large portable mirror. Wendy and Ronan had finished their own stage make-up and were helping Pat with the sound check. It would only take them a few minutes to pull on their costumes, they told Mia, so she should stay in the caravan and have a rest. Gemma was reading the crime novel that Mia had given her in the hospital and Luke was keying a long text message into his mobile phone.

"Writing an essay?" Gemma said archly, looking up from her book. The electronic pips were starting to irritate her, making it difficult to concentrate on the plot. She was finding her leg plaster more and more irritating, curtailing all her usual activities and making her unusually crotchety. How she longed to be able to drive once more, walk to the shops, or even walk down the stairs unhampered. Gemma promised herself that she'd never take the simple everyday things for granted again once she was mobile.

"No," Luke said mildly and resumed his texting.

"Who are you texting?" Gemma asked, ever curious.

Mia looked over and smiled at Luke. "Pay no attention to my nosy sister," she said.

"I'm quite used to her," Luke said. "It's hard to keep any secrets when she's around. Besides, AbbaFab are like one big, happy family. Isn't that right, Gemma?"

"Absolutely! Or should I say Abbasolutely."

Mia and Luke laughed.

"So, go on," Gemma continued, "who's the lucky girl?"

"I'm sending my mother a birthday message if you must know," he answered patiently.

Gemma snorted. "You expect me to believe that? Who's the latest? Go on, spill the beans."

"Gemma, I don't have a girlfriend at present, as well you know. But as soon as the future Mrs Jackman comes along you'll be the first to meet her, I promise." He looked over at Mia and smiled. "See what I have to put up with, Mia? I have absolutely no private life. And as for my text, I'll prove it to you, Gemma." He handed Mia his mobile phone. "Would you mind reading the message out loud for your sister, Mia?" he said rather smugly.

"*Hi Mum,*" Mia read from the screen of his mobile. "*Will ring later. Hope U R having a lovely birthday. Will call in at weekend with present. Have a great dinner this eve — know Mona is taking you out. Best and much love, Lukey.*"

"Lukey!" Gemma laughed. "I've heard it all now. But I stand corrected. My apologies, Luke. Your reputation is safe for the moment. But Lukey, really!"

"Thank you, Gemma," Luke said. "And what does your mum call *you* then? I'm sure you have a nickname." Luke's smile dropped off his mouth quickly when he realized what he'd just said. "Sorry," he murmured.

"It's fine," Gemma said evenly. "And Mum used to call me Charlie if you must know," she remembered. "Charlie the Clown, as I always made her laugh. Wendy was Super Star, she was terribly bossy as a child and always wanted to be on the stage."

Luke laughed. "No, I can't see that at all."

"And Mia . . ." Gemma looked over at Mia who was listening with interest.

"I was Little Star," Mia said softly.

"Yes, you were." Gemma smiled at her. "Mum's Little Star. Mum used to say that Mia had the voice of an angel."

Mia stared at her hands. They didn't talk about Miriam very often, especially in front of others, and she wasn't all that comfortable with the conversation.

"Your mum obviously spotted your potential from an early age, Mia," Luke said kindly. "I like that — Little Star. And speaking of stars, you'd better get changed, Mia, or there'll be no Agnetha on the stage this evening." He studied her face. "Um, have you started your make-up?"

She laughed. "No. Don't worry, I'll get cracking."

"Phew," he breathed a sigh of relief. "I didn't want to put my foot in it again, but you don't exactly look ready. Trowel on some sparkly blue eye shadow and some false eyelashes, there's a girl, and you'll be laughing."

"I'll have a go."

"Why don't I do it for you?" Gemma suggested. She sat up straighter. "It'll make me feel useful."

"Will you do mine too?" Luke asked, lifting one eyebrow suggestively.

"I will not, you big fool." She swatted him on the leg. "Go and do your own."

"Charming," Luke complained, a smile on his face. "See what I have to put up with, Mia?"

"Terrible, isn't she?" Mia agreed.

"You'd better be nice to me or I'll give you an Ugly Sister of a make-up job, Mia," Gemma warned.

"But wonderful at the same time," Mia corrected herself with a grin.

Luke winked at her and Mia felt the strangest sensation in the pit of her stomach. She smiled to herself.

"You're always smiling at some private joke or other, Mia Redden," Gemma said as she dabbed some creamy foundation on to a make-up sponge. Luke had gone into the small caravan bedroom to change. "I often wonder what's going on in that strange little head of yours."

"Not much really," Mia lied. "Nothing very interesting anyway."

"Humm," Gemma murmured. She wasn't so sure. But Mia had always kept herself to herself and she knew she'd get nothing more out of her, especially with Luke practically in the same room.

"He's nice, isn't he?" Mia whispered as Gemma carefully applied Mia's black spider-like false eyelashes.

"Yes, very," Gemma whispered back, "but don't go getting any ideas. He's much older than you are."

"He doesn't look all that old. What age is he?"

"Twenty-eight, I think, or maybe twenty-nine, I can't quite remember."

"Only four years older than me," Mia pointed out.

Gemma said nothing.

"But he'd have no interest in someone like me," Mia continued, fishing. "I'm sure his girlfriends are all very glamorous."

"Humm," Gemma murmured non-committally.

"What was his last girlfriend like?" Mia asked.

"Mia! He's in the next room and the walls are paper-thin. He'll hear us talking about him."

"Not if we keep whispering," Mia said, lowering her voice. "Go on, what was she like?"

"She was a nurse, if you must know."

"A nurse? Really?"

"Now, you're going to have to keep your lips still while I do your lip-liner. So no more talking, understand? And don't distract me while I finish your false eyelashes either unless you want glue in your eye."

"OK," Mia said, "my lips are sealed. But just one more question. When did they break up?"

"Mia!" Gemma hissed.

Mia cocked her head to one side and gave Gemma one of her Bambi looks.

Gemma gave a tut. "OK, but this is the last question I'm answering, I mean it."

"Well? Go on then, when?" Mia asked again.

"Ages ago, before Christmas. Satisfied?"

"Very." Mia sat back in her chair and closed her mouth. But there was no disguising the smile playing on her lips.

Gemma sighed inwardly. Mia was very naive when it came to men and she didn't want to see her get hurt. Mia had had a serious boyfriend in college, a kind, rather gentle French boy called Yves, but it had all ended in tears when he'd gone back to Paris after graduation. As Gemma pressed the false lashes gently against her sister's eyelids, waiting for the glue to take effect, she told herself there was no point worrying about something that hadn't happened yet. Mia was right — she was hardly Luke's type after all. She'd talk to Wendy about Mia and her crush later, Gemma decided. Maybe Wendy could have a word with Luke. Warn him off. It couldn't hurt.

Mia stood at the back of the large marquee and studied the stage in front of her. It had been constructed from matt grey scaffolding and worn-looking wooden planks and boards, and Mia wondered if it would take their combined weights. They'd given it a brief trial run earlier, but that was without the strains of an hour's worth of moving and dancing to contend with. Mia also hoped her costume didn't rip at the seams. Wendy had made it a little too snug for Mia's liking. And what if she forgot the words of the songs? Or the dance moves? And what if she fainted again? Mia bit her lower lip anxiously. She could both smell and taste the sickly-sweet strawberry lip-gloss that Gemma had doctored her pout with. Mia ran her finger over her top teeth, removing a bright pink gloop of gloss. Great, now I'm going to get gloss all over my white costume, she thought. She wiped the pink residue on to the back of her hand and rubbed it into her skin. It made her hand glisten and she held it up to the light and stared at it.

Luke looked over at her and smiled warmly. His dark blue eyes twinkled in the dim light. Even dressed as Bjorn, in his stage make-up, wig and white jumpsuit, he was a sight for sore eyes. Mia could feel herself blush and thanked Gemma for the heavy stage foundation, concealing her discomfort.

"OK?" Luke whispered.

She nodded. "Think so," she whispered back.

"You'll be great," he said. "Chin up."

"Thanks." He really was nice, Mia thought, smiling to herself again.

The band was waiting backstage listening to the Mayor of Dublin's preamble to an opening speech. The marquee was heaving with bodies — the band had all had a peek several minutes earlier — and the excitement in the air was palpable. AbbaFab were the first band on that evening, and the whole Blackrock Music Festival seemed to have caught the attention of the punters and the local and national media alike. The Mayor was currently talking about Blackrock and its place on the music map, citing south County Dublin luminaries from Bob Geldof and Bono to Sinead O'Connor.

"Get on with the music," a member of the audience shouted up at him rather rudely. The crowd clapped and cheered in agreement.

"Right, I will," the Mayor retorted, nonplussed. "And now, to get the evening off to a stellar start, I have the great honour of introducing one of the most popular tribute bands in Ireland, the great, the amazing AbbaFab!" The atmospheric "Arrival" music began to drift from the huge speakers on either side of the stage.

Wendy put her hand on Mia's shoulder and squeezed it. "Here we go. Break a leg," she said softly.

Mia nodded wordlessly, gulping back her fear.

Wendy led the band on to the stage. "Hello, Blackrock," she said in her mock-Swedish accent. "I'm Frida, this is Agnetha, Benny and Bjorn, and together we're AbbaFab." Ronan and Luke went straight into the opening bars of "Waterloo", Luke as Bjorn on lead guitar, and Ronan as Benny on keyboards. The crowd cheered. Mia opened her mouth to sing the first line but no sound came out. Wendy, sensing that something like this might happen, was well ahead of her and also kept silent. Ronan and Luke played on as if nothing had happened, embellishing and extending the opening riffs.

Mia looked out into the sea of faces and then back at Wendy. Wendy smiled at her, her eyes twinkling. "You can do this," she mouthed. "Sing." In the left wing, Mia could see Gemma, whose eyes were glued on her supportively as she gave her a thumbs-up sign. Mia took a deep breath. She had two choices here — she could either sink or swim. And she was damned if she was going to let Wendy and the others down. You can do this, she told herself in Wendy's words, gripping the microphone tightly in her right hand and concentrating on the music. *I* can do this. There was the cue — she opened her mouth and no one was more surprised than Mia at the strength and bell-like clarity of her voice as she sang the first line. Wendy joined in for the second line and the crowd whooped and clapped. By the first chorus, Mia realized that she was operating on autopilot and she wondered why she'd been so nervous. Singing the wonderfully upbeat Abba pop songs, songs she remembered so fondly from her youth, wasn't a chore, it was fun. She turned to the crowd and wiggled her bottom.

Wendy gasped. Gemma cheered Mia on in the wings. Was that really her little sister playing to the audience?

Ronan raised both his eyebrows at Luke. Luke leaned in towards Mia as the last strains of the song filtered out and the crowd began to clap and cheer wildly. "Well done, Little Star," he said warmly. No one except Wendy, Gemma and her mum had ever called her that, but after a moment Mia decided that she quite liked it. In fact, she liked it a lot.

"Thanks, Bjorn," she replied, and gave him a huge smile.

After their set, including a storming encore during which the whole tent joined in, dancing and singing along to a second rendition of "Waterloo", the band collapsed on to the caravan cushions in one sweaty and excited heap.

"You were fantastic, Mia!" Gemma enthused. "You're so much better than me."

"No I'm not!" Mia said, delighted with herself. "You're just being kind. But I did enjoy it. And the crowd were great, weren't they?"

"Yes, they were," Ronan agreed, swigging back some water from Wendy's reservoir of bottles.

"I can't believe it was your first gig," Luke said to Mia. "You looked so professional out there. You've got some career ahead of you if you want it, Mia."

"Thanks," she said a little shyly, smiling at Luke.

He smiled back at her. She blushed and tore her eyes away from his.

Gemma glanced at Wendy. Wendy looked back at her and raised her eyebrows as if to say, "Did you see that?" Gemma nodded almost imperceptibly.

"Anyone free for a drink after we get changed?" Luke asked, oblivious to Wendy and Gemma's disapproving looks. "McCarthy's pub on the main street serves a decent pint."

Ronan looked over at Wendy. "Wendy?" he asked. "Fancy a drink?"

"Not really. But you go ahead if you want to," she said. She was exhausted and a noisy pub was the last place she wanted to spend the remainder of her evening. "I'd better get back to Nadia and the boys. Don't be too late, mind."

"I won't be," Ronan promised. "Anyone else?"

"Count me in," Gemma said. "And I'm sure Pat will join us." Pat was loading the van with their instruments.

"Actually he's going straight home," Ronan said. "He'll see us on Friday at the wedding in Killiney."

Mia pricked up her ears. "I thought the wedding was on Saturday." She turned towards Wendy. "You said the weekend, Wendy."

"Did I?" Wendy said a little vaguely. "Sorry, I probably did. I guess the weekend always starts early for us, I'm afraid. You can still do it, can't you?"

"Yes," Mia said. "And at least we're not working tomorrow."

Wendy sighed. "I wish that was the case, Mia. But we need to spend a couple of hours practising to get you up to speed for the wedding. And I still have to alter Gemma's blue jumpsuit for you, you'll be wearing it on Friday. The alterations shop is too busy so I'll have to do it myself. I'll need you to try it on for me. I'm sorry."

"That's OK," Mia said evenly. "There goes my life!" She smiled.

"So how about that drink, Mia?" Luke asked. "Wendy won't need you all day, will you, Wendy?"

"I suppose not," Wendy said. "I have bookings to confirm, I can do that in the morning and give you a bit of a lie-in, Mia." Wendy had no idea why she was encouraging Mia to go out drinking with Luke, but she didn't have the energy to protest. It would sound petty. And besides, Ronan would be there to chaperone.

Luke grinned at Mia. "See! All the more reason to come out for a little while this evening."

"Thanks," Mia said, "but I have to go home. My friend Alva is staying with me and I don't like to leave her on her own for too long."

"Still? How long is she staying for?" Wendy asked.

Mia sighed. "I'm not exactly sure, to be honest." She figured she might as well tell Wendy the truth — there didn't seem to be any point in keeping it a secret any longer, not now that Sean seemed to have another girlfriend. "Alva and Sean have broken up. I was hoping they'd work things out but it doesn't look like that's going to happen, unfortunately. So she'll be staying with me until she finds her own place."

Ronan whistled. "Poor Alva."

"That's awful," Gemma agreed. "They seemed so happy."

"Appearances can be deceptive," Wendy said. There was silence for a moment.

"Well, why don't you ring your friend and tell her to meet us there?" Luke suggested. "If she's feeling a little down right now a night out might be just what she needs."

Gemma snorted. "Yeah, right! So you can hit on her, Luke?"

"Gemma! That's a terrible thing to say," Luke said.

Mia felt uneasy. Maybe Luke wasn't the gentleman she thought he was. Otherwise why would Gemma have said such a thing? "I don't think she'd be ready for . . ." she began.

"Mia," Luke said gently. "Do you really think I'd take advantage of someone when they're that vulnerable? Going through a break-up is hard on everyone. Were they together long?"

"Years," Mia said quietly. "Since school."

Luke winced. "Poor girl. I know how tough that can be."

Wendy laughed. "Luke Jackman, you're not telling us that you've been unlucky in love, are you?"

Luke smiled enigmatically at her. "Wendy, there's a lot you don't know about me."

Mia looked at him. He caught her eye and smiled back. "Do ask your friend to join us, Mia. Trust me, I'll be the perfect gentleman."

"OK," she said, for some reason believing him, "I will."

"That's sorted then," Luke said. "Now, let's get out of these bloody costumes, troops. McCarthy's awaits."

"Can I have a word with you before you go to the pub?" Wendy asked Ronan as he stepped carefully over Gemma's plaster-flexed leg on his way to the far side of the caravan. "After you've changed."

"Sure," Ronan said a little uneasily. There was a slight edge to Wendy's voice and he feared he was in for a private roasting. When Wendy was tired she had a tongue like a whip when she chose to unleash it.

Wendy leaned against the car and waited for Ronan who was bantering with Mia. "No more of that bum-wiggling now, you hear, young lady?" he joked as he finished packing Wendy's car full of the AbbaFab costumes. "We don't encourage that sort of behaviour."

"Yeah, yeah. Course you don't," Mia thumped Ronan's arm playfully, then turned towards Wendy. "Anything else to do, Wendy?" she asked as Ronan slammed the boot closed.

"No, that's it," Wendy said shortly.

"Right," Mia said. She knew Wendy wanted to talk to Ronan alone and she pitied her poor brother-in-law: Wendy was definitely in a bad mood. "See you tomorrow. What time?"

"Is two OK?" Wendy asked.

"Two's fine. See you then." Mia skipped off in the direction of McCarthy's pub. Luke and Gemma were already waiting for her there. She'd phoned Alva a little earlier and Alva'd said she'd be more than pleased to meet them after she'd changed. It would help take her mind off Sean, she'd said.

"Ronan, please try not to wake up the boys when you come in," Wendy began. "Or me for that matter. I'm wrecked and I could do with a good night's sleep."

Ronan gave her a hug, but she didn't respond with all that much enthusiasm so he drew back quickly. "I'll try not to. I'll have a few pints and then come straight home. I want to do some writing in the morning. The closing date for the Irish song contest for the Eurovision is only a few weeks away and I think I'm on to something."

Wendy smiled. Ronan had been writing songs for as long as she'd known him, but he had yet to have one recorded or win any of the competitions he'd entered. But she admired his eternal optimism.

"And don't forget about fixing the spare mic," she reminded him. "And we have to do some more work with Mia in the afternoon, remember? For the wedding."

"Gemma has already said she'll help. And Luke can fix . . ."

Wendy cut him off with a deep sigh. "I'm a bit worried about Luke and Mia, to tell the truth," she said in a low voice. "Did you see the way she was looking at him earlier, all puppy-dog eyes? He'd chew her up and spit her out! I really don't want to see her get hurt."

"Wendy!" Ronan said. "That's unfair. Luke's a good guy and he'd never do anything to hurt Mia."

"Ronan," she continued, "he might not mean to, but Mia . . . well, Mia's Mia." She shrugged. "I worry about her. I can't help it."

"There's no need to, Wendy. She's not a child any more. Stop fussing."

Wendy's face dropped and he instantly regretted his last comment. "Sorry," he said, "I shouldn't have said that. You have every right to worry about her, but really, Wendy, there's no need, she's fine. But I'll keep an eye on her tonight if it will make you happy. Listen, why don't I come home now and we can have an early night together? I can ring Luke. He won't mind."

"No, it's OK," Wendy said. "You need a night out. I'll go home and take a long bath and watch some bad television. I need to do the supermarket shopping on the Internet anyway if we're to have any food for the weekend. I don't have time to shop tomorrow. Honestly, Ronan, it's fine. Go on, I'll see you later."

"Are you sure?"

"Yes! Sorry for being snappy. I'm just tired."

Ronan smiled at her. "You go home and put your feet up, you deserve it. Watch a movie or something. I'm sure Nadia will have the boys in bed by now."

"Good idea," she said. "And I'm sorry for having a go at you about the mic, it'll wait. Or as you say, Luke can do it. Have a nice evening. And try not to wake me up when you come in."

"I won't," he promised again. "And I'm sorry for saying that about Mia. I know you and Gemma worry about her. But she's fine, really she is." He leaned over and gave her a kiss. "See you later."

Wendy stood and watched as Ronan walked away from the car. She opened the car door and stepped in. And there she sat, arms slumped over the steering wheel, analysing what had just happened. She and Ronan seemed to spend their lives apologizing to each other at the moment. And she was getting tired of it. It hadn't always been like that. What had happened to their relationship, their marriage? They hadn't spent an evening alone together for weeks. She couldn't remember the last time they'd gone out for a meal or to the cinema together, and their sex life had become more of a chore than anything else. Frankly, she was so tired most evenings that she just couldn't be bothered. If it weren't for Ronan's persistence, they wouldn't have a sex life at all.

Wendy looked up. The sky was darkening and a light spitty drizzle was falling on the windscreen. She'd better get home. She turned the key in the ignition and before reversing out, switched on the radio and tuned it to Lyric FM. She needed to listen to something calm and soothing as she could feel her nerves jingling and jangling under her skin. She thought about Ronan. Maybe they could take a holiday, just the two of them — a two- or three-day break to somewhere like Rome or Paris, somewhere romantic. They certainly needed a romantic injection of some sort to get their relationship back on track. Wendy sighed. She was worried — worried about Mia, about her marriage, about her workload. And she hated worrying, it was so tiring and not in the least bit productive. Yet she couldn't help it. She wished she had something to take her mind off things.

"Stop it!" she admonished herself. "Get home and have a bath. You'll feel better then. Stop feeling so sorry for yourself — and thank God that there's nothing really wrong with you or your life." But she knew there was something wrong — she just couldn't quite put her finger on it.

★ ★ ★

Later that evening, on their way home from the pub, Mia and Alva decided to satisfy their drink-induced carbohydrate craving in the local chipper. It was heaving: most of Blackrock's pub dwellers had obviously had the same idea. Ronan and Luke were bringing Gemma home in a taxi as she was legless, in more ways than one. When Luke had ordered champagne to celebrate Mia's first gig, the barman had looked at him sideways.

"Champagne?" he'd asked. "Don't know if we have any, mate. Not much call for it in here to tell the truth." But he managed to find some dusty bottles of Moët in the cellar, which had turned out to be very nice indeed and he'd insisted on giving them to Luke, makeshift ice bucket and all (a small plastic basin), for next to nothing. They'd had to drink it out of wine glasses, champagne flutes being one request too many, but no one had minded.

"Special night for the blonde lady, is it?" the barman had said kindly. "Thought I recognized her all right from AbbaFab — hard to be sure with those wigs on though — caught the first few songs before I had to come in here. Good band. The Missus loves Abba." One bottle had turned into three by the end of the night, and, with a couple of pints each, except for Mia, who was restricting herself to champagne, the evening had ended on a decidedly high note.

And Luke had, as he'd promised, been the perfect gentleman. He'd even spent a good hour listening to Alva talk about Sean and how much she missed him. Mia had felt more than a little jealous until just after eleven, when Alva had slipped to the toilet. Gemma and Ronan were deep in conversation at the far side of the table.

"Alva's lovely," Luke said to Mia, shifting along the pub seat towards her. "It's such a pity that things with Sean didn't work out. But I'm sorry."

"For what?" Mia asked.

"For not spending more time with you this evening."

"Oh?" Mia's heart lifted.

"I wanted to get to know you better. We will be working together after all."

"Oh," Mia said, disappointed. She'd been hoping that their connection went deeper than mere work. But maybe it had all been in her mind.

Luke looked into her eyes. "Are you all right?"

"Sure." She took a sip of her now flat champagne. Apt, she thought to herself. To be honest, she'd had quite enough to drink and was only sipping to find something to do with her hands.

"Do you need some air?" Luke suggested. "I could go outside with you if you like."

Just then, Mia spotted Alva walking back towards them. "Thanks, but I'm OK, really," she said, disappointed again. She would have loved to go outside with Luke — to have him all to herself — but she couldn't leave Alva. Besides, the cool night air always had a bad effect on her at first when she'd been drinking and she'd be mortified if she did or said anything inappropriate. Plus, Alva was a little drunk and it was about time they started to make tracks. Mia wanted to get her friend home in one piece. "We'd better get going. Alva has to work tomorrow and I have to practise with Wendy, remember?"

"Lucky old you." Luke smiled. "Maybe we could go out for dinner one night? What do you think?"

"Um," she murmured. "I'm not sure. With the band, you mean?"

"No, just the two of us." He smiled at her. "A proper date," he added just to make himself crystal-clear.

"I'd like that," she murmured as Alva sat back down beside them. Her heart leaped. Yes! she thought to herself. It wasn't my imagination. He does like me.

"What are you pair talking about?" Alva asked with a grin. "You look as thick as thieves."

"You, Alva," Luke said smoothly. "And how lovely you look tonight. Green really suits you. It highlights the hazel flecks in your eyes."

Alva laughed. "You old charmer," she said, chuffed that he'd noticed.

As Alva and Mia waited in the queue at the chip shop, Alva checked her face on the surface of the diamond-shiny stainless-steel counter.

"I'm getting fat," she moaned. She pointed at her flushed face and poked her cheek with a finger. "Look!"

"No you're not," Mia insisted. "You look great."

Alva lifted her head. "Speaking of great, that Luke's a bit of all right," she said. "What do you think?"

Mia shrugged her shoulders. "He's not bad if you like that kind of thing."

"What's not to like?" Alva demanded. "He's not exactly hard on the eye. And he's a really good listener. A real sweetie."

"I wouldn't have thought of him as sweet, to tell the truth," Mia said.

"Two singles," the woman behind the counter said loudly.

"That's us!" Alva said wryly.

The woman smiled at her. "Join the club, love. Wrapped separately?"

Mia nodded. "Please."

"Salt and vinegar?"

"Lots!" Alva said.

As they walked out of the chipper, steaming, greasy brown paper bags in their hands, Alva said, "I'm starting to feel a little better about the whole Sean thing."

"Really?" Mia asked.

"Yes. Thanks to you." Alva gave her a hug, stumbling slightly on the pavement and sending Mia lurching sideways.

"It's nothing," Mia said, supporting Alva's weight. "You're squashing my chips, woman!"

"Sorry," Alva said, letting go and straightening up. "I love you, Mia."

"I love you too." Mia grinned. "Now, let's get you home."

Early the following evening, Mia was sitting in a café in Monkstown waiting for Sean. She was a little paranoid that Alva would somehow find out about their rendezvous, so she'd chosen a discreet table towards the back of the café, tucked behind a rather large and leafy potted plant. He'd rung to say he was on his way, but he was already ten minutes late. Still, Mia didn't mind. She'd just spent three hours with Wendy and Gemma practising songs over and over again, as well as being prodded, poked and needle-pricked by Wendy, so she figured she deserved a large coffee and something sweet and full of calories. After the bustle of the afternoon, she was rather enjoying sitting quietly on her own, flicking through the newspaper that someone had fortuitously left behind them.

"Hi, Mia." Sean bent down and kissed her on the cheek. "Sorry I'm late." He pulled out the chair beside her and sat down.

Once they'd placed their order Mia said, "So, tell me all about Sadie."

"Jeepers, woman," Sean complained. "You don't waste much time, do you?"

Mia cocked one eyebrow.

"OK, OK." He smiled. "On the understanding that you hear me out without interruption, Mia."

Mia put one hand in the air. "Scout's honour."

"You weren't in the Scouts," he said. "You were in the Guides, remember."

"Sounds better than Guide's honour," Mia reasoned.

"I suppose it does."

"So?" Mia asked. "Go on, tell me all about Sadie."

Sean satisfied Mia's curiosity. And she didn't like what she heard. Not one little bit. She decided she'd have to do something about this Sadie lady. But what?

CHAPTER
FIVE

Voulez-Vous?

In the early hours of Thursday morning, after the session in McCarthy's pub with Luke, Mia, Alva and Gemma, Ronan jabbed his door key in the general direction of the lock of his front door. "Clink." He'd hit metal all right — but the door-knocker, not the lock.

"Damn," he muttered. "Must try harder." He squinted up his eyes and tried to focus on the lock. It was no use, Wendy hadn't left the outside light on and the navy-blue door was only dimly illuminated by the grubby street light on the opposite side of the road to their semi.

"I know," he murmured. He put both hands on the door and felt his way along the paintwork, Braille-like. "Aha," he said as he came across the lock. He tried the key again, this time it went in a little way but then stopped. He thought he'd better not try and force it — even in his less than lucid state, he knew that Wendy would kill him if he broke the key in the lock again.

He pulled out the key and then had a brainwave. Maybe it was upside down. He tried again, this time with more success.

"Bingo," he said as the door swung open. He staggered in and slammed it behind him with his shoulder.

"Oops." He snorted with laughter. "Quiet!" Wendy was going to be mad with him for waking her up — she was a light sleeper and usually woke at the slightest disturbance.

He cocked his ears. Nothing. Good, she must still be asleep. And the boys and Nadia were all heavy sleepers so he didn't have to worry about them.

Ronan looked at the stairs ahead of him — Will I manage all of those without waking Wendy up?" he wondered. Doubtful, he decided after a few moments swaying on his feet. Maybe I should drink some water. And take some of those fizzy vitamin C tablets. And some painkillers. Might have a bit of a headache in the morning otherwise. Shouldn't have drunk all that champagne. Or gone to that nightclub with Luke after dropping Gemma home. And that red wine in the nightclub wasn't the best.

Ronan walked slowly into the kitchen. "Shush," he told himself as he closed the kitchen door carefully behind him, remembering Wendy this time. He flicked on the lights and winced slightly as the brightness hit his pupils, causing them to widen.

As soon as he saw the fridge he remembered that he hadn't had dinner, and sure, wouldn't a nice feed be just what the doctor ordered? He wrenched open the fridge door with a loud clink of the sauce and jam jars. Excellent! Ronan smiled to himself — eggs, sausages *and* bacon — his mouth watered in anticipation. He could have a lovely big fry-up!

He pulled a frying pan out of the pan drawer with a clatter and clunked it on to the ceramic surface of the hob. Then he gnawed open the thick plastic packaging on the bacon, wrestled out three rashers and threw them into the pan. He listened for the satisfying sizzle. Nothing. Then he remembered — he hadn't turned on the hob. So he turned the dial and waited. Within a few seconds the ring began to glow red and the bacon started to sizzle. He then dropped four sausages into the pan, jumping back as hot fat splattered on to his hand.

"Damn," he muttered, licking the fat. He turned down the heat. Then he pulled an egg out of its cardboard egg-carton bed and cracked it on the side of the pan. Unfortunately he applied a little too much force and the sticky innards fell straight on to the kitchen counter and then slithered their way on to the floor tiles.

"Feck!" he swore, bending down to pick it up. He tried to scoop the egg yolk up with his hand but lost his balance and banged his forehead on the kitchen cabinet instead. He stood up gingerly, rubbing his temple. He looked at the egg carton. Maybe eggs weren't such a good idea after all.

He abandoned the eggs and prodded a sausage with his finger. It was warm but still a sickly pink colour. He decided to sit down at the kitchen table and take the weight off his feet. The tiles were slippery under the soles of his shoes, still covered in an egg slick, and he almost lost his balance again. "Slowly," he murmured, "slowly." Once sitting safely on a kitchen chair, he slumped over the table and rested his head on his hands. He was feeling rather sleepy so he thought he'd have a rest, a little one mind you, just until his fry was ready.

Wendy sat up in bed, startled. She looked to her left; no Ronan — he couldn't have come home yet. What the hell was that shrill noise? It sounded like the smoke alarm. She listened for a moment. It *was* the smoke alarm, she decided. She immediately pushed herself up, swung her legs out of the bed, ran to the door, threw it open and stepped into the hall. There was a terrible smell of burning — she sniffed the air and put her head over the banisters — and it seemed to be coming from downstairs. Her heart began to race and her head was thrown into a blind panic. The house was on fire! The boys! She rushed into their room.

"Get up, quickly. There's a fire." She put both her hands on Greg's shoulders — he was the heavier sleeper of the two — and shook him firmly.

He opened his eyes and looked up at her. "A fire?" he mumbled sleepily. "Where?"

103

"Downstairs," Wendy said, trying to keep calm. Please God, she thought, give me enough time to get my boys out.

"What's happening?" Steve asked, his head hanging over the top bunk, blond hair spilling over his rapidly blinking eyes.

"There's a fire in the house. You both have to go outside, quickly. I'll wake Nadia. Wait for me in the front garden, OK?"

"What about Dad?" Greg asked, climbing out of bed.

"He's still out," Wendy replied. "Hurry up."

Nadia met them all on the landing. "What's that noise?" she said sleepily.

"Outside boys, now!" Wendy said loudly.

For once they did as they were told, racing down the stairs, opening the front door and walking outside. They're going to freeze, Wendy thought as it registered that Steve had no pyjama top on.

"Where are the boys going?" Nadia asked in confusion.

Wendy put her arm around the girl's shoulders and ushered her towards the top of the stairs. "There's a fire, Nadia. Come on, we have to get outside." She grabbed some coats from the hooks by the door on her way out.

Once in front of the house, Wendy turned towards Nadia. "Keep an eye on the boys, I'm going back in." She handed Nadia the coats. "Here. Keep warm."

"Is it safe to go back?" Nadia asked, taking the coats off Wendy. "There's many smoke in the hall."

"I'll be careful," Wendy promised. "And I have to get to the phone to ring the fire brigade."

"You go, I look after the boys." Nadia shivered. It was a cool evening and she was only wearing a skimpy vest top and some thin cotton pyjama bottoms. She threw one of the coats, a large black fleece of Ronan's, over her shoulders, swamping her slight frame. "Come here you two," she said kindly. "I get you warm." She shrugged coats over their slight bodies. Greg and Steve watched their mother walk back into the house with wide eyes.

"Mum!" Greg said, running towards Wendy, the coat falling off his shoulders and landing on the grass in his wake.

Wendy turned back and put her hand up. "Stay with Nadia!" she said firmly. "I'll be fine. And don't get cold."

She walked back inside. The hall smelt of smoke. She looked at the kitchen door. There were curls of noxious-smelling smoke wafting under it. She put her hands on the surface of the wood — it felt cool to the touch. She put her ear to the door; she could hear something all right, but couldn't quite make out what it was. What was going on in there? She knew she probably shouldn't open the door but she wanted to know the extent of the damage before she rang the fire brigade. After all, she didn't want to call them out unnecessarily. But if it was bad . . . she suddenly remembered the fire extinguisher and fire blanket under the stairs. She pulled open the cupboard and reefed them both off their fixtures on the wall. At least this way she'd go in prepared.

Suddenly she felt a tap on her shoulder. Her heart leaped into her throat and she screamed in fright. She swung around violently.

"Wendy?" Ronan was standing in front of her. "Easy! It's only me. Do we have a fire blanket?"

The door to the kitchen was open now and smoke was billowing out in a foggy, swirling mass.

"What the hell are you doing?" she shouted at him. "Close that door. There's a fire. Where were you?"

"In the kitchen," he said loudly over the still-ringing smoke alarm. "The pan's on fire."

"What pan?" Wendy demanded in confusion. What the hell was he talking about?

"I was frying some rashers and I fell asleep," Ronan explained.

Wendy stared at him: his eyes were droopy and his facial features slack — it was a look she was all too accustomed to. "Are you mad?" she screamed, pushing past him. "You drunken idiot."

She dropped the fire extinguisher at his feet and pushed roughly past him, opening the fire blanket as she entered the kitchen. Ronan was right — flames and smoke were engulfing the frying pan. Wendy screwed her eyes up, the smoke was starting to make them water. She walked towards the hob and placed the fire blanket over the burning pan. Within seconds the smoke diminished. She ran over to the back door, turned the key with her shaking hands and swung it open. Then she grabbed the oven gloves, pulled them on, picked the frying pan up by its handle and carefully walked towards the back door, down the step and over the decking. She could feel the heat of the handle beneath her palms but luckily the padded oven gloves were nice and thick. She put the pan down on the gravel of the patio, where it settled on to the damp stones with one last dramatic sizzle.

Wendy watched the smoking pan and began to cry, huge hot tears of relief flooding down her face. "Wendy?" She heard Ronan's voice behind her. "I turned the smoke alarm off. Are you all right? I'm so sorry. I can't believe I was so stupid. I'd never do anything to intentionally hurt you or the kids, you know that."

She ignored him.

"Wendy?" he said again. "Talk to me."

"Oh, Ronan!" she said, spinning around to face him. "You could have killed us all. I know you didn't mean to, but that doesn't excuse your behaviour."

"I'm sorry . . ." he began.

She strode past him, through the still-smoky kitchen, into the hall and back outside, wiping away the tears with the back of her hands.

"Is everything all right?" Nadia asked with concern. Wendy looked on the verge of tears.

"Yes, thank goodness. The frying pan was on fire. Everything's fine now. Nothing to worry about." She put her arms around the boys, spooning one in on either side and sheltering them under her strong arms. "How are my two big boys?" she asked in what she hoped was a calm manner.

"Mum, is the house going to burn down?" Steve asked, morbidly excited at the thought.

"No, love. It was a false alarm," Wendy said.

"You have wet bits on your face," Greg said, his face pale. The whole experience had obviously worried him. "Are you crying?"

"No," Wendy said, shaking her head. "It's water from, um, putting out the fire." Luckily Greg seemed to accept this unquestioningly.

Steve rubbed his eyes and yawned. "Can we go back to bed now?"

Wendy smiled at him. Nothing fazed him. She patted him gently on the head. "Yes, love, of course you can."

Greg looked up at her with a worried expression on his face. "Is the house safe, Mum?"

"Yes. Your dad just had an accident with the frying pan."

"An accident?"

"That's right." Wendy didn't want to get into it. She was livid with Ronan, who was wisely keeping out of her way.

"Where's Dad?" Greg asked looking around. "Dad!" he shouted.

"He's busy fixing the kitchen," Wendy said. She had no idea what he was doing but the boys worshipped their dad and thought he could do no wrong. To her knowledge, they'd never seen him drunk and she didn't want their illusions shattered — not at this young age. He could be knocking back a swift whiskey right at this very minute, she thought, and then checked herself for being unkind. She knew that Ronan was distraught about what he'd done, but she wasn't going to let him off lightly. Chastising him in front of Nadia and the boys wasn't the answer, however. "Now, go upstairs like good fellows and I'll be up to you in a few minutes. Nadia, can you see they get into bed? I need to clean the kitchen."

"No problem," Nadia said. She wondered where Ronan really was but didn't like to ask. Recently she had heard them arguing in bed late at night, usually after Ronan had been out, Wendy's raised voice cutting through the darkness. Nadia hated to hear them fighting but Nadia wasn't naive enough to think that all marriages were perfect.

Wendy saw the boys up the stairs and then went back into the kitchen. It smelt terrible and there were sooty black silhouettes on the wall behind the hob and the ceiling above it.

"My beautiful kitchen," she murmured, staring at the smoke damage.

"Wendy?" Ronan lifted his head from the kitchen table where he'd been waiting for her. He didn't dare start to clean up without her — he might make things even worse. "I'm so sorry. I'll clean up, you go up to bed."

"Thanks for the offer," she said, "but I'll do it myself. You go on up. I'll come up when I'm finished. I'd prefer to do it on my own if you don't mind."

"I'm so sorry, Wendy," Ronan said again. "You're right, I'm an idiot. I won't drink again, I promise. Ever."

Wendy sighed. She knew it was an empty promise and she was too tired to have this conversation. She opened the cupboard under the kitchen sink and took out a tube of J-cloths and some cleaning materials. The kitchen walls would have to be repainted but some of the smoke stains might come off the units, she hoped. She'd do as much as she could now, and leave the back door and all the kitchen windows open while she was working — that way the smell might not be so bad in the morning. She eased a pair of tight-fitting yellow rubber gloves over her hands, squirted some cleaning fluid on to one of the cloths and set to work on the charred-black counter top beside the cooker.

"Can I help?" Ronan asked tentatively. "Please?"

Wendy ignored him for a moment, then murmured, "No, go up to bed."

He pulled another J-cloth out of the tube. Wendy spun around, tears in her eyes. She was tired to the bone and she really didn't need this. "Ronan, I need to be alone right now. Go on upstairs. Please, just go."

"OK," he said reluctantly. "I'll see you in the morning. I'll ring a painter first thing. Is there anything else I can do?"

"No," Wendy whispered. "Nothing."

"I'm so sorry . . ." he began.

"I know you are. That makes two of us. Goodnight, Ronan," Wendy said quietly, turning her back on him again.

As she scrubbed at the wall behind the cooker with all her might, taking as much of the sooty shadows off as was humanly possible, she sobbed. It wasn't the first

110

time Ronan had come home blind drunk, but he'd never endangered his family before. Usually he just fell asleep on the sofa with the television blaring, or came home with kebab stains all over the front of his shirt. Once he'd fallen asleep with a large glass of red wine balanced on his chest, which had subsequently fallen, staining all his clothes and the living-room sofa in the process. She'd had to get the sofa re-covered in the end. But this was different — and it had to stop.

The following morning, Wendy woke and turned to see if Ronan was awake, but he wasn't beside her. Then she remembered what had happened last night. She was sure she could still smell smoke, even in their bedroom with the door firmly closed. She had a raging headache and she felt as though she hadn't slept at all. She hadn't made it to bed until after five in the morning and her head had been so full of spinning thoughts that, exhausted though she was, she'd found it difficult to sleep.

She dragged herself out of bed. She could hear the boys and Nadia in the hall. Thank goodness for Nadia — what would she do without her? She suddenly realized how much she relied on the au pair and vowed to give her a pay rise and some extra time off.

Wendy grabbed her waffle-cotton dressing gown from the back of the door and put her weary arms through the generously large armholes. Was it her imagination or did it also smell of smoke? She sniffed it suspiciously. It wasn't the dressing gown. She ran her hands through her hair and held them up to her nose.

111

It was her hair and skin — her whole body reeked of smoke. She opened the door and walked into the hall. She could hear voices coming from the kitchen. She padded down the stairs wearily.

"Morning. How's everyone after last night's little excitement?" she asked, slapping a big smile on her face for the sake of the boys. Ronan, Nadia, Greg and Steve all looked up from the kitchen table.

"Are you still mad with Daddy?" Steve asked astutely.

"Don't talk with your mouth full," Wendy admonished. "And no, I don't have time to be mad with Daddy. I have far too much to do today. And anyway it wasn't really his fault," she added generously.

Ronan smiled at her gratefully. "I phoned the painter. I told him it was an emergency and he's going to come over this evening."

"This evening? Are you sure?" Wendy asked. Painters were notoriously difficult to pin down in Dublin.

"Yes," Ronan assured her. What he didn't tell her was that he'd offered to pay the man a whopping 100 euros an hour for his trouble.

"Good. Well done." Wendy was relieved. "I have to have a shower now, I reek of smoke. Ronan, are you OK to take the boys to school?"

"Sure."

Wendy nodded at him. "Thanks. I have to drop my car in for a service. I'll be gone for at least an hour or so. And Mia and Gemma will be here at two." She looked at her watch and sighed. No time for breakfast this morning, not if she wanted to shower, and she couldn't bear the lingering smell of smoke for one minute longer.

"Nadia, can you collect the boys later? I'll be putting Mia through her paces in the garage. And if you're in this morning, would you mind leaving the back door and the kitchen windows open? It's still very smoky in here."

"No problem. And no worry, I make sure they do homework later," Nadia said.

"And can we make chocolate buns this afternoon, Nadia?" Greg asked her, anticipation written all over his little face. "Please? You promised."

"Can we use kitchen, Wendy?" Nina asked.

"What time is the painter coming at?" Wendy asked Ronan.

"He said sixish."

"As long as everything is tidied away by six that's fine. Thanks, Nadia."

"No problem. I feed the boys early and we be go of kitchen by six."

"Perfect." Wendy smiled warmly at Nadia. Her English still wasn't quite there but she was getting better. "Thanks, Nadia. I really appreciate it. Now, I have to have a shower and get going. I'm in a bit of a rush. See you all later."

Ronan waited for his customary goodbye kiss but none was proffered. "Bye, Wendy," he said to her disappearing back. "Hope the service goes well." He was going to keep well out of her way until this evening, he decided. And in the meantime he'd do all those jobs around the house that he'd been promising to do —

like putting up bookshelves in Greg and Steve's room and fixing the loo seat in the downstairs bathroom. Hopefully that would get him back in Wendy's good books. He'd forget about the song-writing session. Shame, though, he nearly had his Eurovision song nailed. If only he could come up with some catchy lyrics.

Wendy drove to the garage in Deansgrange and parked in the designated area. One of the hazard lights on the dashboard had been flashing on and off intermittently for the last week and was worrying her, and one of the brake-light bulbs needed replacing. Unfortunately the service did take a large chunk out of her already jam-packed day. The answering machine at home was full of unanswered calls — several had come in this morning by fax — and her computer had seventy-seven unopened emails sitting on it. She also had to chase up several unpaid invoices, pay some bills in the Credit Union, do the Internet shopping which she hadn't got around to doing last night, ring the phone company about an annoying buzzing on the line, and pay her television licence in the post office — all in the space of one day. And that didn't include working with Mia in the afternoon and making alterations to Gemma's blue satin jumpsuit. Where was she going to find the time? Plus there was a fabulous Victorian house on show in Sandycove that she was dying to see. She could check it out online, she supposed, but it wasn't the same as seeing it in the flesh. But she really didn't have time today, that was for sure. Or on Saturday. She'd have to arrange a private viewing the following week. What an exciting life, Wendy sighed. Tonight would be another thrilling late night at the computer finalizing bookings, answering emails and sending out invoices, she supposed. She switched off the car engine and pulled the keys out of the ignition.

"Wendy Redden." She handed the relevant documents to the man behind the desk in the garage office. "My car's here for a service."

He checked his desk diary and then looked up at her. "You're bang on time," he said. "Can you go and wait by your car, please, and one of the mechanics will be out to you shortly? And if you can leave the service book on the front seat that would be great. Once he's taken the keys off you, you can wait over there if you like." He gestured at a sofa.

"Thanks," Wendy said. "How long will it take, do you think?"

The man rubbed one of his eyes with an oil-stained knuckle. "Hard to tell really. Depends what needs to be done. I'd say about an hour. Maybe an hour and a half tops."

"Thanks, that's great." Wendy was glad she'd brought some paperwork to do.

She went back outside and leaned against her Volkswagen Golf. It was a reliable little car and she'd never had any problems with it. It wasn't exactly the most luxurious thing on four wheels, but it did the job.

"Excuse me, Miss." A young man dressed in oil-stained blue overalls walked towards her, wiping his hands on his thighs.

"Yes, sorry, can I help you?" Wendy asked him.

He smiled at her. "Keys?"

"Yes, of course." Wendy handed them over. "One of the hazard lights on the dashboard keeps coming on, and one of the brake-light bulbs has just gone. The one on the right."

The mechanic nodded. "No problem."

The man in question was actually rather attractive in a rough-and-ready sort of way. He was tall and lean with strong-looking shoulders and a fine head of silky dark brown hair. And he filled his overalls rather well, Wendy thought.

Snap out of it! she admonished herself swiftly. You're a married woman and a mother of two. But I do miss the thrill of the chase, she thought wistfully as she watched the man drive her car into the test building. Ronan's a good husband but . . . A glimmer of the single, up-for-anything girl she used to be nudged its way into her mind and planted itself there. Wendy hadn't always been the sensible one in the family after all. She'd been wild in her own way, a fact she was strangely proud of now. Not that Gemma or Mia knew anything about her former life, of course. She'd always been careful to shield it from them.

Wendy sat down on one of the hard plastic seats in the waiting area and worked for a while before allowing her mind to wander. Damn the paperwork, she didn't have the energy to do any more. She was so tired; her lids felt heavy and her eyes gritty. She closed them slowly and sat back, resting her head against the wall

116

behind her. She began to drift away, allowing her imagination to fly.

"Hello," the mechanic said to her in her daydream. "I need some help. Are you free?"

"Why, yes. How can I help you?"

He grinned at her. His overalls were gaping open. Her eyes rested on his firm, tanned chest, exposed to his waist. Not a hair in sight, Wendy noticed. Like a model from a glossy magazine. That's it, he's a model in his spare time. And he's in a band, she added. He's the lead singer. She'd always had a thing about singers.

"Follow me," he said.

He led her by the hand towards a room at the back of the garage and closed the door behind them. Wendy looked around. There was nothing in it except a large desk and an office chair. He locked the door and gave her another wide grin.

"You're incredibly hot," he said. "Has anyone ever told you that?"

"Not for a long time," Wendy said. "So what's on your mind?"

"I think you know." He moved towards her and stood in front of her.

Wendy could feel her breath quicken. The mechanic smelt of fresh sweat and his skin glistened in the light. His chocolate-brown eyes smouldered. She put out a hand and ran it down his taut chest. He grabbed her hand and pulled her towards him. She gasped. He began to kiss her passionately, his tongue probing her mouth forcefully. He moved her towards the desk and

117

pushed her down on to its surface. She could feel the hardness of the wood against her back.

"Tell me you want me too," he said in a low growl, pressing his body against hers.

"Wendy? Wendy Redden. Is that you?"

Wendy reluctantly snapped herself back to reality and opened her eyes. An attractive blond man was standing in front of her, smiling widely. He looked vaguely familiar but she couldn't quite place him.

"It's Des, you know, from Westport — Henry's friend? You look a little flushed — are you all right?"

"Um, yes, fine," Wendy mumbled. She sat up and willed her cheeks to cool down. Of course, Des Sullivan. But he'd changed almost beyond recognition. He used to be the bad boy of the set they'd hung around with when the Reddens had lived in Westport, County Mayo, before Mia was born — all long, dirty-blond hair, black leather biker jacket, torn stone-washed jeans, crooked teeth and crooked smile. All the girls were mad about him, Wendy included, but he was always flitting from one girl to another. She noticed that he still had that tiny scar on his eyebrow — the one she knew for a fact that he'd got running through a glass door as a child, and not in a fight, as he'd always claimed to his peers.

"I'm not surprised you didn't recognize me," he continued, sitting down beside her. "It's been an age. I've been living in Sydney for years now. How've you been? Your family moved to Dublin or something, didn't they? It was all pretty sudden. Just after all that

Henry business." He gave a loud snort. "That was the talk of the town, wasn't it? Probably still is."

"Yes, yes," Wendy said quickly. "Dad got a job in Dublin. We moved when I was fourteen." She really didn't want to talk about the past, especially her Westport past. And *most* especially Henry Reilly. Henry was her first real boyfriend; and it was all over and done with, end of story. She'd loved him and he'd broken her heart; he'd left her for the thirty-seven-year-old mother of a friend of theirs, a woman called Thelma Dickens. Henry and Thelma had run away to Boston, never to be heard of again, leaving two devastated families behind them. It was like something from a bad American made-for-television movie and no one could believe it. Henry was only seventeen at the time and it had caused quite a stir in Westport. Wendy had lost her head a little and she certainly didn't want to be reminded of it now. It had devastated her and she'd never really got over it, not properly. Henry had no idea what an impact he'd made on Wendy's life.

"You look great," she said, meaning it. Des had filled out a lot; his skin was tanned and his hair was bleached blond from the Australian sun. Both his teeth and his smile were still crooked, but this just added to his appeal.

"Thanks. I'm enjoying being back in Ireland for a bit."

He didn't elaborate, so Wendy asked, "And what do you do in Sydney? Are you still working or have you retired on your millions?"

He smiled. "Not yet. I'm in computers."

"Really?" Wendy asked out of politeness rather than real interest. "Programming?"

"Yep. Programming, servicing, troubleshooting, the works. There's not much I don't know about computers at this stage." He stretched his long legs out in front of him and crossed his arms over his chest rather too smugly, Wendy thought. But he'd always been full of self-confidence, even as a teenager. "There's good money in it, I've done OK for myself."

"And what are you doing here?"

"Dropping my mum's car in to be fixed. It's making a strange noise apparently. I couldn't hear it myself, but you know what mothers are like. Always worrying."

"No, I meant what are you doing in Ireland?"

"Oh, sorry. I'm over visiting Mum. She had a bit of an old heart attack recently so I thought I'd better see her before she, you know, pops her clogs."

"I'm sorry to hear that," Wendy said.

"Thanks. She's a tough old bird though, she's not going anywhere for a long time yet."

"And where are you staying?"

"With Oonagh, my sister. Do you remember Oonagh? She's a couple of years younger than me."

"Vaguely," Wendy said.

"She lives in Bray, she married a Dublin guy a couple of years ago. Mum lives with her; she moved up after Dad died."

"How long are you staying?"

Des shrugged. "A couple of weeks. I'll see how it goes. I thought I'd check out the computer scene in Dublin while I'm here. Maybe see if there are any jobs

120

going, you know? In case I decide to come and work here at some stage."

"Are you thinking of moving back to Ireland for good?"

He shrugged again. "Maybe. Might even settle down if I meet the right girl. Know any?" He looked at her intensely and raised his eyebrows.

Wendy blushed and looked away. Des hadn't changed. She held her right hand out in front of her. "I'm married," she said with a laugh, fingering her wedding band. "With two children," she added to cement it.

"Shame." He smiled at her. They sat saying nothing for a few awkward moments. Eventually he broke the silence. "How about a cup of coffee while we're waiting? Give us a chance to catch up. No strings. You can tell me all about your husband if you like."

Wendy didn't quite know what to make of that last statement. "I'm not sure," she began. "I'd better wait here. My car's nearly finished and . . ."

"Ah, come on. Live a little," he cajoled. "Just one cup of coffee. It won't do any harm. Unless you're in a rush?"

Wendy looked at his handsome face. She could do with a little distraction after the night she'd had.

He smiled at her, sensing her hesitation. "And I won't mention Henry, OK? That's all in the past, isn't it? Man, did he make one bad decision. You're even better-looking now than you were then."

"Thanks," Wendy faltered, realizing that he was now officially flirting with her. "But I don't think . . ."

Just then the mechanic walked into the office and nodded at her. "All finished," he said, handing her the keys to her car.

"That was quick," she said, remembering her daydream and trying not to blush. "What was wrong?"

"Nothing much. The brake fluid needed topping up," he said, "and I put a new brake-light bulb in for you. She's all set now. But you were right to bring her in. There's no point in messing around when it comes to brakes. Important things, brakes. Your brake-pads will need to be replaced soon enough. I'd give them another six months, then bring her in again."

"Thanks." Wendy smiled at his rather sweet use of the feminine adjective to describe her car. The mechanic handed her the keys and walked away.

She tore her eyes from his young buttocks and turned towards Des. "I'm sorry, I really do have to go. I'm really busy today and . . ."

"No need to explain," Des said. "Give me your hand."

"What?" she asked. And before she had time to protest he pulled a pen out of his pocket, held her left hand firmly and wrote a telephone number on her skin.

"Just in case you change your mind," he said with a smile, letting her hand drop. "About coffee."

"Um, sure. Bye." She avoided his gaze and practically ran out of the office. She put the key into the car door with shaking hands. Once she was sitting in the car she looked back at the doorway — she just couldn't help herself. Des was standing there, staring into her car. He lifted his hand and waved. Wendy felt flustered. She glanced in the rear-view mirror — she was very pink and her forehead was shiny. She waved back and turned the key in the ignition. The sooner she was out of there the better.

As she drove home, Wendy realized with a start that she'd run out of the garage without paying her bill. She'd ring them and apologize as soon as she got home. How embarrassing. But she had been rather distracted.

She wondered what would have happened if she'd gone for a coffee with Des. Maybe nothing. But maybe . . .? She felt a rush of adrenaline power through her veins, and then another warmer feeling suffused her body. With a shock she recognized it as desire. As she waited in a queue of traffic, she looked down at the number Des had etched on her hand in bold blue. After the number he'd written *Ring Me!*

Des Sullivan finds *me* attractive. Wendy smiled to herself, feeling deliciously empowered. Des Sullivan! As she sat at the traffic lights at Baker's Corner she ran her fingers over the blue number. She turned on the radio and tried to concentrate on what Ryan Tubridy, one of her favourite presenters was saying. But it was no use, she was utterly distracted. At least it took her mind off more mundane things. And what if I did ring him? she asked herself. What would happen then?

CHAPTER SIX

Knowing Me, Knowing You

On Friday afternoon, Wendy stood on tiptoe in the back garden of Hollyhock House on Killiney Hill Road, trying to save her pink suede kitten-heeled sandals from sinking into the grass. She knew she shouldn't have worn them, they were going to get ruined, but they did go so well with her jeans and her pink silk kimono top and she loved them; they made her feel good and she could do with all the instant pick-me-ups she could find these days. She was staring up at the hillside in disbelief, Luke and Pat flanking her. A large white marquee was just about visible through the leafy trees.

"You're not serious?" Wendy was horrified. "They said the marquee would be on the lawn at the top of the garden." She pointed in front of her. "That's not a garden, that's a bloody mountain."

"Deadly serious," Pat assured her. "I'm really sorry, but it's all hands on deck, Wendy, or we'll never get the gear up there and ready in time. That marquee is on level ground, thank goodness, but there are some pretty steep steps to negotiate on the way up to it."

"We need Ronan. Where's Ronan?" Wendy looked around a little frantically. She put her hands to her mouth and yelled, "Ronan!"

"I don't think he'll be able to hear you," Luke said, trying not to raise his voice. He understood Wendy's panic but she wasn't exactly helping the situation. "He's in the marquee sorting out the power cables."

"How big is the *garden* exactly?" she asked.

He shrugged. "Four or five acres apparently. Mostly on a slope."

Wendy raised her eyebrows. "Tell me this is some sort of elaborate nightmare." Luke and Pat watched as she visibly slumped in front of their eyes. Her usually rigid shoulders collapsed and she put her hand to her head. She looked crumpled, exhausted.

"Wendy?" Luke asked, concerned. He put his arm around her. He'd never seen her in this state before. It was rather unnerving.

"I'm sorry, Luke," she said softly. "I'm just having a bad day. I haven't had much sleep the last few nights. Ignore me. Sorry for being so short with both of you."

"It's fine, Wendy, honestly. We'll manage. But we are going to need some assistance. Is there anyone you can think of who'd be free to help? Anyone at all?"

Wendy blew the air out of her mouth with a "whoosh" and thought for a second. She shook her head. "Not really. The local rugby team?"

"Do you know any rugby players?" Luke asked hopefully.

"No." She sighed deeply and put her head on his shoulder. "Oh, Luke, what are we going to do?"

He was a little disconcerted by her tone. Wendy was always so positive, so upbeat, and she always had an answer for everything. It wasn't like her to admit defeat.

"How about . . . students?" he offered haltingly. "They're on their holidays, aren't they?"

"Yes, I suppose so," Wendy said, her head still resting on his shoulder.

"Where would we find them at this time of the day?" Pat asked, lighting a cigarette and pulling deeply on it.

Wendy lifted her head. "I have no idea," she said. "Students," she murmured. "Students." She thought about it for a few seconds and then her brain flicked into action. "But I know someone who might. Give me one minute." She punched a familiar number into her mobile.

"Where's Luke?" Ronan asked Pat. He was leaning against Pat's van — his heart was pounding in his chest and he felt as if he'd just run a marathon. Beads of sweat were popping out all over his forehead and he wiped them away with his forearm.

"No idea," Pat said, looking around. "No sign of Wendy either. When's Mia due?"

126

Ronan looked at his watch. "Round about now," he said. "We're never going to be ready in time."

The way things were looking, Ronan was right. The guests would start to arrive in less than an hour, and the stage wasn't fully erected yet. The marquee company were working flat out to finish the job.

"Poor things." Pat gestured towards several of the waiting staff, each carrying armfuls of large white dinner plates, winding their way up the hillside like black and white ants. "There's a mini-kitchen at the back of the marquee, but the chef's doing his nut. Luckily all the courses are cold. There was supposed to be soup, but the catering company refused to let their staff carry the tureens up the hill — they say they're not insured to transport hot liquids like that."

"Too right," Ronan said. "We'd better get back to work, I suppose. But I have no idea how I'm going to last the evening after all this exertion. I feel like my heart's going to jump out of my chest."

"Know what you mean, mate," Pat empathized. "At least I don't have to sing. I don't envy you." He ground his cigarette into the gravel with his boot, took a swig from his bottle of water, put the cap back on, wiggled the bottle into the pocket of his denim jacket and lit another cigarette. "Lights next?" he suggested.

Ronan winced and nodded. At least they weren't as heavy as the amplifiers — *they* were going to be a killer.

Ronan and Pat heard engines powering up the gravel driveway and looked over. "Someone's in a hurry," Ronan murmured.

As soon as the two cars came into view Pat let out a hoot of laughter. "It's Wendy," he said, clappings his hand together in delight and relief. "Followed by Luke. But what the hell?"

Ronan and Pat stared at the two cars in amazement. They were jammed with people — a large, unfamiliar-looking young man was sitting on another man's knee in the front of Wendy's car, and at least seven people were squashed into the back, including a beaming Nadia and a very excited-looking Greg and Steve. Luke's car was equally packed. As soon as the cars came to a halt, the doors sprang open and everyone poured out on to the gravel in a good-humoured wave of chatter and laughter.

Wendy walked towards Ronan, a smile plastered on her face. "I've brought some reinforcements," she said.

"No kidding!" Ronan grinned back. "Where did you find them all?"

"In the Internet café in Dun Laoghaire. They're friends of Nadia's."

Ronan leaned towards her. "Are we paying them all?" he asked in a low voice.

"No," Wendy said. "But I will give them something for their trouble. Nadia talked them all into it. She's quite a popular girl with the local male population as you can see. At least two of them have introduced themselves as Nadia's boyfriend."

Ronan laughed. "Why am I not surprised?" He clapped his hands together again. "Right, better put them all to work. We have a show to run."

128

"Looks like Luke's beaten you to it," Wendy pointed out. Luke had already started to direct everybody towards the side of the van. Pat was helping him.

"Daddy!" Steve and Greg came running towards Ronan and wound themselves around his upper legs and waist. "Isn't this fun?" Steve said, his eyes sparking with excitement. "Nadia said we had to be good and help. What can we do, Daddy?"

"You can be my assistants, how about that?"

"OK." Greg nodded.

"What's going on here?" Mia asked. She'd just walked the short distance from Killiney train station. "Are the guests here already?" she asked, staring at Wendy's new army of helpers. Luke had lined them up and was passing out the AbbaFab equipment and giving them instructions. He'd already mentally handpicked several tall, burly lads for the amplifiers. Pat was climbing up the hillside towards the marquee, his arms full of bags of electric leads, showing the AbbaFab troops the way.

Wendy laughed. "They're Nadia's friends. They're here to help us lug the equipment up the hill." Wendy filled Mia in on what she'd missed.

"Sorry I wasn't here earlier to help," Mia said.

"Not to worry, we weren't expecting you until now."

"So when will the guests start arriving?" Mia asked.

"In less than twenty minutes. But there's a drinks reception on the lawn first, so they won't be in the marquee until later."

"So the idea is to do a quick sound check and then we have a couple of hours off?"

"Correct," Wendy said. "I want to make sure you see the stage before we go on later. There'll be a big enough crowd and . . ."

"How big?" Mia cut in.

Wendy shrugged her shoulders. "Couple of hundred."

"How many?" Mia asked again. "Exactly?"

"Nearly three hundred," Wendy admitted. "Much smaller than the Blackrock gig."

"But that was only a few songs. This is a wedding. The newly-weds will be relying on us to make it the best night of their lives." Mia bit her lip.

Wendy put her arm around Mia's shoulders and gave her a squeeze. "You'll be fine," she assured her. "Stop fretting. Now for the mountain climbing."

Wendy and Mia made their way across the garden and towards the path to the side of the hill. "You're going up there in those?" Mia asked, pointing to Wendy's shoes.

"Mia, in my cruise-ship days I used to dance all night on the stage in six-inch heels." Wendy smiled. "If there's one thing I can do, it's heels."

"I remember the photos," Mia said. "I used to borrow Mum's black feathery wedding hat and dress up in my swimming costume and dance around the house, pretending to be you."

"Did you?" Wendy asked.

"Yes, for years."

Wendy smiled. "I didn't know. It's a pity we didn't have video cameras back in those days; I would have liked to have seen that."

"You brought your gold costume home to show me one year, remember? You let me try it on. We have photos of that somewhere."

"Of course. How could I forget? You nearly broke your ankle in my sandals."

Mia giggled. "I've never been good in heels. Unlike you."

"Speaking of which, we'd better get going," Wendy said. "Follow me."

Mia followed Wendy under the elaborate metal, flower- and silk ribbon- festooned decorative arch and up the steep natural stone steps that led towards the marquee. "Mountain goats, eat your hearts out," Mia murmured as they climbed up and up. They were followed by some of Nadia's friends and more catering staff, now lugging up the dessert plates and clinking boxes of cutlery.

After several minutes' steep climb, they finally reached the top. "I can see why they put the marquee up here," Mia said as she stood on the lawn, panting a little. "Even if it is a bit of a trek."

Wendy stood beside her. Stretched out in front of them was the shimmering blue expanse of Killiney Bay. It was a bright day and the sun was threatening to peep out from its scanty cloud cover at any moment.

"And I can see why they call this the Naples Bay of Ireland," Wendy said. "Look, there's Sorrento Terrace, the most expensive terrace in the country. I recognize it from the property pages. What beautiful houses."

"Is that an outdoor swimming pool over there?" Mia asked, pointing into one particular back garden to their left.

Wendy squinted. "I think so. Or else a rather large pond."

"A swimming pool, imagine that." Mia was impressed.

Wendy looked at her. "Maybe you'll live in Killiney one day, Mia, you never know. And have a swimming pool in your back garden."

"Maybe." Mia smiled back. "After I make my millions in AbbaFab, you mean?"

Wendy snorted. "I wouldn't hold your breath."

"Hey, girls!" Pat shouted over from the entrance to the marquee. "They've finished the stage. Ready for your trial run? The amps are almost ready, Ronan's just wiring them up now."

"Coming," Wendy said. "No rest for the wicked and all that." She held her hand out to Mia. "Come on, you. Enough sight-seeing for one day."

"Hi, Mia." Luke strode towards them, his eyes fixed on Mia. He gave her a hug and a kiss on the cheek, then stepped back and smiled at Wendy.

"No kiss for me then, Luke?" she asked archly.

"Oh, sorry." He leaned forward and kissed her too.

"Hey, hands off my wife," Ronan shouted from the back of the tent. "She's taken. Isn't that right, Wendy?"

"Do you want to do a quick run-through of some of the songs?" Wendy turned and asked Mia.

Mia looked at her sister. It wasn't like her blatantly to ignore Ronan like that. But she thought it best not to say anything. She was sure Wendy meant nothing by it. "Yes, that would be great. And could we go over the dance routine for 'Does Your Mother Know?'? I'm a bit confused about the turns."

"No problem," Wendy said. "We'll do that first while Ronan and Pat finish wiring up the amps." She clicked towards the stage on the exposed wooden floorboards. They hadn't got around to laying the carpet yet. "Ronan, we're just going to go through 'Does Your Mother Know?' with Mia and Luke. Are the mics working yet?"

"No, it'll be another few minutes," Ronan said. "Do you need me?"

"No, you finish what you're doing."

"OK. And we'll try and keep out of your way."

"Great, thanks."

"How are you today?" Luke asked Mia as they walked slowly towards the stage.

"Fine. Good, actually."

"How was the head yesterday morning?"

"A bit muzzy but not too bad. Alva was in a bad way though. She was lying on the sofa moaning when I left. She rang in sick to work."

Luke laughed. "Poor Alva."

"Come on, slow coaches," Wendy said, staring down at Mia and Luke. "Up on the stage with the two of you."

"Yes, Boss," Luke said with a grin. He climbed up and held out his hand for Mia. She took it gratefully. His grip was firm and she felt the power in his upper arms as he pulled her up.

"Thanks," she murmured.

"Right, Mia," Wendy said. "As you know, Luke sings 'Does Your Mother Know?', and Ronan backs him up. He usually sings to Gemma, but I think it's better if he sings to me today. It'll make things easier. So we'll swap the steps around a bit. You stand there . . ." But before she had a chance to finish, Ronan interrupted.

"It's probably best to leave the steps as they are," he said. "Save yourself the extra work. Mia will pick it up quickly enough. But, Mia, try not to laugh at Luke too much when he's singing to you, you'll put him off if you do."

"Gemma always tries to make me laugh," Luke explained to Mia. He shook his head, realizing what he'd just said. "I shouldn't have told you that, should I?"

Mia smiled at him. "Probably not. If it's a family tradition, who am I to . . ."

"That's all very well," Wendy interrupted the banter. "But I really do think that Luke should sing to me."

"Why?" Ronan asked Wendy. She was in a very strange mood.

"I thought you were fixing the amps?" she said, glaring at him.

He shrugged. "Sorry, I didn't mean to interfere. I was just trying to help. I'll get back to the amps."

"I'm sorry, I didn't mean to snap at you, Ronan. I'm just trying to get things right. And to make things easy for Mia. But we'll do things as normal if that's what you'd prefer."

"I don't mind, Wendy," Ronan said, putting his hands up in front of him defensively, "really I don't. You do what you think best, OK?"

Wendy nodded at him. "OK. Thanks." She turned back to Mia and Luke who were waiting for their directions. "Luke, you sing to Mia. I'll do backing with Ronan."

"Sure," Luke said. He took his place on the stage and showed Mia where to stand. "Will I start singing, Wendy? Can Ronan accompany? It would make things easier."

"Ronan, I know you're busy, but would you mind?" Wendy asked him.

"No problem." Ronan jumped behind the keyboard and began to play the jaunty opening bars to the song.

Mia stifled a grin when Luke sang the first, rather cheesy line to her. "*You're so hot, teasing me, so you're blue but I can't take a chance on a chick like you, it's something I couldn't do.*"

Mia licked her lips suggestively.

"And I told you not to make me laugh," Luke said, singing it to the music.

Mia giggled.

"And here's where you dance with your back to him," Wendy said over the keyboard. "When he says '*Girl, you're only a child*'. Turn your head, Mia, flick your hair and smile, good, good. You're supposed to be a young girl flirting with an older man."

Mia did as requested.

Luke changed the first chorus from "Does Your Mother Know?" to "Does Your Sister Know?" and Mia

135

couldn't contain herself. She stopped dead and gave a hoot of laughter. Then Luke started laughing and couldn't sing any longer. Ronan had to stop playing, he was laughing so hard.

"What was that all about?" Wendy asked with a frown.

"Sorry, Wendy," Luke said. "I couldn't resist it."

"Well, it's not funny," she replied, sniffing. "And we don't have much time, so stop messing around. We need to get on with it."

"Yes, Boss," Mia said, then started laughing again.

"Mia!" Wendy said. "You need to take this more seriously."

"And you need to lighten up a little," Mia said. As soon as the words had left her mouth she gasped at her own audacity. She had never spoken to Wendy like that before in front of anyone. Wendy gave a tiny squeak, then jumped off the stage and stormed out of the tent.

Mia looked at Ronan. "Should I go after her?" she asked him.

"Best to leave her alone for a few minutes. She's pretty tired today. We had a bit of a problem with a frying pan on Wednesday evening and she was up most of the night cleaning the kitchen. She hasn't really caught up on her sleep."

"A frying pan?" asked Mia.

"It went on fire," Ronan said sheepishly. "My fault. I put it on the hob and forgot about it. Wendy's not too pleased with me, as you can imagine. Listen, why don't we go through that song once more? Wendy's right, we don't have much time."

Wendy listened as the strains of "Does Your Mother Know?" rang out again. She was sitting outside on the grass, staring down at Killiney Bay. She still couldn't believe that Mia had spoken to her like that, in front of Luke, Ronan and Pat. Her mobile phone was digging into her bottom and she shifted sideways and wiggled it out of her back pocket. She stared at it for a moment and then decided to ring Gemma.

"Hello?" Gemma answered. "Wendy?"

"Hi."

"Are you not working? What's that music in the background?"

"That would be the band practising without me," Wendy said.

"Without *us*," Gemma pointed out.

"Sorry, you're right. Without *us*."

"And why are they doing that?"

Wendy explained what had just happened.

"Ah," Gemma said. "And I take it you're not well pleased with Mia for talking back to you."

"It's not that!" Wendy protested.

"Really?"

"Well, OK, maybe it is a little. But I think Luke's having a really bad influence on her. She seems totally smitten, Gemma, it's really sad. She's being all silly and giggly. And he's not right for her."

"I agree completely. But there's not much we can do about it, is there? Mia has to make her own decisions. I tried talking to her about Luke but she wasn't even listening."

"When? You never told me."

"On Wednesday evening, before you went on stage in Blackrock. And I wanted to talk to you about it yesterday afternoon but I didn't get a chance. But you know, I don't tell you everything, Wendy."

"Well, when it comes to Mia, you should. Maybe I should try talking to Luke myself."

Gemma said nothing. She had no intention of telling Wendy *everything*, even when it came to Mia's life. Wendy sounded tired and Gemma didn't want to argue with her.

"Is everything else OK, Wendy?"

"Let me see, Ronan tried to burn the house down in the early hours of yesterday morning, as you know; I got little or no sleep last night, we've just finished hauling all our gear up a mountain, and Mia hates me. Apart from that, everything's just peachy. Listen, I have to go, Ronan's waving at me."

"Wendy! You can't go now. You're obviously upset."

"Everything's fine, I'm just a bit fed up. I'll ring you back later."

"Promise?"

"Promise."

"And take it easy, Wendy. I'm here if you need to talk. You know that."

"Thanks."

"There you are," Ronan said as Wendy clicked off her phone. "I was looking for you. Are you all right?"

"Yes. I am now. I just needed a little air."

"Mia didn't mean to upset you."

"I know she didn't. I'm tired, that's all. I shouldn't have taken it to heart."

"Will you come back inside?"

"Sure." Wendy pushed herself up with her hands and followed Ronan. "I had to make a phone call," she said to a rather startled Mia and Luke as she approached the stage. "Now, where were we?"

An hour later, Wendy rang Gemma back. "Gemma, it's Wendy again."

"What took you so long? Now I want to hear all about the mountain climbing. You have no idea how bored I am, and I'm in desperate need of some real news. I'm sick to the teeth of reading about celebrities' vacuous lives and ridiculous problems. But that's all my magazines seem interested in writing about. And I've run out of books. It's driving me nuts."

"Sorry to disappoint you, but the marquee is up a hill, that's all."

"How disappointing."

"But I did manage to corner Luke after our practice and have a word with him."

"Really? Alone?"

"Yes. I asked him to check one of the hazard lights on my car. Complete fabrication, of course, there was nothing wrong with it. The others went to Dalkey in the van to find somewhere to eat."

"And?"

"I don't think it went all that well to tell the truth," Wendy admitted.

"Go on," Gemma encouraged her.

"I asked him what his intentions were towards Mia."

"You did not!" Gemma snorted with laughter.

"Why not?" Wendy asked defensively. "What's wrong with that?"

"Intentions! That sounds like something a Victorian father would say, not a sister."

"Yes, well." Wendy sniffed. "I was just letting him know I had my eye on him."

"As if he hadn't noticed! Poor Luke, I'm starting to feel a little sorry for him. I was thinking about it after you rang earlier, Wendy."

"And?"

"I think we have to let Mia make her own mistakes. She's twenty-four after all."

"But she's a very young twenty-four," Wendy said. "You have to admit."

"We're always saying that and you know, maybe that's our fault," Gemma mused. "And maybe it's time for us both to loosen the reins a little. Let Mia live her own life."

"Ronan would agree with you. But I'm not so sure. She still needs us, Gemma." Wendy's phone beeped. "Hang on one second." Wendy put Gemma on hold. Ronan had sent her a text message asking where she'd got to. "Gemma, I have to go. Ronan's looking for me and I have to sort out the costumes and do Mia's make-up."

"Bye then," Gemma said. "I'll talk to you tomorrow I suppose."

"Are you OK? You sound a little down," Wendy asked.

Gemma sighed dramatically. "I'm just fed up with being cooped up at home all the time. I hadn't realized how much of my time is taken up with work. I don't really have any other friends, Wendy. You lot are my friends, and my family for that matter."

Wendy didn't know what to say. "I'm sorry, Gemma, I have been trying to include you in everything. Training Mia in, for example. And you're welcome to come to as many weddings and gigs as you like, you know that."

"Thanks. But it's not the same. I'll just be glad when my ankle's healed. But maybe you won't want me back now that you have Mia. She's much better than I am."

"Gemma, you know Mia's only filling in for you. Yes, she's a great singer, I can't deny it, but she doesn't have your stage presence or your experience. So stop worrying."

"Ah, pay no attention to me. I'm just feeling a little sorry for myself, I guess. And I know you have to go. I'll be fine."

"Are you sure?"

"Yes, yes. Now go!"

A little later that afternoon, Mia and Wendy followed the housekeeper of Hollyhock House — a nice woman in her fifties called Mrs Tibbet — up the rather grand main stairs.

"Talk about a bathroom with a view," Wendy said as soon as Mrs Tibbet had closed the door behind her, leaving them alone. Wendy looked around. She wondered if the housekeeper would give her a guided tour later. It was a stunning period house — many of the original features were still intact and she was dying to see the reception rooms.

"Look at that bath," she said. "Wouldn't you just love to soak in it?" The oversized oval marble bath had pride of place in the large room, positioned against the uncurtained sash window, commanding stunning views of the garden.

"It's gorgeous," Mia agreed. She ran her finger over the curved rim of the bath, the white marble cool beneath her skin. "It's a bit exposed though, isn't it? I'm not sure I'd want people spying on me in the nip."

"Good point," Wendy said. "I'd put a crisp white canvas blind on the lower half of the window myself. And I'd paint the walls a soft cream instead of the blue. To match the bath."

Mia murmured assent. She'd apologized to Wendy about her "Lighten up" comment several times, but was still a little wary. Wendy had seemed fine in the restaurant, though, her usual chatty self. On the other hand, Luke had been rather quiet and withdrawn, which had unnerved Mia. She'd asked him several questions and he'd answered her rather shortly; he wasn't his usual charming and funny self at all. Maybe he was going off her. Maybe he had never really liked her in the first place. Or maybe Wendy had said something to him. Mia wouldn't put it past her. Luke and Wendy had arrived at lunch together in Wendy's car after all.

Mia watched as Wendy set her vanity case in front of the large mirror, sat down on the upholstered bench and opened it with a click.

"*Heigh ho, heigh ho, it's off to work we go,*" Wendy sang under her breath. "This evening's going to be fun," she said as she dotted some cleanser on her cheeks, chin, forehead and neck.

"I hope so," Mia said. There was a slight quiver in her voice which her sister recognized as nerves.

Wendy stroked cotton wool over her skin, removing her daytime make-up. "I know so," she said confidently. "Sit down beside me. I'll budge over."

"Wendy," Mia began, "did you say anything to Luke? In the car, I mean."

"About what?" Wendy asked, staring into the mirror.

"About me."

Wendy said nothing for a moment. Then she turned to face Mia. "He's not right for you, Mia. He's too old."

"Wendy, he's only four years older than me! You're five years older than Ronan."

"Thanks for pointing that out," Wendy said a little tetchily. She didn't like being reminded of the fact.

"And you have no right to tell me who I can or can't see. You're not my mother! So keep out of it, OK?"

Wendy was shocked. Mia rarely raised her voice to her.

"Sorry," Mia murmured. "But it's my life, Wendy."

Wendy sighed. "That's what Gemma said."

"The two of you are always talking about me behind my back."

"No we're not!"

"Yes you are. I'm not stupid. It's been going on for years. And I don't need you and Gemma trying to protect me all the time. Just stop it!"

"I know," Wendy said. "You're right. I shouldn't have said anything to Luke. I just wanted him to . . . oh, I don't know. Treat you with respect, I suppose."

"I'm so embarrassed, Wendy. No wonder he was being so odd earlier. He probably thinks I'm not worth the hassle."

"It won't happen again," Wendy said. "I promise." She stroked Mia's hair. "And he thinks the world of you. Nothing will change that. Nothing *has* changed that. He was probably just trying to play it cool in front of me."

"Do you think so?"

"Yes."

"And he really does like me?"

"What's not to like, Mia? You're wonderful."

"Thanks." Mia's heart lifted. Maybe Luke did like her after all. She smiled at Wendy. "I'd better put some make-up on now."

"So you forgive me for interfering?"

"Yes. But don't do it again." Mia stuck her face inches away from Wendy's and glared at her, making them both laugh. "Promise?" she said in her most threatening voice.

Wendy laughed. "I promise. Here." She handed Mia a thick white towelling band. "Put this on to hold your hair back. Would you like me to apply your foundation?" Wendy rummaged in her vanity case and

144

pulled out two tubes. "Try mixing these two together, that should be a good colour for you."

Mia rarely wore foundation and certainly not the heavier cream type. She took the tubes from Wendy and turned them over and over in her hands. "Gemma did it for me the night before last. I guess I'd better learn how to do it myself. You guys won't always be around after all. Do you have a sponge?"

Wendy fished one out and handed it over. "Good idea. It'll go on easier if you dampen the surface slightly." She smiled gently at her sister. "You've always had such beautiful skin, Mia. You're really lucky. Mine's like old leather at this stage. I used to sunbathe far too much on the cruise ship."

"You were a sun goddess long before that," Mia pointed out. She poured some of Wendy's moisturizer onto her fingertips and began to massage it gently into her skin. "Like the time you were over from London on your holidays and you lay on tin foil in the back garden and got me to pour baby oil all over you? You got terrible sunburn and Mum had to bring you to the doctor, remember? She was so cross with you. 'You're not a turkey, Wendy,' she said. 'There's no need to cook yourself.' And we couldn't stop laughing at that and Gemma kept making gobble, gobble turkey noises. And then Mum got really cross with us for being silly."

Wendy winced. "Don't remind me. Some holiday! It hurt even to laugh. I had third-degree burns and I was in agony for weeks. I'll never forget spending most of the first few days lying in a cold bath; and even that felt scalding hot to me. My poor old skin. The things I put it through, all in the name of beauty. I shudder just thinking about it."

Mia held the small wedge of sponge under the cold tap for a moment, then squeezed it out. "Wendy?" she said as she put some foundation on to the back of her hand. It looked a little too dark for her complexion so she added a lighter dollop from the other tube and mixed them together. Wendy was right — it was almost the perfect shade. She really knew her make-up.

"Yes?" Wendy looked over at Mia. "Do you need some help?"

"No. I was just wondering . . ." Mia tailed off.

"What?" Wendy prompted.

Mia was staring at the top of her own hand intently. "Do you ever think about Mum?" she asked in a quiet voice, still staring at her hand.

"Of course," Wendy said after a moment.

"You never talk about her," Mia said.

"No. No, I don't."

"Why?" Mia raised her head.

Wendy was leaning towards the mirror and carefully patting her crow's feet with a fingertip's worth of wrinkle cream. She held her hand in mid-air and looked at Mia. "At first it hurt too much," she said honestly. "And then, I don't know. I didn't see much point in it, I suppose. She was gone and we had to get on with our lives."

"But you never talk about her now," Mia said softly.

"I'm sorry," Wendy said. "I don't know what to say, Mia. Would you like me to talk about her more?"

"It's not that," Mia said. Then she sighed. "Oh, I don't know what I mean. Ignore me."

"No, it's obviously on your mind, Mia," Wendy said, putting down the tiny pot of cream. "And you're right, we should talk about Mum more. It's her anniversary soon, isn't it?"

"Yes," Mia whispered. Miriam Redden had died in June, not that they ever mentioned the date, not really. Gemma and Wendy always made sure to ring Mia on the day, but Miriam was never mentioned. "Seventeenth of June," Mia added.

"Maybe we should do something this year," Wendy suggested. "Put flowers on her grave or something. What do you think?"

"Not flowers," Mia said.

"Oh." Wendy was stumped. "Why not?"

"Mum didn't like cut flowers. She preferred plants."

"You're right. I'd forgotten that. A plant then. A rose bush in a pot or something. What do you think?"

Mia nodded wordlessly. There was a lump in her throat and she didn't trust herself to speak.

There was a sudden rap on the door. "How are you getting on, girls?" It was Ronan. "Are you ready?"

"Not yet," Wendy said. "We're putting on our faces and we're not changed."

"Right, I'll leave you to it. See you downstairs in what, ten minutes? The room at the back of the kitchen. Luke's with me."

"Fifteen," Wendy replied.

"Fifteen it is."

Wendy and Mia listened as Ronan and Luke's muffled voices grew fainter and then disappeared.

"We'll do something this year," Wendy promised. "For Mum," she added, just to be clear. She looked at Mia again.

"Are you OK?"

Mia nodded slightly. "Yes, I'm fine. Sometimes I just miss Mum, you know. And I feel I can't really talk to you about it."

"Well, you can," Wendy said. She could feel tears prick the back of her eyes and she willed them not to spill. "You can talk to me about anything. I know I'm not always the easiest person to talk to, but I do love you, Mia. And I'd do anything to make you happy. You know that, don't you?"

Mia wiped away a tear.

"Ah, Mia." Wendy leaned over and put her arms around her. "What is it?"

"I don't know," Mia said, wiping back the tears. "I really don't. Some days I just feel lonely. Is that stupid?"

"We all feel like that at times," Wendy said soothingly, holding her close.

"But you have your own family. You have Ronan," Mia said, sniffing slightly. "And the boys. How could you possibly feel lonely?"

"Sometimes being lonely when you have people all around you is the most wretched feeling of all," Wendy said. She shook herself inwardly. Mia didn't need to hear about her worries and insecurities. She needed a sensible, stable sister, not one riddled with self-doubt.

"But you're right, I have Ronan and my boys. And you and Gemma, of course. I'm very lucky, I know that."

Mia had stopped crying now. "I'm sorry, Wendy. I don't know where all that came from. I'm fine, really I am."

"I know you are. But there's nothing wrong with having a bit of a cry now and again. It's good for you. Lowers the stress levels."

"Really?"

"Absolutely." Wendy ruffled Mia's hair affectionately. "You'll be fine, Little Star."

"Thanks, Wendy."

"For what?"

"For always being there for me."

Wendy suddenly felt a wave of guilt. She knew Mia wasn't being sarcastic — that wasn't Mia's style — but at that moment she realized that she was starting to become very self-absorbed. Mia deserved a lot more of her attention, and so did Greg and Steve. Mia was an adult, but she still needed mothering at times, whatever Gemma and Ronan said, Wendy knew that. But she wasn't feeling all that positive about her own life at the moment and she'd have to do something about that too. She needed to be strong and happy for Mia's sake, for the boys' sake. For Ronan's sake.

She wondered if she should talk to Mia, *really* talk to her? Tell her everything. But now wasn't the time. And who would benefit in the long run? Maybe it would only make things harder for everyone concerned. Gemma hadn't mentioned their Westport past in many,

many years and maybe it was best left alone. After all, every family had some sort of skeleton in the closet.

"I love you, Mia," Wendy said eventually, her mind racing. "Always remember that. I always have and I always will. Even if I don't always show it."

"I know you do," Mia murmured, touched but at the same time a little embarrassed by Wendy's declaration.

After sitting in silence for what seemed like forever, Mia pulled away from Wendy and picked up the make-up sponge again. "Better get ready," she said. There were so many things that she wanted to say, but she didn't know how to put them into words. Standing up to Wendy about Luke, and talking to her about Miriam had had a cathartic effect, however, and she now felt calmer and more content than she had in a long time. Maybe things would be different from now on, or maybe not, but at least she'd tried to voice her thoughts to Wendy. That was a start.

Wendy nodded wordlessly. She felt strange, as if all her nerve endings were raw and exposed. Emotionally open. Just like she'd felt after giving birth and the heady first few minutes with her brand-new babies. Everything seemed hyper-real, and she felt vulnerable and sensitive. At that moment she really wanted to talk to Gemma, but she knew it wasn't possible. They were due on stage in a short while and she had to collect herself before that. If she didn't, there was a distinct possibility that one of the more sentimental songs would send her over the edge.

Ronan gave a loud wolf whistle as soon as Mia and Wendy walked into the basement of Hollyhock House.

They were in the authentic "Arrival" white jumpsuits, Wendy's with plunging neckline and gathered trouser legs, and Mia's complete with stainless-steel zips and dark pink edging on the collar and cuffs. "Looking good, ladies!" he quipped as the girls stode towards them in their white platform boots.

"How are you feeling, Mia?" asked Luke.

"Terrified," she admitted.

"Good!" Luke said.

Mia stared at him.

"Nothing like a bit of adrenaline to get the old blood pumping," he continued. "All the best performers are scared witless before they go on stage. It's a well-recorded fact. Even Agnetha herself suffered from stage nerves."

"Really?" Mia asked, slightly mollified.

"Would I lie to you?" Luke winked at her and she smiled. She was more relieved to see that he seemed back to normal rather than to hear that the real Agnetha suffered from stage fright, but she kept this to herself. She looked over at Wendy and her sister smiled back at her.

"It's true," Wendy confirmed.

"In that case," Mia said, "show me the stage."

"That's better," Luke said. "Now, are we all set? The speeches are almost over and it's almost time for the bride and groom's first dance."

"What are they dancing to?" Mia asked. "I thought our first song was 'Dancing Queen'? Strange choice for a waltz really."

Ronan and Luke stared at Wendy. "Did you not tell her?" Ronan asked Wendy, trying to keep the shock out of his voice.

Wendy hit her forehead with the heel of her hand. "Oops! I knew there was something. I'm so sorry, Mia."

"What?" Mia asked.

"I never told you about the song, did I?"

"No. What song?" Mia asked. "Would someone please explain what Wendy's talking about?"

"The bride and groom have requested a special song," Ronan began, "It's 'their song' apparently."

"Which means it's the bride's favourite song," Luke quipped.

Mia's face drained. Please no, I really don't want to faint again, she said to herself as she willed her body to stay upright.

Luke, noticing her pallor and slight lurch, sprang into action and put his arm around her. "Easy there, Mia. Why don't you sit down?" He steered her towards a chair by her shoulders. "Wendy can sing the first song on her own. Really, there's no drama. It's only 'Still the One', you know, the Shania Twain song?"

"I know that song," Mia murmured.

"Sorry?" Wendy asked. "What did you say?"

Mia raised her head and gave a half-smile. "It's one of Alva's favourite songs, sad person that she is. She plays it all the time. I know it backwards."

"Great," Luke said. "As long as you know it forwards, we're in business!"

"Excellent!" Wendy said with relief. "Problem solved."

152

"Now, ready for the ascent?" Ronan asked. "Everyone got their ropes and crampons?"

They all laughed. "We'll follow you," Wendy said. "And will you go behind Mia, Luke? I don't want her tumbling down the slopes in her boots."

"My pleasure." Luke grinned.

Wendy regretted her request as soon as she realized that Luke now had her blessing to check out Mia's bottom the whole way up the hill. But there's nothing I can do about it without drawing attention to myself, she thought crossly. And I did promise Mia I'd keep out of it after all. But I do wish her jumpsuit wasn't quite so tight around the bum.

Mia stepped on to the small stage that evening feeling a lot more confident than she had in Blackrock Park. She sang a little nervously during "Still the One", not a song she'd ever attempted to sing before, regardless of Alva's drunken cajoling, but no one seemed to notice. And once the first strains of "Dancing Queen" played, Mia was soon in her element. Gone was the slightly shy and nervous Mia, and in her place was the confident and self-possessed Agnetha. Wendy watched in wonder as Mia danced and strutted around the stage, throwing herself into the songs and imbuing them with such heartfelt emotion that Wendy realized that she herself had become quite blasé about the lyrics and decided there and then to put more effort into her own delivery. During "Knowing Me, Knowing You", singing about "walking through an empty house", "memories, good days, bad days" and "children", Wendy felt real tears in her eyes. And for the very first time in her long singing career she cried on stage.

AbbaFab left the stage to storming applause. They had sung two encores, finishing up with "Take a Chance on Me" on Wendy's instruction, much to Mia's delight. During the song, Wendy changed the chorus lyrics to "Take a Chance on *Mia*" as their mum had always done while singing along. And just like Miriam, Wendy had leaned in towards Mia and sung "*Mia*" in her little sister's ear every time the chorus said "Me". Mia had smiled to herself, delighted and touched that Wendy had remembered. She hadn't felt so close to her sister for a long, long time and if she closed her eyes, it almost felt like having her mum back.

"Girls, you were brilliant!" Luke said after they'd climbed back down the hill and were congregated around the van. A DJ had taken over for the rest of the evening, and was playing a selection of late-eighties hits at the request of the crowd. The band had caught their breath in the small catering marquee, unwinding for a few minutes before their descent, all on a high and eager to compare notes on their performance. "And that was the best version of 'Knowing Me, Knowing You' I've heard in years. You'd almost believe that Wendy was really crying. What an actor!"

"Thanks," Wendy said, trying to sound calm and levelheaded. She was still a little shaken by her own uncharacteristically emotional reaction to the lyrics.

"Who's on for a pint?" Luke asked as he unzipped the top of his jumpsuit. "Anyone interested in checking out a new club in town?"

Mia couldn't but notice his smooth, almost hairless chest and his taut stomach, both glistening with fresh, tangy sweat.

"Luke," Wendy said, "could you not wait till we're inside? There are ladies present."

"Where?" he asked with a grin, looking around and feigning surprise. Wendy laughed and raised her eyebrows. "Sorry, Wendy," he said. "But I'm boiling. It was sweltering in that tent. As I was saying, I'm off to the opening of a new club. A friend of mine, Bert, runs the place and I'm sure he wouldn't mind if I brought along a few friends if anyone fancies it."

Wendy groaned. "Wish I had your energy, Luke. I'm heading straight home to bed. The boys will be up at the crack of dawn tomorrow."

"On a Saturday?" Luke asked.

"They don't have any problem getting out of bed at the weekend," Wendy explained. "School mornings are the problem."

"I'm heading home with Wendy," added Ronan, eager to stay in her good books. "Early night for me too."

"Where's the club?" Mia asked. She wasn't usually a big fan of nightclubs, but she was on a high, her head was buzzing and she didn't think she'd be able to sleep for hours and hours. Besides, she quite fancied the idea of spending some time with Luke away from Wendy and Gemma's over-protective eyes.

"In town," Luke replied. "Just off Grafton Street. It's called Atlas. Bert's promised me a booth in the VIP area if you're interested."

"I might be," she said.

Wendy looked at Mia. "We're working tomorrow, you do know that, don't you?"

Mia nodded.

"That's not until the evening, Wendy," Ronan said, eager for Mia to enjoy herself.

"I suppose you're right," Wendy murmured. "But don't get too tired, Mia."

"Maybe I should just go home," Mia began.

"You should definitely go to the club," Ronan cut in, nudging Wendy in the side. "Have a bit of fun."

"Yes, of course you should," Wendy added quickly. She knew she was being over-protective. "I'd go myself if I wasn't so tired. You can tell me all about it tomorrow. And you should give Gemma a ring. If she's still up, I'm sure she'd be interested."

"Good idea," Luke said. He looked at Mia. "Go on, it'll be a laugh."

"Can I bring Alva?" she asked.

"Of course, bring whoever you like. The more the merrier." Luke clapped his hands together. "That's settled then. Let's go home, get changed and hit the town, Mia. I'll pick you and Alva up in a taxi in an hour. And then we can go and collect Gemma if she wants to join us. How about that?"

She smiled at him. "Sounds good."

★　★　★

As Ronan and Wendy drove past the garage beside the Purty Kitchen pub in Dun Laoghaire, Ronan driving and Wendy staring out into the darkness, she was reminded of her car's service and of Des. She should have wiped his number from her hand and all memory of him from her mind, but she hadn't on either count. He had seemed very interested in her and it was flattering. No one had looked at her in that way for a long time, especially not Ronan. Maybe she'd give Des a ring. Just to meet for coffee, mind, nothing else. She could do with a little confidence boost, and what was wrong with a little male attention anyway? It wasn't as if it meant anything.

Who are you kidding, Wendy? she asked herself rationally as Ronan pulled into their driveway. Grow up. Coffee with Des isn't going to solve anything, in fact it's only likely to make things worse.

Later that night, lying in bed unable to sleep, Wendy turned towards Ronan. "Ronan, are you happy?" She nudged him in the side. "Are you awake?"

"Uh? Awake?" he grunted, still half asleep. "I am now. What did you just ask me?"

"Are you happy?" she repeated.

Ronan opened his eyes. He could see the whites of Wendy's eyes staring at him in the murky darkness.

"Sure," he said. "Are you?"

Silence.

"Wendy?" He sighed. "Is this about the other night? And the frying pan? You know I'm sorry. I was an idiot, a complete idiot . . ."

"No," she said softly. "It's not about that." She'd just about forgiven him now that the kitchen had been freshly painted and was almost back to normal except for the annoying scorch mark on the ceramic hob, which was so far resisting all manner of cleaning products.

Ronan waited for her to elaborate, but she didn't. She put her head back on the pillow and closed her eyes tightly.

"Wendy?" he said softly several minutes later. But there was no answer. He gave up. He rolled over, closed his eyes and went back to sleep.

As soon as she heard him gently snoring, Wendy slowly swung her legs over the side of the bed and climbed out, taking care not to wake him. She pulled her dressing gown on and tied the belt firmly around her waist. She opened the bedroom door gingerly and crept into the hall, lingering for a moment outside Greg and Steve's door. "Sleep well, my babies," she murmured before making her way downstairs and into the kitchen.

She sat down on a kitchen chair and stared out of the window. There was an almost full moon outside, illuminating the deck and the neat patio garden. They had had grass several years ago, but Wendy had become sick of mowing it — Ronan's job of course, one of many he never actually got around to doing. So she'd had the whole area paved and gravelled. The boys were always complaining about the lack of grass, but as far as she could make out, they only really missed digging it up to find worms to "play" with. And as they'd quickly discovered, if they dug deep enough, there were still worms aplenty. Looking outside, Wendy suddenly longed for grass; she longed to stand in the garden in the dark and feel the cool, damp blades beneath her bare feet. She leaned forward and put her elbows on the table and her face in her hands. Large tears fell on to the wooden surface of the table. What was happening to her life and why did she feel so out of control these days? She stood up, wiped away the tears with the sleeve of her dressing gown, and walked over to the kitchen counter where she'd left her mobile phone on recharge. She flicked through the phone book and found the number she was looking for. It was late but she was sure he'd still be up.

"Hello?" Des answered. "Hello?"

CHAPTER
SEVEN

The Name of the Game

Sean's date, Sadie, was also crying on Friday night.

"Sean, that was such a lovely film. I can't believe Hannah died in the end, it was so sad, wasn't it?"

"Yes, very sad," Sean said, trying to sound sympathetic. He'd felt more like laughing than crying at the end of the terrible Hollywood weepy, *Dying for Love*. The leads — well-respected actors, one of whom had even been nominated for an Oscar a few years back — should have known better. In Sean's humble opinion the film was brutal. But there had been no seats available for the one he had planned to take Sadie to, and *Dying for Love* had been the only other viable option. He wondered what Alva would have made of it. Alva had no time for sentimental films, which was strange, Sean always thought, as she had no problem with sentimental and far-fetched soap operas.

"So realistic too," Sadie added.

Sean nearly choked on the dregs of his bottle of water. Realistic? Where else but on the silver screen would a stunning nurse in her late twenties fall for a rotund, balding man in his mid-sixties who was dying of cancer? And as for having the poor nurse die in a freak tree-felling accident in a redwood forest, what were the screenwriters thinking of? And was Sadie mad?

Sean grunted non-committally. "Would you like a drink?" he asked before she had a chance to quiz him any further on the film. "It was really warm in there, I'm parched."

"Yes. But how about going into town? There's a new club opening this evening. I have an invitation to the launch. It's called Atlas, have you heard of it yet? It was all over the papers last weekend. It sounds cool. There's a huge globe beside the dance floor apparently and . . ."

Sean zoned out. Sadie loved the sound of her own voice, but luckily she didn't seem bothered that he was only half listening. A nightclub? He thought about it while Sadie prattled on. He wasn't normally a big nightclub fan. Alva tended to go clubbing with her friends from work, or Gemma (Mia wasn't a fan either), leaving him happily at home. But he should really start making an effort now that he was single again, he supposed. And tonight was as good a time to start as any. "I'm not really dressed for it," he said, gesturing at his plain white shirt and dark blue denims.

"You look great," she said. She took in his wide shoulders, trim stomach and strong-looking legs admiringly. "And you're with me anyway." She clung to his arm possessively. He'd wondered earlier if she wasn't a little overdressed for the cinema. Her short, flirty red dress and matching red jacket and heels seemed a little over the top to him, but what did he know? He wasn't all that attuned to fashion, as Alva was always pointing out to him, like when he'd questioned her habit of wearing summer dresses over jeans. He wasn't sure if Sadie was what you'd call fashionable exactly: her hair was a rather unnatural ash white, as straight, shiny and still as a sheet of metal; her skin was a dark, nutty brown, as if she'd just spent a month in the Caribbean (which Sean knew for a fact she hadn't); and her thin, perfectly arched eyebrows gave her face a permanently startled look. Her cheeks were whippet-thin; her tiny, five-foot-nothing body doll-like, although she had remarkably muscular upper arms for a woman of her size. She was very attractive — there was no denying that — but there was something missing, Sean thought, although he couldn't quite put his finger on it.

Less than half an hour later, after striking it lucky with a taxi, they were in Atlas. Sadie oohed and aahed at the interior decor: the huge illuminated globe, the thick carpet underfoot, the generously oversized red and dark purple velvet sofas. She clung to his arm like a limpet, her head only just reaching his chest. "Isn't this something?" she gushed.

"Would you like a drink?" he asked, gazing at the huge, brightly lit bar that ran the full length of the right-hand wall. He was gasping for a pint. And he hoped that with a drink to sip on, Sadie would stop talking so much.

"Yes, please. A white wine spritzer," she said. "I'll come with you."

Sean wondered if Sadie would let go of his arm at any stage during the evening; she seemed inordinately fond of it. I'll have to fish my wallet out of my pocket to pay for the drinks, he thought, she'll have to let go of it then.

Alva and Mia stepped out of their taxi and started to walk up Grafton Street towards Atlas. It was a mild evening; just as well as they had both decided to wear dresses — Mia all romance heroine in floaty cream chiffon with a fitted denim jacket thrown over it to dress it down a little, and Alva resplendent in a plain but beautifully cut black number from an Italian designer (which had cost an arm and a leg but which she'd never actually worn) with a light, black ballet-style cardigan over her arms and tied just under her neat bust. Mia had sent Luke on in the taxi as Alva had only just jumped into the shower when he'd arrived and she didn't want to keep him waiting for ages. She'd also rung Gemma at home as her mobile wasn't switched on, but Gemma wasn't in the humour for a club, she told Mia, she was on her way to bed. Watching everyone dance would be most frustrating when she couldn't join in, she explained.

Mia and Alva linked arms as they tripped up the cobble-locked pedestrian street in their heels, stopping every now and then to admire a particularly fine leather bag or pair of shoes in one of the brightly lit shop windows.

"Left!" Alva pulled on Mia's arm and steered her down a side street.

"Look at those lights!" Alva exclaimed as they approached the discreet doorway of the club. The sky above Altas was a fiesta of multi-coloured strobes, criss-crossing each other with rainbow intensity. There was a clamour of smartly dressed people queuing against the redbrick wall of the street, chatting and laughing animatedly, all waiting patiently to be admitted. There were four bouncers outside the club, two stationed at the rather innocuous-looking plain black front door, and two roaming up and down the side street, talking to punters in the queue; recognizable only by their matching long-sleeved T-shirts, printed all over with a map of the world. Unlike stereotypical burly bouncers, the two men and two women were of normal stature, and each wore an earpiece and a wrap-around microphone.

One of the girls bounced up to Mia and Alva who were debating whether to join the queue or not. "Hi, can I help you?" she asked politely.

"Please. We're friends of Luke Jackman's: he's on the guest list. Do we need to queue?" Alva asked the smiling woman.

"No, not at all. Follow me." She led them towards the entrance. "I met Luke earlier; he was in school with

Bert, he told me. These guests can go straight in," she said to the woman to the left of the doorway.

"Thanks," Alva said.

"Enjoy yourselves," the woman said and bounced off again.

Once inside, Mia poked Alva in the ribs. "Is it my imagination or was that the most polite bouncer you've ever met in your life?"

"No kidding." Alva nodded. "And look at this!"

The inside of the club was lit in soft, glowing shades of deep blue and purple. It was dark enough to be interesting, but not gloomy enough to be dingy. Swirling, exotic-sounding dance music drifted out of hidden speakers. The walls were decorated in swathes of red and dark pink heavy silks and there were fresh flowers on a dark wood console table to the left of a large stairwell.

"What's that smell?" Alva asked.

Mia sniffed the air. "I don't know. Cinnamon? Vanilla maybe? Is this place for real?"

Alva shrugged. "Seems a bit too good to be true. Has someone really opened a club with polite bouncers, tasteful decor and music that doesn't deafen you?"

"Maybe," Alva murmured.

Two tall, identical-looking clean-cut men stood to the left of the stairway. "Do you need to check coats?" one of them asked politely.

Alva and Mia shook their heads. "No, we're fine, thanks," Alva said.

"In that case, welcome to Atlas, ladies," the other man said, gesturing towards the staircase with a flourish of his left arm. "Enjoy your evening."

"Thanks," Alva murmured. She looked at him and smiled. "This is *Candid Camera*, right?"

"Sorry?" he asked.

"Nothing, don't mind her." Mia put her hand in the small of Alva's back and guided her towards the top of the staircase. As they made their way down the stairs, they both noticed the thick carpet under their feet — manna to heel wearers.

"Look!" Alva said pointing towards the middle of the room. In front of them was a huge floor-to-ceiling globe whose interior, softly glowing lights pulsated to the music.

"How cool is that?" Alva asked, very impressed. "Hey, is that blonde girl Nicola from *Fair City*?" Alva knew all her soap stars intimately.

"Where?"

"On the dance floor. To the left."

Mia stared over. "It looks like her all right. But I've only seen *Fair City* a couple of times, so I'm not the best person to judge." They walked past the globe and had another peek at the woman.

"No, that woman's hair isn't naturally blonde," Alva said wickedly. "Look at those roots. She's not as pretty either. And she's too short. Nicola's quite tall."

"You're right. And look at that dress, it barely covers her."

As they watched, the woman smiled at her dancing partner and swatted him playfully on the arm. The man

166

looked very much like Sean. Alva focused her eyes on the man's face. It *was* Sean. What the hell was he doing here? And who was the Barbie doll dancing with him? Her stomach lurched towards the floor. She felt numb.

Alva stood rooted to the spot and dug Mia in the ribs. "It's Sean," she hissed.

"Where?" Mia looked around.

"On the dance floor. With the fake blonde."

Mia looked closer. Alva was right. It *was* Sean.

"Over here!" They heard a shout behind them. Luke and another dark-haired man were waving at them from a small booth against the wall.

"Are you OK?" Mia asked Alva who was still staring at the dance floor. Barbie had now wrapped her arms around Sean's neck and his hands were cupped around her tiny waist. Alva felt as if someone had stuck a knife in her heart and was slowly turning it.

"Alva?"

"I'm fine. Let's just ignore them, shall we?"

"OK. But do you want me to say anything to Sean?"

"Like what?"

"I don't know. Ask him to leave maybe?"

"Don't be silly, it's fine. I'm over him, really. He can cavort with whoever or whatever he likes, I don't care."

"If you're sure."

"I am." Alva nodded curtly. "We'd better join the others."

"Hi, girls." Luke grinned as Mia and Alva approached. "I was wondering when you'd turn up. Great place, isn't it? I saw you both checking out the dance floor." He slid over on the dark red velvet sofa and patted the seat cushion beside her. "Jump in." Alva and Mia sidled in.

"Bert, this is Mia and Alva," he said to the dark-haired man. "And, girls, this is Bert. Bert owns Atlas."

Bert winced. "The bank does more like, but I'm delighted to meet you both. Ladies," he said formally, standing up and brandishing his arm with a flourish, "welcome to Atlas."

"Or should I say, Mr Smooth?" Luke laughed.

"And what about you, Luke?" Alva said, looking Luke up and down. "You're looking pretty smooth yourself." She'd forgotten how attractive he was. Much better-looking than Sean. And he'd look incredibly good on my arm, Alva decided immediately. That would show Sean and Bimbo-features.

"Can I get you both a drink?" Luke offered.

"Please, drinks are on the house," Bert said. "Tell the barman you're with me, Luke, and he'll sort you out."

"That's very kind of you," said Mia. "A white wine and . . ." she looked at Alva. "What about you, Alva?"

"Do you think they have cocktails?" Alva asked Luke, her eyelids doing more batting than Babe Ruth in his glory days.

"Absolutely," he said. "What do you fancy?"

Alva raised her eyebrows slightly and smiled her most dazzling smile. "A Sex on the Beach," she purred. "Or maybe an Orgasm. Or a Long, Slow Screw. What do you think?"

"I've never had any of them." He laughed. "So to speak."

"You're making those up," Mia said a little crossly.

"No, I'm not, honestly," Alva insisted with a girlie laugh. She flicked her glossy dark brown hair back with a whip of her head.

"What about a Cosmopolitan, Alva?" Mia said quickly. "I know you love them. Get her one of those, Luke." She recognized that Alva was in full-on flirting mode and was keen to stop her in her tracks. I shouldn't have bothered inviting her in the first place, she thought. I want Luke all to myself tonight. Mia hadn't told Alva about her feelings for Luke. She'd agreed that he was attractive and good fun, but that was about as far as it had gone. Things had moved pretty quickly after all, she was only starting to get to know him. Nothing had happened yet, not really. But she realized now that she should have said something earlier. Alva *was* in a vulnerable state after all. Maybe she should say something now, she thought; that would probably be the best idea. Better nip things in the bud before Alva started getting any ideas. She'd talk to her as soon as she got a chance.

"Sounds perfect," Alva said, looking at Mia. Was it her imagination or was Mia frowning at her?

"I'll give you a hand," Mia said to Luke, jumping to her feet.

"Great," said Luke, a little nervous at Alva's change of demeanour. She hadn't been so blatantly flirtatious the last time they'd met and he wondered if she wasn't a little drunk tonight.

Alva watched Mia and Luke walk towards the long chrome-topped bar at the far right of the large room.

Then she whipped her eyes back to the dance floor, looking frantically around the club: she'd lost sight of Sean and the blonde who were no longer dancing. They've obviously gone somewhere private for some high-octane canoodling, Alva thought with a sick feeling in her stomach.

"Are you all right?" Bert asked her.

"Yes, sorry, I didn't mean to ignore you just now. I just spotted someone I know earlier and I was looking for him. So, how long have you been in the nightclub business?" she said, realizing that she'd been rude. Bert began to tell her about his previous business enterprises and Alva listened, trying to pay attention to what he was saying while her mind was elsewhere.

Mia and Luke reached the bar. Mia stood there and put her hands and her pulse points against the deliciously cool metal surface. "It's hot in here," she said to Luke.

He smiled at her. "Sure is."

"I'm not usually a nightclub fan, but this place is great. And Bert seems really nice."

"Bert's great. We go back years. We were in school together and we meet up whenever we can. He has a young family so he's pretty busy most of the time."

A new song came on, a remix of an early Madonna track, and Luke tapped a coin against the top of the bar in time to the music. "I love this one," he said. "Want to dance?"

"What about the drinks?" Mia asked. They hadn't even ordered yet.

Just then Bert appeared beside them. "I thought I'd give you a hand. Alva said she was fine on her own for a few minutes. I need to have a quick word with one of the barmen anyway."

"Great timing." Luke slapped Bert on the back. "Get the drinks in, will you? I haven't ordered yet. I'm taking Mia for a quick spin on the dance floor."

Bert laughed. "Go on."

"Thanks," Luke said. He took Mia by the hand and led her towards the centre of the room.

"I'm not a great dancer," Mia said loudly over the music.

"That makes two of us." Luke smiled at her.

He was lying of course, but Mia had just started to enjoy herself when Alva shimmied her way towards them. She sidled up to Luke, turning her back to him and looking over her shoulder while she moved to the music. She raised both hands to either side of her head, lifted her long, chestnut hair on top and let it drop back down in a swish, like a sleek living curtain.

Mia looked at Luke. He seemed transfixed by Alva, and Mia felt as though she'd been kicked in the solar plexus. She mumbled "Excuse me," to no one in particular, and practically ran into the Ladies. She locked herself into a cubicle and sat down on the closed toilet lid. She leaned forward and put her head in her hands. What had she been thinking of? Of course — Luke and Alva — what an obvious couple. Both stunningly attractive, with everything going for them. How could I have thought that Luke was interested in me, she wondered.

At the wedding gig earlier Mia could have sworn that Luke had been flirting with her, but it had obviously been no more than wishful thinking. He was just being nice and she had read too much into it. Maybe it was Alva he was really after. No wonder he'd practically insisted that she come out this evening.

Mia stayed in the cubicle until she felt a little better and then made her way back to the table where Bert was sitting, minding the drinks. She watched Alva flutter around Luke like an exotic butterfly and her heart sank even further in her chest. "Can you tell the others that I'm going home?" she said, dragging her eyes off the happy couple. "I'm exhausted. But best of luck with the club. I'm sure it will be a huge success."

"Is everything all right?" Bert asked gently. Mia was staring at the dance floor and she seemed very out of sorts.

"Yes, fine, really," she said. "I was working this evening and I'm just a little tired. It was lovely to meet you."

"And you. And please ask one of the bouncers at the door to order you a taxi. We have an account with a taxi company."

"Oh, thanks. I'll do that."

As Mia walked out she spied Sean just to the left of the staircase. Men! she thought as she made her way towards him. The woman clinging to his arm was tiny, and looked a little old to be dressed in such a provocative manner. The plunging lacing on the front of her red dress left little to the imagination, and, Mia thought in an uncharacteristically catty way, was certainly not a good choice for someone with such a droopy chest.

"Mia!" Sean said in surprise as she plonked herself in front of him.

"Sean," Mia replied.

"Mia, this is Sadie," Sean said, trying to sound less nervous than he felt. He hoped to goodness that Mia wouldn't say anything inappropriate. "Mia's an old friend of mine."

"Hello, Sadie. I'm also Alva's friend." Mia looked at the woman, whose head was tilted up towards Sean, a simpering smile on her thin face. Mia took an instant dislike to her. "And Alva's here," she added, coming straight to the point.

"Alva?" Sean stared at Mia. "Are you serious?"

"Alva?" Sadie asked, ignoring Mia and looking up at Sean. "Alva, your ex?"

"Where?" Sean asked Mia, in turn ignoring Sadie.

"On the dance floor, with Luke." Mia nodded over at the couple. Alva was doing her hair-lifting trick again and Sean winced visibly as he watched her sashay her hips suggestively to the music.

"Luke from AbbaFab?" Sean asked, unable to take his eyes off the couple. "She didn't waste much time."

"Would you like to dance, Sean?" Sadie asked, following his gaze on to the dance floor. She'd been single for far too long now and she wasn't going to let Sean go without a fight. Damn it, she could hair-flick for Ireland and she was far thinner than that girl.

Sean shook his head. He couldn't bear to watch Alva enjoying herself with Luke any more. "Let's just go home," he said gruffly, turning his attention back to his date. "OK with you?"

Sadie nodded. Going home with Sean was even better.

"Bye, Mia," Sean said. He took one last look at the dance floor. Alva had stopped dancing and was staring over at them, as if sensing their collective gaze. Sean pulled Sadie even closer.

"Bye, Mia," Sadie tittered. "Nice to meet you." Sean swung Sadie around and practically frogmarched her towards the bottom of the stairs.

"Good riddance," Mia muttered as she watched Sean and Sadie leave.

Alva appeared beside her. "So what did Sean have to say for himself?" she demanded.

"Not much," Mia said. "You've just driven him away. Enjoying yourself, Alva?"

"What's wrong?" Alva asked. Mia's eyes were sparking.

"What are you playing at?" Mia asked in disdain. "I thought you wanted Sean back."

"I do."

"You're going a funny way about it."

"He's the one who's with someone else!" Alva said.

"A very silly little someone who won't last the week. She's so not his type. And you've just blown it, Alva. And by the way, I'm going home. Alone. I'll see you later, or tomorrow, or whenever."

"What do you mean, tomorrow or whenever?"

"I guess you'll be going home with Luke."

"No, Mia. I won't be. In fact he's spent the whole time talking about . . ."

Mia cut in. "Give my apologies to Luke for not saying goodbye, won't you? But he has been rather busy, hasn't he?" Mia ran up the stairs without looking back.

". . . *you if you must know,*" Alva whispered the end of her sentence. Right now she felt very stupid and very lonely. What must Sean think of her? And Mia. And Luke. Her stomach lurched and she felt ashamed. She'd been so caught up in her own little world that she had failed to notice what was going on in Mia's life. Of course, she realized, Mia likes Luke, it's so obvious now. But it's too late to do anything about it. Why didn't I notice it earlier? I'm a terrible friend and Mia deserves better. I'm a horrible, horrible person.

At the top of the stairs Mia lingered for a moment. Was she overreacting? Luke and Alva had just been dancing after all. But she'd seen the way Alva was gazing at Luke, a look Mia had seen many times before, and she knew that if Alva had set her sights on him he didn't stand a chance . . . whatever Alva protested to the contrary. Besides, there was another gig tomorrow, well today actually, and she had no business being out at all really. She should never have agreed to it in the first place. Wendy had been right, as usual. Mia yawned. She suddenly felt dog-tired.

"Mia?" A bouncer appeared from nowhere.

She nodded.

"Bert asked me to order you a taxi. It will be here in about five minutes."

"Thank you," Mia said, almost tearful at Bert's kindness. If only other men were as thoughtful.

"I'm sorry," Alva faltered as she sat back down in the booth with Luke. Bert was busy talking to a couple who had stopped to congratulate him on the club.

"Not to worry," Luke replied. He lifted his drink and took a long gulp.

"I hope I haven't spoiled things," Alva said. "With Mia, I mean. She left in a bit of a state."

"Why?" Luke asked.

Alva decided to come clean. "Because I was flirting with you. And I shouldn't have been. But . . . I hadn't realized. About you and Mia, I mean. And Sean's here and I wanted to . . . it's stupid," she finished lamely. "I hope I haven't ruined things."

Luke said nothing for a moment. "Ruined things for you or for me?" he asked.

"Both," she replied honestly.

"So do I." He lifted his glass and drained the dregs of his drink. "It's not always a good idea playing games with people's feelings like that, Alva," he said after a moment. "Especially not Mia's feelings. She's been a good friend to you."

Alva felt about an inch tall. "I know," she said softly. "I'm sorry. I had no idea that she, well, you know . . . that you guys . . ."

"How would you? And it's as much my fault as it is yours. I was just flattered that such a beautiful girl

176

would want to dance with me. You're a great dancer and I got a little carried away I guess. Talk to Mia. I'm sure she'll forgive you."

"But what about you?" Alva asked. "Will she forgive *you*?"

He sighed deeply. "Who knows?"

"I'm so sorry."

"I know you are. But, please, do me a favour?"

"Yes?"

"Is Sean still here?"

"No, he left just before Mia," Alva said.

"Try talking to him about how you feel. Ring him tomorrow."

"But he has another girlfriend now. She was with him this evening."

"What's she like?"

Alva described Sadie in detail.

"That won't last the night," Luke said. "Trust me, I know her type. And from what you've told me about Sean she's not for him. Not after you."

"Thanks," Alva murmured. "You know that's what Mia said." She suddenly brightened. "You know, you're right! You're absolutely right. I should talk to him." She jumped to her feet. "And there's no time like the present. Thanks, Luke."

"I didn't mean . . ." Luke began, but it was too late. Alva was already striding away from him.

"Where's Alva off to?" Bert asked, looking over at Luke.

Luke shook his head. "Don't ask. I think I've just made another big mistake."

★ ★ ★

177

Alva could hardly contain herself in the taxi as it drew nearer and nearer Sean's house. Luke was right — Sean couldn't like that blonde woman, she wasn't right for him, that was obvious. He'd dropped her home of course, that was only polite, but now he'd be sitting up watching late-night television on his own, like he always did when he couldn't sleep. She would apologize for her appalling behaviour in Atlas, he'd admit that he'd been really jealous, and they'd hug, kiss and finally tear each other's clothes off. And then . . .

"Which way at the lights?" the taxi driver asked, interrupting her reverie.

"Right, please," she replied. "And then second left."

He grunted.

Ten minutes later the cab pulled up outside Sean's cottage. Alva paid the driver, adding a generous tip — for good karma — and hopped out. The lights were on in Sean's front room: excellent, he was still up.

Alva stood on the doorstep, weak with anticipation. "I'm sorry" was on the tip of her tongue. "I'm sorry, Sean. Let's start again. I love you."

Before knocking on the door, she had a quick peek in through the window; Sean never pulled the curtains properly.

"What's wrong, Sean?" Sadie asked in the taxi. He was staring fixedly out of the left passenger window, his right arm stiffly around Sadie's shoulders.

She put one of her hands in his and squeezed it tightly, her other hand snaking up his leg towards his crotch. "Is there anything I can do to make you feel

178

better?" she whispered in his ear, her breath hot and moist. She gave his ear lobe a playful nip and he winced.

"Sadie!" Sean nodded at the taxi driver.

She giggled. "I'm sure he's seen it all before."

An image flashed into Sean's mind, the image of Alva wrapping her lithe, toned legs around Luke's body. He couldn't shake it off. What had he done? Alva was so completely over him — that was obvious from her behaviour with Luke in the nightclub. But try as he might, he still couldn't get her out of his head. In fact, spending the evening with Sadie had convinced him even more that he belonged with Alva. But there was no point thinking about that now — it was too late. Alva was with Luke and he was with . . . He glanced sideways at Sadie. She wasn't the worst; she seemed to like him anyway. And he certainly didn't want to spend the evening alone, thinking about Alva and what he'd lost.

"Sorry," he said, turning towards Sadie. "I'm just a little tired, that's all. But let's wait until we get home. It will make it even better, I promise." He threw her a smile.

Sadie's heart turned a somersault. Sean liked her. Really liked her. She'd been worried that his ex-girlfriend had unsettled him, but that obviously wasn't the case. She stroked his leg and beamed up at him. "I can't wait," she purred.

As soon as Sean shut the cottage door behind them, Sadie was all over him like a giant cat, rubbing her body up and down his and licking his ear enthusiastically. "Would you like a drink?" he asked her, trying to slow things down.

"No, but let's go into the kitchen," she suggested. "See what's in the fridge."

"Um, OK," he said with a gulp. He hoped this wasn't all going to turn a little *9½ Weeks*. He wasn't sure he wanted peanut butter and Nutella smeared all over his private bits, thank you very much. Let alone ice cream. In the early days, he and Alva had experimented with paint-on chocolate, but they'd both agreed that it tasted disgusting and that sharing a romantic dinner *before* sex was far more of an aphrodisiac than involving actual food in their lovemaking.

He led Sadie into the kitchen and she immediately opened the freezer section of the fridge and took out the ice-cube tray.

"Can I have a glass?" She smiled at him. "Actually two."

"What would you like to drink?" Sean asked.

"No drink," she said. "Just ice. And warm water."

Sean handed her two tumblers and watched as she filled one with ice, each cube dropping into the glass with a hollow plunk. She filled the other with warm water. "Follow me," she said, walking back into the living room and putting the glasses down on the coffee table in front of the sofa. "Sit down." She put her hands on his chest and pushed him gently on to the soft seat. He leaned back and watched her, getting more and more nervous by the second.

"Sadie, what are you doing?" he asked as she knelt down in front of him and grinned, showing lots of her

180

slightly off-white, rather large teeth. Sean was reminded suddenly of a rabbit. "Sadie!" He almost jumped in fright as she leaned forward and began to open the buttons of his fly with her red-taloned fingers.

"Shush," she said. "You'll love this. I read about it in *Cosmopolitan*." She reached back, took an ice cube in her mouth and began to suck on it.

"Sadie!" he said again. He tried to swat her hands away with his own, but Sadie was nothing if not determined. She took the ice out of her mouth, held the dripping cube between two fingers and sat up again. "Will I turn off the light? Would that make you more comfortable?"

"No, it's just . . ."

"What?" She looked at him in amazement. "It said all men love this. Just shut your eyes. I'll be gentle, I promise."

"Sadie!" he protested for a third time as she popped the ice back in her mouth and delved both her hands rather roughly into his trousers. He'd had enough. What was wrong with him? Whatever the question, Sadie really wasn't the answer, and he'd just have to tell her to . . .

Suddenly there was a loud rap on the window.

Sean took both Sadie's hands firmly in his own and pulled them away. "There's someone outside." He stood up, made his way over to the window and pulled back the curtains fully. He recoiled in horror as he recognized the face pressed against the other side of the glass.

"You prick!" he heard distinctly, even through his extra-thick double-glazing.

"Alva!" He ran to the door and wrenched it open. "Alva!"

Alva looked over and stared at him, an expression of complete disgust on her face. She looked down at his crotch and then back up again. Without saying a word, she turned on her heel and powered off down the street, leaving Sean staring in her wake. He looked down. His fly was gaping open, his white boxer shorts framed by the dark denim. "Oh, shit!" he muttered. What had he done?

"Sean," Sadie called from inside.

Sean felt sick to the stomach. He was an idiot, a complete idiot. Alva would have no respect for him now and she'd be right. How could he have been so stupid? He had to do something. Something drastic. But what?

CHAPTER
EIGHT

Arrival

"Mia, you have to start talking to me," Alva pleaded the following Wednesday morning. "We're living together, for heaven's sake, and I've apologized till I'm blue in the face. Please, this is getting ridiculous."

Mia ignored her. She left the jumper she was carefully hand-washing dripping in the sink and walked out of the kitchen.

"Mia!" Alva followed her.

Mia walked into her room and closed the door in Alva's face.

"Mia, you're being really childish. Just talk to me. We need to sort this out. It's getting beyond a joke."

Mia hadn't said a word to Alva for four days now and Alva was beginning to despair. They'd had their

183

arguments over the years all right, but nothing like this. She waited outside the door for a few minutes but there was silence from inside the room.

"I'm going to work now," Alva said finally. "I'll see you later. I'll cook this evening, OK? Something nice."

Still nothing.

Alva gave up. She grabbed her bag and jacket, and closed the front door behind her. "Damn it," she muttered, getting into the car and thumping the steering wheel with her fist. This can't go on, it's ridiculous. As she drove towards Dublin city, she decided to make one final effort to make Mia forgive her. And if that didn't work she'd move out.

Later that morning, Mia raised her head from her book. Someone was ringing her doorbell. It had better not be Alva again, she thought darkly. At first, she'd got quite a kick from sending her friend to Coventry, but now it was becoming rather tiresome. She wanted Alva to think about her behaviour in Atlas, but it had all got rather out of control and now Mia didn't know how to stop it. She couldn't start speaking to Alva again, just like that. Alva still hadn't apologized properly. Oh, she'd said sorry all right, but Mia didn't think she'd meant it, not really.

Mia got up and looked out of the window. Sean was standing on the doorstep, staring up at her.

"Can I come in?" he shouted through the open window.

"Depends," she replied. "Do you have any food?"

184

"Of course." He grinned up at her. "I'd hardly call in empty-handed this close to lunchtime, now would I?"

"I'll be down in a second." Mia looked around the sitting room. Alva had made more of an effort than usual to keep it tidy, but there were still clothes draped over the back of the sofa and a pile of work-related folders spilling their contents all over the coffee table. But it wasn't too bad. And, in any case, Sean would hardly notice.

Mia left her flat, snibbing the door lock to make sure she could get back in, and went downstairs to the communal hallway. The owner still hadn't got around to installing buzzers for each flat, as he'd promised to do two years ago, but Mia didn't really mind running up and down the stairs to open the door for guests — it kept her fit. But she did feel sorry for old Mrs Carmody in the flat upstairs, who wasn't at her most mobile after two hip operations and had taken to lowering her keys through the window in a small basket whenever anyone came to call. Mia always smiled as she saw the basket swinging past her window on its way down to Mrs Carmody's guest.

Mia opened the heavy front door and stood back to let Sean in. "To what do I owe this unexpected pleasure?"

"Can't an old friend call in without wanting anything?" he asked, feigning hurt.

"No." Mia was no fool; she knew exactly what or who he wanted to talk about. "Come on up."

He followed her up the stairs and into her flat. "I see Alva's still living here," he commented, nodding at the sofa.

"Yes." Mia said, leaving it at that.

He showed Mia a large brown paper bag. "Salads and bread from the deli," he said. "Hungry?"

"Always. Want to eat now?"

He nodded. "Why not?"

They climbed the few steps to the kitchen. Sean put the bag down on the table and began to fish out its contents. "Potato salad," he said, lifting out a large round plastic container. "Apple and walnut; baby roast potatoes and rosemary; and that carrot one with the poppyseeds that get caught in your teeth."

Mia laughed. "Thanks, Sean, I know it's not exactly your favourite."

"Bloody rabbit food," he said. "And pâté and bread."

Mia handed him a breadboard and a knife. "Will you do the honours?" she asked.

He nodded.

She put plates and cutlery on the table and filled two large tumblers with water from the fridge. "Sorry, I don't have any juice to offer you."

"Water is fine."

"Thank you," she said, sitting down at the table and looking at the spread. "I was going to have a sandwich, but this is much better."

"No problem." He watched as she helped herself to some bread and smothered it with pâté. Then she heaped salads on her plate and began to tuck in.

"What?" she asked when she'd swallowed her first mouthful. Sean was staring at her blatantly.

"Aren't you going to ask me anything?" he asked.

"Like what?" She cocked her head and looked at him innocently.

"You know, about Saturday night. About Sadie."

"It's none of my business, Sean," she said evenly and took another large bite of bread.

"Mia," he said, his voice a little mournful, "I need your help. I've been really stupid."

Still nothing from Mia.

"Mia, why are you being like this?"

"Like what?"

Sean waved his hands in the air rather aimlessly. "Oh, I don't know. Uninterested, I suppose. As if you couldn't care less about me and Alva."

Mia shrugged. "Sean, I've had it up to here with 'me and Alva'. I thought you wanted to move on. What about Sadie?"

Sean winced. "That was a mistake. I presume Alva told you what happened?"

"In the nightclub, you mean? I was *there*, Sean."

"No, afterwards."

"Afterwards?" Mia shook her head. "No." Alva had tried to tell her something about Sean and Sadie all right, but Mia seemed to remember that she'd walked out of the room in the middle of Alva's account, even though Alva had been visibly upset. Mia felt ashamed. It wasn't a nice thing to do to her friend.

"So you don't know?" asked Sean.

"No. Go on," she said, curiosity getting the better of her. "Tell me."

Sean stared down at his hands which were pressed against the tops of his thighs. Then he looked up, a red slash of embarrassment spreading up his neck. "Mia, it was terrible. I'm so ashamed. Alva called into the house and caught me . . ." He stopped suddenly.

"Yes?" Mia encouraged. He'd certainly caught her attention now.

"With Sadie."

"Having sex?" Mia stared at him in astonishment.

"Not exactly, but close." Sean explained how he'd answered the door in a rather compromising state.

"Poor Alva," Mia murmured. "No wonder she was so upset on Sunday."

"She was upset?" Sean asked his voice an octave higher.

"Yes, of course she was. Don't sound so pleased about it. Hurting Alva is nothing to be proud of."

"No, no, of course not."

"Sean, what am I going to do with the pair of you?"

He shrugged. "I have no idea. All I know is that I want Alva back. I do love her, Mia. Do you think there's any hope?"

Mia felt like laughing. They certainly deserved each other, that was for sure. "What are you like?" she asked eventually.

"Would you talk to her for me, Mia? Please?" He put his hands together palm to palm in a prayer gesture.

"To tell the truth, I'm not exactly on speaking terms with her myself at the moment."

188

Sean looked at Mia in amazement. "She's still living here, isn't she?"

"Yes. But I haven't said a word to her since the early hours of Saturday morning. We had a bit of a fight."

A smile played on Sean's lips.

"What?" Mia asked.

"You did that to me once."

"Did what?"

"Stopped talking to me."

"Did I?"

"Yes, in sixth year. When I made a joke in biology class about women being inferior to men, remember? You didn't say a word to me for two days."

Mia blushed slightly. Now that he mentioned it, she did recall some incident in sixth year all right. "What happened after two days?" she asked, her voice low.

"It was the weekend and I took you to the movies to say sorry. Something with Richard Gere in it, I think. Who, as you know, I can't stand. It was an act of great charity on my part."

Mia nodded. "Right. Well, this is different."

"Is it?" Sean asked gently. "I presume it has something to do with Luke from the band."

Mia shot him a look. "No, it doesn't!"

"I know Alva," Sean continued, "and she didn't mean to upset you, Mia. It had nothing to do with Luke and everything to do with me. I see that now, even if I didn't on Saturday night. She obviously didn't realize."

"Realize what?"

"How you feel about Luke."

"I have no interest in Luke!" Mia said strongly.

"Mia, don't be like that. It's me you're talking to."

Mia sighed. It would be a relief to talk to someone about it. And she trusted Sean. And she was sick of being angry. "Maybe I like him a bit," she conceded. "But, Sean, Alva was all over him. Hair flicks and all. I just couldn't take it. I thought he liked me." She broke off, embarrassed at her outburst.

"He'd be mad not to," Sean said gently. He put his hand on Mia's. "Talk to Alva. I'm sure she feels awful, Mia. Let her apologize."

Mia pushed the food around on her plate. "It's not that simple," she said.

"It is really," Sean said. "When she walks in the door, just say hello and take it from there."

"I'll see." Mia took a sip of her water and put it back on the table. "So what about you?" she asked. "Are *you* going to apologize to Alva?"

He sat back in his chair and gave a deep sigh. "If she'll let me, yes."

"And if she won't forgive you?"

"I have no idea. But I'll think of something. I haven't given up hope."

"That's the spirit."

Sean looked at his untouched plate. "Haven't done very well on the eating front, have we?"

Mia shook her head. "But I'm starting to feel hungry again now. Let's forget about Alva and Luke for a while and tuck in."

Sean smiled at her. "Good idea. And Mia?"

"Yes?"

"Thanks."

"For what?"

"You know." He nudged her shoulder affectionately with his. "For listening. To Alva and me. I know it can't be easy sometimes and I think Alva . . ."

Mia interrupted him. "Enough! Eat!" she commanded.

It was almost seven and Alva hadn't returned from work yet. Mia was sitting by the window waiting for her, attempting to finish reading another of her old favourites, *Rebecca*, by Daphne Du Maurier, but the type was swimming in front of her eyes and she couldn't concentrate on the plot. Sean was right — she'd have to start talking to Alva again and there was no time like the present. So she'd been waiting for her for the last hour. It wasn't like Alva to be home so late; Mia hoped nothing had happened to her.

"Ping!" Her thoughts were interrupted by a sharp rap on the window. "Ping!" There it was again. Mia glanced towards the noise and recoiled in shock as a small stone hit the glass with another loud "ping!"

"What the hell?" she muttered, rising from her chair and making her way towards the window. She jumped back in fright when she heard a loud bang outside.

"OK, what's going on?" She stared out, and suddenly her view was blocked by a barrage of colour as a cloud of red, pink, blue, green, yellow and purple balloons floated into her line of vision.

She opened the window and tried to push the balloons away so she could look down, but it was no use, there were too many of them. So she began to pull them into the flat through the window instead. Just as she'd succeeded in wrestling three of them in and had cut their rather tough ribbon-like strings with her teeth, allowing them to float up to the ceiling, she heard music from outside. It was one of her favourites, an old eighties song about lions sleeping in the jungle that Wendy used to sing to her when she was a child. Back from London for a two-day visit, Wendy had choreographed a dance for Mia and Alva, and Mia smiled as she remembered the happy summer day when she'd spent the whole afternoon with the two of them, learning the dance and the song. She pulled a few more balloons into the room and then looked down. Alva was staring up at her from the pavement.

"Hi, Mia." She waved up, a hopeful look on her face.

Mia couldn't help but smile. "Hi, Alva," she shouted down. "You're mad, do you know that? Come on up and help me with the bloody balloons."

"Will do."

The music, courtesy of Alva's car stereo, stopped, and seconds later Mia heard her friend bounding up the stairs. She practically ran into the living room where Mia was still struggling with the helium balloons. "Do you like them?" she asked a little shyly, still wary of Mia.

Mia smiled. "Yes. And they seem to like the high ceiling." Sure enough, the balloons had all drifted to the ceiling, where they nestled around the central rose and plasterwork. "Thanks. And where did you find that song? It's pretty old."

"On a compilation album in HMV in town. I knew it would make you smile. You used to play it all the time when we were kids. Mia, I'm so sorry. Really I am. I behaved like an idiot and . . ."

"It's OK." Mia let go of the balloons she'd been holding and they floated up to join the others. She gave Alva a quick hug and then drew back. "I'm sorry too. Sean told me about that thing with him and Sadie. It must have been a shock for you to see him in that state, even if there wasn't really anything going on."

Alva snorted. "Nothing going on? Sean's trousers were practically around his ankles. I know what I saw, Mia."

Mia thought for a moment. "Things aren't always as black and white as they look," she said eventually. "Sean swears that nothing happened and I believe him. He sent Sadie home as soon as you left. He made a mistake, Alva. But we all make mistakes. Talk to him."

Alva snorted again.

"What?" asked Mia innocently.

Talk to him? That was fine advice coming from Mia, Miss Grudge Holder herself! But Alva thought it better not to go into it. Mia had only just started speaking to her again after all. "Nothing. But Sean and I are history, Mia. I have to accept that. It's just not meant to be."

"Ah, Alva."

Alva flopped down on to the sofa and brushed her hair away from her glowing face. "I'll be fine, Mia. Really. I just need some time to adjust to being single again."

"It's not so bad," Mia said gently. "Being single has its advantages, Alva. At least your heart never gets trampled on."

Alva looked up. Mia had a strange expression on her face. "Luke's a good man," Alva said gently. "He also made a mistake. But don't punish him for it, Mia. He doesn't deserve it. It was as much my fault as his."

Mia shrugged. "It's irrelevant now. I'm not interested." She stared up at the ceiling. "Where did you get the balloons?"

"The Balloon Man shop in Dun Laoghaire, but stop changing the subject." Alva took a deep breath. "Mia, there are some good guys out there and although I don't know him all that well, I think Luke is one of them. If I can say that after what I've been through, then isn't there some hope?"

"Maybe," Mia conceded.

"At least give him the benefit of the doubt."

"Like you're giving Sean?" Mia asked archly.

"That's different!"

"Is it?"

"Totally. He betrayed me and our relationship."

"But you're not together at the moment, Alva, and you certainly weren't on Friday night either. So how did he do that?"

"He just did."

"Are you sure it's not a simple case of jealousy? Sean was with someone else and you're punishing him for it. Please, just swallow your pride and talk to him."

"No!" Alva exclaimed. "I can't."

"Can't or won't? Just tell him how you feel."

"I tried, Mia, remember?" Alva said with a wobble in her voice. "You know I did. But *he* wouldn't talk to *me*. I think you're being a little harsh."

"Sorry," Mia murmured. "You're right. But Sean called in earlier and I spent hours listening to him telling me how much he loves you and what a fool he was to let you go in the first place. I suppose it just annoys me." She looked Alva in the eye. "Alva, you love Sean and he loves you. Can't you get over all that's happened and give it one more try? None of this makes any sense."

Alva shook her head. "I can't, Mia. Maybe before Friday night . . ." she shrugged. "Seeing him with Sadie like that, in our house, on our sofa; I feel sick just thinking about it. You say he still loves me, but how could he if he behaved like that?" Alva put her head in her hands. "I know what you're going to say, that nothing actually happened. But don't you see? Men don't bring women home late at night for a little by-the-fire chat. Of course he was going to sleep with her. And maybe she turned out to be a little nuts and not his type. But don't you understand? She was in his house, our house. He *would* have slept with her if things had gone well. That's what matters. Not what he did or didn't actually do."

"I hadn't really thought about it like that," Mia admitted. "And I suppose you're right. But can't you forgive him, Alva?"

"No, I don't think I can."

Mia hugged her friend. "Ah, Alva. What am I going to do with the pair of you?"

"Well, you can keep me busy for a start," Alva said. "Stop me thinking about it all too much. What are you doing this weekend? I still owe you lunch."

"We're singing at a festival in Skibbereen. Want to come?"

"Where's that?"

"West Cork."

Alva smiled. "You know, that sounds ideal. I'm in Limerick on Friday and Saturday at a work thing. I could drive up and meet you there on Saturday afternoon if that suits."

"Of course. That sounds great. I'm sure the others won't mind. And you can drive back with me on Sunday."

"Perfect. And Mia?"

"Yes?"

"I am sorry."

Mia smiled at Alva. "You can stop apologizing. I believe you. Now, you promised to cook this evening, remember?"

"I did?"

"Yes, this morning."

"Oh, right." Alva thought for a moment. "How about a curry?"

"Lovely. I didn't know you could cook Indian."

"I can't. But I know a man who can."

"Sean?" Mia asked hopefully.

Alva frowned. "No! The chef in the Bombay Pantry. He does mean garlic naan bread too."

★   ★   ★

196

Later that evening Mia was woken by the phone ringing. She lowered herself out of bed and staggered into the hall.

"Hello?" she said groggily.

"Hi, Mia." It was Sean.

"It's almost one in the morning," she said. "Is anything wrong?"

"I'm so sorry, Mia. But I had to talk to you."

"Go on."

"It's about Alva."

Mia sighed.

"Before you say anything, let me finish. I know you've had enough of the both of us, but I haven't given up. I've been thinking about it all evening. I need your help."

"Yes?" Mia said, willing him to get on with it so that she could get back to sleep.

"Where will Alva be this weekend?" he asked.

"Actually, I think she'll be in Skibbereen with me. We're singing at a festival. Alva's coming down to join us on Saturday after working in Limerick," Mia said in a low voice. She didn't want Alva to overhear the conversation. Luckily she was a heavy sleeper and was unlikely to hear them conspiring.

"Perfect," Sean said. "Skibbereen? That's about an hour's drive from Cork city, isn't it?"

"I think so."

"Skibbereen," he repeated. "Great. You're an angel, Mia."

"I don't know about that," Mia murmured. "Listen, I'm exhausted. Can I ring you tomorrow?"

"Of course, you go back to sleep. Talk to you tomorrow."

Mia put the phone down, crawled back into bed and switched off the light. And as soon as her head hit the pillow, she was asleep.

Sean, on the other hand, was having another bout of insomnia. But this time at least he had something positive to think about and a plan to concoct. Because he wasn't going to let Alva go without a fight.

CHAPTER
NINE

Gimme! Gimme! Gimme!

"Come on, computer, please co-operate this time." On Thursday morning Wendy pressed the power button on her laptop for the umpteenth time, scrunching her eyes tightly shut and willing it to behave. When she opened them again the screen in front of her was still full of illegible multicoloured lines.

She cursed under her breath and put her hands to her face. Not this morning, please not this morning. Unless she sent the invoices out immediately there would be a major cash-flow problem and no one in the band would get paid next month. Wendy knew for certain that their bank would be none too pleased if she and Ronan were late with yet another mortgage repayment. She'd already used all the excuses in the book on previous occasions, from having to organize several grannies' funeral arrangements (although it was hardly normal for anyone to have quite so many grannies), to sick pets and flooded bathrooms. I could always fall back on the cremated kitchen excuse, Wendy thought wryly. I haven't used that one before.

She took a deep breath and shut the computer down once more. She then opened and closed the lid of the laptop, trying to bring the screen back to life. This particular problem had happened once before, but had righted itself after a few minutes.

Wendy's work station was an old late-nineteenth-century clerk's desk, stained to look like mahogany, which she'd found in an auction house and bought for a song; much less than the cost of a brand-spanking-new but anonymous computer desk from one of the office supply furniture shops, with their unappealing wood-effect surfaces and wobbling legs. Ronan had sanded, stained and varnished it for her and it now sat proudly in the corner of the sitting room. It was, truth be told, a little large for the room, but it had real character and Wendy loved it. At the front was a panel of square cubbyholes and there were large, deep drawers on either side, ideal for holding some of her paperwork. She also kept a small utilitarian filing cabinet on castors beside the desk, which was wheeled under the stairs whenever they had company. And best of all, the desk had its original roll-top — restored to working order by Ronan — which when closed cutely hid away all Wendy's in- and out-trays and mountains of paperwork from Greg and Steve's prying eyes and sticky fingers.

Wendy's living room was her pride and joy. At present its walls were a tasteful shade of eau de nil, but she was about to change them again. She'd recently found the most delightful Designers' Guild curtain fabric, flamboyant pink, turquoise-blue and purple flowers on a plain white background — very retro, and jewel colours were the latest thing, after all. But she'd have to paint the walls to match. Plain white, she thought, white with a touch of blue maybe. Or that lovely Farrow and Ball colour she'd discovered in an interiors magazine only last week — pale powder white. It would cost an arm and a leg, but it would be perfect.

"Ronan!" Wendy yelled from her seated position. "Ronan!"

She heard him run down the stairs. "What's wrong?" he said as he walked into the sitting room.

"Were you asleep?" she asked suspiciously. I left you in bed over an hour ago, you lazy lump, she felt like saying, and you promised me you were about to get up. I've washed the kitchen floor, hung a full load of washing on the clothes-line, cleared the floor in the boys' room, extracted their dirty underpants and socks from under their beds; all this — and you've been bloody asleep.

Wendy gritted her teeth. She knew there was no point saying a word. Ronan would just apologize as he always did and nothing would change. And besides, she had more important things on her mind right at this moment, like her banjaxed laptop; a lecture on Ronan's domestic responsibilities could wait. It didn't usually bother her so much, but in the last few days her energy levels had hit an all-time low and domestic chores which she usually found easy had started to get on top of her.

"Were you using my computer last night?" she asked, trying not to sound accusatory.

"Yes. I was checking some sites for Steve on the Internet. He has to find out about the Egyptians for school. They're studying the Pyramids this week and next week they're doing . . ."

"Did you move the screen?" Wendy cut him off.

"The screen? I probably did. They both wanted to look at the site I found from the Ancient History Museum in Cairo and . . ."

"What did I tell you yesterday morning about the computer?"

Ronan gazed at her blankly. "Sorry, Wendy, I don't remember."

"I told you that there was a loose connection between the screen and the keyboard and . . ." She looked at him expectantly.

"And not to close the computer," Ronan finished. He hit his forehead with the heel of his hand. "Oh, Wendy, I'm sorry, I didn't think . . ."

Wendy sighed. "Ronan, I have so much to do, I can't be without my computer today. I have to finish setting up the Skibbereen gig for one thing. It's next weekend and I still haven't given all our press details to the organizers."

"Can't you ring them?"

"They need photos and biogs for the local papers and radio station. And it's all in here." Wendy tapped the top of the laptop with her nails.

"Can't it be fixed?" Ronan asked. "I'm sure there are companies that do that kind of thing. I'll have a look in the Yellow Pages. Give me a few minutes to ring around, I'm sure I'll come up with something."

"Thanks, that would be great. I'd really appreciate it. Sorry for snapping at you, I'm just under a lot of pressure. You know how it is."

"Of course. And I'm sorry about the computer, really I am. It was stupid of me. While I'm in the kitchen, I'll make you some nice strong coffee. Would you like anything to eat? Have you had breakfast?"

"No, but I'm fine. I'll return a few phone calls on my mobile while I'm waiting."

Ten minutes later, Ronan came back into the sitting room and handed Wendy a steaming mug of coffee and a round of hot buttered toast on a plate.

"Thanks," she murmured, blowing on the surface of the hot liquid and taking a careful sip. "Any luck?" She put the plate down on top of her groaning in-tray.

Ronan shook his head. "Not yet. There's one company that can have a look at it all right, but they're really busy with their regular accounts at the moment. They can squeeze us in tomorrow afternoon."

"Tomorrow!" Wendy spluttered. "Are you serious?"

"I'm afraid so. But I'll keep trying other places."

As soon as Ronan had left the room Wendy had an idea. She picked up her mobile phone, found Des's number and stared at it on the screen. Maybe it's fate, she considered. Wendy wasn't a great believer in fate, she tended to think that you made your own, largely by a mixture of hard work and being in the right place at the right time. But in this case she was prepared to suspend her disbelief, because it suited her to do so. Besides, she told herself, it's an emergency.

She made a deal with herself. If Ronan can't find anyone to fix the laptop, I *will* ring Des, she decided. And this time I'm not going to put down the phone as soon as I hear his voice. A shiver of excitement ran up and down her spine. It's business, she tried to convince herself. Strictly business.

"Ronan," she called through the open door, sealing the deal, "if you don't find anyone, there's someone I can ring. An old friend from my cruise-ship days. I bumped into him at the garage the other day."

"Why don't you ring him now?" Ronan said, walking back into the room. "I'm having no luck and I have to go out soon."

"I will in a few minutes," Wendy said. "I just have to do a few other things first." There was no way she was going to ring Des with Ronan standing beside her.

As soon as she was sure Ronan was otherwise occupied, Wendy picked up her mobile, her hands shaking. She pressed the call button before she had the chance to change her mind.

"Wendy Redden," Des said, "now there's a surprise. Did you ring me late on Friday night? Actually more like Saturday morning?" Wendy could picture the lopsided smile on Des's face.

"No, I did not!" she lied. Shit, shit, shit, she thought.

"OK," he said, letting it slide. He knew she was lying. Out of curiosity, he'd rung the unfamiliar number back the following morning, and had got her voice on the message-minder. "I was hoping you'd ring."

"Des," she said, grateful that he'd let it drop, "I need a favour. My laptop's acting up. Do you think you could have a look at it?"

"Oh, sure, sure," Des said lazily. "I can have a look at it all right."

"It's a bit of an emergency," Wendy explained, ignoring his less than serious tone. "There's a loose connection and the screen's gone all fuzzy. I can't read a word."

"That's pretty common with laptops," he said. "What make is it?"

Wendy gave him all the details.

"Right," he said. "Here's the thing. It could be something simple, like you say, a loose connection. But it might need a new video card and that's a bit more complicated."

Wendy groaned. A video card? That sounded serious.

"How urgent is urgent?" he asked.

"Very urgent. You have no idea."

"I can come over and have a look at it this morning, if you like. There is one temporary option if you do need a new video card, so don't panic yet. I'll see what I can do."

"I'd be so grateful, Des. Really." She gave him the address and directions.

"You know I'll expect the favour returned, Wendy, don't you?" Des said, his voice treacle-thick.

"Um, this is just business, Des," Wendy faltered. "Ronan's here," she blurted.

"Well, we'll have to save the pleasure for later then, won't we?" Des said smoothly.

"No, I don't think you understand . . ." Wendy began.

"Oh, believe me, I do," Des murmured before cutting her off.

Wendy put her mobile down on her desk and put her hands to her face. She could feel her cheeks burning and willed them to cool down. What had she done? Emergency or no emergency.

"Did you ring your friend?" Ronan asked, coming into the room. "Is he able to do it? Are you all right? You look a little flushed."

"I'm fine, just hot." Wendy stood up. "Yes, he'll be here within the hour."

"Thank goodness." Ronan smiled at her. "That was lucky, wasn't it? How do you know this guy exactly?"

"He worked for the cruise ship," Wendy said vaguely. "Administration."

"I see." Wendy had lots of different friends and acquaintances from her cruise-ship days and Ronan could never remember all their names. He'd stopped even trying long ago.

"Hopefully it'll be fixed by the time I get back. Do you want anything?" he asked kindly.

"Where are you going?" Wendy said in a slight panic.

206

"Town. With Pat, remember? I have a meeting with Dino Fairfield, Mr Eurovision himself. It turns out he's Pat's brother-in-law. He's offered to listen to my song and give some helpful advice, I hope." Ronan grinned. "Exciting, isn't it?"

"You never said anything to me about it." Ronan was forever having meetings with people in the music industry; Wendy found it hard to keep up. God bless his enthusiasm, she always said.

"I'm sure I did. I'll be back in a couple of hours. I'll be on the mobile if you need me."

He kissed her on the cheek. "Are you all right, Wendy? You look a little shell-shocked."

"Um, I'm fine," she managed.

What the hell was she going to do now?

"So where's hubby?" Des grinned at her as he strode into her hall a little later that morning. It seemed almost too small to hold his tall, self-assured frame.

"Upstairs," she lied. "Can I show you the computer?"

"Talk about getting down to business." He cocked his head and looked at her. "Like the boots."

Wendy had changed out of her tracksuit and into a skirt and high-heeled boots as soon as Ronan had left. It would make her feel more confident, she told herself. She'd also slicked on some lip-gloss and run a brush through her hair. No point in looking less than professional, she reasoned.

"Nice perfume," Des commented as he followed her into the sitting room.

"Thanks."

Ronan had long stopped noticing her signature vanilla-based scent.

"This is the problem." Wendy clicked on the computer and they both studied the distorted screen.

Des nodded. "I'll get cracking." He sat down on the chair in front of the desk and began to run his fingers along the join at the back of the screen.

"Would you like a coffee?" Wendy asked.

"Love one." He gazed at her for a little longer than was strictly necessary.

"Back in a moment," Wendy mumbled, and practically fell out of the door.

In the kitchen she stalled for time, taking a few deep, calming breaths before clicking the kettle back on to boil. Why is he having this effect on me? she asked herself. Get yourself together, woman. Get your computer fixed and stop this ridiculous behaviour before it gets you into serious trouble. Even if Des does find you attractive, you're hardly going to do anything about it now, are you? It wouldn't be right. What about Ronan?

As soon as the kettle had boiled, Wendy poured steaming water on to the coffee granules, put the two mugs, the sugar bowl and a small jug of milk on to a tray, and after taking another deep breath walked back into the sitting room.

"It's actually one of the fittings at the base of your screen," Des said without looking up. "It needs to be replaced, I'm afraid."

"How long will that take?"

208

Des shrugged. "An hour, tops. But I'll have to order the part for you and that could take a day or two, depending on availability."

Wendy's face drained. She felt like crying. A few days — what the hell was she going to do now? She muttered an expletive under her breath.

"But while I'm waiting for the part I can hook up your hard drive to a different monitor. That way you can use your computer as normal."

"Really?" Wendy was so relieved. She sat down on the sofa and put the tray on the floor in front of her. She began to laugh. "Sorry, I just had to sit down there, it's been quite a morning."

"You don't realize how much you depend on computers until something goes wrong, do you?" asked Des. He stood up. "I have another monitor in the car. I'll get it. I was setting up some new computers in my brother-in-law's office this morning and I have two left over. I don't need to return them for a few days so I can borrow one of the monitors for your laptop."

"Great. But do drink your coffee first," Wendy said. "A few more minutes won't make any difference at this stage and it'll get cold." She was itching to get back to work but didn't want to appear rude.

Des sat down on the sofa beside her. "Are you a bit of a workaholic by any chance, Wendy Redden?" he asked and then grinned.

She picked the tray up off the floor and nodded down at it, ignoring his question. "Here's your coffee. Sorry it's only instant. I'm out of the real stuff."

Des added a large splash of milk and wrapped both his hands around the mug cosily. Wendy placed the tray on the floor again, then leaned down and picked up her own mug.

"So here we are," Des said, staring straight ahead of him, a hint of amusement in his voice. "Would your husband not like a cup of coffee?"

"No, he's fine. He's just had one," Wendy said.

"I see." Des took a sip.

Neither of them said anything for several minutes. Finally Wendy became uncomfortable with the silence.

"Thanks for coming over so quickly," she said. "I really appreciate it. Ronan spent hours this morning trying to find someone to help."

"So I was the last resort," Des said evenly.

"I didn't like to bother you on your holidays," Wendy explained. "And I didn't want you to get the wrong idea."

Des raised his eyebrows. "And what idea would that be exactly?"

Wendy stared at the floor. "That it was anything other than strictly business."

"Unfinished business," Des murmured. He took another swig of his coffee and replaced the half-full mug on the tray.

Wendy held her breath. Unfinished business, what does he mean by that? What will I do if he tries to kiss me? I haven't kissed anyone but Ronan for so many years — will it feel any different?

Stop it, Wendy! she chastised herself. That's quite enough. He's not interested in kissing anyone, especially not you.

210

But he stood up. "Thanks for the coffee. I'd better get back to work. I know you're anxious to be rid of me. I'll get the monitor from the car."

Wendy watched him as he walked out of the room. She felt strangely disappointed.

Twenty minutes later, the computer was working again. "Bless you," Wendy said in delight as her familiar files popped up on to the new screen. It was slightly awkward as her keyboard now sat beside the new screen and not directly in front of it, forcing her to twist her neck and head slightly to read it, but it would be fine for a few days. It was working — that was the main thing.

"My pleasure."

"And what do I owe you?"

"Wendy, you insult me. You don't owe me anything."

"Please. You've saved my life. Let me do something." The words were out before she had the chance to stop them.

"You can let me take you out to lunch," Des suggested instantly, his eyes twinkling. "How about that?"

"Um, I'm not sure . . . I'll have to check when Ronan's free to babysit," she said, fishing for an excuse.

"Why don't you go upstairs and ask him?" Des said smoothly. "If he is upstairs."

"Why don't I just get back to you?" Wendy said.

Des grinned at her. "He's out, isn't he?"

"Um, yes," Wendy admitted. "But I didn't want . . ."

Des put his finger on her lips and pressed gently. "Shush." He took some of her long blonde hair in his hand and brushed her face with it. "Wendy, I won't do anything you don't want me to do."

Wendy felt a frisson of excitement, mixed with a pit-of-the-stomach feeling of guilt. "I don't want to do anything," she gulped. "Really." She flicked her head to the side, pulling her hair out of his hand, leaving a few ripped-out strands lingering in his fingers. It hurt a little, but she didn't care.

"Feisty," he said. "I like that." He put his hand behind her head; she could feel the power in his firm, strong fingers as he pulled her face towards his.

"Des!" she protested. "Stop, please."

"Just one kiss and then I'll leave," he said. "I promise. One kiss for old times' sake."

Wendy faltered for a moment. What harm would it do, she asked herself, knowing full well that just one kiss never meant just one kiss. But she hadn't wanted anything so much for as long as she could remember. Her legs were practically buckling under her and the blood was pumping through her veins. She felt wanted, special, alive.

"Not now," she murmured. "Not here."

"Just one kiss," he whispered, leaning towards her.

She could feel his warm breath in her ear and it made her whole body tingle. He planted a tiny, fluttery, warm kiss on her neck, which melted on to her skin. He put his hands on her shoulders and gazed into her eyes. Wendy closed her eyes, willing him to kiss her properly, all her nerve endings tingling and her lips waiting to be kissed.

"Ring me," he said in a silky-smooth voice.

212

She opened her eyes, mortified.

His eyes were caressing her face. "I don't want to keep you from your work."

"But . . ." Wendy began.

Des silenced her with a finger on the lips again. "Later," he said.

He turned away from her, opened the front door and left without turning round.

Wendy stood rooted to the spot, unable to move. Her blood was still pumping through her body, her lips still aching for his. She heard his car pull away. Finally she shut the door and rested her back against the wood. As if I could do any work now, she thought, her neck still poker-hot from his caress.

A few hours later, Ronan returned to find Wendy sitting at her desk, gazing into space. It wasn't like her; usually she was doing at least two things at once — talking on the telephone, the receiver lodged between her neck and her ear, leaving her hands free to type an email; or printing out some booking details while simultaneously filling in figures on her complicated expenses spread-sheets and talking to Sid in the tax office, the kindly official with whom she was on first-name terms due to her regular calls to his desk. As well as everything else, Wendy filed all the band members' tax returns.

"Is everything all right?" Ronan asked, a little concerned. "Is the computer still broken?"

"No, Des fixed it, temporarily anyway."

"Des?"

"My friend. You know, the computer guy."

"You never told me his name."

"Didn't I? It's Des. Des Sullivan."

Wendy felt strange. She should feel guilty even saying Des's name out loud, especially in front of Ronan. But she didn't. She felt elated, reckless, dangerous and capable of anything.

"So you were able to work this morning after all?" Ronan encouraged.

Wendy really was in an odd mood. Usually you couldn't stop her talking about all the work she had to do. But now she'd gone all quiet and there was a wicked glint in her eye that he hadn't seen for a long time. When he'd first met her, the glint was often there, but the daily grind of work, running the house and looking after two lively boys had dulled her sparkle a little. Ronan felt very, very nervous. Something was up, he could sense it.

"Yes, yes," she said distractedly.

She stood up and smiled at him a little too brightly. "I have to go out for a while. I'm viewing a house."

"Right now?" Ronan asked. "Can't it wait? I thought you were snowed under with work."

"I am, but I need a break," she said evenly. She looked at her watch. "I won't be long; it's only in Sandycove, one of the big Victorian houses on the seafront. I'll be back within the hour. If the woman from the Skibbereen Festival rings, could you ask her if she received the attachments? I sent her two photographs — one black and white and one colour, a press release and some reviews."

214

"Sure," Ronan said. "Anything else?"

"No, that's it. We have that corporate gig in Booterstown tonight, but they only want us to play for an hour. We're collecting Mia on the way." She leaned over and gave him a peck on the cheek. "See you later."

"See you."

As soon as Wendy had closed the front door behind her, Ronan looked out of the window. She crunched over the gravel in her boots, opened the car door and hitched up her snug-fitting leather skirt so she could get in without stretching it. He watched as she pulled the rear-view mirror down in order to check her make-up and only when satisfied turned the key in the ignition and reversed slowly out of the gateway, her brake lights still on. She'd left the handbrake on again.

Wendy wasn't wearing those boots or that skirt earlier, Ronan noticed with a start. He felt hollow inside. For a long time he'd suspected that he wasn't enough for Wendy, that sooner or later she'd realize how amazing she really was and would leave him for someone more exciting, someone who could give her the type of lifestyle she deserved. A life of luxury, allowing her to have everything her heart desired, from top-of-the-range leather bags to handpainted velvet cushions — all the things she lusted after in the glossy magazines she loved to read. And a house with many, many rooms that she could renovate and change to her heart's content. A house where velvet cushions wouldn't appear out of place.

If she was having an affair, how could he blame her? In fact, he'd suspected as much for a long time. Some of the house viewings had to be a ruse for clandestine meetings — surely no one could be that interested in other people's property, especially when they had no intention of buying?

This time he had to know for sure. He jumped to his feet. Within seconds he was also driving towards Sandycove.

Wendy's mobile beeped just as she pulled up outside Sandycove House, the imposing Victorian house on the seafront with its own designer-renovated, ultra-modern mews. She reached down and checked her screen. "*Thinkin of U*," she read. "*I need U — ring me. D.*"

Wendy looked around her furtively. She was being paranoid; there was no one staring into the car. Why would there be? And it was only a text message after all. She stared at the screen. A shiver of delight ran up her spine. She'd heard about text flirting, but it was usually in the context of teenagers or famous footballers. And it was pretty harmless, wasn't it? A bit of fun. She ran her fingers over the keys of her mobile. No, she decided. Not a good idea. She deleted the message quickly before she was tempted to reply and buried her mobile in the bottom of her bag.

"Wendy, is that you?"

Wendy was absorbed in the amazing white-walled, double-storey living room in the renovated mews at the back of the main house. Its wooden ceiling was punctuated with large skylights and light flooded the simple, minimalist interior. It was stunning.

She spun around on her heels. An elegantly dressed woman with long dark hair pulled back off her face in a sleek, glossy ponytail was smiling at her.

The woman cocked her head to one side. "It's Nora, Nora Queen. Nora Valerio now, that's my married name."

"Nora!"

Wendy was bowled over. Nora had changed beyond recognition. When working on the cruise ship she had had short, spiky, henna-red hair, a mahogany perma-tan, and a penchant for skimpy bikini-style tops and bum-hugging cut-off denim shorts — when she wasn't in showgirl mode, that was. Nora, Wendy remembered, had enjoyed a varied career as a pole dancer, post woman, and farm hand on her brother's farm in Donegal, ending up as one of the chorus girls in Wendy's show before disappearing off the face of the planet.

"Nora, you look great. Last time I saw you was on the *Emerald Star*. On the Mediterranean leg. You upped and left the ship without saying goodbye to anyone. Whatever happened? Where did you go? It was the talk of the ship at the time."

Nora gave a deliciously deep and throaty laugh. "A man, that's what happened. Isn't it always? Luca was one of the passengers, and you know what the powers that be were like about dating passengers. When we docked in Sorrento, he whisked me off the ship and we

217

spent a wild week in the most adorable family-run hotel in Positano down the coast."

Nora held out her left hand and an enormous diamond nearly blinded Wendy. "He proposed at the end of the holiday and I said yes, of course. He was the best thing that had ever happened to me. Still is. We lived in Rome for a few years before moving back to Dublin last Christmas. We're married now, with our second on the way." Nora patted her stomach and grinned.

"You wouldn't know it," Wendy said. "You always were annoyingly skinny. I bet you still eat like a horse too."

"Sure do. Even more so now that I'm pregnant again. And what about you? Any family?"

"Two boys. Greg's six and Steve's five."

"And you're in AbbaFab, aren't you? I see your photo in the papers from time to time. I'd love to hear you play, I adore Abba."

"I'll send you tickets to one of our gigs," Wendy promised. "So what are you doing here? Are you moving house?"

Nora laughed again. "Not at all. Luca works for my brother-in-law's estate agency. Lowan's?"

"Ah." Wendy nodded. She recognized the estate agency's name instantly, it was one of the biggest and most successful in Dublin. She was au fait with them all.

"I fill in for him when he's stuck, showing the properties." Nora lowered her voice a little. "It's not really my cup of tea to tell the truth, but it gets me out of the house."

Wendy sighed. "You're so lucky. I love old houses like this, I could spend hours showing people around them. I'd love your job."

"Really? Well, if you're ever interested, I'm sure Luca would take you on in a heartbeat. He swears by pretty women in their thirties. Too young and it's distracting for the punters, he always says. Bit of a dinosaur, my Luca is when it comes to being pc, but his heart's in the right place."

"If I ever leave the band I'll seriously consider it," Wendy said.

"Listen, we should meet up for coffee or lunch. I'd love to hear all about your family. You're married, I presume."

"Oh, sorry, did I not say? Yes, to Ronan Borza, he's also in the band."

"How funny, is he Italian too?"

"His father is, but Ronan's lived here all his life. I met him just after my mum died."

"Oh, I'm sorry to hear that. You used to talk about her a lot on the ships; you two were pretty close. It must have been hard on you. And your sisters. You have two, don't you?"

"Yes, that's right. Well remembered. Gemma and Mia. It was hard on us all, but it's a long time ago now."

"I suppose."

A couple walked towards Nora, intent in their eyes. "Here comes trouble," she murmured to Wendy.

Wendy smiled. Nora always was a tonic. "I'd love to meet up." She handed Nora one of her cards. "Give me a ring. We can do lunch."

"I will." Nora nodded, running her fingers over the tasteful white AbbaFab card with its gold lettering. "Definitely. I look forward to it. I've never been a lady who lunches."

"Me neither," Wendy said. "But for you, Nora, I'll make an exception."

Wendy suddenly realized how little she saw of her old cruise-ship friends these days and made a mental note to look some of them up when she had the time. She sighed inwardly. If she ever did have the time.

As she walked back into the main house, she could hear the couple quizzing Nora on the unusual ceiling roses and original wall friezes. "Italian or French?" they asked.

"Um, I'll have to check for you," she heard Nora say.

Italian, Wendy thought to herself. She was tempted to tell the couple herself, but refrained. It wasn't her job after all.

As she wandered from room to room in the main house, admiring the generous proportions and the high ceilings, Wendy thought about what Nora had said. Would her husband really give her a job? Maybe she could squeeze it in during the day, after the paperwork and before singing. If she got up an hour earlier, it might just be possible. Wendy sighed. Who am I kidding? I already get up at six most mornings. I'm already wrecked enough without even more work.

As she walked into the bathroom, which needed a complete rehaul, often the case with older houses, she heard a muffled bleep. I wonder if it's Des again, she considered, the very thought making her smile. She whipped her mobile out of her bag and checked the screen. It was! As she read the massage she blushed. It was pretty graphic this time, leaving her in no doubt of his feelings towards her. She was shocked but delighted. Imagine inspiring those kinds of emotions in anyone, she thought guiltily. This time she didn't delete the message. You never know, I might just need his number urgently, she reasoned. I'll keep it just in case.

Ronan sat outside Sandycove House in his car. He could see Wendy's car parked two spaces up. He felt terrible. How could he have doubted her? Of course she was viewing a house, she viewed houses most Thursday afternoons if she got the chance. Yes, normally in her tracksuit if that's what she happened to have on, but maybe today she just needed to change for some reason. He drove home feeling like a fool. What would Wendy have thought if she'd seen him? He was a paranoid idiot.

That evening Ronan drove Wendy and Mia to the corporate headquarters in Booterstown where they were playing. He'd been in a quiet, reflective mood all afternoon, but Wendy and Mia didn't seem to notice, they were too busy planning the weekend in Skibbereen. They were travelling down together on the train the following morning, while Ronan and Pat went

221

on ahead in the van, and Wendy was giving Mia the final details.

"There's a press reception tomorrow evening," she said, "and we have to play one song. Then the official opening is on Saturday at twelve, followed by the gig itself on Saturday evening."

"Has Wendy told you that she's cutting the ribbon, Mia? Along with the head of the Skibbereen Business Association," Ronan said. "Some fellow called Gubber O'Shea."

"Really?" Mia asked. "What fun! And what a name, is he really called Gubber?"

"Apparently." Ronan gave a snort. "He owns one of the local pubs."

Wendy groaned. "I'm sure he'll be ancient and he'll probably try to snog me. Might even slip me the tongue if I'm lucky," she quipped.

"Wendy!" Mia was shocked. "That's disgusting!"

"Sorry, little sis," Wendy grinned. "But it's true. I've met a lot of Gubber's type in my day and some of them are randy little buggers."

"Wendy!" This time it was Ronan's turn to be shocked.

"Keep your pants on," Wendy said. "Gubber won't have his evil way with me, I can assure you."

Ronan gripped the steering wheel tightly. He didn't know how to deal with Wendy at the moment. She wasn't her usual self at all. She was extra feisty and some of her old energy seemed to have returned.

Unfortunately, Ronan thought he knew why she was behaving differently. He'd come across a graphic text message on her phone earlier and he was still reeling from the shock. He had no idea how the hell he was going to confront her, or deal with her explanation, for that matter. As far as he could see, he had nothing to win and an awful lot to lose by accusing Wendy of adultery without any solid evidence. But he knew in his heart that her mind was elsewhere, and this cut him to the quick.

At least he could keep an eye on her in Skibbereen, he supposed. There was something to be said for its distance from Dublin. And at some stage over the weekend, he decided, he would confront her about her affair. He couldn't go on like this. Thinking about Wendy with another man was torture. He'd just have to pick his moment.

CHAPTER
TEN

Eagle

As soon as Alva arrived at the Ardilare County House in Limerick on Friday afternoon for the BodyFest event, she felt out of place. She was there to represent Bluewater, who were sponsoring the event, but she was beginning to regret offering to go. For starters, she seemed to be the youngest person in the main reception room by at least twenty years. She was surrounded by women in their fifties and sixties, and they all seemed to know one another. Then she noticed a few younger women as she looked around, and she began to feel a little less self-conscious.

She wasn't sure how much demand there would be for the streamlined Bluewater Cobra range though. As far as she could see, most of the women were wearing baggy grey or dark blue tracksuit bottoms, teamed with all manner of different tops — from skimpy vests that wouldn't look out of place on a Spanish beach to woolly jumpers and T-shirts emblazoned with all kinds of designs and pc logos such as "Save the Whales" and "Keep Dublin Bay Clean". One small, red-haired woman was kitted out from top to toe in a rainbow-coloured tie-dyed creation and Alva had to make an extreme effort not to stare at her. Maybe the Cobra gear is just what they need after all, she smiled to herself. She spied a manned desk to the far left of the room and made her way through the chattering throng.

"Hi, I'm Alva Ryan," she said to the white-haired woman behind the desk. "From Bluewater."

"Alva," the woman said warmly. "I'm Evie. We've been expecting you. It was so nice of your company to sponsor our event." She gave Alva a generous grin.

Alva could feel her whole body relax. Maybe this wasn't going to be so bad after all.

"Carol, could you man the desk for a while?" Evie called over to another woman. "I'm going to show Alva around. Alva's from Bluewater."

Carol, also white-haired, and small and fit-looking, her toned body resplendent in dark blue leggings and a lighter blue vest top — all the more astonishing as Alva reckoned she must be at least sixty — came bustling over.

"Welcome." Carol shook Alva's hand enthusiastically. "We so appreciate Bluewater's sponsorship. With your

225

support, we were able to fly in Alia Oberone from Amsterdam to give classes."

Alva looked at her blankly.

"Alia's one of the most respected and influential yoga teachers in Europe," Carol explained. "You should go to her class this afternoon. It's ideal for beginners and you look pretty supple."

"Supple? Really?"

Carol nodded. "Certainly. You hold yourself well. Excellent posture."

Alva was flattered. No one had ever commented on her posture before. "I'll certainly check it out," she promised.

"Follow me," Evie said. "I've set up some tables for you in the dining room. But feel free to move them elsewhere if it suits."

"Let's go and have a look," Alva said, "and then I can fetch the Cobra boxes from the car."

"Cobra." Evie smiled. "Very good."

"It's a yoga pose, isn't it?" Alva said, glad that she'd read the Cobra brochures carefully.

Evie smiled again. "Are you a yoga virgin by any chance?"

Alva laughed. "Is it that obvious?"

Evie nodded. "But not to worry." She touched Alva's arm gently. "We'll have you sorted out by tomorrow."

Alva wasn't all that sure that she wanted to be "sorted out", whatever that meant. But she said nothing.

The space in the dining room was ideal and Evie helped Alva carry in the clothes from the car and set up the lightweight chrome travelling rail. They heaped the tops and jumpers in neat piles on the table and hung the trousers and longer tops on plastic hangers from the rail. Then Alva decorated the poster boards behind the tables with Cobra information and glossy photos of models wearing the clothes, and pinned up a price list.

Evie ran her fingers over a rich purple velour top with a generously-sized hood. "This is rather lovely," she said. "Do you think it would suit me?"

Alva looked at Evie's conservative black sweatshirt and matching black leggings. "Yes, definitely. Why don't you try it on?"

Evie pulled her sweatshirt over her head, dislodging her glasses, then eased on the Cobra top, pulling the hood over her short hair and zipping it right the way up.

"The colour's great on you," Alva said.

Evie looked like a young girl, her big brown eyes peeping out from the depths of the hood.

"How much is it?" she asked.

"Nothing." Alva smiled at her. "It's a present."

"No!" Evie cried. "I can't accept it." She scrambled to take it off, undoing the zip with a loud crack.

"Please," Alva insisted, stopping her in her tracks. "You'll be doing me a favour. Just tell everyone it's a Cobra top when they ask. Honestly, it's the best possible publicity for the range."

"If you're sure," Evie said hesitantly, fingering the velour.

"Positive."

"In that case, thank you so much."

"My pleasure."

After a healthy but surprisingly tasty lunch of salads and quiche, Alva attended her first yoga class, with the aforementioned and rather strangely named Alia Oberone. Alva wasn't usually one for exercise — even the word "gym" practically made her break out in a rash — and she never walked anywhere if she could help it. After all, she reasoned to Mia and Sean whenever either of them scolded her for being so lazy, that's why cars were invented.

The class was being held in a large wooden-floored reception room, completely empty of furniture. Most of the women were clustered in groups against the walls, chatting quietly, but two were sitting on the floor with their legs stretched out in a wide "V" in front of them, bending forward like ballet dancers limbering up. Alva gulped. She couldn't touch her toes on a bad day, let alone touch her head to her knees as they were currently doing.

"Don't mind them," a tall, elegant woman with white hair piled on top of her head whispered to Alva, gesturing at the women. "That's not what yoga's about." The woman had a slight accent but Alva couldn't quite place it.

"Really?" she asked.

The woman nodded and continued, "Yoga's not supposed to be a competitive sport. It's about finding your inner calm, finding your own sense of well-being. Some people would be better off joining a gym."

"Is it good for dodgy backs?" Alva said, joking.

"It is actually." The woman smiled gently. "Very good. It's also good for restoring equilibrium in a busy life." She looked Alva in the eye. "Modern life can be very stressful, yoga is a great way to take some time out for ourselves."

"That sounds excellent." Alva smiled. "I wasn't sure what yoga was going to be like, to tell you the truth. I've never done it before. I've always wanted to give it a go but . . . you know what it's like. By the time I get home in the evening I'm usually wrecked. I tend to just slob out in front of the telly."

"I know exactly what you mean. I'm prone to laziness myself."

Alva was taken aback. The woman looked incredibly lithe and toned. Not slim exactly, but fit and healthy. Just how Alva would like to look in her sixties.

"I'm Alia by the way," the woman said. "And you are?"

"Alva," she stammered.

This was the famous Dutch teacher — how embarrassing. Alva could feel her cheeks redden.

"Welcome to my class," Alia said kindly, sensing her discomfort. "I'm very honoured to be your first yoga teacher."

Alva felt relief flood through her body. "Um, thanks," she mumbled.

Alia patted the small of Alva's back. "Better get on with the class. See you later."

She moved to the top of the room and stood there as still as a statue, with her hands in prayer position. Her head was bowed, the tips of her fingers resting gently on her mouth, her eyes fixed on the floor. Within seconds everyone stopped talking and gazed at her in expectation.

"Good afternoon," she said in her calm yet strong voice. "I'm Alia Oberone and I'm delighted to be here in Limerick for BodyFest. Let's get started, shall we? There are mats against the right-hand wall, so if you don't have your own, please take one. And then if everyone could find a space on the floor and lie down with their heads towards the centre of the room, we'll begin with some relaxation and breathing exercises before moving on to some asanas and breath-awareness exercises."

Alva did as Alia asked and rolled out her pristine sky-blue Cobra yoga mat on the floor in a space between two other mats and their owners. Minutes later, she was following Alia's voice as it commanded her to focus her attention on different parts of her own body, from her toes to her fingertips. As she concentrated on the hypnotic voice and its instructions, she felt her body relax on to the floor. Her mind kept flitting away, but Alia's deep, soothing voice brought Alva's attention back to her body.

After the relaxation, Alia talked the class through a series of stretches and twists; her instructions were precise and easy to follow and Alva found that by concentrating on her breathing when her thoughts began to drift, her mind was almost totally focused on the moment, only lapsing now and again. Soon her niggles and worries were long forgotten as she focused on Alia's voice. As Carol had correctly surmised, Alva was more supple than she'd expected and was surprised to find her body responding well to the teacher's instructions.

"Now let's move on to the asanas, or body poses," Alia said after giving them all a few moments to rest following the stretches. "Remember not to push your body, let it tell you when to stop. And also remember your breathing. First, Tadasana, the Mountain. Stand in the centre of your mat, feet together, big toes and ankle bones gently touching. Arms hanging loosely but actively to the side. Gazing gently ahead. Concentrating on the breath."

After a while, Alva was so caught up in the practice that she didn't notice the time pass. Resting after a fun pose called the Dog, which involved balancing her body on her hands and feet and moving her weight upwards and backwards, she glanced at her watch for the first time and was amazed to find that an hour had passed already.

After another hour, Alva began to wonder why she hadn't found the time to take a yoga class before. She'd toyed with the idea when yoga was the "next big thing", somewhere after spinning and before Pilates, and was being offered in every gym and parish hall in Dublin, but had never quite got around to it. Now she felt more refreshed than she had felt for many years — tired yet energized. And calm; calmer than she'd felt for a long, long time.

During the final relaxation, Alia asked everyone to make a resolution, to repeat it three times and to do something about it in the weeks to come. Alva made two. One: to find a yoga class when she got back to Dublin and make it a regular part of her life; and two: to talk to Sean, to sort things out once and for all. Only then, she felt, would she be able to really move on with her life.

She opened her eyes and felt as if a huge weight had been lifted from her shoulders. She smiled to herself. She felt in control, ready to face anything.

As she rolled up her mat and popped it into its bag, Alia appeared beside her. "Did you enjoy that?" she asked.

Alva beamed at her. "Oh, yes. It was wonderful. Thank you so much. I'm going to find a class in Dublin when I get back."

Alia thought for a second. "Evie's class might suit you. She's based in Glasthule, is that near you?"

Alva smiled. "What a coincidence. I'm in Sandycove, just down the road."

Alia winked. "No coincidence, fate," she said, her eyes twinkling. She leaned in towards Alva. "Let go of that stress," she whispered. "And face your fears. They might not be as scary as you think." She squeezed Alva's arm. "Will you be at my class tomorrow?"

"Try stopping me."

"And one more thing."

"Yes?"

"You'll have to give up the cigarettes."

"How did you know?" Alva was flabbergasted. She hoped her breath didn't stink or something. Or maybe it was her fingers.

"It's affecting your breathing. I used to smoke too. But you *can* give up when you're ready to."

"Um, thanks," Alva murmured, not knowing quite what to say. "I'll certainly give it some thought."

Alia nodded at her and smiled. "Good luck."

Alva strode out of the class with her head held high, her yoga mat in its bag slung across her shoulder. On her way out she heard the two young women from the class behind her who had been stretching before the class started.

"Did nothing for me," one of them said in disgust. "What about you?"

"Boring. And that bloody relaxation thing at the end, the resolve, what was that all about? I didn't get it. I think I'll stick to the gym from now on."

Alva hugged her arms around her body and suppressed a smile. *I* got it, she felt like telling them.

That afternoon and evening Alva had great success with the Cobra range. As she had predicted, many people had admired Evie's new top and had also noticed Alva's smart yoga mat and matching bag.

"You're a godsend," one woman told her after purchasing two pairs of cotton stretch trousers in a warm moss green and a matching hooded top. "It's impossible to find nice yoga gear in Kildare where I live. I've been wearing these old leggings for years," she said, pointing down at her legs. "I'll be only too delighted to throw them out."

As Alva was selling the range at a hefty discount — part of the sponsorship deal — everyone was delighted with the prices, and she felt reassured that she wasn't ripping anyone off, which enabled her to talk up her products with confidence.

The stand was thronged with women until seven, only letting up when food was served. Alva would have liked to attend another yoga class or one of the other sessions, much to her surprise, but unfortunately work came first.

She sat with Evie and Carol during dinner and they charmed her with tales of their children, husbands, dogs and friends. Both were yoga teachers with many years' experience between them, and Evie was also a baby-massage practitioner and sold special natural products for mothers-to-be and newborn babies' sensitive skin. They were quite a pair and Alva was entertained all evening.

Carol and Evie had jokingly fought over who would have Alva in their class, but Evie won out in the end, due to the close proximity of Alva's house and Evie's studio. It was only afterwards that Alva realized that, of course, she didn't actually live in Sandycove with Sean any more, but she was too embarrassed to point out her mistake. She'd find a nice flat in the general locality, she decided, Sean or no Sean. She loved Sandycove, it was home to her now, and Mia lived nearby, which was an added bonus. It was time to take charge of her life and to move forward.

Alva had planned to leave early on Saturday morning and meet Mia in Skibbereen for lunch. But first she wanted to attend one more of Alia's classes.

"Mia, there's been a slight change of plan," Alva told her on the hotel phone on Saturday morning at half past eight.

"Jeeze," Mia said sleepily from her hotel bed. "What has you up? It's not even nine yet. It's not like you to be up so early on a Saturday."

"I thought you weren't playing till tonight?"

"We're not, but I had a late one last night. I'll tell you about it over lunch."

"Sounds interesting. But I won't be down until three or four. I want to take another yoga class this morning."

"Yoga class? Are you serious? I thought you said yoga was for crusty vegetarians."

Alva laughed. "Did I? I was wrong. Listen, I have to run, the class starts soon and I have to take a shower. Talk to you later."

"See you down here. We'll be in the Town Hall at a reception from three. After that we'll be back in the hotel, so try ringing my room. If I'm not there for some reason, try Wendy's mobile."

"Mia, you really do need a mobile."

"Yes, yes," Mia murmured. "See you later."

"Great, see you in Skibbereen."

Alva clicked off her mobile. Mia sounded in chipper form, if a little tired. Alva pulled her T-shirt over her head, shimmied her light cotton shorts down her legs and stepped into the shower. She closed her eyes and let the hot water caress her face. I'm going to be OK, she told herself. And for the first time in many days, she actually believed it.

CHAPTER
ELEVEN

Another Town,
Another Train

"Mia!" Luke waved from the head of the queue in Dublin's busy Heuston railway station.

Mia made her way towards him, her large travel bag hitting her calves. It wasn't all that heavy really, just awkward, but she couldn't fit all her clothes into her small overnight case, so she was stuck with it. She swung the bag over her shoulder and continued.

"Where's Wendy?" she asked as she joined Luke in the queue, ignoring the irritated glances and tut-tuts of the passengers behind him. She knew she was queue-jumping, but she didn't want to miss the train to

Cork. She'd cut it pretty fine, but luckily Luke had been a little more organized and was almost at the ticket desk.

"She's flying down later. Ronan rang me a few minutes ago. He's already on the road with Pat. Wendy has to do something this morning apparently. Some sort of last-minute thing."

"What?" Mia asked in a slight panic. "She didn't say anything to me about flying down, and I was talking to her earlier. What's happened?"

Luke shrugged. "Sorry, I don't know any more than I've just told you. Why don't you ring her?" He passed her his phone. "You really do need to get a mobile, Mia."

"I know, I know," she said a little crossly. She keyed in Wendy's mobile number and waited, but it went straight to messages.

"Any luck?" Luke asked.

Mia shook her head. "Her phone is switched off." She handed the mobile back to Luke.

"It's fine," he said, putting his phone back into his pocket and then nudging Mia gently with his shoulder. "I don't bite."

"It's not that . . ." she mumbled, her head lowered slightly. She looked up and attempted a smile. "I just wish she'd told me, that's all."

"Warned you, you mean?"

"No! Honestly, I don't have a problem with travelling down with you. Really I don't."

"It might be nice to get to know each other a little better," Luke suggested.

"I suppose." Mia was sceptical. Luke had shown his true colours in Atlas and she wasn't sure how much more she needed to know. "Can you hang on here? I want to get a paper in the shop."

"Sure. Leave your bag, you'll be quicker that way. I'll get you a ticket if the queue gets a move on. If I'm not still here, I'll wait for you at the platform gate. It's platform two."

"Thanks." Mia dumped her bag beside him and walked quickly towards the newsagent's. She browsed through the few shelves of bestsellers for a few minutes before selecting an entertaining-looking novel about an Irish female GP with a disastrous love life. She also grabbed a newspaper and two glossy magazines. If she was going to be stuck on the train with Luke for three hours, she'd need some ammunition.

There was no sign of him at the ticket office, and Mia found him waiting for her as promised, at the gate. He smiled as he saw her approaching and handed the tickets to the inspector, who glanced at them, looked at Luke a little suspiciously and then handed them back with a grunt.

Moments later they were sitting in the train. Mia spread her reading material out on the table in front of her. The mid-morning train was empty and they had the whole carriage to themselves.

"Help yourself," Mia said, picking up the paper as soon as she was seated, bag safely stowed under the table, and gesturing at the magazines.

"Not quite my scene," Luke said, perusing the covers of the first glossy. "I don't have any man problems so to

238

speak, and my breasts are quite big enough, thank you very much." He read the cover of the second. "But this sounds a little more interesting." He read out loud: " 'Learning to Live as One: letting go of your ex.' Might be good advice for Alva, what do you think? We should save the magazine for her."

Mia stared at him. Was he trying to be funny?

"Sorry," he mumbled. "Probably not appropriate."

The driver made an announcement about the doors closing and seconds later the train began to move.

"You're stuck with me now," Luke quipped. "There's no escaping."

"I can always get out at Thurles or somewhere."

Luke shook his head. "This one doesn't stop at all, it's the express."

"I'll survive," Mia said, sticking her head back in her paper.

Luke picked up a magazine and began to read. He was hoping that Mia would mellow in a little while. He'd been delighted when Ronan had told him about Wendy's change of plan this morning; he wanted to set the record straight with Mia, and saw the long train journey as the ideal opportunity. But it didn't look as if that was going to happen now. In a way he didn't blame her — he'd behaved badly and he had no one to blame but himself. He should never have danced with Alva like that; as soon as he'd realized she was flirting with him he should have made his excuses and left the dance floor. But to be honest, he'd been flattered by the attention. Alva was one of the best-looking women in the place, bar Mia, and she'd had him in the spotlight of her wide and generous smile.

After a while, Luke tired of the magazine and put it back on the table. He stared out of the window. Nothing much to look at except green fields and more green fields.

He looked back at Mia. She was still buried in her paper but at least he could see her face now as she'd lowered it a little. Her arms must have tired, he surmised.

"We could have flown down with Wendy, I suppose," he opened. "But it's probably quite expensive, especially at the last minute."

Mia made an "um" sound but said nothing.

"Skibbereen's going to be fun, isn't it?" he tried again. "It's a lovely town. Have you ever been there?"

Mia lifted her eyes and glanced at him briefly this time. "No." She looked back at her paper.

"Anything interesting in the paper?"

"Luke! I'm trying to read."

"And I'm trying to start a conversation."

"I can see that. But it's early. I'm not in the mood."

"It's not that early," he pointed out. "It's almost ten."

"And I'm not a morning person," Mia said. "Why don't you go and see if the buffet car's open? I'd love a coffee. White, please, no sugar."

"OK." Luke climbed out of his seat. "Don't miss me too much."

"As if."

Luke came back with two paper cups of coffee in his hands. He placed them on the table and sat down again.

"Thanks," Mia said, prising the plastic lid off the top and taking a sip.

"What's it like?" Luke asked.

"Not as bad as I'd expected," Mia admitted.

"Mia, will you please let me say something and then I promise I'll let you get back to your paper?"

Mia pre-empted him. "It's fine," she said a little wearily. "I know what you're going to say. Don't worry about it. Alva was just trying to wind Sean up, I know that. I'm not in the least bit bothered, honestly."

"It's not fine, Mia, is it? Or else you wouldn't be acting like this."

"Like what?" Mia glared at him.

"You're clearly annoyed with me and I don't blame you. I felt awful after you left but I didn't know what to do."

"I presume you just left with some blonde, like Sean," Mia said archly. "Isn't that what you all do?"

"No I did not!" Luke spluttered. "I'm not like that, Mia."

"Really?"

"Really."

"As I said, don't worry about it. Now can I go back to my paper?"

"No, I haven't finished. I made a mistake, Mia. But we all make mistakes. I shouldn't have danced with Alva like that." He ran his hands through his hair, making it stick up in funny little spikes. It quite suits him like that, Mia thought, then stopped herself. What did she care what his hair looked like?

"I've had a difficult two years," he continued. "And I'm just getting back on my feet again. I was a mess for a long time and that's why I haven't been in a serious relationship for a while. But I'm not afraid to commit, Mia. That's not a problem for me. It's just . . ."

"Hold it right there," Mia interrupted him. "I really don't need to know any of this, Luke. Please. We're in the band together and that's it. Work friends. OK?"

"Is that really what you want?" Luke asked, his voice low. "I thought there was something between us. I thought . . ."

"You thought wrong," she cut him off again.

"What's up with you today? You're not yourself."

"What do you mean?"

"You're usually so kind. The old Mia would have listened to me."

"You don't really know me, Luke."

"Maybe not. But I do know that you'd do anything for your sisters. You even replaced Gemma in the band when you didn't really want to. You've put up with Alva staying in your flat even though you haven't found it easy. And Ronan told me that Alva's joining us tomorrow night, so you must have forgiven her for hurting you." He stopped for a moment and gave a small sigh. "Mia, I'm so sorry if *I* hurt you. If I could turn back the clock you know I would. But please, just give me one more chance."

Mia was shocked to find a lump forming in her throat. She was being terribly hard on Luke, but she didn't know how to forgive him. It was like Alva all over again. She shut people out to protect herself, she knew that. But only the people she was really close to, like her sisters, Sean or Alva, knew to keep knocking. Others just stayed permanently outside.

Luke sensed her confusion. "Why don't we start again?" he suggested gently.

Mia looked at him. "What do you mean?"

"Pretend we've just got on the train. Just me and you, no agenda, no past, no history. Just two strangers sharing a journey. Let's get to know each other properly. Don't shut me out, Mia. Please."

Mia felt that lump again. Could he really know her so well after such a short space of time? They'd practically only just met after all. She nodded curtly. "OK. Tell me something then. Something interesting about you that I don't know."

Luke stared at the table top for a moment, then looked her straight in the eye. "I was engaged," he said evenly. "Almost a year ago. We'd set a date for the wedding and everything."

Mia was amazed. She didn't know quite what to say. "Go on," she prompted.

Luke sighed. "She changed her mind, basically. Broke my heart. End of story."

"What was her name?" Mia asked. "If you don't mind telling me, that is."

"No. Ciara. Ciara Halpin. She was a nurse in St John's Hospital, sorry, *is* a nurse in St John's. We met at a wedding, how ironic is that?"

"Lots of people do," Mia said.

"Is that where Ronan and Wendy met?" he asked.

"No, they met in a pub. Well, to be precise, Ronan saw Wendy in a pub. He didn't actually meet her until later. He went out with Gemma first."

"Are you serious?" Luke asked in amazement.

Mia nodded. "It didn't last long. Then he went out with Wendy. They got married quite quickly, fairly soon after Mum died in fact. He'd been in love with her all along, apparently. He just didn't think she'd be interested in him."

"And what about Gemma? How did she feel about the whole thing?"

"Fine, apparently. I was only young at the time so I don't really remember much about it to tell the truth. I think Gemma found him a little too sensible, too straight. But for goodness' sake don't tell him that."

"Of course I won't." Luke smiled.

"Gemma went out with one of Ronan's friends soon after the break-up," Mia continued, "so she can't have been all that bothered. I can't remember the exact details. But she's certainly OK about it now."

"Ronan never said anything to me about going out with Gemma," Luke mused.

"Why would he?" Mia said. "It's ancient history."

"I suppose. So what about you? Do you have a chequered romantic past like your sisters?"

"No." Mia smiled gently. "I've had a few boyfriends but nothing serious. Teachers in the music school mainly. And a French guy in college. Nothing like you. That must have hurt. Do you still keep in contact?"

"No. It's easier not to."

"I understand."

Luke gazed out of the window for a second. "It's taken me a long time to get over Ciara." He looked back at Mia. "Life can be hard, can't it? But it's so minor compared with what happened to you. How did you cope, losing both your parents like that?"

Mia was taken aback. It wasn't something she was in the habit of discussing, even with her own sisters.

"Sorry," Luke murmured. "Maybe you'd prefer not to talk about it."

Mia took a deep breath. Luke had told her about Ciara, which couldn't have been easy for him. She should at least make an effort. "No, it's not that," she said after a moment. "I was very young when Dad died, so it didn't have a huge impact on me to tell the truth. But Mum, well, that was different. I was fifteen when she died and I adored her. She was everything to me." Mia could feel tears prick the back of her eyes and she blinked them back.

"Stop if it's too much for you," Luke said kindly.

"I'm all right," Mia assured him.

He handed her a tissue and she dabbed her eyes gently. "Wendy was twenty-nine at the time so she kind of took over. Mum had put her down as my guardian in her will, which came as a bit of a shock to us all, but Wendy took it in her stride. She's always been the practical one. I don't know what we would have done without her — she organized our lives like a military campaign and sorted everything out. I didn't have to worry about a thing." Mia glanced out of the window for a moment and then looked back at Luke. "She didn't really encourage me to talk about Mum much. 'We need to get on with our lives, Mia,' she'd say. She was right, I suppose. And it was her way of coping. We might have all gone to pieces otherwise. But I missed Mum so much and I couldn't really talk to anyone about it. We actually talked about it for the first time last weekend, me and Wendy. Isn't that funny? It's the anniversary of Mum's death soon and we're going to do something for it. Something special."

Luke reached over and put his hand on Mia's. Tears were streaming down her face now. She felt stupid but she was powerless to stop them. She dried her cheeks with the sleeve of her shirt.

"What about Gemma?" he asked. "How did she deal with it all?"

"Gemma was like me, in bits; she just didn't show it as much. Wendy was the strong one, the one who kept us all going. She still is."

"It must have been hard on Wendy," Luke said. "All that responsibility suddenly."

Mia nodded. "No kidding. She was amazing. But, you know, I still miss Mum, even now."

"Of course you do," Luke soothed. He got up and moved so that he was sitting beside her. "That's only natural." He put his arm around her and she rested her head on his shoulder.

"Sorry," she said, dabbing at her eyes again and giving a huge sniff.

"Don't be stupid. It's fine. It's good you can talk about it."

They sat in silence for several minutes while Mia's tears subsided.

Finally Luke broke the silence. "How are you feeling?" he asked kindly.

"Not too bad," she said. In fact, she felt surprizingly good. She smiled at him, realizing that her eyes must be red and her face blotchy. "I must look a sight."

"Not at all." He smiled back at her. "You always look beautiful to me."

Her heart skipped a beat and she could feel her cheeks begin to blush.

"Oh," she murmured. She began to laugh. "You really are a charmer, aren't you, Luke?"

"Don't make fun of me. I mean it, Mia. You're beautiful." He kissed her tenderly on the forehead. "Now, are you going back to your paper?"

She shook her head. "I don't think so. Let's talk. It's far more interesting."

"So I'm forgiven?"

Mia nodded.

Luke put his hand on hers and squeezed it. "Good."

Mia and Luke arrived in Cork city just after one and walked across the river towards the bus terminal. They were lucky; their timing was perfect and they only had to wait a few minutes for the direct bus to Skibbereen. By half past two the friendly bus driver had dropped them outside a hotel on the main street.

Mia looked around her as soon as the bus had pulled out. "What a lovely town," she remarked. "It's pretty big, isn't it?"

"What were you expecting?" Luke asked, the hint of a smile on his lips.

Mia shrugged. "A few shops, some pubs, a supermarket maybe — nothing like this."

"Come on, you city slicker." Luke took her bag off her and swung it over his shoulder with his own.

"Luke, I can . . ." she began to protest but he ignored her and strode up the street. She followed him.

"Almost there," he said after they had walked a short distance, past O'Donovan's Bookshop and a large, bustling supermarket called Field's. Then he stood back against a shop window, put down the bags and pointed at a grey building. "The Town Hall. That's where the reception is later."

Mia stood for a moment, studying the Town Hall and the square in front of it, which was thronged with people. There were busy, cosmopolitan-looking shops along the interconnecting side streets — a deli called Kalbos, a peacock-blue-fronted shoe shop called Shoe Candy; and several upmarket clothes shops which Mia promised herself she'd have a browse in after the civic reception.

Luke watched her taking it all in and smiled. "Dublin isn't the centre of the universe, you know. I grew up in a town just like this."

"Really?" Mia was intrigued. "Where?"

"A place called Oranmore, near Galway city."

"But you don't have a Galway accent," Mia pointed out.

"Ach, sometimes it creeps in," Luke said, allowing his voice to lilt. "But I've been in Dublin so long now that it's been practically beaten out of me."

The Town Hall clock chimed once and Mia and Luke gazed up at the clock tower. "Bang on half two. We'd better get a move on," Luke said. "Wendy will be getting ants in her pants if we're not ready in good time."

"You said it." Mia laughed. "You can tell me more about Oranmore later, OK?"

Luke picked up her hand and kissed it. "I will, I promise."

Mia frowned a little.

"Don't worry," he said with a grin. "I won't kiss you in front of your sister."

"It's not that!" Mia protested.

"Yes it is. You should tell her about us."

"Us?" Her heart soared. She hadn't been an *us* for so long and it felt strange. Strange but good.

"Yes, *us*," he said, taking her slightly dreamy state for confusion. "Me and you. You and me."

"You know," Mia said, thinking about Wendy, "I think I will tell her. Today."

"Good. Now, come on. The civic reception awaits and we still have to get ready. Our hotel is just down the road."

"Would you let me carry my own bag?" Mia began, reaching down and picking it up, but he took it from her and swung it seemingly effortlessly over his shoulder where it nestled against his own.

I'd love to hold his free hand, she thought to herself with a start. And he's such a gentleman, carrying my bag for me. She smiled.

"What are you smiling about?" Luke asked as he led the way down the road.

"Nothing." Mia grinned back at him. She felt in remarkably good humour and was looking forward to later that evening when she'd find out even more about Luke Jackman.

"About time," Wendy said as soon as they walked into her hotel room in the Skibbereen House Hotel. "I was starting to worry." She was in her costume, face bare and hair scraped back off her forehead with her customary white towelling headband. With her hair like that and her skin *au naturel*, she looked years younger, Luke realized with a start, and far prettier. He'd never seen Wendy without her full complement of make-up.

"We had to get the train and the bus," Mia said evenly, "unlike some, who were travelling in the lap of luxury."

"I'm sorry," Wendy said. "There was a problem at home this morning. Steve and Greg had a pillow fight; Steve hit Greg in the mouth and almost knocked out one of his teeth. I had to take him to the dentist. Couldn't be avoided, I'm afraid."

"Is Greg all right?" Mia asked.

"Fine, thank goodness. He has strong teeth apparently. The dentist just pushed it back into place." Wendy shivered. "It gives me the creeps just thinking about it. Greg was really brave. But there'll be no more

250

pillow fights in our house, that's for sure. How was your trip?"

Mia looked at Luke who winked at her surreptitiously, and then back at Wendy. "Good, thanks. Where are Pat and Ronan?"

"Doing a sound check in the main hall. The reception starts at three so you two had better get changed quickly."

Mia looked around the small double room. "Where? Will I change in my own room? We haven't checked in yet so I don't have a key."

"No," Wendy said. "I have everything laid out here and we're a bit short on time."

"And Luke?" Mia didn't think she was quite ready to change in front of Luke, she'd be too embarrassed.

Wendy smiled at her. "Luke has his own room, down the corridor. He can change there. Here's the key, Luke, and your costume."

"Thanks." Luke handed Mia her bag and then took the key and his costume from Wendy. "See you in a minute," he said, leaving the room.

"Oh, Mia," Wendy said as soon as Luke had closed the door behind him. "I shouldn't have dumped you with Luke like that without telling you. I meant to ring, but with Greg and everything . . ."

"It's OK," Mia said. "Honestly. Don't worry about it. We got on fine." Mia opened her bag and fished out her boots and tights.

Wendy handed her her costume. "Fine?" she asked, her eyebrows raised. "Is that it? Fine? Is that all you're going to tell me?"

Mia hadn't said anything to Wendy or Gemma about the night at Atlas or the associated fracas, so she knew she was safe there. "What do you mean?" she asked, feigning innocence.

Wendy leaned towards her and lowered her voice. "He didn't try anything on, did he?"

"On the train?" Mia laughed. "Wendy, are you serious? Of course he didn't. He was the perfect gentleman." She whipped the plastic wrapping off her costume. "Ah, karate suits again. Did you hear that crackle? I'm surprised we didn't see sparks flying with all that static electricity. I hope I don't get electrocuted on stage when I'm rubbing up against Luke." She grinned at Wendy.

"Mia! Please tell me there's nothing going on between you and Luke."

"You've got him all wrong, Wendy," Mia said, slipping off her runners and pulling her jeans down her legs. She was very grateful that Luke wasn't present to witness her prickly stubble. At least it wouldn't show through the thick stage tights. She'd have to shave her legs later. "Luke's a nice guy," she added.

"Hum," Wendy murmured. She had to restrain herself forcibly from commenting further, remembering what Gemma had said about letting Mia make her own mistakes. Her little chat with Luke obviously hadn't had the desired effect on him from all accounts, quite the opposite, in fact. So if something was going on, maybe it was all her own fault. Maybe by meddling she'd pushed them together.

Mia knew Wendy's mind was working overtime. "You always analyse things too much, Wendy," she said. "Stop worrying about me. I'm fine."

"But I do worry about you, I can't help it, it's my job," Wendy said honestly.

"I know." Mia gave Wendy a smile. "I appreciate that. I won't do anything stupid, I promise. But I like Luke. And he likes me too. So can you just be happy for me? Please?"

"I'll try," Wendy murmured. So there was something going on. At least she knew now.

"Thank you." Mia sat down on a chair and began to ease the thick brown tights on to her left and then her right leg. She jumped up and pulled the top of the tights over her stomach. "Very flattering," she said with a grin. She put the tiny white skirt on and shimmied her hips. "It's a bit short, isn't it? I wouldn't want to twirl too enthusiastically. Might give the photographers a bit more than they bargained for."

"I don't think they'd mind too much," Wendy said. "The press like a bit of leg."

Mia laughed. "I hope I don't disappoint them."

"Are you kidding? With your legs?"

Mia smiled. "You're biased. You have to say nice things about my anatomy, you're my sister. We share the same genes."

"Trust me," Wendy said. "There won't be any complaints."

There was a discreet knock on the door. "Ready?" Luke asked, his voice muffled by the wood.

"No!" Mia and Wendy chorused in unison.

"Hurry up then. Can I come in?"

"No!" Mia yelled.

"In a minute," Wendy added.

Mia pulled off her long-sleeved T-shirt. Wendy handed her the white karate top and helped her put it on over her plain white bra, wrapping the thick blue belt tie firmly around Mia's waist and checking that she wasn't showing too much cleavage.

"Can I let him in now?" Wendy asked.

Mia nodded.

Luke walked in and smiled at Wendy and Mia, resplendent in his own matching white karate suit. "What do you think, ladies?" he asked, putting his hands on his hips and spinning round. "Will I do?"

"Just about," Wendy said, surveying the back of the costume nervously. "The seam across your shoulders is looking a little taut, Luke. I hadn't noticed until now. So be careful. No wild stage jumps for you, understand?"

"Wendy, we're AbbaFab, not Van Halen." Luke laughed.

"Are you all ready?" Ronan said, coming into the room. "Everything seems to be running on time and the press are dying to meet the girls."

"Dying to get a look at Mia's legs, more like," Wendy said.

"Probably true," Ronan conceded.

"Stop that!" Mia said. "You're making me nervous. And I'm not ready at all," she squealed. "I don't have my face on yet. Give me a few minutes."

"Neither do I," Wendy added.

"Hurry up, you lot," Ronan said. "Wendy, I thought you'd have them all organized by now."

Wendy shrugged. "Keep your shirt on, it'll be fine. We'll be ready in a few minutes. Tell them Agnetha's putting her thigh-high boots on, that'll shut them up."

Ronan looked at her. "Fine," he murmured. It wasn't like Wendy to be so *laissez-faire*. Especially regarding timekeeping. She was usually a stickler for punctuality.

The Town Hall reception went without a hitch and, as Wendy had predicted, the press were much taken with Mia's legs and other parts of her anatomy.

"Show us your famous bum, Agnetha," one of the older men quipped after the band had finished their rendition of "Dancing Queen" on the small stage at the top of the room.

Mia looked at Wendy, who smiled and shrugged. "You really don't have to," she whispered.

"It's fine," Mia said. "I'm not me, remember, I'm Agnetha. I'm sorry, you'll have to come to the show tomorrow night for that," she said and smiled, fluttering her spider-like false eyelashes at the man.

"Oh, I'll be there all right, Agnetha," the man said, "in the front row. Try stopping me."

That evening AbbaFab played a private gig for the Skibbereen Business Association, a short set lasting just over an hour. The band were all tired after the journey down and arranged to meet in the hotel bar for a nightcap, after removing their costumes and make-up, and having a rest. They'd been invited to join the Business Association for drinks following their set but had declined the offer, knowing it would lead to a long night of carousing and dangerously free drinks; the locals were well known for their partying and their stamina.

The Skibbereen House Hotel was a comfortable four-star hotel only five minutes' walk from the centre of town, overlooking the River Illen. They didn't always stay in such nice hotels, but the owner was a member of the Business Association and the rooms had come as part of the package. Mia's room, a large and tasteful if rather blandly decorated double, had a view of the river, and her en suite held a deliciously large bath, which she'd filled with lashings of steaming water and some of the complimentary lavender bubble bath. She was taking a long soak in the fragrant suds, relaxing back against the cool ceramic end of the bath. She folded a hand towel and popped it under her head, its edge trailing in the water, something she never did at home, considering it an extravagant waste of a clean towel.

Mia loved hotel bathrooms with their abundance of clean, fluffy white towels to use and abuse as she liked; their wall-to-wall tiles which (as long as it was a decent hotel) didn't have grotty grey grouting and weren't hanging off the wall, unlike the ones at home; the tiny bottles of shampoo, bubble bath and paper-wrapped soaps; the dinky little shoe-shine and sewing kits; and most of all the fact that someone else had to clean up after her. Mia didn't feel too guilty about this. She'd worked for a summer as a chambermaid in a hotel in Dublin city so she'd certainly paid her dues. Even at her messiest, she'd never plummet to the lows that some people did when staying in hotel rooms, that was for sure.

As she shut her eyes and relaxed back in the bath, Mia thought about Luke. She was looking forward to talking to him again this evening. And maybe once the others all retired to bed . . . Mia felt a warm glow in the pit of her stomach. She imagined Luke kissing her, his firm lips moving against hers, his strong hands caressing her shoulders. She imagined what it would be like to sleep with him. Mia hadn't had much experience with men in the past. She'd slept with one of her boyfriends, Yves, but she'd found it all rather disappointing to tell the truth. In her opinion, sex wasn't anything to write home about. After a few glasses of wine, Alva often told Mia what a great and considerate lover Sean was, although thankfully she never divulged too much information. But Mia had heard enough to understand that they had a healthy and active sex life, which they both enjoyed immensely.

She had hoped all along that she just hadn't met the right man yet. That sex would be wonderful with a special guy, one who loved her with all his heart and whom she loved back and trusted with all her being. Otherwise she wouldn't be able to relax and enjoy herself. Maybe Luke was the one?

Mia opened her eyes. Life isn't some sort of elaborate fairy tale, she chastised herself. And Luke isn't my knight in shining armour, coming to rescue me. *But*, a little voice in the back of her mind protested, *what if he is?* Maybe there is such a thing as

Mr Right, Mia mused. Look at Wendy and Ronan. They've been together for years and they're still happy. Mia sat up. What time is it, she wondered. I'd better get out. Besides, I'm beginning to feel overheated.

She turned on the cold tap and splashed some water on her face, wincing as the cold droplets hit her warm skin. Then she climbed out of the bath and wrapped one of the huge bath sheets around her body. She pulled out the plug and listened as the water began to drain with a loud gurgle. She looked in the mirror; her face was red and flushed — not a good look — she'd been in the bath for far too long. After drying herself off and tying her damp hair back, she strode into the bedroom. She allowed the bath sheet to drop to the floor and dithered for a moment, completely naked. Simple white cotton underwear or the black lace? She decided on the cotton — the black lace would show through her dress — and put it on. Then she shimmied a pale blue summer dress over her head, slipped her feet into a pair of sandals and pulled a cardigan over her arms. It was a warm enough night, but not that warm. She dried her long hair off — which never took as long as people expected as it was so fine — slicked some lip-gloss on her lips and touched up her eyelashes with mascara. When she was satisfied with the result she took a calming breath and left the room.

"There you are," Wendy said as Mia walked into the bar. She was sitting at a table with Ronan and Pat. "We were wondering where you'd got to."

"Where's Luke?" Mia asked before she could stop herself.

"At the bar," Wendy said. "Getting drinks."

"I'll go and tell him what I want," Mia said, eager for the excuse to talk to him alone.

"Hi, there," she said, sidling up to Luke and giving him a tentative smile. She tried to banish her earlier, furtive bath thoughts of him from her mind, but all hope of this was dashed when he took her hand in his, raised it to his mouth and kissed it tenderly, his lips making her skin tingle.

"So you talked to Wendy?" he asked, surprised that she hadn't pulled her hand away.

"Yes." Mia felt proud that she was able to answer him in the affirmative. She *had* talked to Wendy.

"Good," he said simply. "So what are you having?"

"Sparkling water, please."

"Nothing stronger?"

Mia shook her head. "It's been a long day. I feel ready for bed, to tell the truth."

"So do I," Luke murmured, gazing at her with unabashed longing in his eyes. Mia looked away. She could feel her cheeks burning.

"Sorry," Luke said quietly. "I didn't mean to embarrass you."

"That's OK," she replied, trying not to let her eyes meet his. "It doesn't matter."

"It matters to me," he said. "I want to do things right this time, Mia. After Ciara, I went through a bad patch, drinking too much, going out every night, having one-night stands, that sort of thing. I really wasn't myself for a long time. It helped to deaden the pain I suppose. Sorry, I'd better order the drinks." One of the barmen was standing patiently in front of Luke, waiting for him to order. After he'd done so, he turned back to Mia. "I'm not explaining myself very well, am I? What I'm trying to say is I don't want to rush things with you. That's all."

"You're not," she said honestly. "I'm not used to flirting and male attention in general, I suppose. I'm completely out of practice. I'm sorry, I'm sure you're used to far more sophisticated women than me. I must be a real let-down." She gave a small laugh, regretting it instantly. What kind of idiot must he think I am? she wondered.

Luke smiled at her. Far from finding her awkwardness and inexperience offputting, he found it rather endearing. "Well, you'd better start getting used to *me*, Mia. I intend to be around for quite some time."

Mia was taken aback. She smiled at him, relieved that he didn't appear to find her gauche. "Oh really? And do I have any say in the matter? I might not want you around for very long."

"No, you don't have any say whatsoever," he replied firmly.

"I see," she said with a laugh.

"Here are our drinks," he said as the barman approached them.

"I'll carry some of them over for you," Mia offered.

"Thanks. I'll join you in a minute. I'll just pay for them."

"Thanks," she said. "I'll get the next round."

"What were you and Luke talking about?" Ronan asked as Mia put a pint of Guinness on the table in

260

front of him and a large gin and tonic in front of Wendy, making sure it was resting on a beer mat. Wendy was a stickler for things like that.

"Timing," she said without thinking. "In one of the songs," she added.

"Which song?" Ronan asked. "Maybe I can help?"

"No, it's fine," Mia said. "I think we've got it covered."

"I think there's something going on between Mia and Luke," Ronan whispered to Wendy as soon as Mia had deposited their drinks and walked back to the bar. "Look at them flirting. And he just kissed her. Wendy! Are you watching?"

"Ronan, stop staring at them. And yes, Mia and Luke are together. She told me about it earlier."

"You've changed your tune." Ronan stared at her. "I thought you were dead set against Luke going anywhere near Mia."

"Things change," Wendy said mildly.

"But . . ." he began.

"Ronan!" she said. "Can't you just be happy for them?"

"Of course," he murmured, picking up his own drink. "I think Luke's a great guy and he'll be good for Mia. But *you* said . . ."

"Ronan, just drop it, will you? They're coming over."

Ronan kept his mouth shut for the remainder of the night. He was upset that Wendy had snapped at him, but he'd talk to her about it later. And maybe confront her about his suspicions, if he could work up the courage.

An hour later Ronan couldn't stop yawning. "I'm going to head up," he said. "I'm exhausted. Wendy, are you coming?"

"No," Wendy said. "You go on, I'll be up soon."

Ronan thought for a moment. He didn't want to cause a scene. He leaned towards her and said in a low voice. "It would be nice if you'd join me. Please, Wendy, we need to talk."

"I have another drink on the way, Ronan, and I'm enjoying myself. It's usually the other way around, isn't it? Me going to bed early and you staying in the bar. But tonight it's different. For once in my life I don't have to get up early in the morning to deal with the boys and we have nothing on until lunchtime."

"Fine," Ronan said a little stiffly.

An hour later he was still lying in bed, wide awake, wondering what Wendy was doing. Was she still in the bar? Was she with someone else? He leaned over and switched on the bedside light. This was torture, he had to know. He got up and pulled on his jeans and shirt.

"Ronan!" Wendy said as he appeared beside her in the bar. "What are you doing here? I thought you'd gone to bed."

"I couldn't sleep," he said. His eyes lingered on the empty glasses in front of Wendy, all smeared with her tell-tale dark red lipstick. "How many have you had?"

"A few," she said, and giggled.

"I have to check the equipment in the morning," Pat said quickly, standing up. He sensed trouble. "So I'll be off. 'Night."

"'Night, Pat." Wendy waved her hand at him and gave him a bleary smile.

"I'm taking you up to bed," Ronan said.

"Well, there's an offer," Wendy quipped. She stood up, swayed a little and then sat down again. "Oops," she giggled.

"Come on," he said. He put his arm around her and helped her up.

"Thanks, love," she said, lurching into him.

"Where are Luke and Mia?" he asked, looking around.

"They've just gone up," she said. "Together," she added. She looked at him. "Bet you don't approve, do you? Sex before marriage is very, very naughty." She giggled again. "Not that I'd know anything about that, of course. Would I, Ronan?"

"Let's get you to bed," he said, anxious to stop Wendy before she said anything else. So much for having any kind of meaningful conversation, he thought wryly as he helped her stagger out of the bar.

A few minutes earlier, Mia had rubbed her finger over the condensation on the side of her glass. It was warm in the bar and she was feeling a little flushed.

"Mia, don't take this the wrong way, but would you like to go up to your room?" Luke asked. "You look a little hot. I could join you if you wouldn't mind and we could have a drink there."

Mia considered this for a moment. She wasn't sure how she felt about having Luke in her room. The suggestion seemed to interest her and make her nervous in equal measures. Be brave, Mia, she told herself.

"OK," she said with a gulp.

"It's not that late," he said, sensing her unease. "Maybe we could watch a film or something. What do you think?"

"I'd like that," she said, relieved but also a little disappointed.

And, after saying their goodbyes to Wendy and Pat, that's exactly what they did. The hotel had a fine collection of films on its pay-per-view service, and as they flicked through the trailers, Mia wondered what Luke would say if she suggested a porn film. Not that she would of course. In fact, she had never even watched one, not a proper one anyway. In their teens, she and Alva had daringly taken out a few notorious films from the video shop (which didn't seem to mind what age its clients claimed to be), from *Betty Blue* to *9½ Weeks* (which neither of them had understood at the time), and watched them when Wendy and Gemma had been out singing, but that was about the extent of it. In fact, now that Mia thought about it, she really was quite innocent when it came to sexual matters. She wondered whether Luke would think her terribly childish and inexperienced. She hoped not. Anyway, she had no intention of suggesting a porn film, and wondered why she had even considered it.

Luke chose an American romantic comedy starring Julia Roberts and they settled down to watch it, taking some heinously overpriced chocolate from the fridge of the mini-bar. Luckily they'd had the foresight to bring some drinks up with them. Mia baulked at paying six euros for a bottle of water. She'd rather drink from the tap in the bathroom than pay that.

Luke arranged the pillows against the headboard of the bed. "There you go," he said. "Ready for your own private viewing?"

Mia nodded. I know what I'd like to see, popped into her head before she could stop it. Mia, she chastised herself, stop that! She hopped on to the bed and leaned back against the soft pillows. He jumped up beside her and put his arm around her shoulders. "Is that OK?" he murmured.

"Yes." She snuggled in towards him and rested her head on his shoulder. "Lovely."

The film was entertaining enough and Mia tried to concentrate on the plot and characters, but her mind kept drifting back to Luke. Luke's arm, Luke's leg pressing warmly against hers. Luke's breathing, Luke's . . . damn it, she felt an overpowering urge to kiss him.

"Luke," she whispered.

"Um?" he murmured, his eyes still fixed on the screen.

She put her hand out, raised her body a little and kissed him on the cheek. He smiled at her, gave her shoulder a little squeeze and then looked back at the screen again.

"Luke!" she hissed.

"You're missing a good bit," he said, eyes still glued to the film, a smile playing on his lips.

"Luke!" she said crossly.

"I'm only joking." He gave her his full attention. "You're so cute when you're angry."

"I'll give you cute," she said, grabbing a pillow from behind her head. She swung her legs under her body and sat up on her hunkers.

"Are you threatening me, Mia Redden?" he asked. "I'm a bit of a pillow-fight expert, I'll have you know."

"Are you now?" she said, a glint in her eye. She swung the pillow and it smacked him in the jaw.

"Mia!" he exclaimed, rubbing his jaw and then picking up a pillow. "You're asking for it. I warn you."

"The Reddens are well known for their pillow-fighting expertise," she said.

"I hear they knock each other's teeth out all right." Luke laughed. "I suppose a gum shield is out of the question?"

"Poor Greg," Mia mused. "But no face shots, how about that? Just in case it's a family jinx?"

"Deal." Luke swung the pillow at Mia's waist with such force that it knocked her off her hunkers.

"You brat!" she shrieked. She jumped to her feet, sinking into the soft mattress, and gave him a blow to the chest. He retaliated with a bash to her upper legs. And so they continued for several minutes, laughing and shrieking until they were both quite breathless.

When she stopped to try to catch her breath, Luke rugby-tackled Mia around the waist and brought her down to lie flat on her back.

"Luke," she panted, "that's not in the rules."

"Says who?" He smiled down at her. His face was flushed and his breath was short and ragged. He kissed her firmly on the lips and then drew back. "Is that in the rules?" he said.

"Yes," she said. "And so's this." She put her arms around his neck and pulled him towards her. Their lips touched, gently at first, then with increasing force and passion. Mia's roaming thoughts were silenced, her mind totally and utterly concentrated on the moment. She'd never been kissed like this before — like it mattered, like there was nothing more important than getting every nip, every lick, every caress completely perfect. She used her fingers and hands to explore Luke's face, neck and shoulders, roaming over the rough and smooth landscape of his skin with her fingertips.

"Mia," he murmured, coming up for air, "you're amazing." He gazed down at her and grinned. Then he began to plant tiny kisses on the nape of her neck, moving down towards her chest. His hands brushed back her cardigan and the top of her dress.

Mia stiffened. "Stop!" she clamoured, her hands scrambling at her dress as she sat up.

"Sorry," Luke said immediately. His eyes flickered nervously to hers. "I didn't mean to . . ." He ran his hands through his hair and sighed. "You're just so damn sexy, Mia. I couldn't help myself."

"No, it's not your fault," she said, "it's mine. I'm not ready. I'm sorry."

He sat staring at her. "You're so lovely, Mia. I'd never do anything to hurt you, you know that. If you want to wait, that's fine by me."

"Are you sure you don't mind?"

"Of course not."

"Can we just kiss, Luke? Is that OK? Or is it terribly teenage?"

He grinned at her. "No. I don't think so. It's sweet."

"Sweet?" Mia frowned.

"That's the wrong word." He thought for a moment. "It's nice."

Mia groaned. "That's worse."

"Sorry, I'm not expressing myself very well." He took her hand in his and held it tight. "Mia, whatever you want to do is fine by me. As I said before, I don't want to rush you. Kissing is absolutely great, brilliant. Really. It just feels a little odd to be talking about all this, to be honest."

"Sorry, I think I get that from Wendy." Mia yawned.

"That interesting, am I?" Luke smiled.

"Sorry."

"No need to apologize, it has been a long day. Why don't I leave? Let you get some sleep."

"No, no, it's fine." Mia yawned again. "Gosh, sorry. I've suddenly come over all tired."

"You go to bed," he said kindly. He leaned down and kissed her on the forehead. "I'll see you in the morning." He sat up and made to go, but Mia stopped him.

"I feel like I've wrecked everything," she said, looking at him earnestly. "I'm sorry for encouraging you and then asking you to stop like that. I wasn't trying to lead you on, I just ..." She halted in mid-sentence and looked down at her hands. "You must think I'm so stupid. I don't know why you're wasting your time with me, Luke. I'm an idiot."

He put his hand under her chin and raised her face gently. "Listen to me," he began, "I like you, a lot. And I don't think you're stupid, far from it. I think you're wonderful. You like to get to know someone before you sleep with him, that's nothing to be ashamed of. In fact, far from being childish, I think it's actually rather sensible. And it's really, really fine, honestly. This isn't just some fling for me, Mia. Do you understand that? And I hope it's not for you. It's not, is it?"

Mia shook her head. "No. No, of course not," she said, realizing as soon as the words had left her mouth just how much she meant it.

"Good." He kissed her on the lips, firmly yet gently. "Goodnight. Sleep well. I'll see you in the morning."

She swung her legs off the bed.

"No, don't get up," he said. "I'll see myself out."

As soon as the door closed, Mia suddenly felt very alone. Luke had said he didn't mind leaving, but she wondered if he really meant it. She gave a huge sigh. What was she like?

A moment later she heard a quiet knock on the door. What now? She went over to answer it, half expecting to see Wendy standing there, ready to question her as to why Luke had been in her room so late at night. But it was Luke.

"Oh!" She almost jumped backwards in surprise.

"I didn't get a proper goodnight kiss," he said with a grin. "And my bed's a bit uncomfortable to be honest. I was wondering if I could share yours? I'd like to wake up beside you, Mia. If that's OK with you. Nothing else."

"Yes," she whispered, standing back to let him in. A smile fluttered to her lips and she put her hand up to cover it. Her heart felt as light as a feather and she had to suppress the tiny bubbles of joy that threatened to gurgle out of her throat. "I'd like that too."

CHAPTER
TWELVE

Alva
I Do, I Do, I Do, I Do, I Do

"Mia!" Alva called across the bar of the hotel late on Saturday afternoon. "Over here!"

Mia waved and made her way towards Alva, impeded somewhat by several squat bar stools which had come adrift from the mothership of their tables.

"Hi, Alva." Mia sat down beside her friend and gave her a warm hug and a kiss on the cheek.

"Sorry I'm late," Alva said as she sat back against the upholstered seat. She studied Mia's face. "What has you in such a good mood? You look positively radiant."

Mia just smiled at her. "Isn't it a lovely day? How was the drive from Limerick?" Without waiting for an answer, she whipped up the menu and began to read it. "Gosh, I'm famished. Are you having something to eat? I had a huge cooked breakfast, so I didn't have any lunch. What about you? How about some lasagne and chips?"

"Mia, you're gabbling. What was the first question again?"

"Oh, sorry, was I? Sorry." Mia shrugged and smiled again. "I've no idea."

In fact, she was finding it hard not to smile. Her mouth seemed to be hot-wired to her heart, which was zinging like it had never zinged before.

Alva looked at Mia carefully. Mia's cheeks were flushed and she seemed rather over-excited about something. "You've had sex!" she said finally after noticing what looked suspiciously like stubble rash on the side of Mia's neck.

"No, I have not!" Mia said indignantly. "I'm just in a good mood, that's all. It has nothing to do with . . . you know."

"Well, you've had something," Alva said. She tried to catch Mia's eye, but she had buried her head in the menu.

"Mia! What is it?" Suddenly it dawned on Alva. "Something's happened with Luke, hasn't it?"

"No!" Mia exclaimed a little too vehemently.

"That's it!" Alva cried. She knew when Mia was lying. She nudged her in the side. "Go on, tell me what happened."

Mia couldn't hold it in any longer. She had to tell someone or she'd burst. She'd been keeping it to

272

herself all morning and the strain was getting to her. She'd almost rung Gemma several times before thinking better of it. Gemma would only tell Wendy after all, and then Wendy would want to talk about it. And she didn't want anything or anyone to bring her down to earth just yet, especially not Wendy. "OK. I'll tell you. As long as you promise to keep it to yourself."

"Cross my heart and hope to die," Alva said. "Go on!" She was dying to hear the news.

"I mean it, Alva. Don't breath a word of this to anyone, do you hear me? Especially not Wendy."

"You can trust me, I won't," Alva said.

Mia said nothing for a moment. She considered bringing up the Atlas night but thought better of it.

Alva caught Mia's eye. "Are we OK?" she said. "Mia?"

Mia nodded. "We're fine." There was no point in being petty. It had been a minor blip in their friendship and Mia was happy to put it firmly behind them.

"Really?"

"Yes. Now do you want to hear about Luke or not?"

"Are you mad? Of course I do."

Mia took a deep breath and began at the beginning. She told Alva all about the eventful train journey and the late-night pillow fight. "And that's about it," Mia finished up. "We kissed and then he stayed the night."

"And?" Alva encouraged.

"Nothing happened, Alva. I know what's going through your dirty little mind, but we just kissed, that's all. It was lovely. I woke up and his arm was still wrapped around me."

Alva knew from Mia's tone of voice that she was telling the truth. "How sweet," she murmured.

Mia laughed. "That's what Luke said."

Alva gave Mia a hug. "Mia, I'm so pleased for you. I think it's brilliant." She leaned towards her. "Is he a good kisser?"

"Alva!"

Alva grinned at Mia. "I bet he is."

"I'm saying nothing. So tell me all about your yoga retreat. Was it awful?"

"No, it was great. I met some really nice women and I took a few yoga classes and really enjoyed them. I'm quite supple actually."

Mia snorted. "*You!* Supple? Are you serious? Are you sure you have any muscles, Alva? You haven't exactly used them much."

"I know, I know. But the teacher was fabulous and I really loved it. I'm going to sign up for classes back home too."

"Wonders will never cease," Mia said. "My friend the yogi."

"I wouldn't go that far." Alva laughed. "And I did a lot of thinking while I was there. Yoga really clears your mind, allows you to focus on the important things."

"And?" Mia prompted.

"I'm going to talk to Sean. I want to sort everything out so we can both move on with our lives."

"Good," Mia said. "It's the right thing to do, Alva."

"I know it is. It just hurt so much — Sean dumping me like that — I didn't know how to deal with it. But from now on things are going to be different. I'm not going to take anyone or anything for granted ever again. I've lost one good man and I almost lost my best friend, both through my own stupidity. Neither of which are ever going to happen again, not if I can help it."

Mia touched her shoulder against Alva's. "You'll never lose me, I'm here for the long haul."

"I don't deserve you," Alva said.

"I know."

"Hey!"

"Only joking," Mia said with a grin.

"So what's happening this evening?" asked Alva, looking around. "The town is really hopping. It took me ages to drive down the main street."

"We're on stage from nine until eleven. There's some sort of Irish dancing competition before that, if you're interested."

"I think I'll give that a miss, thanks very much. I'll just watch you sing, if that's OK. I'm really looking forward to seeing you on stage. I'm sure you're brilliant. I'm sorry I haven't made it to anything yet."

"That's all right. You've been busy and it's not as if you can just arrive at someone's wedding or business do uninvited. You're here now."

"You're brilliant, Mia. Do you know that? You have such a big heart. I'm lucky to have you as a friend."

"Thanks," Mia said. She was touched. "Now, can we please eat?"

Alva watched AbbaFab belt out their first number, "Waterloo". Alva and Pat were sitting in the wings on a flight box and Alva couldn't keep her eyes off Mia, who had been transformed by more than just make-up and a costume. She seemed a completely different person on stage: confident, fizzing with energy, dancing and singing her little heart out.

Alva felt a strange sort of lump form in her throat. Mia looked so happy and carefree. She realized with a jolt that Mia needed to be on stage, she'd always needed it, even as a child. It was part of who she was. It enabled her to be a different person for a while, to stretch her limits. And by suppressing her desire to perform since Miriam's death, Mia had been stifling part of her own personality, her safety valve. Being in AbbaFab is so good for her, Alva thought. And it's nice and safe because Wendy is there to back her up, and Ronan too. And now Luke. Long may it last.

As soon as the second song, "Knowing Me, Knowing You", had finished, Pat stood up. "Give me a yell if anything goes wrong," he said to Alva, speaking loudly to be heard over the enthusiastic applause.

"Where will you be?" she asked.

"In the van."

"Doing what exactly?" Alva asked, expecting him to be loping off to roll a joint, or to drink a beer at the very least. If she hadn't been glued to Mia's performance, she might have joined him.

"Ronan's writing a song for the Eurovision," Pat explained. "He has to submit it by Wednesday. He nearly has the lyrics nailed but they need a little more work. I promised I'd look over them, give him a few suggestions."

"The Eurovision?" Alva asked in amazement. That wasn't very rock and roll. "Really?"

Pat gave her a grin. "There's decent money in it. Nothing to be sniffed at. And it's good exposure."

"I suppose." Alva wasn't convinced.

"He wants to write ballads, you see, for boy bands and the like."

"Boy bands?" Alva couldn't contain her mirth.

"Alva, well may you laugh, but do you have any idea how much commercial songwriters earn?" He gave her some ballpark figures.

Alva's eyes opened wider and wider. "Are you serious?"

"Not so funny now, is it? And once he has that market cracked it will leave us time to write some other stuff together. We have a few ideas for an Irish rock musical."

Alva was impressed. "That's great. But what about AbbaFab?"

Pat shrugged. "It pays the bills. But it won't last forever."

"I suppose not," she murmured.

"See you later." Pat walked away just as Ronan and Luke began to play the opening strains of "Dancing Queen". The end of AbbaFab — that didn't sound like good news for Mia. Then again, it was only supposed to be temporary while Gemma recuperated, Alva knew that. But whatever happens, Mia has to keep performing, Alva thought as she watched Mia interact with Wendy on the stage. I'll make sure of it, AbbaFab or no AbbaFab. She's a star.

★   ★   ★

"Pat! It's Sean, Alva's boy — um, ex. We met at one of Wendy and Ronan's parties."

Pat stopped in his tracks and smiled in recognition. "How are you? How are the house renovations coming along?"

They'd spent the evening discussing old houses as Pat had been thinking of buying a cottage in Wicklow which needed to be completely rebuilt. He'd changed his mind in the end, going for a town house near Bray instead, but Sean had been most kind and generous with his advice and had even offered to have a look at the house before Pat bought it.

"Good, thanks. Almost finished, I hope."

"What brings you down here?" Pat asked. He looked Sean up and down. "And what are you wearing under your jacket. Is that Luke's?"

Sean smiled. "It is. And I'm here because of Alva. Is she here?"

Pat nodded. "She's watching the show from the side of the stage."

"I thought she might be."

Sean told Pat his intentions. Pat smiled as Sean unfolded his plan and then began to laugh out loud. "Are you sure?"

"Yes. Positive."

Pat shrugged. "In that case, follow me. If we get separated in the crowd I'll meet you at the right-hand side of the stage. Alva's on the left."

"Thanks, Pat."

"I wouldn't thank me yet," Pat said a little ominously.

★ ★ ★

Alva smiled as she caught the subtle change to the chorus from "Take a Chance on Me" to "Take a Chance on *Mia*". Alva felt happy. It was good to see Wendy and Mia getting on so well. Alva knew that Mia worshipped Wendy, and nothing made Mia happier than pleasing her sister, who wasn't always the easiest of people to please. This evening was just getting better and better. In fact, Alva was getting quite emotional watching AbbaFab play and she wondered if it had something to do with Alia and her classes. Maybe my emotions have been all stirred up by the yoga, Alva thought. Whatever it is, I do feel rather strange.

She began to sway to the music and mouth some of the words. She'd forgotten how catchy Abba's songs were. I must buy one of those Abba compilation albums for the car, she thought. As the song finished she took a swig of water from the bottle at her feet. When she looked at the stage again she was surprised to see a man talking to Wendy and Mia. He was dressed in an Abba costume, one of the "Arrival" jumpsuits, which was a bit too small for him. He looked familiar but she couldn't quite make him out under the stage lights.

"Ladies and gentlemen," Wendy said as the applause for "Take a Chance on Me" petered out. "This is Sean Malone and he has something to say. All yours, Sean." Wendy handed him the microphone.

Alva nearly fell off the flight box. What the hell was Sean doing on the stage? Was this a joke? She stared at him in disbelief.

"I have a story to tell this evening," Sean began. There were one or two groans from the audience. "It won't take long. It's about a man who made a stupid mistake. That man is me."

"Hey, we all make them, buddy," Luke said into his microphone, and the crowd laughed.

"I had a girl, a wonderful, beautiful girl and I loved her with all my heart. And I'm here this evening, making an eejit of myself, to tell her that I'm sorry. That I love her." He stopped for a moment. "And to ask her to marry me." He looked towards the wing where Alva was sitting and put his hand over his eyes in an attempt to catch her eye. "Alva, what do you say?"

The crowd began to clap and cheer. "Go on, ya good thing!" someone yelled.

Sean stared at Alva who was standing, rigid with disbelief. "Alva?" he asked again.

She blinked, like a deer caught in the headlights. Had Sean really just proposed to her? On stage? In an Abba costume? What was he thinking of?

"Alva?"

Blood rushed to Alva's head. She felt sick and dizzy. Air! She needed air. She turned on her heels and ran out of the back entrance of the tent.

"Alva!" Sean said, dropping the microphone on the stage floor and following her. The crowd gasped and then a few people began to clap.

Mia's heart was torn. She wanted to follow Sean and find Alva, but she knew she couldn't. She also knew it was time for them to find their own way, together or separately.

"Are you OK?" Wendy whispered to her.

280

"I think so," Mia said. "And the show must go on, as they say. They'll be fine."

Wendy nodded at her and then turned back towards the crowd. "We thought you'd enjoy that little bit of drama," she said into her microphone, rescuing the situation. "It wasn't real, of course. And thank you to our wonderful actor." The crowd clapped and cheered. "Back to the music, folks," she added. Luke began to sing "Does Your Mother Know?" with as much energy and animation as he could muster.

After a few minutes of frantic searching, Sean found Alva at the end of the large field, leaning against a wall which separated the makeshift car park from a farmer's land. Her body was leaning forward, her hands supporting her weight, and she was staring at the river that flowed through the neighbouring field.

"That's the River Ilen," Sean said softly as he approached her.

"Oh," she said flatly. She continued to stare at the dark, slowly moving water.

Sean sat down on the wall and waited for a moment before speaking. "I'm sorry, Alva. It seemed like a good thing to do. I know how much you like grand gestures and all that."

She snorted. "Do I? I suppose you're right. But I don't necessarily like being on the receiving end of them, Sean."

"Sorry," he murmured again. He stared down at his hands. "I've really messed up this time, haven't I?"

She turned her head and looked at him. He looked completely ridiculous in the Abba costume and she stifled a giggle. "We're quite a pair, aren't we?"

"We are that," he agreed.

She hopped on to the wall and they sat in silence for a few minutes. "Do you really want to marry me?" she asked finally.

"Yes," he said. "Yes."

"Why?" she asked.

"Because I can't live without you, Alva. Lord knows I've tried. You're under my skin. I love you — it's that simple. I can't help it."

She nodded and stared at the river again. "I know what you mean."

"So what's your answer?"

"You're not serious?"

"Ah." Sean shook his head and sighed.

"Ah, what?" she asked.

"I take it that's a no then."

"Not necessarily."

Sean looked at her. "Is it a yes?"

She shook her head. "It's a maybe. We have a lot of things to talk about before we get to that stage, don't you think?"

"You're probably right. So what happens now?"

"I have to find somewhere to live for a start. Somewhere near you and Mia."

"You're not moving back in then?"

"No. I think I need to live on my own for a while." She smiled at him. "Wash my own dishes, cook for myself."

Sean was disappointed. "Are you sure? I don't mind doing all that stuff, Alva, you know that."

"I know, but it's not right, Sean. I think we both need to have our own space for a while. Let's get our relationship back on track first."

"Our relationship? You mean you want me back?"

"Yes. I guess I do."

Sean put his arm around her and drew her closer and gave a huge sigh.

"What was that sigh for?" she asked.

"Relief," he admitted. "I miss you so much, Alva. I wasn't sure if you'd have me back. Especially after that Sadie business."

Alva thought for a moment. "I wasn't sure if I could forgive you for that. But we all make mistakes. And don't let it happen again. Understand?"

Sean nodded. "Alva, you're an amazing woman. I'm so lucky. God, how I missed you."

She wrapped her arms around him. "You're a good man, and I missed you too. You're part of me, Sean Malone. You're like my second liver."

"You always were the romantic." Sean laughed. "Could you not have said second heart?"

"Livers are far more interesting organs." Alva smiled at him. "Sure, where would we be without our livers?"

"You're terrible," Sean murmured. "Now quiet, Alva. I want to kiss you."

For once in her life, Alva did as she was told.

Later that evening in the hotel's nightclub Mia watched Alva and Sean dancing, their arms wrapped around each other, moving in rhythm to the music.

"They look so right together," Mia said to Wendy. "Don't you think?"

"Yes," Wendy agreed. "Do you think they'll ever get married, Mia?"

"I expect so. Not for a few years though. I think they have a lot more living to do first. Getting married so young isn't always a great idea after all."

Wendy said nothing. Her eyes were fixed on Sean and Alva.

"Oh, sorry, Wendy," Mia said as soon as she realized what she'd said. "I didn't mean . . . you and Ronan are different."

Again Wendy said nothing.

"Is Ronan all right?" Mia asked, gesturing towards him. He was sitting beside Wendy, his head resting against the back of the seat and his mouth open, snoring gently.

"He's fine," Wendy replied tersely. "He's just had too much red wine; it always sends him to sleep."

"It's been a busy day," Mia said, anxious to defend Ronan for some reason. "And Ronan always works so hard."

Still Wendy said nothing.

"Wendy, is something wrong?" Mia asked. Wendy certainly didn't seem herself.

Wendy sighed. "No, everything's fine." Her eyes were still fixed on Sean and Alva.

"You can talk to me, you know," Mia said tentatively. "I'm not a bad listener."

Wendy looked at her sister and smiled. "Thanks, but really, there's nothing wrong."

284

"Excuse me, are you the girl from AbbaFab?" a tall, blond man stood in front of them and stared down at Wendy. "I saw you earlier, I'm a big fan."

Wendy looked up and smiled. He wasn't bad-looking really, if you overlooked the yellow teeth and the slight paunch. And he did seem to be rather taken with her if the eager expression on his face was anything to go by. "Yes, that's right."

"I'm Carl. Would you do me the honour . . .?" he said rather formally, holding out his hand. "I'd love to dance with you."

"Why not?" Wendy said, standing up. "Are you OK on your own here, Mia?"

"Um, sure. Luke will be back in a few minutes. He's at the bar." Mia was completely taken aback. What was Wendy playing at? She made it a rule never to dance with fans. "More trouble than it's worth," she always said.

Mia watched as Carl began to swing Wendy around the dance floor, oblivious to the fact that it wasn't exactly in keeping with the slow, melodic music. He was quite a good dancer for his size, Mia considered as she watched Wendy smile and laugh.

"Who's that with Wendy?" Ronan asked, rousing from his nap.

"An admirer," Mia said honestly. "He's called Carl."

They both stared at Wendy and Carl.

"She seems to be enjoying herself," Ronan said, a slight edge to his voice. He wasn't slurring his words, but he didn't seem altogether sober either.

"Ronan, is everything all right between you and Wendy? I don't mean to pry but . . ."

Ronan sighed. He'd love to talk to someone about his suspicions but Mia wasn't the right person. Gemma maybe. But certainly not Mia.

"Fine." He patted Mia's hand. "Everything's just fine."

CHAPTER
THIRTEEN

Wendy
Head over Heels

"Ronan, I'm off now." Wendy popped her head around the kitchen door. "I'll be back later. I'll grab a sandwich while I'm out."

Ronan lifted his head from the paper. He was extremely tired this morning. The drive back from Skibbereen had taken even longer than it should have due to several sets of roadworks, with associated tailbacks, and Greg had been up several times during the night with nightmares about getting lost. He was a perceptive child and Ronan worried that he could sense the growing tension between his parents. "Where are you going?" he asked Wendy, trying not to sound accusatory.

"Bank, post office, shopping centre to buy a new sports bra — my old ones are starting to look really grotty — chemist and supermarket. Nothing very exciting, I'm afraid."

"What time will you be back?"

"Two or three. But you'll be out, won't you? You're going over to Pat's."

"That's right," Ronan nodded. "You look nice, by the way." He took in the navy dress which wrapped around her body and tied at the front, one of his favourites; the navy sandals with peep-toes; the freshly washed hair which hung loose around Wendy's face; the broad smile which lit up her expression.

"Thank you."

Was it his imagination or did she seem a little uneasy? Nervous, even? "See you later then," he said.

"Bye," she said breezily, before shooting out of the door.

Ronan stared at his paper but he couldn't concentrate, the words were swimming in front of his eyes. He shut his eyes tight and then opened them again. Maybe he was being paranoid. Just because Wendy was dressed up and obviously in a good mood didn't mean she was having an affair. Maybe the text had been a mistake, sent to Wendy in error or something.

"Stop it!" he muttered to himself. "Try not to obsess."

But it wasn't easy. It was all he could think about. He glanced at his watch. Pat would be expecting him. He folded up the paper and stood up. He wished he could get the picture of Wendy dancing with that blond man in Skibbereen out of his head, but he couldn't.

★ ★ ★

Wendy's heart was still thumping in her chest. She was sure that Ronan suspected something. It was the way he'd looked her up and down, she decided, his eyes lingering on her dress. Just as well he's not Superman, Wendy thought, a delicious shiver thrilling up her spine. Because if he did have X-ray eyes he'd see quite clearly that Wendy was wearing new and rather risqué underwear: a daringly low-cut black lacy basque with matching lacy almost-not-there knickers. Because she was not on her way to do mundane, boring shopping. Oh, no. She was on her way to a small, discreet hotel just outside Wicklow, where Des would be waiting for her.

They'd been texting each other all weekend and Wendy had finally relented and agreed to meet him, and not just for an innocent lunch either. She knew exactly what he wanted, because she wanted it too. Or at least she thought she did. She certainly wanted something, and maybe furtive sex with Des would stop the gnawing itch, the growing feeling that there was something wrong with her life and her marriage; that there was something missing. She was feeling rather out of control these days, as if her life was just ticking over and she was being pulled along in its wake, powerless to change anything.

Wendy had also been thinking about her teenage days in Westport ever since she'd bumped into Des in the garage, thoughts she'd tried to consign to the dumping ground of her memory a long time ago. What would Ronan do if he ever found out about Westport? She shuddered just considering it. And as for Mia . . .

"Stop!" she told herself. "I can't bear thinking about it." Maybe sex with Des was just what she needed. It would certainly stop her mind churning over the past and place it very firmly in the present.

As Wendy drove up the long gravel drive towards the Glenford House, a small boutique hotel just outside Wicklow town, she started to feel butterflies of anticipation in her stomach. She pulled up outside the large, red-bricked house and the butterflies rose up to her throat. She held back her excitement and tried not to grin as she walked into the primrose-yellow hall, her eyes resting on the glorious stained-glass arched window on the stair landing, the rich, jewel-coloured damask drapes on the windows, the Victorian-looking parlour palms in their huge tubs, and the rich, antique mahogany furniture.

"Can I help you?" A woman appeared from nowhere. A smartly dressed woman in a plain black suit and crisply ironed white shirt. A respectable woman.

"Yes, I'm looking for Des Sullivan. He's booked a room." Wendy willed her cheeks not to redden, but it was no use. She felt as guilty as hell and wished now that she'd worn different underwear. She knew this nice woman could see right through her.

But the woman simply smiled.

"Ah, yes. Mrs Sullivan. It's your wedding anniversary, isn't it? How romantic. I do hope you have a lovely afternoon. Mr Sullivan has arrived and is in your room. I'll take you up now. He's already ordered champagne and lunch."

"How lovely," Wendy murmured.

290

Now she felt even worse. Wedding anniversary? Champagne? Her heart sank to the bottom of her shoes. What was she doing? As she followed the woman up the impressive staircase, she castigated herself. What kind of person are you, Wendy Redden? Lying to your husband, lying to this nice lady. Well, she hadn't lied exactly (she discounted lying by omission on this occasion because it suited her), but Des most certainly had.

"Here you are," the woman said, leaving Wendy outside a door on the first floor. "Happy anniversary."

"Thanks."

As soon as the woman walked away, Wendy opened the door. She was struck immediately by the strong, heady scent of hyacinths. Des looked up at her from the small sofa by the window. In front of him was a coffee table with a silver champagne bucket and an empty flute sitting on it. He was already sipping some of the pale, sparkling liquid.

"Hello," he said in his silky-smooth voice. "Isn't this place heavenly?"

Wendy nodded and closed the door behind her. "Where did you find it?"

"On the Internet," he said. "It was recommended as one of the most romantic hotels in Ireland."

"It's beautiful," she said, still rooted to the spot.

"You look gorgeous." He grinned wolfishly. "Good enough to eat. Would you like a glass of bubbly? It's rather good."

Wendy nodded. "Please." If she was going to go through with this, she certainly needed some Dutch

291

courage. "And in case I forget to say it later, thanks for fixing my computer — you're a life-saver. Nadia told me you called by on Saturday. I really appreciate it. How much do I owe you for the work?" Wendy had been delighted to find her laptop working again on her return from Skibbereen.

"Nothing," he said. "On the house. A favour for a special friend."

He lifted up the heavy dark green champagne bottle and poured expertly, tipping the glass sideways to prevent any frothing bubbles from cascading down the side.

"Come and sit down beside me," he cajoled, patting the seat of the sofa.

Wendy placed her wrap on the back of the sofa and her bag on the seat and did as he requested, her heart quickening as she felt the warmth of his thigh pressing against hers through the thin material of her dress. He handed her the glass and clinked his own against it.

"To us," he said.

"To us," she murmured.

He took a long sip, then put his fingers into his glass, reached over and splattered some drops of champagne just under her neck.

Wendy jumped. The liquid was ice-cold.

"Des!" she exclaimed, her hand moving up to brush the champagne away.

"Leave it!" He moved towards her, cocked his head and began to lick up the drips. His tongue felt hot and rough on her skin and she winced. But she also felt remarkably aroused. She willed herself to fight it.

Wedding anniversary, she reminded herself. What the hell was she doing here? Des wasn't . . .

Des silenced her racing thoughts with a long, sensuous kiss which tasted deliciously of champagne and something sweet. Wendy let herself be kissed, her body beginning to respond to his caresses, her mind befuddled with endorphins. Chocolate, she thought suddenly as Des's tongue caressed hers. That's what the taste was. Sweet, rich and dark.

As they came up for air, she noticed the chocolate-covered strawberries in a small silver dish on the table.

"Want one?" Des asked, following her gaze.

He took one in his fingers and played it over her skin, up and down her arms, lingering on her neck and finally popping it into her mouth while still holding its stalk. "Suck the chocolate off," he said.

She obeyed, the delicious taste filling her mouth.

"That's what I'm going to do to you," he whispered.

Wendy could feel her whole body melt with desire. He stood up and put both arms around her waist, lifting her off the sofa.

"Des!" she said. "What are you doing? I'm not sure I'm ready . . ."

"Shush," he murmured.

He sat back down on the sofa and placed her on his knee, straddling him, their faces almost touching. He pulled her towards him and began to kiss her passionately, one of his hands pressing against the back of her head, making her feel trapped.

Wendy shook her head, forcing his hand away. "Don't," she said, her eyes flashing.

He nodded wordlessly and began to kiss her again. This time his hands roamed her neck and back, inching their way along the seam of her dress towards her breasts. She gasped as he cupped them firmly yet gently, playing with her nipples through the thin lace basque. Then he moved his hands down and began to snake them up her thighs.

Wendy tried not to squirm beneath his touch. She had terribly ticklish inner thighs. In fact, Ronan loved taking advantage of this fact and they often had tickling matches before or after sex. Ronan's side was his weak spot, just above his hipbone. Ronan. His smiling, kind face slipped into her head. Sex with Ronan was safe, comfortable and involved lots of laughter. Of course, it hadn't always been like that; in the early days it had been passionate and intense. But as the years had passed it had changed, they'd changed. Now they knew each other's bodies intimately and enjoyed pleasing each other. At least, they had done. Sex had been a little low on the agenda lately. She hadn't felt like it recently and Ronan hadn't forced the issue. In fact it was weeks since they'd last made love.

Wendy tried to concentrate on kissing Des. This was like the old days with Ronan. Her whole body was quivering under his touch, her nerve ends jangling with anticipation.

"Wendy?" Des said, drawing away. "Will we move to the bed?"

Wendy gulped and nodded wordlessly.

He led her by the hand over to the huge four-poster bed and gently pushed her on to her back. He began to kiss her from the top of her head to her toes; quick, nibbling kisses that Wendy found a little irritating to tell the truth. She watched the top of his head as he took her big toe in his mouth. This did nothing for her and she stifled a laugh. She used to suck the boys' toes when they were babies — they loved that, she remembered. Her two little angels. They'd been darling babies, Steve especially with his unruly mop of white-blond hair.

Des started to tug a little roughly at the front of her dress. Wendy was afraid that he'd rip it. It was one of her favourites, which she'd picked up for next to nothing at an Irish designer's sample sale, and she was damned if she was going to let him damage it.

"I'll do it," she murmured, untying it with shaking fingers.

As soon as she'd done so, Des pulled back the material and gasped. "You're so beautiful," he said, drinking in her pale, smooth skin, almost luminescent against the black lace, his hands roving up and down her flat stomach. He pulled her basque down, freeing her breasts.

Wendy suddenly felt self-conscious. She was practically naked and he was fully dressed. Plus it was broad daylight. However well preserved her body was, after having children it wouldn't stand up to much close scrutiny.

She pulled her dress around her. Des whisked it open again. "I'm not finished," he said in a husky voice.

Wendy began to unbutton his shirt. He helped her, his fingers faster than hers. She smoothed the shirt off his body and it fell to the ground. He had a firm, hairless and tanned chest and Wendy ran her hands over his toned shoulders. He leaned forward, opened her dress again and rubbed his chest gently over her nipples, sending waves of sensation crashing through her body. She scrambled at his jeans, opening his belt buckle and working at the fly buttons. He pulled them down his legs, kicking them off the end of the bed. He still had his socks on and Wendy noticed with a smile that they were Homer Simpson socks, similar to the ones Greg and Steve wore. She stifled a laugh.

"What?" Des asked, noticing her smile.

"Like the socks," Wendy joked.

He leaned down and pulled them off. He didn't seem too impressed by her quip.

"At least you don't have matching boxers on," she said.

Des glared at her. Then she realized that his shorts had a Man United logo on the waistband. She couldn't help but laugh. Des wasn't amused.

"What's so funny?" he demanded.

"My sons have almost the same shorts," she explained. "I'm sorry." She tried to stop laughing but couldn't.

"Wendy!" he said in a whining voice.

She looked at him. His tanned cheeks were flushed, his hair was tousled and his teeth gleaming. Does he bleach them, she wondered. They look unnaturally white.

Wendy pulled her dress over her exposed chest again and sat up. "I can't do this," she said.

As soon as she said it she realized how ridiculous the whole situation was. She might have thought she could have an affair, but she was kidding herself. It just wasn't right. It just wasn't her. Not any more. Not ever.

"What?" Des demanded. "I shelled out a small fortune for this room — champagne, lunch, the works. You're joking, right?"

She shook her head. "No. I'm really sorry."

Des looked completely defeated. "But why?"

Wendy shrugged. "I have no idea."

"Is it me?" he asked a little petulantly.

"No. It's me."

"And there's nothing I can do to change your mind?" He ran his finger along her leg. But instead of feeling turned on, she felt ticklish.

"No, I'm sorry."

He said nothing for a long moment, then grabbed his jeans from the floor and stepped into them. "I'm sorry too. But I don't fucking believe this, Wendy. You're a real prick tease, you know that? You always were."

Wendy fastened her dress and stood up. "That's unfair. I'm sorry I can't go through with this, but I did intend to, really I did. I just . . ."

"What? Changed your mind? Maybe you're just trying to get back at me for ignoring you in Westport, is that it? Some sort of retribution? Or are you trying to

297

get back at Henry through me?" He laughed nastily. "That's it, isn't it, Wendy?"

"No!" Wendy exclaimed. "That's not true!"

"Are you sure?"

"Yes! I'd forgotten all about Henry until I met you in the garage."

Des gave a hard laugh. "I find that hard to believe. According to rumour he left you with a little reminder."

Wendy's face paled. She was speechless with anger. "Get out!" she screamed. "Get out of my sight."

"Touched a nerve, have I, Wendy?" he sneered as he grabbed his jacket. "Don't worry, I'm leaving. My fiancée is flying in from Sydney tomorrow to meet Mum, so I won't be ringing you again. You're some piece of work, Wendy. I pity your husband. Does he even know about . . . ?"

Wendy gave a loud shriek and shoved him towards the door. "Get out!"

"Take your hands off me," he said. "I'm going." He slammed the door behind him.

Wendy crumpled to the ground and began to sob.

"Hello?"

"Yes." Ronan answered the phone that evening.

"Can I speak to Wendy Redden, please?"

"She's in the bath. Can I take a message?"

"Please. She left her mobile phone in our hotel this afternoon. She asked us to ring her when we found it. Can you tell her it's in the safe and she can collect it whenever convenient. We found it down the side of the sofa."

"Hotel?" Ronan said his mind racing. "Sorry, what hotel?"

"Glenford House," the woman said.

Ronan racked his brains. Glenford House, Glenford House? Wendy hadn't said anything about a meeting at Glenford House. Or had she? He couldn't remember. "Ah, right. Of course."

"Did you enjoy your wedding anniversary?" the woman asked.

"What?"

"Your wedding anniversary. The special champagne lunch. I know you had to leave early for a business meeting . . ." The woman tailed off, worried that she'd put her foot in it. Glenford House was often used as a discreet rendezvous for married lovers — lovers who often weren't actually married to each other. She'd seen it all in her time.

Ronan put her out of her misery. "Thanks. Lunch was lovely."

He put down the receiver and sank into the chair. What the hell was Wendy doing in a hotel all afternoon? And what was the woman talking about — a wedding anniversary? What wedding anniversary? The blond man from Skibbereen flashed into his mind. And then the penny dropped. Wendy *was* having an affair. He wasn't going mad after all. He felt sick to the stomach and angry blood raced through his veins.

He ran upstairs, taking the steps two at a time. The boys were in the living room watching television with Nadia. Of course, he thought, Wendy was in the bath washing away the evidence. She'd been avoiding him ever since she'd come in. He banged on the door of the bathroom.

"Wendy!" he shouted. "Wendy, come out right now!"

"What's the matter?" she asked, hearing the edge to his voice. "Are the boys all right?"

"Yes. I want to talk to you."

"Can't it wait?"

"No. Glenford House rang. They found your mobile."

Wendy gasped and put her hand to her mouth. She took a deep breath and tried to calm her heart which was threatening to beat out of her chest. How was she going to explain herself? She tried to think of a valid excuse but failed miserably. What the hell was she going to do? How could she have been so stupid? She should never have asked them to ring her at home, but she hadn't exactly been thinking straight at the time.

At least Des had had the decency to tell the woman at the desk that he'd had to leave urgently for a business meeting. But he hadn't settled the bill which had come as quite a shock to Wendy. Luckily she'd had her credit card on her or it would have been very embarrassing.

It was all such a mess. And for what? She began to cry, hot, heavy tears running down her cheeks and dropping into the bath.

"Wendy, you'd better come out right now, I'm warning you!" He banged on the door again.

Think of something, she thought. Anything.

"Ronan," she began. "I can explain. I was at a meeting about a gig. They're thinking of holding weddings there and they need a band . . ."

"You're lying!" Ronan shouted. He banged on the door again. "Why, Wendy? And who is it? That blond man from Skibbereen? Who?"

Wendy felt like laughing. Carl? As if she'd go near *him*.

"I know you're having an affair, Wendy. I have proof. I've seen the messages on your phone. There's no point denying it. And if you won't even talk to me about it, then our marriage is over. Do you hear me? Over!"

Wendy held her breath. Ronan didn't say anything else. She heard him march down the stairs. She jumped up and grabbed a large towel, sending a wave of soapy water sloshing over the edge of the full bath.

She unlocked the bathroom door and flung it open. Ronan was at the front door.

"Ronan. Where are you going?" she asked, panic-stricken.

He turned and looked at her, his face pale and his eyes glittering through the tears. "I love you so much, Wendy. How could you . . ." He broke off and stared at her. "But I can't take this."

Wendy's heart lurched. Why had she hurt him so badly? She had to tell him it had all been a horrible mistake, that nothing had happened. She began to run down the stairs, her hands clutching her towel around her body.

"Ronan!" she cried. "Don't go. Ronan, I'm sorry. Please come back."

Her foot tripped on something and she fell head first down the stairs. The last thing she remembered was Ronan's voice.

"Wendy!"

CHAPTER
FOURTEEN

One of Us

Gemma and Ronan were sitting in the corridor of St John's Hospital.

"Wendy hates the lighting in here," Ronan murmured, staring at his hands, clenched tightly together in his lap. "She says it's too harsh. It shows up everyone's wrinkles."

"She's right," Gemma said gently, pleased that he was talking at last. He hadn't said a word for at least ten minutes and she was worried about him. "It's not the most flattering, is it?"

Gemma had been sitting with Ronan for almost half an hour. He hadn't really told her what had happened, except that Wendy had fallen down the stairs and hit her head on the hard ceramic tiles of the hall floor. She had been knocked unconscious and still hadn't woken up. They'd arrived at St John's in an ambulance and Wendy had been whisked straight into the emergency rooms. The doctors were worried that she might have a haematoma or blood clot on the brain — Gemma had taken that much in when the doctor, a slightly crumpled-looking but nice man in his thirties called Dr Tobin, had spoken to her briefly about Wendy's injuries, but other than that they were all in the dark. Like Wendy. Ronan seemed to be in severe shock. He kept muttering to himself about being stupid and about a bag, but Gemma couldn't make out what he meant. When she asked him to explain, he just shook his head and put his face in his hands.

"Gemma! Where's Wendy? Is she all right? What happened?" Mia came flying down the corridor towards them, followed closely by Alva. Mia's eyes were wide and her face was pale, with two spots of high colour on her cheeks. Her hair was in a messy ponytail and she was wearing a denim jacket over an old tracksuit, which Gemma knew she wore in bed.

"That was quick," Gemma said. "You didn't get caught in traffic?"

"I drove in the bus lane," Alva explained. "It has its uses."

"Wendy?" Mia asked, her eyes wild. "Where is she?"

"The doctors are keeping her under close observation," Gemma said more calmly than she felt. She didn't want to worry Mia unduly.

"Is she awake now? Can I see her?" Mia asked.

Gemma hesitated for a moment. "Not yet, Mia. She's still unconscious."

"Still unconscious? Does that mean she has brain damage, Gemma? Will she be all right? Tell me she'll be all right." Mia began to cry, huge sobs racking her body. She brushed the tears away. "Where's the doctor? I want to talk to the doctor." She looked around. "There's one over there."

A young female doctor was talking to a nurse in the corridor.

Gemma put her hand on Mia's arm. "That's not Wendy's doctor, Mia, so there wouldn't be any point in talking to her. Wendy's doctor is called Dr Tobin. He said he'd be back in a little while and I'm sure he'll have more news for us then."

"I'll go and find him," Mia said.

"It would be better if we all stayed here," Gemma said firmly, thinking on her feet. "Ronan needs us. Alva, would you get Mia a cup of coffee?"

"Of course," Alva said, checking in her wallet for change.

"I don't want coffee," Mia said in a tiny voice. "I want to see Wendy." She began to cry again.

"Why don't I go and find the doctor?" Alva said to Gemma. "He might be able to put Mia's mind at ease."

"Thanks," Gemma replied. "That would be great. Try asking in the nurses' office." She pointed up the hallway. "Up there and to the right."

Watching Alva's back as she walked down the corridor, Gemma took Mia's hand in hers and

305

squeezed it. "Wendy will be fine, Mia. Try not to worry."

Mia squeezed back but said nothing. Gemma offered up a silent prayer. She wasn't particularly religious, but she was prepared to try anything at this stage. Please God, make Wendy be OK. Mia couldn't cope if anything happened to her. Mia deserves a break, God. Please. She's a good kid. Tears came to her eyes and she blinked them away.

As Alva walked down the corridor, her runners squeaking on the hospital floor, Ronan looked up. The last time he'd been in this hospital was with Wendy when they were visiting Gemma after her ankle operation. Wendy's runners had made a similar noise on the floor, he remembered. He looked down again. Wendy. How would he survive without her? What if she never woke up? He began to rock backwards and forwards in his seat. He didn't care what she'd done, he still needed her. She was his life.

"Try not to worry, Ronan," Gemma said, putting her arm around him.

He stopped rocking and looked at her. "What if she dies?" he asked, his face racked with anguish. "It's all my fault."

"Hush, Ronan. She'll pull through. Wendy's a strong woman, you know that. And of course it wasn't your fault. She fell down the stairs. How could it have been your fault?"

"But it is," he insisted. "She fell because of me. She was running after me and she tripped over my bag,

Gemma. I left it on the stairs. How could I have been so stupid? It's all my fault."

"Why was she running after you, Ronan?" Gemma asked gently.

He put his head in his hands and stared down at the floor, rocking backwards and forwards again.

"She just was," he said after a long pause. "It's not important now."

"What's Ronan talking about?" Mia whispered to Gemma. Her eyes were wide and Gemma knew that she was also in shock.

Gemma shrugged her shoulders. "He's very upset, Mia. I'm not sure he knows what he's saying. Best just to leave him be, I think."

Alva walked towards them with Dr Tobin in tow. Ronan looked up, his face hopeful. "Is she awake?" he asked.

"No, Wendy's stable but she's still unconscious," Dr Tobin said, coming straight to the point, for which Gemma was grateful. "I know how concerned you must all be but I'm afraid I can't tell you much just yet. There is some swelling on the front right-hand side of the brain, at the point of impact. She probably has a skull fracture . . ." Mia gasped. "But to be honest," he continued, "that's the least of her problems. The fracture isn't depressed, which is good, but we won't be able to tell the exact extent of it until we take an X-ray."

"And what about the swelling?" Gemma asked. "Is that dangerous?"

"I won't lie to you," he said, his kind eyes locking with hers, "it can be. But we're monitoring the intracranial pressure very carefully and she's on a ventilator to ensure a good oxygen supply to the brain."

"Will she wake up soon?" Mia asked. "Can I see her?"

"It's probably best to leave her alone for the moment," he said gently. "And hopefully she will wake up soon, though it's impossible to tell. But when she does wake up she may be quite confused and even have amnesia."

"Amnesia?" Ronan asked. "Will she know who we are?"

The doctor nodded. "Yes, probably. Post-traumatic amnesia tends to affect the short-term memory. But sometimes patients can't remember the accident or what happened for days before it."

Ronan thought about the implications of this, but said nothing. It was all too much to take in.

"Will she be OK?" Mia asked, tears streaming down her face.

Dr Tobin looked at Mia and then back at Gemma, recognizing her as the strong one. "It's impossible to say, I'm afraid. But let's hope so."

Mia could feel the blood rushing from her head and all around her everything began to move in slow motion. She staggered awkwardly and collapsed forward on to the chair beside Gemma. Dr Tobin and Alva lifted her properly on to the chair.

"Mia!" She heard Gemma's voice, foggy and distant. Gemma put her arms around her sister and held her close. Mia crumpled in a heap on to Gemma's shoulder. She could feel her sister's hands stroke her head and hear Gemma whisper, "Wendy will be fine, Mia. She's as strong as an ox. You know that, Mia. She'll be fine, you'll see. She'll be fine," over and over again like a mantra.

"I'll get some water," Alva said, jumping to her feet.

Dr Tobin knelt down and put his hand on Mia's forehead, his palm cool and smooth against her flushed skin.

"You're very hot," he said. "How do you feel?"

"OK," she murmured.

"Mia and Wendy are very close," Gemma explained. "Our mum died when we were young. Mia was only fifteen when it happened and Wendy pretty much brought Mia up."

Dr Tobin nodded. "You've had a terrible shock, Mia. Try to stay sitting." And to Gemma. "Has she ever fainted before?"

Gemma nodded. "Quite a few times."

"Recently?"

Gemma nodded again.

"Is she vegetarian?"

"No."

"Still, she's quite pale. You might encourage her to get her iron levels checked. She might be a touch anaemic."

"I will, thanks, Doctor."

He stood up and gave Gemma a half-smile. "You're welcome. I'll be back with any news."

"Thanks," she said again, continuing to stroke the top of Mia's head. She looked at Ronan who had just stood up. "Where are you going, Ronan?"

"To stretch my legs. I need some air. I'll be back in a few minutes."

"Do you have your mobile on you?"

He stared at her. "Mobile?" he murmured, his eyes glazing over a little. Wendy wouldn't be in this mess if it weren't for her damned mobile, he thought irrationally.

"Yes. Your mobile. Is it switched on?"

"Yes. Yes," he answered a little vaguely.

"Good. We'll ring you if there's any news. Don't go too far."

"I won't. Thanks."

"Water," Alva said, appearing in front of them. She opened a bottle of still water and handed it to Mia. "Sorry it took me so long, the first machine I found wasn't working so I had to go upstairs. All very boring." She looked at Mia who had already gulped down almost half the bottle and was taking a breather. "You were thirsty. Are you feeling any better?"

"A little."

"The doctor said she might be anaemic," Gemma commented.

"Makes sense," Alva said. "Wendy was very anaemic after having the boys, remember?"

"Now that you say it," Gemma said, "maybe it runs in the family."

"How long has Wendy been unconscious now?" Mia asked sitting up. She was starting to feel more alert.

Gemma studied her watch. "Just over an hour."

"Is that bad?" Mia asked. "Is she in a coma, Gemma?"

"I don't know," Gemma said. "I only know what the doctor told us. I'm sorry." She patted Mia's hand. "I know this is hard for you."

Just then Dr Tobin strode towards them. "Good news," he said. "Wendy's just woken up."

Gemma felt a flood of relief rush through her veins. Mia gave an audible cry of relief and sat up even straighter.

"But I must warn you," Dr Tobin continued, "she's a little confused. She keeps asking for Miriam. Who's Miriam?"

"Miriam was our mum," Gemma explained. "She's dead."

"Oh, I'm sorry, you did say . . . how stupid," he faltered.

"Not to worry," Gemma said kindly.

"Is Wendy's daughter here then?"

"Daughter?" Gemma's stomach lurched. No, not now, please not now, she begged silently.

"Yes," he said. "Wendy's asking for her daughter. Is she on her way?"

Mia stared at Gemma, whose eyes were fixed on the doctor's face. Gemma could feel her whole body trembling. She felt icy-cold. "No," she gasped. She tried to say more but the words stuck in her throat.

"Is she already here?" Dr Tobin asked, a little confused. He looked at Alva. "Wendy keeps asking for her daughter, M . . ."

"No!" Gemma cried out. But it was too late.

"Mia," Dr Tobin finished.

Mia stared at Gemma. "Gemma?" she demanded. "What's he talking about? Gemma?"

Alva also stared at Gemma. Mia was Wendy's daughter? Was it true? She had heard of this happening in Irish families of course — it was common enough in the fifties and sixties. Everyone knew, or knew of, a family where the grandmother had brought up an unmarried daughter's child as her own. But had it really happened in the Redden household?

"Gemma!" Mia said, her voice rising to a dangerous level. "Is it true? Tell me! Gemma?"

Gemma said nothing. She opened her mouth to say something and then closed it again, still unable to force the words out.

Alva looked at Gemma's stricken face and knew the answer immediately.

"Gemma?" Mia continued, almost shouting now. "It's true, isn't it? Why didn't you tell me before this? Years ago. Gemma?"

Gemma looked terrified. Mia was standing in front of her, the spots of colour on her cheeks standing out from her ashen face, her eyes black and flashing with emotion.

Alva knew she had to do something. She turned quickly towards Dr Tobin. "Gemma will go and see Wendy now, Doctor. I'll take Mia outside for some air and we'll find Ronan."

Dr Tobin had seen enough family dramas in his day to realize that he'd just stumbled into an emotional minefield. "Of course," he said. "Gemma, this way please."

Gemma put her hands in her crutches and rose to her feet. He put his arm around her shoulders and guided her slowly down the corridor, Mia staring in their wake.

"I won't forget this, Gemma!" she shouted at Gemma's back. "I trusted you. You're supposed to be my sister, for God's sake. Some sister you are." Tears were streaming down Mia's face and her body racked with sobs. "But you're not my sister, are you? Not my sister at all."

"It's OK now, Mia," Alva said, trying to comfort her but not knowing what to say. "Let's go outside and find Ronan."

"But . . ." Mia looked like a crumpled doll.

"Come on," Alva cajoled. "Let's get some fresh air." She took Mia's arm gently and led her outside.

Gemma stood and waited at the nurses' desk as Dr Tobin talked to the staff nurse. Wendy had been moved into her own private room in the intensive care unit, the nurse told him, and then asked him a question regarding another patient's chart.

After a moment, Dr Tobin turned towards Gemma. "Sorry about that. I'll take you in to see Wendy now. Follow me."

Gemma gasped when she stared through the small window in the door of Wendy's intensive care room. Wendy looked terrible. She had two drips attached to her, one in either hand, and a small tube was feeding what Gemma presumed was oxygen into her nostrils. Her face was horribly bruised on the right-hand side and the bridge of her nose resembled a war zone; both her eyes were sunk into dark sockets and there was dried blood in her hair.

"She was amazingly lucky," Dr Tobin said. "The X-rays are back and she didn't break any bones."

"What about her skull?" Gemma asked. "I thought you said she had a suspected skull fracture."

"No, she has a tiny hairline fracture, but nothing to worry about. She's one tough woman, your sister."

"And the swelling?"

"She's awake and that's a very good sign. And the swelling seems to be reducing, which is excellent. But there's still a risk of bleeding and we'll have to keep her under close observation for the next few days. She's through the worst, though."

"Is she very confused?"

"Yes. She keeps saying, 'I was only fourteen'. Does that mean anything, Gemma? Maybe you can shed some light on it. Did something traumatic happen then?"

"She had a baby daughter," Gemma said in a monotone, staring at Wendy through the window. She looked back at Dr Tobin. "Traumatic enough for you? The blonde girl outside, Mia, is her daughter."

"Did she have the baby in Dublin?" he asked gently.

"No, in a small hospital near Westport where we used to live. We moved away immediately afterwards, to Dublin, and the baby was brought up as our sister," Gemma said in a strangely even voice. It was the first time she'd ever told this particular piece of the Redden family history. But she'd rehearsed it so many times it

314

was a relief finally to be able to say out loud the words that she'd had to keep repressed for so long.

"Mum thought it was for the best. I was only eight at the time, but I remember it vividly. Wendy didn't say a word for weeks afterwards. The birth went smoothly apparently, but it can't have been easy going through childbirth at that age. Or handing your baby over like that. Pretending nothing had happened."

She put her hands on the door and leaned towards the glass. "We've never really talked about it, to be honest. It was a taboo subject when Mia was around, obviously. I used to try and make Wendy talk to me about it in private, but she wasn't interested. She wanted to forget it had ever happened. Mia's her sister, not her daughter, as far as she's concerned. It's as simple as that. Her husband, Ronan, doesn't even know."

Gemma gave a deep sigh and turned around to face Dr Tobin. "I don't know how any of us are going to handle it." She looked him in the eye. "How is Mia going to handle it?"

"I don't know what to say," Dr Tobin began. "But Wendy is going to recover, isn't that the important thing?"

"Of course," Gemma murmured. "But at what cost?"

"It seems to me that Wendy has some explaining to do to her daughter," Dr Tobin said, lifting his eyebrows. "Don't you think? But not right now. She doesn't need any more excitement today, that's for sure."

"I suppose you're right."

"Let me know if there's anything I can do. But try not to say anything that might upset Wendy. She's still in a fairly fragile state. Her memory should start returning slowly, but it could be a very gradual process. Or it could happen in a matter of hours. It's hard to tell."

"Thank you, Doctor, you've been very kind."

"Let me know what happens, won't you? I'll check on Wendy later, but if you have any questions ask one of the nurses to come and find me. Otherwise, well, good luck with the family, um . . ."

"Secret?" Gemma suggested.

"Yes." He smiled at her gently. "Hope it all works out for you. Is this her husband?" Ronan was striding up the corridor.

"Mia said Wendy's awake, is she awake?" Ronan gabbled. "Can I see her? Is she all right?"

Dr Tobin nodded. "Yes, but she's a little confused. Maybe . . ." He looked at Gemma.

"I need to talk to her first," Gemma interjected. "She thinks Mum's still alive. I'm going to sit with her for a while, try to calm her down. It's better that way."

Ronan looked at Dr Tobin.

"Maybe you'd like to sit in the relatives' room," the doctor said. "It's nice and quiet in there."

Ronan nodded. "And you'll come and get me as soon as Wendy's settled?" he said to Gemma.

"Of course," Gemma promised. "Where's Mia?"

"Still outside with Alva. She's crying. I couldn't make out what she was saying. Something about her mother. She wasn't making any sense, Gemma. Alva's having a cigarette and Mia's sharing it. I didn't know Mia smoked."

Thank goodness for Alva, Gemma thought. "She doesn't," she said. "Must be the shock." She looked at Wendy again through the window. She seemed to be stirring and her eyelids were flickering. "I'd better go in now. I'll come and find you as soon as I've talked to Wendy."

"Wendy?" Gemma leaned over the bed and studied her sister's eyes. They flickered again and then opened.

"Gemma? Is that you? Where's Ronan? Are the boys all right?"

Gemma felt a huge surge of relief. Wendy seemed to be back in the present. "Outside in the relatives' room. And the boys are fine. They're at home with Nadia."

"And Mia?"

"She's with Alva." Gemma tried to keep her voice even but it was difficult. She wasn't sure if Wendy realized what she'd let slip to Dr Tobin.

"What is it?" Wendy asked. "Have you been crying?"

"Just a little."

"Tell me, what's wrong?"

Gemma looked at Wendy. "Nothing. Really. Everything's fine."

"Where's Mia?"

"Outside."

"Ask her to come in. I want to see her."

"The doctor said no more visitors for the moment. You're stuck with me, I'm afraid." Gemma gave her a half-smile.

"What's happening? There's something going on. Gemma?" Wendy tried to sit up but her head throbbed so badly that she was forced back against the pillows by the pain. She winced and put her right hand to her head, touching her bruise gingerly. "My head," she murmured.

"Wendy, take it easy. You've had a very bad fall."

"Mia," Wendy said again. "I want to see Mia."

"I'll go and get her as soon as the doctor . . ."

"I want to tell her the truth," Wendy said, a sense of urgency in her voice. "What if I'd died, Gemma? What if I hadn't woken up? What then? Would you have told her? Or would she have spent the rest of her days living a lie?"

"Wendy, I don't think . . ."

"She deserves to know the truth, Gemma. I should have told her a long time ago. Have I made a terrible mistake lying to her all these years?"

"I don't know," Gemma said honestly. "And there's no point worrying about it now. Maybe you should wait to talk to Mia until you feel a little better. Until you've had a chance to think things over. We've all had a terrible shock. Talk to Ronan first, see what he says. Maybe get some counselling."

Gemma's mind was racing. She wanted to protect both Wendy and Mia, that was her job as their sister, wasn't it? Sister and aunt, she corrected herself. But things were spiralling beyond her control.

Wendy closed her eyes tight and then opened them again. "Ronan," she murmured. "Oh, Gemma, I've done the most terrible thing. I have to tell you. I feel so guilty."

She told her sister about what had happened just before the fall and what had or, to be accurate, what hadn't happened in the hotel earlier that day. Gemma listened in amazement. She knew Des Sullivan of old and wasn't all that surprised — he always was a bit of a chancer. But Wendy — the mind boggled. She couldn't think of anyone less likely to have an affair.

"Gemma, I've been such a fool," Wendy moaned. "I've ruined everything, haven't I?"

Gemma reached over and held Wendy's hand, careful to avoid the drip. She noticed a dark, angry-looking bruise on her wrist. "You poor old thing," she said. "That looks nasty."

"My body I can deal with," Wendy said with a snort. "But as for my head ... and I don't mean the concussion. What have I done to my marriage? To Ronan?"

"Ronan's in bits," Gemma confided. "He blames himself for your fall. He left his bag on the stairs apparently and you tripped over it. Explain what happened, Wendy. Talk to him. He'll forgive you, I know he will. He still loves you, that hasn't changed."

"I'm so ashamed." Wendy began to cry, but her eyes were so sore that it hurt to squeeze out every tear.

"Wendy, will I talk to him for you?" Gemma suggested.

"It's too much," Wendy said.

"What's too much?"

"All of this. The affair, Mia. Because I'm going to tell her, as soon as I see her. It's only right. He won't forgive me, Gemma. It's too much."

"Wendy, he nearly lost you. Don't you think that everything else will pale into insignificance?"

"I don't know." Wendy was still crying. "Oh, Gemma, I'm so tired."

"I know you are. Try to get some sleep. Things will seem better in a little while. Try not to upset yourself."

Gemma sat with Wendy, holding her hand firmly and dabbing away her sister's tears with a tissue. She didn't know what to do. Nothing she'd said to Wendy had seemed to help. This was something that Wendy would have to face on her own and Gemma didn't envy her.

Wendy drifted asleep and Gemma extracted her hand carefully. Wendy stirred a little and then settled back to sleep. For a moment Gemma wondered if she was supposed to be asleep. What if she never woke up? She felt anxious and pressed the call button. Within seconds a nurse arrived.

"Can I help?" she asked Gemma.

"She's asleep," Gemma whispered, gesturing at Wendy. "Is that all right?"

The nurse smiled at the worried-looking young woman in front of her. She checked the monitor beside Wendy's bed. "Everything seems fine," she said after a moment. "I'll be back in a little while to check again. And Dr Tobin will be back in an hour or so. Try not to worry. Rest is the best thing for her at the moment."

"Thank you. Can you tell me where the relatives' room is?"

The nurse gave her directions. Gemma looked at Wendy one last time and, satisfied that she was in good hands, went to talk to Ronan. She wasn't relishing it, but someone had to tell him about Mia, and it would be better for her to do it than Mia herself. Once she'd talked to Ronan, she'd tackle Mia. And if talking to Ronan was going to be difficult, talking to Mia was going to be even worse.

Gemma opened the door of the relatives' room.

"Ronan?" she said.

He lifted his head. Gemma sat down beside him.

Ronan looked at her expectantly. "Wendy?" he asked.

"She's doing well," she reassured him. "She's asleep now and the nurse said that everything's fine, that rest is the best thing for her at the moment. Her head hurts, but that's to be expected. Her memory seems fine."

She paused, choosing her words carefully. "Wendy's still a little confused but she remembers everything that happened last night. She's very upset, Ronan. She feels horribly guilty." She looked at Ronan. He had a strange expression on his face. "She told me about the hotel and about the other man," she continued. "But nothing happened. She couldn't go through with it. You know that, don't you?"

Ronan shook his head. "No. I wouldn't listen to her."

"She didn't know what she was doing, Ronan. Wendy knows she's made a huge mistake. She loves you."

Ronan shook his head again.

"Please, just listen to me," Gemma said.

"I suspected she was having an affair," he said. "But I stupidly thought that if I didn't say anything, didn't confront her, it would all go away. I should have talked to her days ago. It's all too late now."

"Ronan, it's not too late. Did you hear what I said? Wendy didn't have an affair. Yes, she thought about it, almost went through with it, but in the end she didn't. She knew it wasn't right, that it would ruin everything."

Ronan looked at Gemma, his eyes glittering, "Do you believe her, Gemma?"

"Yes. But the important thing is, do you?"

Ronan shook his head. "I'm not sure what to think right now. I want to believe her, really I do, but . . ." He gave a deep sigh. "Oh, I don't know. Things keep going through my head, you know?" He looked down at his hands for a moment and then raised his head again. "But I don't know what I'd do without her." He stopped for a moment. "I need to see her, talk to her face to face."

"She's sleeping now. Probably best to leave her. The nurse said she needs her sleep right now, remember?"

"As soon as she wakes up then," Ronan said. "I really want to believe her; I don't want to lose her, Gemma. But I just don't know if I can."

"There's something else," Gemma began. She hoped that once he talked to Wendy he'd see that she was telling the truth. She was about to drop another bombshell and she hoped he was strong enough to take it. But Gemma knew that if she didn't deal with it now, once Mia talked to Ronan things would be even more difficult. Better he should hear it now and have a chance to talk to Wendy first.

"I don't know how you're going to take this, Ronan, you've had such a difficult evening, but I have to tell you. It's about Mia. Wendy and Mia. And their, um, relationship." Gemma paused for a moment, afraid to go on. How was she going to explain?

"Gemma, it's Mia you should be talking to, not me," Ronan said, filling the silence. "I already know that Wendy is Mia's real mum. I've known for years."

"What? How?" Gemma was so shocked she could barely get the words out. Whatever reaction she'd expected, it wasn't this.

"Miriam told me a few days before she died. She was worried that something might happen to Wendy. She wanted Mia to know and she wasn't convinced that you'd tell her. She knew how much you love them both and how much you'd want to protect Mia. But it's part of who Mia is. Your mum knew that. In the end I think she felt that she'd made a mistake by bringing Mia up as her own, but it was too late to do anything about it. Miriam thought that all of you had enough on your plate, with her being so sick, without adding to it by telling Mia the truth. The last thing you all needed at that stage was extra emotional trauma. And I wanted Wendy to tell Mia herself. I believed that when the time was right she would. So I've kept it a secret all these years."

"And what about Wendy? Have you ever talked to her about it?"

"No, Wendy has no idea that I know." Ronan smiled at Gemma. "I'm good at keeping secrets."

"You're a dark horse, Ronan Borza, do you know that?" Gemma was still in shock.

He smiled again. "And how are *you*, Gemma? This is a lot for you to take in, I know."

"I'm all right. I'm worried about Mia though."

"Go and find her." Ronan stood up. "I'll sit with Wendy if I'm allowed. We have a lot of talking to do. But now's not the time. I'll just tell her that everything's going to be all right and that I'll look after her. And I really do think it will be all right, Gemma."

"I think so too," Gemma said, trying to sound more optimistic than she felt.

Gemma walked out of the hospital and took a deep breath of the cool, fresh air. It was always so stuffy in hospitals, she thought as she looked around for Mia and Alva. She spotted them sitting on a bench to the right of the entrance. They were both staring straight ahead, puffing on cigarettes. Mia was blowing the smoke out almost as soon as she'd drawn it in, billows of it lingering in front of her mouth until she fanned them away with her hand. Gemma smiled to herself. Mia never could smoke properly. Alva, on the other hand, was drawing deeply and very little smoke was coming back up.

Gemma watched until Alva noticed her and waved her over. Mia glanced at Gemma and then looked away, refusing to meet her eyes. Gemma's heart sank.

"Hi, you two," she said, standing in front of them. "Enjoying your nicotine rush?"

Alva nodded. She dropped her spent cigarette to the ground and extinguished it under the sole of one of her runners. "I must give up one of these days."

Gemma said nothing. She'd heard that one before.

"I'll go," Alva said getting up. "I'll leave the pair of you alone. To talk." She looked pointedly at Gemma.

"Don't go," Mia said, looking up at Alva. "I have nothing to say to *her*."

Alva sighed. "Mia, none of this is Gemma's fault," she pointed out. "Just listen to what she has to say."

"Only if you stay."

Alva nodded. "OK then. But Gemma's . . ."

"Been lying to me for years," Mia cut in, her voice full of anger. "How do you think that makes me feel? I don't know what to think or who's telling me the truth." She swung her eyes to Gemma's face and stared at her. Gemma could see the anguish behind Mia's glare and longed to be able to soothe her.

"I have nothing to say to you, Gemma," Mia said. "Just leave me alone. And Wendy too. I don't want anything more to do with either of you."

"You don't mean that!" Gemma cried. "We're sisters!"

"But Wendy's *not* my sister, is she? And neither are you! Why didn't you tell me, Gemma? Why did you never say anything? I've always trusted you to tell me the truth. My whole life is a lie. How could you let that happen?"

"It wasn't my place to tell you," Gemma said, fighting back the tears. "It was Wendy's secret, not mine. It all happened such a long time ago. I was only eight when you were born, Mia, you have to remember that. I just went along with everything. I didn't have much choice. Mum thought it was for the best . . ." Gemma stopped when she saw the dark expression on Mia's face.

"I'll never forgive you," Mia said in a chillingly calm voice. "Never." She stood up and with one last dagger look at Gemma, strode away.

"Mia!" Gemma said, walking after her. She put her hand on Mia's arm but Mia shook it off. "Mia!"

"It's probably best to leave her be for a while," Alva suggested. "I'll take her home and stay with her."

"Thanks," Gemma said. She felt absolutely wretched. What am I going to tell Wendy? she thought. It's all my fault. I should have stopped Dr Tobin when I had the chance. I've ruined everything.

"It's been a very emotional day for everyone," Alva said kindly. "I'll take care of Mia. And I'll ring you later to let you know how she's doing."

Gemma nodded. She was all out of words at this stage and she was desperately trying to fight back the tears. A few moments later she watched Alva drive out of the car park, a stony-faced Mia staring rigidly ahead of her in the passenger seat.

Only then did the tears begin to flood down Gemma's face.

CHAPTER
FIFTEEN

When All Is Said and Done

Wendy was finally allowed home four days later, with explicit instructions from Dr Tobin to rest and to avoid anything stressful. He'd also forbidden her to even think about singing for at least three weeks, much to her horror. But even that failed to prevent her from attempting to do the paperwork. She'd asked Ronan to bring her laptop to their bedroom so she could work from bed, but he'd refused. She'd already insisted on ringing the insurance company herself to check her serious illness cover. Luckily, being her ever-efficient self, the premiums were up to date and she qualified for six weeks' benefit. After Ronan had consulted the other band members, including Pat, he'd withdrawn enough from the band's emergency coffers to cover everyone's expenses for a month. He'd then transferred this into each of their accounts. Wendy allowed herself a small rush of pride when she realized that the financial safety nets she had carefully put in place over the years were now being put to good use.

Nadia had taken the boys to school that morning and was proving invaluable to the family: as well as looking after the boys, she had taken over all the cooking, washing, ironing and housework. From this morning, when Wendy had arrived home from the hospital, Nadia had also checked on her every hour, replenishing her water jug and giving her snippets of news gleaned from the TV and the radio while Ronan worked downstairs.

"Wendy, the doctor said to rest," Ronan protested when she asked for her laptop for the third time that day. "And work is certainly not rest."

"But I've so much to do!" Wendy protested. "What about this weekend's gigs?"

Ronan stared at her incredulously. "Wendy, please tell me you're joking. There's no way you can get up on a stage in two days' time, no way. I won't allow it. And you know what the doctor said."

Wendy snorted. "I meant to cancel them, Ronan," she explained. "I'm not that bad. My head still throbs a bit," she touched the bridge of her nose gingerly, followed by the side of her head, "and no amount of make-up, thick stage make-up included, is going to cover this lot."

"I'm very relieved to hear you say it." Ronan sat down on the edge of the bed. "Please, you've been through a terrible time. I know you're not very good at doing nothing, but you have to, really. I've already cancelled some of the gigs and I can do the rest later. Now please just rest."

"I'll try." Wendy sighed. "But my mind is working overtime without work to distract me. And I keep thinking about what's happened. You know, I deserved to fall down those stairs. I'm a horrible person."

"What! How can you say that?"

"Because it's true." Wendy stopped for a moment and looked Ronan in the eye. "I know you keep saying that we have all the time in the world to talk, but I'd like to start now if that's OK with you. We've been putting it off long enough. We need to clear the air. I can't just lie here thinking about it all, wondering about what's going to happen when we do talk."

Ronan nodded. "But are you sure you won't find it all too much? The doctor said . . ."

"I know, I know," she interrupted, "no work and no stress. But it's important, Ronan. I want us to get on with our lives, and until we face up to what happened I don't think we can. I certainly can't. Do you understand?"

He nodded again, silently.

Wendy waited for a moment before she spoke, collecting her thoughts. She stared straight ahead of her, her eyes resting on the soothing blue and green Monet water-lilies print on the wall opposite the bed. "I haven't been happy for a long time, Ronan. And before you say anything, it has nothing to do with you, or us, honestly. It's all about me." She gave a dry laugh.

"Goodness, I sound so selfish, don't I? And I was being selfish. Horribly, horribly selfish. I don't really know where to start to tell the truth." She pulled her eyes off the painting and rested them on Ronan's face. "I've worked so hard over the last few years to make AbbaFab a success and I think I overlooked the fact that I had no life of my own outside the band. And I was just fed up with it all, I suppose. I wanted something for myself, something that had nothing to do with the band, or my life with you and the boys. And then I met Des O'Sullivan at the garage in Deansgrange when I was getting the car checked."

Wendy glanced at Ronan. He was gazing at her intently. "I know him from Westport, not from the cruise ships like I told you. He lives in Australia now but he was over visiting his mother. He invited me for coffee, but I said no. But he gave me his number and I kept it. He works in computers and I rang him when the laptop went mad." She paused again, looking at Ronan. He deserved her complete honesty. "But I was only looking for an excuse to get in touch with him. I would have rung him anyway."

"Des is the guy who came to fix your laptop?" Ronan asked, needing to clarify things.

"Yes."

"And?" he encouraged.

"After that Des started to text me. He made it obvious from the start that he fancied me, and he knew I was married, that didn't seem to bother him. He made me feel attractive, I suppose, wanted. I was flattered by his attention. At the start I never intended for anything to happen. It was a bit of fun, a distraction." She stared down at her hands and fingered the white indent where her wedding ring usually rested. She missed her ring. The nurses must have taken it off her hand in the hospital. "And nothing did happen, not really. Not until the other day. At the hotel." She looked up again. "He kept pestering me for a date and eventually I . . ." She paused and then said in a rush, "I met him in that hotel, Glenford House in Wicklow, the afternoon of my fall. The hotel that rang about my mobile. I'm not proud of it, Ronan, but I want you to know everything. It was so, so stupid. I don't know what I was thinking."

Ronan's face drained. "You were wearing your navy dress," he managed eventually. "The one I like."

"Yes." Wendy gulped and then continued, trying to get her confession over with as quickly as possible for both their sakes. "But I couldn't go through with it. Once we were in the room we kissed, but it felt wrong, terribly wrong. I couldn't stop thinking about you. And I realized just how much I had to lose. Nothing else happened, absolutely nothing. I asked him to leave and he wasn't too happy with me. But he did and that was the end of it. I haven't heard from him since, thank goodness. He's probably back in Australia by now with his fiancée. I hope I never set eyes on him again."

"And you left your mobile in the hotel room?"

"Yes. I was in such a panic to get out of there, I left it behind me on the sofa."

"What if you hadn't forgotten it, Wendy? What then? Would you have told me eventually? Or would it have been yet another secret?"

"Secret?" she faltered. "What do you mean?"

"Let's deal with this first," Ronan said, leaving Wendy hanging. "If I hadn't found out, would you have told me?"

"I don't know," she said honestly. "But I do know this. It made me realize just how much I love you. And that I was the one with the problem, not you. You've always been a good husband, I know that now."

"I've had my moments," Ronan said. "Like the fire . . ."

"No one's perfect," Wendy interrupted. "Forget about the fire. What I'm trying to say is that I'm sorry. For everything. And not just for the business with Des. For putting the band before my family, for snapping at you, for making you feel second best, for not being there for you . . ."

"Wendy!" Ronan said. "You're the most wonderful woman I've ever met. You could run the country far better than any of our damned politicians; hell, you could be President if you set your mind to it. You're incredible. You never cease to amaze me."

"But that's just it!" she said. "I don't want to be President or run the country. I don't even want to run AbbaFab any more. I'm tired, Ronan. That's the truth. I'm tired to my bones. I want to stop being Superwoman and try just being myself for a change. And above all, I want to give our marriage another go.

I know it will take time, but do you think you can forgive me?"

Ronan said nothing for a moment. Wendy felt as though her life was passing in front of her eyes and she held her breath.

Finally he said, "I already have."

She felt so ashamed. "After everything I've done?" Tears ran down her cheeks.

He nodded. "Yes. Losing you would be the end of me. Sitting in St John's, waiting for you to regain consciousness, was the worst hour of my life. I felt so out of control, so alone. You're everything to me, Wendy. You're all I've ever wanted. We make sense together."

"I know," Wendy whispered. She brushed back her tears. "I'm so, so sorry. And I do love you."

He shifted up the bed, put his arm around her shoulders and kissed the top of her head. "I know you do."

They sat in silence for a few minutes, Wendy crying gently and Ronan holding her. "Hush now," he soothed, stroking her head. "It's all over. We'll put all this behind us and start again."

"Thank you," she murmured. "And Ronan, do you know where my wedding ring is? I miss it."

He pulled the ring out of the pocket of his jeans. "I was hoping you'd want to wear it again." He slipped it on to her ring finger, put his arms around her and gave her a gentle hug. Then he drew back and tenderly brushed her hair back off her face. "Nadia will be back with the boys soon and they'll be dying to see you."

"I'm just so tired," Wendy sighed. "I feel like I could sleep forever."

"That's natural after a head injury."

"I was tired long before that."

"You work so hard, Wendy. I'm not surprised you're tired. You haven't had a holiday in almost two years and you take on so much. Singing, booking, everything really."

"I've been thinking . . ." Wendy began. "About the band."

"Yes?"

"Would you manage without me for a while? I'd like to spend more time with Steve and Greg. I'd still do all the booking and everything of course."

Ronan looked at Wendy in surprise. "I thought you loved performing."

"I do. But I need a break. I could try finding someone else for you until Gemma's back on her feet. It won't be easy but at least the mad wedding rush is almost over. I'm sure I'd be able to find someone to fill in. Then when Gemma's on her feet again Mia could take over from me. Gemma and Mia would be brilliant together."

"Is that really what you want?"

She nodded.

He patted her hand. "You really have been doing a lot of thinking, haven't you?"

"Not much else to do confined in hospital and in this bloody bed."

"True."

"I met an old cruise-ship friend recently, a lovely girl called Nora, and she seemed to think that her husband might give me a job showing houses. He's an estate agent."

Ronan grinned.

"What are you smiling at?" she asked.

"I was just thinking it would be the perfect job for you. A licence to legitimately nose around other people's houses. It's a great idea."

She thumped him on the arm. "Ronan!"

"Good to see you're feeling a little better," he quipped.

"There's something else," Wendy said, a smile lingering on her lips. "What about trying for another baby?"

"A baby?" Ronan was dumbstruck. Wendy had always said that her baby days were most definitely over. He'd always hankered after a larger family, but he'd learned to accept the fact that Wendy wasn't interested in going down that road again.

"Say something," she said. "What do you think?"

"You know I'd love another baby," he said. "But are you sure?"

Wendy nodded. "Positive. I'm thirty-eight, Ronan. It's now or never. If I leave it any longer it could be too late."

"Isn't there something you need to sort out first?" he asked. "Your other baby," he prompted gently. "You have to talk to Mia."

Wendy looked at him in astonishment. "What?" she whispered. "You know? I don't believe this. Did Gemma tell you? How long have you known?"

"I've known for years, Wendy. Gemma had nothing to do with it. Miriam told me before she died. I came to terms with it a long time ago. So you have nothing to worry about."

Wendy was in shock. "I can't believe it," she whispered. "You never said a word."

"I promised Miriam I wouldn't. Not unless something happened to you. And I always keep my promises."

"I know you do. It's one of the reasons I love you so much. But I can't take this in. You knew? All this time?" She shook her head gently from side to side and winced at the throbbing in her temples.

Ronan began to stroke her head again. "I'm glad it's all finally come out. Mia deserved to know the truth. It's part of who she is. And it's part of who you are too, Wendy."

"*Deserved?* You mean she knows too?"

Ronan explained to Wendy about how Dr Tobin had inadvertently let the secret out in the hospital.

Wendy buried her head in her hands and began to moan. "Oh no, not Mia. Little Mia. My Mia." She raised her head. "She must hate me, Ronan."

"She doesn't hate you," he said, "she's just confused. She'll be OK. She needs to be left alone for a little while. You and Gemma have been living with this secret for years; to Mia, it's come as a huge shock."

"Yes," she murmured. "Yes, of course." Her voice changed. "But has she rung yet? She must be so confused. I really need to talk to her, explain to her

336

what happened when she was born, why I gave her away like that," she said frantically.

"No," Ronan said gently. "She hasn't rung yet. You need to take it easy, Wendy. Try not to get upset. I'm sure she'll ring very soon. Just give her time. Gemma's been talking to her."

Wendy didn't like the sound of that. "What did Gemma say?"

"Just that Mia would come and see you when she was ready. That she needed some space to think things over."

Wendy lay back against her pillows and rubbed her eyes gently. "What a mess. And it's all my fault. When's Gemma coming over?"

"This evening, if you feel up to it."

"I'll be fine. But Mia's . . ."

Just then they heard loud voices in the hall, an excited squeal and footsteps running up the stairs.

"Boys!" Nadia's voice rang out. "Careful. We no need any more accidents in this house."

"Too right," Ronan murmured.

Greg and Steve burst into the room.

"Mummy!" Steve said throwing his arms around her. She winced as he kissed the tender part of her head. "You still look like you've been in a fight."

"Steve!" Ronan admonished. "That's not very nice."

Wendy laughed. "It's fine." She ruffled Steve's hair. "It's good to see you both. It was far too quiet in the hospital without you." She looked at Greg. He was staring at her.

"Does it hurt a lot, Mummy?" he asked solemnly. "Your head looks sore."

"It is a bit sore, pet. But it's getting better. Come over here and give me a hug."

Steve moved over and allowed his brother to snuggle in beside Wendy.

"I'm glad you're back, Mummy," Greg said looking up at her. "I missed you."

"And I missed you both too. Steve, could you ask Nadia to come up? I want to tell her something."

A moment later, Nadia entered the room. She smiled at Wendy. "The boys have been very good today," she said. "Very helpful."

"I wanted to thank you, Nadia," Wendy said. "We wouldn't have got through the last few days without you. I do appreciate it. Really I do."

"They are good boys," Nadia said kindly. "It was no trouble. And I decide to stay in Ireland for another six months. If you have me."

"Of course we will!" Steve said quickly, throwing his arms around Nadia's neck.

"Steve!" Ronan frowned at him.

"Sorry," Steve said. He stopped strangling Nadia. "But can we keep her?"

"Of course." Wendy smiled at Nadia. "But I think the question should be, will she have us?"

Nadia laughed. "You are not the baddest."

"There's no such word!" Steve pointed out. "No wonder you need to stay in Ireland. Your English is . . ."

"Steve!"

"I know, I know. Sorry, Nadia."

"That's OK." Nadia smiled at him. "I used to it now. And it true. My English, how you say?"

"Sucks!" Steve added helpfully.

They all laughed.

"What are we going to do with you?" Ronan asked Steve, ruffling his hair.

Steve shrugged. "I'll probably grow out of it."

"We can always hope," Wendy said and gave him a huge smile. "But I kind of like you all just the way you are."

CHAPTER
SIXTEEN

The Day Before You Came

"Mia, can you hear me? Are you there?" Gemma shouted up at the open window. She'd already tried ringing the intercom, but there'd been no reply. Mia hadn't answered her phone over the last few days and Gemma was at her wits' end. Alva had assured her that Mia was reasonably all right in the circumstances, but she still didn't want anything to do with either Gemma or Wendy at the moment.

Gemma felt as though her heart was breaking. It was all her fault. Mia was right, she should have told her the truth a long time ago. She felt wretched. Wendy was home from hospital today and she was going to visit her that evening. Gemma had no idea what she was going to tell her. She'd have to lie, she decided. Wendy was

340

still in a fragile condition after all. No stress, the doctor had said.

Gemma walked over to the front door and tried the intercom one last time with no success. Then with a heavy heart she walked slowly away on her crutches. She was completely fed up with hobbling around, but she'd sent the taxi away in the vain hope that Mia would let her in. It had seemed to Gemma to be tempting fate by asking the taxi to wait. She made it up the hill and on to the main road, palms throbbing a little from the exertion and waited for the bus. It wasn't as if she had anything else to do that afternoon, after all. Life without AbbaFab was proving to be rather tedious and she had far too much time on her hands to think: about the past and about her future. She was dreadfully bored and itching to get back to work.

Walking slowly up her road after the short bus ride, Gemma was surprised to see Alva sitting in her car outside her door. Alva's head was lowered and she was engrossed in something. Gemma rapped on her side window. Alva looked up and smiled. She lowered her window.

"There you are," she said. "I wondered where you'd got to. I had to visit an account in Dun Laoghaire so I thought I'd call in here on my way back to the office. Lucky I had a paper to read."

"You could have rung my mobile," Gemma said.

"I did. You didn't answer."

Gemma balanced on one crutch and pulled her mobile out of her pocket. "I forgot to switch it on," she said with a grimace. "Sorry."

"Not to worry. Can I come in for a coffee?"

"Of course."

A few minutes later they were sitting at Gemma's kitchen table waiting for the kettle to boil.

"So how's Mia?" Gemma said.

"I was wondering how long it would take you to ask," Alva said. "Mia's OK." She paused for a moment. "Actually, to tell the truth, she's not great. But it's hard to get her to talk about it — you know what she's like sometimes. She just clams up."

"Tell me about it," Gemma said. "I just don't know what to do. It's all my fault. I should have stopped Dr Tobin saying anything while I had the chance. I wasn't fast enough."

"Ah, Gemma. Stop blaming yourself. If you ask me, Wendy should have told Mia years ago. It wouldn't have been such a shock to her then."

"I know, you're right. I should have made Wendy see sense. Or told Mia myself."

"Gemma! It wasn't up to *you* to do anything. It wasn't your secret to tell. You have to stop protecting your sisters. And this is all between Wendy and Mia now. I don't think you should get involved. I'm sorry to sound harsh, but Mia's a big girl. Let her fight her own battles for a change."

"What are you talking about?" Gemma demanded. "Of course I should get involved. And Mia needs my help. Wendy does too."

"No, Gemma. They need your support, not your help. You can't fix this one, however much you try."

342

Gemma seemed to slump visibly in front of Alva's eyes. "But they're my family," she murmured. "What else am I supposed to do?"

"Get on with your own life," Alva said gently. "You must have dreams, ambitions. Don't you want to meet someone, have your own family?"

"Yes, at some stage I suppose."

"Well, unless you stop living your life through Wendy and Mia you're not going to, ever. You'll be too busy trying to fix their lives instead of your own. When was the last time you had a boyfriend?"

Gemma opened her mouth to answer.

"A proper boyfriend, not just a fling?" Alva added.

"A few years ago," Gemma admitted.

Alva raised her eyebrows. "When we were kids you used to have to fight them off with a stick. Remember? What happened?"

"Things change," Gemma pointed out. "I haven't really had time . . ." she finished lamely.

"Don't let things change too much or you'll be left behind," Alva warned. "I've been doing a lot of thinking since Wendy's fall, Gemma, and I'm worried about you, all of you. I've known the three of you all my life and Mia's practically like a sister to me."

"At least she has one real sister then," Gemma said.

Alva smiled wryly. "It's all a bit of a mess, isn't it?"

Gemma nodded. "And I understand what you're saying, really I do. But I *have* to get involved, don't you see?"

"No, I don't."

Gemma sighed. "Then we'll have to agree to disagree, I'm afraid."

"Just think about what I've said. Please?"

Gemma nodded. "OK."

Alva looked at her watch. "Shoot. I have to go."

"What about that coffee?"

"Another time. But thanks anyway. And Gemma?"

"Yes?"

"Mia's lucky to have you both. And I'm sorry if I was hard on you. But I'm only trying to help."

"I know you are."

"You stay there, I'll see myself out."

As soon as Alva closed the front door behind her, Gemma felt her body slump. She put her arms on the table and rested her head on them. Her head was throbbing with thoughts. Maybe Alva had a point. Maybe it was time to let Wendy and Mia sort things out for themselves.

And then Gemma had an epiphany: maybe it is time for me to leave AbbaFab, she thought. Stand on my own two feet for a change. She smiled to herself. When I have two working feet, that is. A plan began to form in her head. It won't be easy, she thought, but sometimes taking a chance is worth the risk.

That evening, Gemma stood nervously outside Wendy and Ronan's house. She wasn't looking forward to this visit one little bit.

Ronan let her in.

"How's Wendy?" Gemma asked.

"Dying to get out of bed," Ronan said. "You know Wendy."

"Only too well." Gemma smiled. "Is she upstairs?"

Ronan nodded. "Do you need a hand getting up?"

"Are you offering to carry me?" she joked. "I'm quite a weight."

Ronan frowned. "Um . . ."

"I'm only teasing." She put his mind at rest. "I'll manage."

"That's a relief. No offence, but I'm not sure if my back could take it."

Gemma slapped him on the arm. "Don't be so cheeky."

It took her a few minutes, but she got there eventually. Ronan followed behind her just in case. The stairs made him distinctly nervous these days.

"Gemma!" Wendy sat up in the bed and smiled widely at her sister. "I'm so bored. Thanks for coming. How's the leg?"

"Fine. The plaster will be off soon, thank goodness. But not soon enough — I'm counting the weeks. Talk about being bored. I'm sick to death of hobbling around the place."

"I can imagine. I've only been laid up a few days and I'm doing my nut."

"But you're being a very good patient." Ronan grinned down at her from the bedside.

Gemma sat down on the side of the bed and allowed her crutches to fall on to the carpet with a dull thud. "That's better." She rubbed the base of her palms together to ease them out.

"I'm sure you girls have lots to talk about," Ronan said, turning to leave.

"Please stay," Gemma said. "I have something to tell you both."

Ronan came back and leaned against the bedroom wall, his arms folded casually around his chest.

"Is it about Mia?" Wendy asked immediately.

"No," Gemma said. "It's about me." She looked at Wendy and then at Ronan. "I'm leaving AbbaFab."

"What?" Wendy cried. "But you can't!"

"Now you have Mia you don't need me," Gemma pointed out. "And I think it's time for me to move on and do my own thing."

"But *I'm* leaving AbbaFab," Wendy said before Ronan could stop her.

Gemma stared at Wendy in astonishment. "Are you serious?"

Wendy nodded. Ronan started to laugh.

"What's so funny?" Wendy demanded.

"I'm not quite sure," he admitted. "Is this a good time to tell you both *my* news?"

"What news?" Wendy demanded.

"I've just got off the phone. My song has been accepted for the Eurovision song contest competition."

"That's brilliant!" Wendy enthused. "Congratulations, darling. You're so clever."

Gemma looked at Wendy and then at Ronan. Darling? Wendy hadn't called Ronan darling for as long as she could remember.

346

"Good on you," Gemma added. "About time too. How long have you been entering the Eurovision competition now?"

"Hey, it's only been ten, no, eleven years." Ronan snorted. "No time at all. And I'm hoping to start writing full-time soon. Widen my song repertoire. Maybe write a rock musical with Pat."

"But what about AbbaFab?" Gemma asked. "I presume you're talking about leaving the band too. What about Mia and Luke?"

Wendy looked at Ronan and then back at Gemma. "This is all news to me, Gemma. We haven't talked about any of this yet. But we can't *all* leave. It wouldn't be fair on Mia."

"Mia's a big girl, Wendy," said Gemma. "She'll cope."

"But . . ."

Gemma continued, "Really, Wendy, she'll be fine. Changing the subject slightly, that's the other thing I wanted to talk to you both about. Mia. You and Mia to be precise," she said to Wendy.

"Yes?" Wendy looked at Gemma expectantly.

Gemma took a deep breath. "I'm sorry, Wendy, but she doesn't want to talk to either of us. Alva called in earlier and she says Mia's fine physically, but still very upset. I've rung her countless times and I've also tried calling in, but she wouldn't open the door. I'm at my wits' end, Wendy."

Gemma heard a gasp. Wendy's face drained and she put both hands on the bed covers to steady herself.

347

Gemma felt terrible. She knew she shouldn't have upset her sister. Her heart sank.

Wendy noticed the pained look on Gemma's face. "I suspected as much," she said. "Thank you for being so honest. None of this is your fault. I'm to blame. Me and me alone. And I have to deal with the consequences."

"Are you all right?" Ronan asked Wendy with concern.

"Not really," Wendy admitted. "But I needed to hear the truth. Mia's been kept in the dark for long enough. It's time for me to start facing up to my past, to shoulder my mistakes." Her hands fluttered to her face and she pressed her fingertips to her eyes.

Gemma realized Wendy was crying. "It'll be OK," she soothed, shifting up the bed as best she could and putting her arms around her sister.

"I've been such a fool," Wendy sobbed. "I should have told her a long time ago. How could I have been so stupid? I thought it was for the best."

"I know," Gemma said gently, at a loss as to what to say. She looked over at Ronan but he shrugged slightly as if to say, I'm lost too.

"I'm going to call on Mia again this evening," Gemma continued after a few minutes of holding Wendy and allowing her to cry. "Hopefully she'll answer the door this time. Would you like me to talk to her for you?" she asked before she could stop herself. Alva had warned her not to get involved, but it was so difficult not to. Old habits die hard, Gemma thought

348

wryly as soon as the question had popped out of her mouth.

Wendy shook her head. "Thanks. But no. I need to talk to her myself."

"I understand," Gemma said softly and stroked her sister's head. "I understand."

"Hello?" Mia said tentatively into her intercom that afternoon, an hour after Gemma had called. She hoped it wasn't Gemma again. She had nothing to say to her.

"Hi, Mia. It's Luke. Are you busy? I'm going to take a walk down by the sea, shame to waste this sun. Want to join me?"

"Love to. I'll be down in a minute."

Mia ran around the flat looking for her sunglasses. She knew she'd put them somewhere sensible, but she wasn't exactly sure where. "Sunglasses, sunglasses," she murmured, retracing her steps. She gave up after searching everywhere logical, grabbed her denim jacket from the coat hook in the hall and patted her jeans pocket for her keys. Satisfied she had them, she closed the door behind her and skipped down the stairs. She was determined to put the whole Wendy and Gemma thing behind her for the afternoon and have a nice time with Luke. But now she was starting to feel a little guilty for leaving Gemma standing on the doorstep like that. Still, Mia thought as she opened the main front door, she deserved it. They both did.

"Hi, Mia." Luke bent down and kissed her on the cheek. "You look lovely."

Mia squinted up at him. "Thanks. It's gorgeous out, isn't it? I walked to the shops earlier this morning and it was hot even then." Then she remembered and patted the top of her head. She gave a small laugh when she realized that, yes, her sunglasses were perched there, held in place by her hair. She slotted them down over her eyes. That was better.

"What's so funny?" Luke asked.

"Nothing." She smiled up at him and took his arm.

"You're in good form today," he commented as they walked down the road towards the sea front. "All things considered."

"Yes, I am." Mia said, refusing to be drawn. Luke knew all about the Wendy revelation, Ronan had told him the details. Ronan needed to talk to someone outside the family, someone who would listen, Mia couldn't begrudge him that. But it was rather annoying that that someone also happened to be her boyfriend. Every time Luke tried to broach the subject with Mia, she'd closed up like a clam. Eventually he'd got the message

"I presume you'd rather not talk about your sisters this afternoon?" he asked astutely as they walked down the road towards Monkstown seafront.

"Gemma and Wendy, you mean?" she asked, being pedantic. He nodded.

"Correct," she said shortly. And, changing the subject, "I could kill an ice cream. Can we make a detour to the shop?"

"That's a great idea."

Minutes later they were walking arm and arm along the hard, damp sand, licking their ice creams in companionable silence.

"What are you thinking about?" Mia asked eventually. "You're very quiet."

"Nothing really," Luke said, not wanting to admit that he was pondering the Wendy–Mia situation. "Ronan rang this morning."

Mia remained silent.

"No, nothing like that," Luke said quickly. "There's going to be a band meeting tomorrow. He has something to tell everyone."

"Really? What?"

"He wouldn't say. We'll have to go along and find out."

"I'm not going!" Mia said immediately.

"Don't be silly, Mia. You have to go. You're part of AbbaFab now. You don't have to talk to Wendy if you don't want to. In fact, she may not even be there. She's supposed to be resting after all."

Mia snorted. "This *is* Wendy we're talking about?"

Luke nodded and smiled. "She'll be there all right. But you have to go, Mia. It would be really bad form if you didn't. I know you're hurting at the moment . . ."

Mia spun on her heels and faced him. "No you don't, Luke! You don't know how I'm feeling. No one knows."

"Take it easy, Mia," Luke said evenly. But Mia was having none of it.

"You really don't understand," she continued, "do you? My whole life has been one big lie. I'm not who I thought I was, I'm someone completely different.

351

Wendy and Gemma have been lying to me for years and I trusted them. You have no idea how I feel."

She pulled away from his arm, but he grabbed her hand and refused to let go.

"Luke! Let go of me."

"That's where you're wrong, Mia," he said. "And no, I won't let go of you. Listen to me. I *do* know. I know exactly how you feel."

Mia glared at him. "How could you?"

"I'm adopted," he said. "My parents only told me when I was fifteen. I tried to find my birth mother but she emigrated to America just after I was born. I felt exactly like you do now. Hurt, let down, lied to, the whole works."

Mia felt as if time had frozen. In one instant, everything had changed. Her mind was in a whirl. "I'm sorry," she said eventually, feeling ashamed. "I had no idea. I don't know what to say."

Luke shrugged. "It's not something I'm all that comfortable talking about, to tell the truth, that's why I haven't told you before now. It took a long time for me to forgive my parents for lying to me all those years. They let me think I was their natural son."

"Why?" Mia whispered. "Why didn't they tell you?"

Luke stared out to sea. "For the same reason Gemma and Wendy didn't tell you." He looked back at Mia. "They wanted to protect me," he said. "They loved me. And, as they admitted themselves, they made a mistake." He looked at her again intently. "And I had to forgive them for that. For not being perfect."

"And did you?"

"Yes, eventually." He paused for a moment. "But my dad died before I had a chance to tell him."

"Oh, Luke, I'm so sorry." Mia felt terrible. Poor Luke, she thought, what must he think of me, whingeing on about Wendy and Gemma when he has family history of his own?

"That's why I'm telling you all this, Mia. I've never forgiven myself, but it's something I have to live with. If I could change things, though, turn back the clock . . . well, it's too late now." He blew out his breath. "Let's walk."

Mia nodded, saying nothing. Luke was visibly shaken, and she tried to keep up as he powered along the sand. As she walked, she thought about Wendy. She felt a shiver run through her body. Luke was right: everyone had lied to her because they thought it was for the best — Miriam, Gemma *and* Wendy. None of them had meant to hurt her. Gemma had only been eight when she was born. Eight! Just a little older than Greg and Steve. It must have been very traumatic for her. And as for Wendy, Mia shuddered just thinking about it. Having a baby at any age was scary, but at fourteen . . . Her eyes began to fill with tears and within seconds she was crying.

"Luke," she whispered.

He stopped, and realized that she was crying, the tears sneaking down her cheeks under her sunglasses. He put his arms around her and held her tight.

"I'm sorry," she said through her tears. "I've been so stupid."

"There's no need to apologize to me," he said. "But I think you should listen to what Wendy and Gemma have to say. Don't you?" Before it's too late, he wanted to add, but stopped himself. Mia knew what he was getting at.

Mia buried her head in his chest and continued to cry. Luke stroked the back of her head. "Hush now," he soothed.

After a while, Mia's tears stopped and she pulled away from him. "Can we go home?" she whispered.

"Yes, of course."

"And Luke?"

"Yes?"

"When we get there, would you mind staying with me for a little while?"

"I'd be happy to. I won't leave until you're feeling better."

"Promise?"

"I promise."

That evening, after a delicious meal cooked by Nadia and eaten on trays in Wendy's and Ronan's bedroom (a first — normally Wendy insisted that all food was eaten in the kitchen), Ronan offered Gemma a lift to Mia's house, which she gratefully accepted. He watched from the car as Gemma stood on the doorstep, waiting. Answer the door, Mia, he willed from his vantage point. Please, Mia. He wanted her to talk to Gemma, but he also wanted to get back to Wendy as soon as possible. She was still upset, although hiding it well, and he was worried about her.

Gemma tried the intercom for the second time.

"Hello?" Mia's voice asked tentatively.

"Mia? It's Gemma. Can I come in?"

Gemma heard a male voice say something to Mia in the background. It sounded suspiciously like Luke.

The door buzzed and Gemma pushed it open and made her way slowly up the stairs. Mia's door was open and Gemma pushed it with one of her crutches.

"She's in the living room," Luke said, opening the door properly for her and giving her a nod. "Chin up," he whispered, taking in her anxious expression.

Gemma gave him a small smile and a nod. Chin up. It was a curiously old-fashioned expression, but it fitted the occasion perfectly. She did just that, took a deep breath and crutched herself into the living room.

"Mia?"

Mia was standing at the window, staring out. She turned her head as soon as she heard Gemma's voice. Mia's eyes jumped around the room nervously before finally settling on Gemma's. She didn't say a word.

"Mia, I'm sorry," Gemma said nervously, staying exactly where she was. "You're right; I should have told you a long time ago."

Mia scrunched her nose a little. "Look, Gemma, I'm sorry too. I shouldn't have said those terrible things to you. None of this is your fault. Can you forgive me?"

"Forgive you? Of course." Gemma was surprised. She wasn't expecting *this*. She moved closer to Mia, standing just beside her at the window. "I know you probably have hundreds of questions. And I'll answer them all for you as best I can."

355

Mia shrugged and gave a deep sigh. "I know we have a lot of talking to do, Gemma. But right now, would you mind if we left it? I'm exhausted from it all, to tell the truth. And if I cry any more there won't be any water left in my body."

"Fine by me," Gemma said, relieved. "There's plenty of time. I'm not going anywhere." She stopped for a second. Alva's words rang through her mind. Stop trying to protect your sisters. Live your own life. "And Mia, I'm not going to get involved in this any more — the whole situation between you and Wendy, I mean. You do what you think is right. I won't interfere. I promise."

Mia was taken aback. She was waiting for the "You must sort things out with Wendy" lecture. She wasn't expecting this. "OK," she managed.

"I'm going to go now," Gemma said. She leaned over and gave Mia an awkward hug, her crutches getting somewhat in the way. "I love you, Mia."

"I love you too," Mia said back, a lump forming in her throat.

"I'll see myself out now. You know where I am if you need me. Ring me when you're ready. Take care of yourself."

"And you. And Gemma?"

"Yes?"

"I'll ring you tomorrow. Not to talk, mind, just to say hello."

"That sounds good. Till tomorrow then."

Gemma's eyes were full of tears as she walked carefully down Mia's stairs and towards Ronan's car. But this time they were tears of joy.

356

★   ★   ★

Luke proved as good as his word. He stayed with Mia until she fell asleep in his arms late that evening, emotionally drained. After clearing the air with Gemma, Mia had agreed to talk to Wendy the following day after the band meeting.

Lying in Mia's bed, watching her breathing, Luke realized with a start that he never wanted to leave her, ever.

CHAPTER
SEVENTEEN

Does Your Mother Know?

The following morning Mia and Luke walked to Wendy and Ronan's house for the band meeting. Mia felt sick to her stomach with nerves, but she felt reassured by Luke's presence. They had talked late into the night; about his parents, what he knew about his birth mother, the long years of trying to find her, his fear of abandonment and his devastation when Ciara left him. And then Mia had shared her own feelings with him, something she'd never found easy to do. She felt so comfortable with him. "I could get used to this," she'd murmured as she dozed off to sleep in the safety of his arms.

"Hi, Luke, Mia. Thanks for coming." Ronan opened the door wide and ushered them inside.

Everyone looked up as they entered the living room. Pat, Gemma and especially Wendy. Mia held Wendy's gaze for a second. She knew she should give her a smile, let her know that everything would be all right eventually, but she felt powerless to do so. Her lips were locked tightly together and she felt even more nauseous. Talking to Wendy was going to be one of the hardest things she'd ever had to do. But Mia knew she had to face her fear. Running away from it just wasn't an option. She could always shut Wendy out, she supposed, but then, thinking of Luke's situation, she chastised herself. I'm going to face this head on, she promised herself.

"I'm sure you're all wondering why I called this band meeting," Ronan said, interrupting Mia's thoughts. "Some of us have news that will affect the whole band," he said, looking around the room. "Where will we start?"

"With me," Wendy said. She looked around the room, her eyes lingering on Mia's. "I'm leaving the band."

Mia gasped. "What? But you can't!"

Wendy smiled at her gently. "It's time for me to do other things, Mia. AbbaFab has been my life for many years now, but I need to start thinking of the future. I want to spend more time with Ronan and the boys."

"But Wendy, you *are* AbbaFab," Luke pointed out. "What's going to happen to the band?" Wendy gave a brief nod to Gemma.

"I'm leaving too," Gemma said, sounding a little nervous. "I'm not quite sure what I'm going to do, to

359

be honest. I've had an idea for a cabaret act and we'll see how that pans out. But I'm definitely leaving AbbaFab."

"What about you, Ronan?" Luke asked. "Don't tell me."

Ronan nodded. "Sorry, mate. I've decided to try and make a go of the song-writing lark. One of my songs has been accepted for the Song for Europe."

"The contest that selects Ireland's Eurovision entry?" Mia asked.

"Yes," Ronan said.

"That's great!" Mia said. "Congratulations."

"And I'm going to try my hand at writing a rock musical," Pat added.

"That's all well and good," Luke said in a slightly subdued tone. "But what about AbbaFab? That just leaves me and Mia."

"You're more than welcome to keep the band going," Wendy suggested. "You could find two extra singers and a new Pat."

"I don't think so," Luke said after a pause. "Whatever about the singers, we'd never be able to replace Pat. And it just wouldn't be the same without all of you."

"Thanks, mate." Pat smiled at him and gave him a wink.

"What do you think, Mia?"

Mia shook her head. "Luke's right. It just wouldn't be the same."

She felt deflated. Everyone seemed to have their lives mapped out for them, except for her and Luke. It just wasn't fair.

"But it's such a pity," she murmured. "I've only just started," she began, not knowing quite what she wanted to say.

"What was that, Mia?" Ronan asked gently.

"I don't want to stop singing," Mia said, surprising herself and everyone else by the strength of her conviction. "I can't go back to teaching now. What am I going to do? I want to sing!"

Luke took her hand in his. "We'll be fine," he promised her. "It looks like AbbaFab has come to its natural end. Just like the real Abba. Isn't that right, Wendy?"

Wendy nodded.

"We'll find something else," Luke continued. "Whatever about me, Mia, you have a natural God-given talent."

"He's right," Wendy said firmly. "You're brilliant."

Gemma nodded. "We all think so."

"Really?" Mia asked. "You're not just saying that?" She looked at Pat.

"You've got it, Mia," he assured her. "Star quality. You'll go all the way if you believe in yourself."

"Thanks," Mia whispered, staring down at her hands. She was touched. Pat didn't say much but when he did, he always told the truth.

"So is that it?" Luke asked. "The end of AbbaFab?"

"I guess so," Ronan said.

"It seems like such an anticlimax," Gemma pointed out. "The end of AbbaFab. Just like that."

Wendy sighed. "I know what you mean."

"We should have a party," Ronan said. "And play one last time. When Wendy's better. And we can have two Agnethas."

"Two?" Mia asked.

He grinned at her. "Why not? And if Gemma's still in plaster she can sing from a chair. We can do what we like. And our fans will love it."

"Our fans?" Gemma asked.

"Don't sound so surprised," Wendy said. "We do have quite a number, you know. They're always emailing the AbbaFab website, asking when we're playing next. Speaking of which, why don't we play in the Singing Tree, where Ronan first discovered us?" She smiled over at Gemma. "Where it all started?"

"Would we fit? It's quite a small pub," Gemma pointed out.

"I'm sure they'd put a marquee in the beer garden if we asked them nicely," Wendy suggested. "My man has contacts." She winked at Gemma and Gemma laughed. Ronan's cousin owned a marquee hire company.

"Great idea," Ronan said. "If everyone agrees, I can set it up."

Pat nodded.

"Sounds good," Luke said. "Mia?"

Mia nodded too. She was trying to hold back the tears. She felt overwhelmed. It had been quite a week. First the Wendy revelation, now the break-up of AbbaFab.

Ronan noticed her discomfort. He clapped his hands together. "Who'd like a beer? I put the barbecue on just in case. Anyone up for a steak?"

Gemma laughed. "Always thinking about your stomach."

Ronan patted his stomach affectionately. "But of course."

Everyone stood up except Wendy, who remained on the sofa. "Mia?" she said tentatively.

Luke squeezed Mia's hand. "Stay and talk to her," he said in a low voice.

Mia shook her head. She was almost shaking with nerves.

"Mia," he said. "It's time."

"OK," she murmured. She stayed on her feet as everyone left the room. Luke shut the door behind him and Mia suddenly felt claustrophobic.

"Mia?" Wendy said. "Will you sit down?" She patted the seat of the sofa beside her.

Mia stared at Wendy for a moment. "I'll stand."

"Mia, please." Wendy looked up at her and Mia noticed with a start that she was crying.

Mia shook her head.

"Mia." Wendy looked her in the eye.

Mia held her gaze. And in that moment she realized that Wendy loved her. It was as simple as that.

"I'm so sorry," Wendy began, tears rolling down her pale cheeks. Mia still said nothing. "I never meant to hurt you. You have to believe me. I was so young when I had you, I didn't know what I was doing. If I could go back and change things I would. You have no idea how hard it was for me, living a lie for all those years."

"*You* were living a lie!" Mia snorted.

"I know. And I'll never forgive myself for keeping it from you all that time. I made a mistake, Mia. A terrible mistake. I should have told you, but it never seemed to be the right time. I wish I could turn back the clock, but I can't."

"Why did you give me to Mum?" Mia demanded. "Did you not want me?"

"Of course I did. But I was fourteen, Mia. Fourteen! I had four more years of school ahead of me at the time."

"But Mum could have minded me when you were at school. You didn't have to give me up completely."

"It seemed the right thing to do," Wendy said. "For the family and for you. I wasn't thinking straight. I was in complete denial and I didn't tell anyone for ages. Gemma was only eight, remember. Mum guessed when I was just over seven months pregnant, and after that, she and Dad made all the decisions."

"You could have been my proper mum," Mia said. "You could have looked after me."

"It was what *I* wanted," Wendy admitted. "But Mum and Dad convinced me that it wasn't the right thing to do. They couldn't have any more children; having Gemma almost killed Mum, so I guess they saw it as God's will. They really did think it was for the best, Mia."

"But you went along with it, Wendy. Even though you knew it was wrong."

Wendy nodded. "I thought keeping you was the selfish option. The other option was to give you up for adoption to another family. And that would have killed me. At least this way I got to see you every day. It was hard, but I saw you grow up. It made it a little more bearable for me."

"But then you went away when I was three, to London."

Wendy nodded. "I found it harder and harder to cope with what I'd done as I got older. I realized that if I'd been a little bit more determined and a little older, sixteen or seventeen maybe, I could have kept you as my own. It became unbearable after a while and I had to get away. I couldn't live with the constant reminder of what I'd done. I went a little wild, to tell the truth, especially when I was working on the cruise ship. But I missed you so much. I thought about you all the time and I came back to see you whenever I could. And then when Mum died I got to look after you, like a real daughter. It was a strange twist of fate."

Mia hesitated before she asked the next question. "Who's my father, Gemma? I need to know."

"A boy from Westport called Henry Reilly. He was a few years older than me. He's living in America now. He emigrated with a woman from the town."

"What was he like?"

"Utterly gorgeous," Wendy said honestly. "He was tall and slim with white-blond hair, like yours, Mia. And the most beautiful skin. Even as a teenager, he didn't have one single spot. All the girls were mad about him. He loved music too, he was in a rock band called Tumbleweed and they used to play at parties. He had quite a voice. I always had a thing about musicians."

"Does he know about me?"

"No, I never told him."

Mia stared at Wendy incredulously.

"Don't look at me like that, Mia. He left Westport before I got the chance." Wendy paused for a moment. "But if you want to find him, I'll help you. His family in Westport might . . ."

Mia shook her head. "Maybe sometime in the future. Right now, I think I have enough to be going on with, don't you?"

"Of course. Sorry."

Mia leaned against the side of the sofa. She suddenly felt weary.

"Please sit down, Mia," Wendy cajoled.

This time Mia acquiesced.

"So what now?" Wendy asked, wiping away her tears. She'd stopped crying but she still felt emotionally raw. This conversation wasn't exactly going as planned. She'd hoped that Mia would forgive her, they'd talk honestly, sort things out, and that would be that. But she recognized now that she was being naive.

Mia shrugged. "I'm not sure. There are so many things I want to know, but right at this moment I can't think of any of them."

"It's a lot to take in," Wendy said gently. She looked at Mia. "What about us?" she asked. "You and me?"

"I don't know," Mia said truthfully. "I don't know what or how I feel, Wendy. I'm all over the place."

Wendy took a deep breath. "Mia, you're everything to me. You always have been. I love you more than anything in the world." Wendy moved slowly towards

366

Mia on the sofa. She put her arms around her, but Mia pushed her away.

"Not yet," Mia said. "I'm not ready, Wendy."

Wendy felt as though she'd been stabbed in the heart. She moved away. "We'll work this out, Mia," She murmured. They sat side by side on the sofa in silence.

"It'll never be the same again," Mia said. "You and me. You know that, don't you?"

Wendy nodded wordlessly. Finally she said, "But at least you know who you are now."

"Yes. I always sensed something wasn't quite right, but I could never put my finger on it. As you say, as least I know who I am now."

As they sat, Wendy felt the weight of her secret she'd been carrying on her shoulders for so many years lift, and suddenly she felt pounds lighter. She began to cry again. She smiled through her tears. "At least one of us does."

Epilogue

Take a Chance on Me
Fourteen Months Later

"Mia, I had to ring you. I have news."

"Hi, Gemma. I can't stay on the mobile long, I'm on stage in a few minutes. I'm in the dressing room, sorry if it's a bit noisy."

There was a busy hum of voices in the background.

"Not to worry, I'll be quick," Gemma promised. "Well, to start with, Ronan's song won the Song for Europe."

Mia gasped. "No, really? So his song will be in the Eurovision?"

"Yes!"

"That's brilliant! How exciting! I was so disappointed for him last year when he came second."

"I know. And he has a really good chance of winning the whole thing. Johnny Logan has agreed to come out of Eurovision retirement to sing it."

"What's it called?" Mia asked.

"'Sister, Miss Ya'." Gemma sang the jaunty chorus. "'Sister, love ya; there's never been another quite like ya. Sister, miss ya; never, ever stop thinkin' of ya.'"

"Catchy." Mia giggled hysterically.

"Cheesy, isn't it? But it's so sweet it's bound to win. Wendy wrote the lyrics, can you believe it?"

"Um," Mia murmured. It had been over a year since she and Luke had moved to London together to join the cast of the long-running Abba musical, *Mamma Mia*. Luke was still in the chorus, but Mia had progressed through the ranks quickly and was now understudy to one of the lead parts, the young daughter, Sophie Sheridan. She hadn't been home once in all that time to visit Wendy or Gemma. She'd given them a variety of excuses: "The show's so busy, I can't possibly get the time off," "We have to paint the flat," "Luke's sick, I can't leave him," "I'm exhausted." But the truth was, Mia just wasn't ready to face Wendy again. Not yet. She still had a lot of things to work through first. But Luke was helping, listening to her when she needed a friend, giving her advice when she asked for it.

Mia had also seen Alva recently when she and Sean had flown over to catch the show and for a "non-honeymoon-honeymoon" as they'd jokingly called it. And they seemed more in love than ever, even if they were still arguing. But that just seemed to be their way.

"We're trying to find a way to live together without killing each other," Alva had told Mia and Luke over dinner, while grinning at Sean. "But it's hard. Sean's a very difficult housemate."

"Pay no attention to Alva, she's a bit ratty as she's been off the cigarettes for a few weeks now," Sean had retorted.

"And how's the cabaret show going?" Mia asked Gemma. Gemma now sang as Marlene Dietrich, Edith Piaf and other famous cabaret divas in clubs and at events.

"Great! I'm doing two nights a week now at the Olympia and lots of private gigs. I'm really enjoying it!"

"And your doctor friend?"

It turned out that Dr Tobin's mother was quite the cabaret fan. He'd been dragged along to a show at the Olympia Theatre, had recognized Gemma instantly and afterwards, somewhat smitten, had gone backstage to find her.

"Excellent. Although he's always working. But I have even more exciting news," Gemma continued.

"More exciting than the lovely Dr Tobin?" Mia laughed.

"Oh yes, far more exciting. Wendy had her baby. A girl."

"A girl?" Mia faltered.

"Yes."

"I have a sister?"

Gemma's heart stopped for a moment. "Well, yes, Mia. You do. A little sister."

"Does she have a name?"

"Sorry, of course. Stella. Stella Miriam."

The line went silent for a moment as Mia took this in. "Stella? Doesn't that mean star?"

"Yes," Gemma said. "It does. But Wendy said you'd always be her original Little Star, that would never change."

Mia's heart thudded in her chest and tears flooded her eyes.

"Are you OK, Mia?" Gemma asked gently.

Mia wiped away the tears with her knuckles. "Maybe I should come home," she said, "and meet little Stella. I'm due some time off."

Now it was Gemma's turn to cry. "That's a great idea," she said joyfully. "I'd love to see you and I'll tell Wendy. She'll be over the moon."

Gemma heard a voice shouting in the background.

"Sorry, have to run," Mia said, "curtain call."

"Break a leg," Gemma said.

But Mia had already gone.

Also available in ISIS Large Print:

Bookends

Jane Green

Cath and Si are best friends. Total opposites, always together and both unlucky in love. Cath is messy and emotionally closed, and Si is impossibly tidy and catty. They live near each other in West Hampstead, close to their other best friends Josh and Lucy — who are married, with a devil-spawn child called Max and a terrifying Swedish nanny, Ingrid.

Then the beautiful Portia steps back into their lives. Portia who broke their collective hearts one night, and from whom they have all gradually grown apart. Her reappearance sets off a chain of events that tests Cath and her friends to the limit. Does Portia have a hidden agenda, or is she just looking for happy endings all round? Whatever the answers, none of them could ever predict the outcome . . .

ISBN 0-7531-7618-1 (hb)
ISBN 0-7531-7619-X (pb)[z]

Caught in the Act

Gemma Fox

Carol French — grown up, confident, settled — is about to meet the man of her dreams. Her teenage dreams, that is, because Carol is going to a school reunion with a difference. Brought back together by a website called oldschooltie.com, the old sixth-form drama group that took Macbeth on tour 20 years ago is all set to repeat the performance.

The original tour was dramatic in more ways than one and Carol has carried a torch for the leading actor ever since. Not that it has stopped her marrying, having kids, divorcing — but that memory just won't go away. Now she is about to be brought face to face with the adolescent love god himself, except now he's nearly forty . . .

ISBN 0-7531-7581-9 (hb)
ISBN 0-7531-7582-7 (pb)[z]

THE DROVE ROADS OF SCOTLAND

By the same Author

BY MANY WATERS

THE PATH BY THE WATER

The Highland Drovers' Departure for the South

(*From the painting by Sir Edwin Landseer, R.A., in the Victoria and Albert Museum—Crown Copyright*)

THE DROVE ROADS
OF SCOTLAND

A. R. B. HALDANE,
D.Litt.

THOMAS NELSON AND SONS LTD
LONDON EDINBURGH PARIS MELBOURNE
TORONTO AND NEW YORK

THOMAS NELSON AND SONS LTD
Parkside Works Edinburgh 9
3 Henrietta Street London WC2
312 Flinders Street Melbourne C1
5 Parker's Buildings Burg Street Cape Town

THOMAS NELSON AND SONS (CANADA) LTD
91–93 Wellington Street West   Toronto 1

THOMAS NELSON AND SONS
19 East 47th Street New York 17

SOCIÉTÉ FRANÇAISE D'EDITIONS NELSON
25 rue Henri Barbusse Paris V^e

———

First published June 1952
Reprinted 1952 (twice), 1953

THIS BOOK IS DEDICATED TO
MY WIFE

ACKNOWLEDGMENTS

THE list of those who have helped me in the production of this book is a long one, and I can only attempt to mention by name a few of those to whom I am principally indebted.

In the first place, I must record my very great indebtedness to the staff of the Signet Library, Edinburgh, who have helped me throughout, and particularly to Mr John Robertson, who has not only helped me in my search for sources of information, but has undertaken the long and laborious task of checking the references. Without the help of the Signet Library and its staff the time and labour involved in the collection of material would have been immensely increased. I am also indebted to the staffs of the Central Library of Edinburgh Public Libraries; the National Library of Scotland; the Historical Room at H.M. Register House, Edinburgh; the Public Record Office, London; the Map Room at the British Museum, and The Royal Scottish Geographical Society.

Dr H. W. Meikle and Professor W. Croft Dickinson have helped me greatly with suggestions and encouragement, and I wish particularly to thank them.

I am also much indebted to the following: Mr Charles McInnes, Curator of Historical Records, H.M. Register House; Mr Angus Graham, Secretary to the Royal Commission on Ancient Monuments in Scotland; Mr K. J. Bonser, Leeds, and Mr R. J. Adam, Lecturer in Mediaeval History, St Andrews University, through whose kindness I have had access to material in the Sutherland Estate Papers at Dunrobin.

I wish also to express my thanks to Mr N. G. Matthew for the great care which he has taken in the preparation of the map, to Mr Robert Adam for allowing me to use a number of his fine photographs illustrating the country through which the drovers passed, and to numerous other friends and correspondents who have helped me in my search for illustrations.

In addition to those mentioned, I have received valuable help and information from landowners, factors, farmers, crofters, shepherds and others in many parts of Scotland who have given me the benefit of their knowledge of local history and tradition.

vii

ACKNOWLEDGMENTS

The extent of my indebtedness to other writers, contemporary and modern, is, I hope, sufficiently apparent from the notes and references.

Finally, I must record my thanks to the Carnegie Trust for the Universities of Scotland whose generosity has helped to make possible the publication of this book, and to the publishers for the great care which they have given to every detail of its production.

A. R. B. H.

EDINBURGH, 1951

CONTENTS

LIST OF PLATES

ABBREVIATIONS

In the Notes and References the following abbreviations have been used :

A.P.S.   Acts of the Parliament of Scotland

R.P.C.   Register of the Privy Council

O.S.A.   The Statistical Account of Scotland, 1791–99

N.S.A.   The New Statistical Account of Scotland, 1845

H.R. & B.   Reports of the Commissioners for Highland Roads and Bridges, 1804–60

P.R.O.   Public Record Office

NOTE

The Author wishes it to be clearly understood that the mention in the text or the notes or the marking on the map of routes or areas used as drove roads, rights of way or stances during the period of which he writes, cannot in itself be taken as any indication that these routes or areas retain today the character of rights of way.

Except in the quotations or in passages directly referring to quoted matter, the spelling of the place names is that given in W. & A. K. Johnston's Gazetteer of Scotland, 1937.

INTRODUCTION

DURING the autumn of 1942 I had occasion, in the course of certain work on which I was then engaged, to call to mind an old road which crosses the Ochils immediately behind my home near Auchterarder in Perthshire. For a mile or two back into the hills the road serves as an access to upland farms, but at the sheep farm of Coulshill it loses this character, and from that point to its junction with the main road through Glendevon it is now little more than a lonely grass-grown track crossing the hills. Little used as it now is, the grassy road retains the clear marks of extensive use by the traffic of former days, and it occurred to me that it would be of interest to try to trace something of its history. Local inquiries left little doubt that the road had seen much and varied traffic. Over the Ochils passed at one time coal and lime from West Fife going north to the rich farm lands of Strathearn, while slates from Glenalmond and Glenartney, together with grain, flax, wool and timber went south to the Forth basin. It may be that a part of this traffic crossed the Ochils by this Coulshill road in preference to the parallel routes through Gleneagles or by Dunning to Yetts of Muckhart ; but besides all this, local tradition marked the road as one which was in use in the latter part of the eighteenth and much of the nineteenth centuries by droves of cattle and sheep bound from the Highlands to the great market at Falkirk. I knew little or nothing of the nature or extent of this traffic and my informants were in little better case, but the subject seemed to be one of interest and I determined, as opportunity offered, to get to know more of this droving traffic, the routes by which it reached the Lowlands, its ultimate destination and the methods of the men whose work it was. The material contained in the pages which follow has been gathered over the past eight years, partly from the personal recollection or inherited tradition of men and women in many parts of Scotland, but in the main from scattered references contained in a wide variety of manuscript and printed sources in Scotland and England, from which has been gradually pieced together to the best of my ability the story of the drove roads of Scotland.

The main intention at the outset was to discover the routes

I

by which the cattle of the Highlands were brought to the markets or trysts in the centre of Scotland, and to a substantial extent this intention has been adhered to ; but at an early stage it became apparent that before any intelligent appreciation of the drove routes could be gained, a wider knowledge of the history, nature and extent of the droving traffic must be acquired than could be obtained from any sources then available to me, while the growing interest of the subject, as research proceeded, suggested that a more comprehensive study would be worth attempting.

To anyone attempting to trace the origin and development of the movement of livestock the problem must immediately arise of deciding to how early a date the research is to be carried. In Scotland, as in all other largely pastoral countries, the breeding and movement of livestock was fundamental to the life of the people and can be traced back as far as historical records exist. Part of this movement was clearly of a normal and legitimate character called for by the need to move stock from one grazing area to another, or by the droving of beasts to such markets as then existed. To this extent it forms part of the history of droving which may thus claim to date back at least as far as recorded history. The Register of the Privy Council from which much of the early historical material has been drawn shows, however, that as late as the sixteenth and seventeenth centuries a large part of this movement was the result of cattle thieving. That the cattle traffic of the earlier centuries was largely of a like character seems certain, and the early history of the drove roads is to a large extent the story of the gradual transition from lawless cattle driving to lawful cattle driving. The evidence available suggests that this process of change began to be apparent about the end of the fifteenth century, gradually acquiring momentum during the two centuries which followed. The Union of the Crowns helped the trend towards the legitimate movement of livestock, but it was only after 1707 that droving in the sense of large-scale organised movement of livestock on foot to established markets became a marked feature of Scotland's economy.

The century which followed the Union of the Parliaments witnessed several great developments which fundamentally affected the commercial life of the country and not least the trade in livestock. During these hundred years the Union with England

2

became a reality and Scotland was finally integrated as an essential part of the commercial life of Great Britain, losing in some degree her identity and with it certain Continental markets, but gaining in return the advantages of a growing market in England and the vast markets and resources of the extending Empire. The Union with England had involved Scotland in the full consequences of British foreign policy, and the constant wars which filled much of the eighteenth and early nineteenth centuries were of direct and vital consequence to the droving trade. The eighteenth century saw the final pacification of the Highlands and the transformation of Highland communications brought about first by Wade and the builders of the military roads who immediately followed him, and later by the great work of the Commissioners for Highland Roads and Bridges. Most important of all in its effect on the livestock trade, the second half of the eighteenth century saw the start of a great revolution in farming practice comparable in scope to the industrial revolution with which indeed it was closely connected and to which it was in many ways complementary. Coinciding as it did with other changes, political and economic, the agricultural revolution at first brought a great extension to the droving industry, and only in its later stages in the second quarter of the nineteenth century brought into play factors which led in the end to the decline of the trade. It is, then, of this century and a half which followed the Union of the Parliaments, of the growth, fortunes and vicissitudes of the cattle trade during these years that the story of the drove roads of Scotland mainly tells.

The magnitude of the changes, social, political and economic, which took place during this period of 150 years presents a formidable problem in attempting to construct an intelligible picture of a trade which persisted throughout. The main wealth of the material available for the task comes from the Statistical Account of 1791–99, the New Statistical Account and the many surveys of Scottish agriculture which were undertaken in the years between ; but much comes also from the early and middle part of the eighteenth century. From all we know of them it is very evident that drovers were adaptable fellows. Handicapped by few preconceived ideas or perhaps even by any too rigid code of commercial morality, they were quick to change their methods to suit the needs of their rough-and-ready trade. So it is that the fleeting and scattered glimpses of the droving trade through-

3

out the long years of its continuance reveal a variety of custom and technique. The main outlines are clear, but any comprehensive survey of a drover's life and work must almost inevitably include detail and colour belonging to different phases in the history of the trade.

A similar difficulty presents itself in considering the routes used by the drovers. Without a doubt these changed from time to time according to the political and social conditions of the time, the market requirements, the type of beasts forming the drove, the weather or even the individual tastes, prejudices and idiosyncrasies of the drovers. It can be little, if any, exaggeration to say that there are few glens in the Highlands, even few easy routes leading to the South over moor or upland country, which have not known the tread of driven cattle on the way to the Trysts. At an early stage in the research it became apparent that to construct a map on which were marked all the routes, the use of which at one time or another as drove roads could be established by reasonable evidence, would be an unmanageable task, and that such a map, through the very multiplicity of routes, would lose much of its meaning. It was, therefore, decided to show only the main routes used by the drovers, with such subsidiary routes as appeared to be of substantial importance or interest, and no claim is made that the map is in any way exhaustive.

For the purpose of exact historical record this work has been too long delayed. Had it been undertaken even twenty years earlier, much information now lost might have been secured. The written and printed sources, scanty and widely scattered though they be, remain, but the generation of those who can recall the last days of the droving trade is almost gone, and there survives only a small and fast-dwindling band of old men who themselves took cattle to Falkirk Tryst in the last years of its existence and can speak either from their own recollection or at least from information handed down to them from the generation before. How often in the course of inquiries in all parts of the Highlands has a request for information been met with an expression of regret that it had not been made during the lifetime of those not long since dead. If this has often provoked tantalising speculation as to what might have been, it has no less brought realisation of the importance of securing what can still be secured before that too becomes obliterated by the passage of time ; but perhaps the delay in attempting this research has been not without some advantage, for it may be that had the work been started earlier, at a time when droving was still a part of everyday life or even a very recent memory, the picture might have lost something from over-abundance of detail and from the absence of that perspective which distance lends.

The work has for me been full of interest and growing fascination. Once the initial difficulty of grasping the few scattered threads leading to the true sources of information had been overcome, these threads quickly led to others, and the number and variety of sources finally used have been incomparably greater than seemed at first possible. Throughout I have had the very great advantage of having access to the resources of the Signet Library, Edinburgh, and the ready help of those who care for and know so well that fine collection ; of the National Library of Scotland ; of H.M. Register House, Edinburgh ; of Edinburgh Public Libraries and, through the Central Library for Students, of local collections in Scotland, England and Wales. Apart from the printed and manuscript sources the search has led to many parts of Highland Scotland ; to Wester Ross-shire where on an autumn day a crofter working in his harvest field on the eve of his hundredth year told of his early life as a drover in voluble Gaelic interpreted by his daughter ; to Skye ; to the Lorn and Knapdale districts of Argyll ; to the banks of the Upper Don and to many parts of Perthshire and the Southern Uplands. I can only hope that any who read these pages may perhaps derive a small part of the pleasure which the collection of the information has given to me, and that the picture I have tried to paint may help to preserve for the future a reflection, however faint and imperfect, of what was once a vivid and vital part of the life of Scotland.

1

THE EARLY DROVERS

THE beginning of the story of Scotland's cattle lies far back in her remote past. In all parts of the world, before man came to possess knowledge, skill or implements to enable him to till the ground, hunting and the grazing of livestock provided him with his only means of livelihood, and in the possession of that stock lay almost his only source of wealth. As the years went on, bringing with them increasing knowledge, the richer lowland areas came gradually into cultivation for crops, but in the mountains and upland valleys, sheep and cattle remained the mainstay of the people.

So it has been with Scotland. The early records bear witness to the number of sheep and cattle in the country and the importance of stock grazing. In the early Charters few superficial areas of land are given, the extent being in general measured by the number of cattle and sheep which it would support, while rents, taxes and fines were regularly paid in livestock. The monks and religious houses, particularly in the south of Scotland and the valley of the Tweed, soon became among the best and most prosperous farmers. Indeed it seems probable that at the time of the Reformation the monks, and especially those of the Cistercian Order, had raised the standard of farming in the lands under their control to a level which was not surpassed till well on in the eighteenth century. In this the monks of Melrose Abbey were prominent, and at the end of the twelfth century they were deriving much of their revenue from the pasturing of stock. In 1180 Melrose was given the right to build a 'vaccaria' for 100 cows in Threipwood.[1] Newbattle Abbey had from the Lord of Lynton and Romanno the right of pasturage for 1,000 sheep and 60 cattle—a 'mirabilis concessio,'[2] while the records of the period are full of other references showing the value and extent of stock-raising particularly in the Lowlands. These rights of grazing were often in conflict with the interests

---

[1] *A.P.S.*, I, 387
[2] *Chartulary of Newbattle Abbey*, xxxv, 97 (Bannatyne Club 89). Cosmo Innes, *Sketches of Early Scottish History*, 133

of the huntsman and game preserver. A grant by Robert Avenel of lands in Upper Eskdale to the monks of Melrose reserved deer, boar and other game.[1] In an early Grant of Pasturage in the Lammermuirs it was provided that moveable folds should accompany the flocks of the Abbey to provide shelter, but avoiding the establishment of permanent settlements in the forests, and statutory penalties incurred by the owners of cattle found trespassing in the forests recur frequently in the early Acts of the Scots Parliament.

On Matthew Paris's map of thirteenth-century Scotland he has shown the far North and West of the country as ' marshy and impassable, fit for cattle and shepherds,' [2] and a century later John Fordoun found ' the upland districts and along the Highlands ' to be ' full of pasturage grass for cattle and comely with verdure in the glens along the water courses.' [3] Of the total number of cattle in the country in these early times, no accurate estimate can be made, but the Exchequer Rolls for 1378 show the number of hides exported as being nearly 45,000.[4] Major, writing of Scotland in the early sixteenth century, reported that many men possessed as many as 10,000 sheep and 1,000 cattle,[5] and when, in 1544, Henry the Eighth sent the Earl of Hertford and later in the same year, Sir Ralph Eure to lay waste the Border country, the tale of the losses suffered by Scotland shows that the beasts driven back to England included 10,386 cattle and over 12,000 sheep.[6] Estienne Perlin, describing Scotland in the middle of the century, speaks of the abundance of cattle in the country,[7] and towards the end of the century Bishop Leslie described how ' in the mountanis of Aargyl and Rosse lykewyse and sindrie utheris places ar fed ky, nocht tame, as in utheris partes, bot lyke wylde hartes, wandiring out of ordour and quhilkes, throuch a certane wyldnes of nature, flie the cumpanie or syght of men.' [8] Well might they fly the company of men, for the story of these days and of the two centuries to follow is the story of an unkindly age with cattle the pawns in a rough and

[1] *Liber Sancte Marie de Melros* (Bannatyne Club), I, 178
[2] Hume Brown, *Early Travellers*
[3] Hume Brown, *Scotland before 1700 ; from Contemporary Documents*, 11
[4] *Exchequer Rolls*, II, xc
[5] Hume Brown, *Scotland before 1700 ; from Contemporary Documents*, 48
[6] Brewer, *Historic Note Book*, 105, and Ridpath, *The Border History of England and Scotland*, 1776, 548–50
[7] Hume Brown, *Early Travellers*, 74
[8] Hume Brown, *Scotland before 1700 ; from Contemporary Documents*, 132

cruel game. The early records are full of instances of the cruel treatment of stolen cattle. The Acts of the Lords of Council covering the years 1496–1501 contain a complaint about the chasing and poinding of cattle ' garring thame cast calfis ' and ' spoliation of certane oxin and puttin furth of thair ene,' [1] while in 1668 Sinclair of Dunbeath and others are charged with stealing cattle from the lands of Lord Reay and ' incarcerating and imprisoning them in great dungeons and pitts and keeping them their in great miserie be the space of many dayes.' [2]

In an unsettled age and a lawless country where cattle were the main form of transportable wealth, it was inevitable that much of the early traffic in livestock should be the result of raiding between glen and glen and between Highlands and Lowlands. From the middle of the sixteenth century the Privy Council was responsible for the general maintenance of peace and order. The Records of the Council contain details of the cases heard before it, and during the next hundred years complaints of thefts of cattle follow close one on another with a regularity almost wearisome in its monotony. From all parts comes the same story ; from Caithness and Ross, from Glen Isla and Strathardle, from west Perthshire and Lochlomondside, and above all from the East, West and Middle Marches of the Borders. It almost seems that cattle raiding was in the sixteenth and early seventeenth centuries the chief occupation of the people of Scotland. From the highest to the lowest few could resist their neighbour's beasts. Scott of Harden drives the cattle of Drumelzier and Dreva in Upper Tweeddale,[3] Douglas of Drumlanrig those of Branerig [4] ; Stuart of Ardvorlich steals from his neighbours in West Perthshire [5] ; Forbes of Towie in Strathdon from Glen Farquhar in Kincardineshire,[6] while the Angus glens were the happy hunting ground of the men of Lochaber and Badenoch. From Reay in Sutherland comes news of losses, from Morayshire, from Locheil's country and from the Argyllshire hills. In an attempt to check the traffic in stolen beasts bonds were taken from landowners who controlled the numerous ferries on lochs and rivers, and these included the boat

---

[1] *Acts of the Lords of Council in Civil Causes 1496–1501*, II, Introd., cxiii
[2] *R.P.C.*, 3rd series, II, 566–7   [3] *R.P.C.*, 1st series, IV, 709
[4] *R.P.C.*, 1st series, V, 273   [5] *R.P.C.*, 1st series, V, 28
[6] *R.P.C.*, 1st series, VI, 363

at Aberfeldy, the coble at Fonab, the ferry boat at Pitnacree, the
' curroch of Innergarrie ' and even the ' littill coble of Tulloche.' [1]
It would be hard indeed to find one corner of the Scottish
Highlands, the Southern Uplands or the Border country the
inhabitants of which, now as victims more often as perpetrators
of cattle thefts, do not figure in these records. Many of the raids
were on a small scale involving the theft of the few ' nolts ' and
the scanty household goods of humble folk, and sometimes the
complaint is against the wanton malice of ' houghing and
hounding ' cattle too weak or thin to drive away. Most were
under ' cloud and silence of nycht,' but not all. In a complaint
against Alastair Stuart of Ardvorlich and others for the theft of
160 cattle from neighbouring lands in 1592, the defendants are
charged with having come onto the complainers' lands ' with
twa bagpypis blawand befoir thame.' [2] Some were on a larger
scale, involving a major operation of real war. In 1602, men of
Glen Garry raided the grazings in Glen Isla, Glen Shee and Strathardle, driving off 2,700 cattle pursued by the owners who overtook and partially defeated them near the Cairnwell Pass.[3] In
the following year, a raid by the Clan Macgregor on Colquhoun
of Luss ended in a fight in Glenfruin with the loss of 80 men and
the theft of 600 cattle, an expedition which led to the proscription
of the Clan Macgregor.[4]

Against this flowing tide of lawlessness the Crown and the
Privy Council, as the central body responsible for the maintenance
of law and order throughout the land, could do little. Chieftains
and large landowners were held responsible for their tenants, or
answerable for those to whom they had given protection or for
whom they had acted as resetters of the stolen beasts ; but seldom
did they appear to answer the charge, and time after time all
the Privy Council could do was to find the charge proven and
pronounce sentence of outlawry against the guilty party, safe and
untroubled in the fastnesses of Lochaber, Argyll or the Border
hills.

By an Act of the Scots Parliament in the reign of William the
Lion in 1175 it had been made unlawful for anyone to buy cattle
without ' lauchful borch of hamehald.' [5] This was a form of
' guarantee ' or ' caution ' required by the buyer of cattle from

[1] *R.P.C.*, 3rd series, VIII, 532, 575 [2] *R.P.C.*, 1st series, V, 28
[3] *R.P.C.*, 1st series, VI, 501 [4] *R.P.C.*, 1st series, VI, 534, 535
[5] *A.P.S.*, I, 373

9

the seller that the beasts had not been stolen, heavy penalties being due from the latter or from him who guaranteed the seller's good faith if the beasts should later turn out to be stolen property. As late as 1634 the Baron Court held at Killin found it necessary to provide that no dealer in cattle should buy from strangers or even from neighbours dwelling ' between the ford of Lyon and Tyndrum ' without sufficient ' caution,' of ' burgh and hamer.' [1] In 1606 the Privy Council, acting in its legislative capacity, sought to compel ' dryvers of sheape and nolt ' to buy only from those answerable to the King's Laws under pain of confiscation of their ' whole drifte.' [2] Twelve years later, in an attempt to stop cattle thefts in the Middle Marches, the Privy Council ordered that no carcase be brought to market unless with the skin attached,[3] a precaution which was still in force in the Island of Islay as late as 1725. The Islay regulations required that before cattle or sheep were slaughtered they must be shown to two witnesses who knew the brand-marks of the person in whose possession they were, to prove that they were his own property or that evidence must be brought to show how he acquired them. The hides of slaughtered cattle were to be kept till the carcase had been eaten, to prove the ownership.[4] By such measures did King and Council seek to bring law and order into the cattle dealing of Scotland, but the frequent recurrence of such orders shows with what small success they met in checking or changing what had grown to be a tradition and custom ingrained and deeply rooted in the character of the people.[5] It shows a country stocked with cattle and a people trained up in a warlike school to a hardiness, a way of life and a knowledge of their native hills which was to be passed down from father to son and at last to droving descendants of cattle-reiving ancestors.

In such conditions it might well be imagined that any legitimate trade in cattle was almost an impossibility; but as early as

---

[1] Cosmo Innes. *Sketches of Early Scottish History*, 381–2. *Black Book of Taymouth* (Bannatyne Club), 389   [2] *R.P.C.*, 1st series, VII, 744

[3] *R.P.C.*, 1st series, XI, 289   [4] *Stent Book of Islay*, 280

[5] In many parts of the country the King's Writ did not run and many decrees were dead letters as soon as they were passed. An Act of the Scottish Parliament of 1503 refers to ' greit abusioun of Justice in the northt partis and west partis of the realme sic as the northt Ilis and south Ilis for lak and falt of Justice Airis Justicis and Shereffis and thairthrou the pepill ar almaist gane wild.' (*A.P.S.* II, 249), while in 1527 letters of apprising issued in the King's name against ' Alexander McLeod of Dunveggan ' refers to Alexander as dwelling ' in ye Hieland where nane of ye officeris of ye law dar pas for fear of yair lyvis ' (*Scot. Hist. Rev.* ii, 356).

the days of Alexander II travellers on the King's Highway had a common law right to spend one night on common land through which the road passed and there pasture their beasts ' saving corn and meadow,' [1] while frequent reference to ' viridis via ' in early Charters would seem to be an indication of routes which were at least of the nature of drove roads. To claim this as early evidence of droving in the sense in which the word came to be used in later years may be to claim too much, but that droving existed at least as early as 1359 is shown by a letter of safe conduct of that year granted to Andrew Moray and Alan Erskyn, two Scottish drovers, with three horsemen and their servants, for travelling through England or the King's foreign dominions for a year with horses, oxen, cows and other goods and merchandise,[2] and ten years later the Scots Parliament allowed cattle to be sold to Englishmen, fixing the customs dues on beasts leaving the country.[3]

During the three centuries which followed, the Scots cattle trade, in common with trade in other items on the short list of Scotland's exports, was to be the victim of an uncertain commercial policy. That policy—if policy it can be called—blended of ignorance, opportunism and self-interest, was dictated by a combination of factors, complex and often inconsistent one with another. The relative freedom of export and import trade which Scotland had formerly enjoyed came to an end with the start of the Wars of Independence, and from now on till the close of the seventeenth century antagonism and jealousy towards England

[1] *Chartulary of Newbattle Abbey* (Bannatyne Club), XXXVII, 158
[2] Rymer, *Foedera*, III. Record Comm. Edn., 1825, III, part 1, 415
The opening of the struggle with England marked the beginning of a long period during which commercial relations between the two countries were strained and constantly broken. From the date of the meeting of Edward I with the Scots barons at Norham in 1291 till 1348, only three safe conducts were given to English merchants to trade with Scotland, and during those years there is no record of a safe conduct granted to a Scots merchant to trade with England. (Davidson and Gray, *The Scottish Staple at Veere*, 97 ; Tytler, *History of Scotland*, 2nd Edn., II, 262–3)
In contrast to this, after 1357 very many safe-conducts were granted to Scots merchants trading with England, their number reflecting the desperate efforts made by Scotland to meet the crushing ransom required by Edward II for the release of David II who had been taken prisoner at the Battle of Neville's Cross eleven years earlier. (*Rotuli Scotiae, passim*)
[3] *A.P.S.*, I, 508, 547
In an English Writ dated 1384 mention is made of ' Johannes Kereslegh, Drovere et civis, London ' (Early Chancery Proceedings 61/387,' *Bulletin of the Institute of Historical Research*, III, 68 and *cf.* I, 97). Quoted by Professor C. Skeel in *Cattle Trade between England and Wales from the 15th to the 19th centuries* (Royal Historical Society Transactions, 4th series, IX, 1926, pp. 137/8).

fought with the hard fact that here lay a natural market. High prices at home, constant wars and recurring threats of famine, called periodically for retention in Scotland of the livestock and victuals which were a large part of her exportable products as urgently as the precarious state of her national economy called for export trade. The powerful Convention of Burghs looked on questions of commercial policy solely from the point of view of those privileged trading classes whose interests they so jealously guarded. Free-traders only if the trade passed through their hands, national interests meant little to them, and the development, except by them, of commerce or industry met with their bitter opposition. While the tanning industry wanted hides from home-killed beasts, the Crown, whose revenue came largely from export dues, preferred to encourage the export of hides on the live animals. In such conditions the policy of the Crown, the Acts of the Scots Parliament and the Orders of the Privy Council during the fifteenth, sixteenth and early seventeenth centuries present a maze through which the cattle trade threads a hard, devious and precarious way.

The trade to England which had been, at least by implication, recognised by the Act of 1369 appears to have been carried on partly on a credit or possibly a barter basis, for in 1451 the Scots Parliament prohibited any trade to England except in cash,[1] and during the famine of 1480, while all restrictions on foreign merchants trading with Scotland were lifted, south-bound cattle traffic across the border was entirely forbidden. Five years later the export of hides was prohibited, the object being to increase the livestock population of the country [2]; but men who could brave the perils of droving through fifteenth-century Scotland were not to be deterred by Acts of Parliament, more especially when King and Council possessed little of the will or the power to enforce the law. So the traffic continued without effective check, and the year 1542 saw a complaint to the Scots Parliament, this time that the profit on cattle sold out of the country was not paid to the Customs Officers.[3] A few years later a further complaint that owing to the negligence of the Wardens of the Marches the export of Scottish products has caused great dearth in Scotland, leads to an Order of the Council that no sheep or cattle are to be exported nor are English beasts to be

---

[1] *A.P.S.*, II, 40   [2] Davidson and Gray *op. cit.*, 62. *A.P.S.*, II, 174
[3] *A.P.S.*, II, 424

pastured in Scotland.[1] In the next year the cattle traffic to England is again prohibited, and also the export of barrelled beef, particularly to Flanders,[2] owing to the scarcity of food in the country, a scarcity which for the next half-century is reflected in repeated measures to check both export trade and meat consumption in Scotland. An Order of the Privy Council in 1561 ordained that as meat deteriorates at Lentryne and bad weather has caused scarcity, no one except those who are sick may eat meat before 29th March.[3] Five years later the Council again forbids anyone to eat meat during Lent in that or future years,[4] while in 1592 the King, ' understanding the greit wrang done to the comoun weill be certane privat personis for thair awin comoditie transporting in england yeirlie, woll, scheip, and nolt, abone the nowmer of ane hundreth thowsand punds quhairby sic derth is rasit . . .' prohibited the export of sheep and cattle to England under pain of forfeiture [5]; but once again the trade goes on, recognised, or at least tolerated, and an Act of the King in Council in 1598 aimed against those who ' daylie transportis grit nowmeris of nolt and scheip furth of this realme ' without licence or ' undir cullour of prevey licenceis unlawfullie and surreptitiouslie stollin and purchest ' from the King, annuls all export licences.[6] In such a tangled skein it is hard indeed to find one firm, continuous thread, but, confused as the records are, they do show beyond any doubt the existence at least as early as the sixteenth century of a cattle trade to England spasmodic and interrupted but clearly recognisable as a forerunner of the great droving traffic of the days to come.

While the drovers of the sixteenth century thus strove in the face of so many dangers and discouragements to take their beasts

[1] *R.P.C.*, 1st series, I, 114, 115
Complaints of beasts pastured across the Border were not confined to the Scots. In their *View and Survey of Waste Lands along the East and Middle Marches of England* in 1542, Sir Robert Bowes and Sir Ralph Elleker observed ' also upon the said Elterburne [near the head of Bowmont Water] we did perceive and see two brode waies or rakes commonly used occupied and warne with cattall broughte out of Scotland to be contynually and daily pastured and fedde wythin the ground of England. . . .' (p. 177) : ' also hygher upon the said burne [Elter] appeared twoo comonly used waies or rakes of great bredth where the cattalles of Scotland had bene accustomed to have been dryven into the grounde of England to their contynuall pastures. Also the townes of Scotland boundinge upon England have eared plowed and sowen muche of all the grounde that was wounte to be their pastures and pasture all their shepe and cattall in great nombres within the Realme of England.' (Hodgson *History of Northumberland*, Part III, vol. 2, 219)   [2] *R.P.C.*, 1st series, I, 127
[3] *R.P.C.*, 1st series, I, 200   [4] *R.P.C.*, 1st series, I, 611
[5] *A.P.S.*, III, 577   [6] *R.P.C.*, 1st series, V, 476, 477

to England, the first signs were appearing within Scotland itself of an internal cross-country cattle trade breaking the trail for the droving traffic of later times. By the early years of the sixteenth century Skye had already started sending beasts to the mainland, and before the century ended a regular traffic was being carried on between the island and the East of Scotland, running the gauntlet through the trackless hills of a wild countryside of the losses and dangers which ' discourages all peceable and guide subjectis to direct or send ony guidis to the mercattis and fairis of the incuntrie.' [1] Argyllshire cattle, too, were being driven to the Lowlands, and by 1556 so many Highlanders were coming to the Lowlands to trade that the Privy Council found it necessary to take measures for the preservation of order at the markets.[2]

Like the drovers of later times, these early cattle dealers had no doubt little use for the beaten track or the fixed line of march, and of made roads there were few, but tolls on bridges in the late sixteenth and early seventeenth centuries show the existence of a regular cattle traffic. An Order of the Privy Council of 1594 levies a toll of 2d an ox for the repair of the bridge of Linton in East Lothian,[3] and a similar sum a few years later for the repair of Auchendinny Bridge at Glencorse [4] ' being the only direct passages between Edinburgh and the South. . . .' In 1605, 4d an ox was charged for those crossing the Water of Leith, for building a bridge at Saughtonhall,[5] and in 1607 a toll of 8d an ox was exacted for beasts passing through Dumbarton to any market, for the preservation of the town from flooding.[6]

While the course of legislation towards the Scots cattle trade throughout the greater part of the sixteenth century was determined by few considerations other than the immediate and changing needs of the moment, the last quarter of the century did in fact see the first signs of a new outlook. Scots trade policy, based hitherto purely on fiscal considerations and sectional interests, began now to show some signs of a national complexion, and an Act of 1592 forbidding the export of skins aims for the first time at the encouragement of industry and the increase of employment in Scotland.[7] The new outlook had shown itself in

[1] *R.P.C.*, 1st series, VI, 184
[2] *R.P.C.*, 1st series, I, 470–1. Hume Brown *Scotland in the Time of Queen Mary,* 27–8.
[3] *R.P.C.*, 1st series, V, 216
[4] *R.P.C.*, 1st series, VI, 207
[5] *R.P.C.*, 1st series, VII, 741
[6] *R.P.C.*, 1st series, VII, 431
[7] Davidson and Gray op. cit., 66 ; *A.P.S.*, III, 579, IV, 29

a practical step to improve the trade channels between Scotland and England. The Border areas which presented such a formidable barrier to trade with the South had despite the efforts of the Wardens of the Marches so far remained beyond the effective reach of the law. This was partly the result of the inability of the Crown to make them otherwise; but partly it was an act of policy. The Scots saw something of advantage in having on their southern border a belt of wild unsettled country which, while it cost them dear in raids on the rich lands of Berwickshire, Roxburghshire and Dumfriesshire, preyed equally on Northumberland and Cumberland. Scots and English alike were content that this turbulent land should lie, a buffer state between them, looked on by each as a potential safeguard against invasion, and tolerated by either country for its value as a thorn in the flesh of the other. Hitherto what measures had been taken by Scots and English against the Border dwellers, were aimed only against those who were common enemies, against those who 'stole the beeves which made their broth from Scotland and from England both.' In the middle of the sixteenth century the state of the Border lands was as bad and as unruly as it had ever been. The policy of Henry VIII was hostile to Scotland, but the reign of Elizabeth saw a steady improvement in the political relations of the two countries possessing at last a common interest in the defence of the Reformation. Now for the first time the lawlessness of the Border country began to be regarded by the Scots as endangering peace with England, and an Order of the Privy Council of 1597 reflects the new outlook in providing for the release of prisoners and the return of cattle and other booty taken by Border raiders in a recent raid on England.[1] On the English side of the border the power of the great family of Percy had at last been broken, and Redesdale and Tynedale had come finally under the effective control of the English Crown. On the Scottish side, the hard core of Border unrest was attacked in the gradual eviction of the raiders from the strongholds which had hitherto proved inaccessible and unassailable. So the last quarter of the century saw the first successful efforts of Scots and English alike to put an end finally to what had been for centuries a disturbing influence in the relations of the two countries, now linked by a common religion and soon to have a common Crown.

If the close of the sixteenth century saw the end of the most

---

[1] *R.P.C.*, 1st series, V, 405

bitter period of antagonism between England and Scotland, the Union of the Crowns in 1603 had little immediate effect in drawing closer the commercial bonds between them. The old jealousies and prejudices largely remained, and the trade passing between the two countries continued to be regulated by few considerations other than the immediate and individual needs of each. For the drovers of Scotland's cattle the gradual pacification of the Borders had removed one of their main sources of anxiety, but their trade still remained at the mercy of a legislative policy marked as in the past by opportunism rather than continuity. The conflict of interests which had so hampered the drover of the sixteenth century largely continued, and the first half of the seventeenth century showed only a gradual, tacit and unofficial recognition of the trade ; but from now on the emphasis is laid less on efforts to stop the trade than on measures to secure that the fullest advantage is obtained from its existence. The Commission which under James VI had been appointed to consider terms for a treaty between the two countries had recommended the virtual adoption of free trade between them, and that the inhabitants of either Scotland or England should enjoy the privileges of free-born subjects in the other. The Scots Parliament agreed to the Commission's proposals, and in 1607 passed an Act providing that, with certain exceptions, all such wares as were the growth or handiwork of Scotland might be exported to England without paying any customs dues or other exaction.[1] Cattle, sheep, wool, hides and linen were among the items which were still to be subject to customs, and the first step to give effect to this was an attempt to canalise the traffic crossing the Border and to ensure that it passed through certain fixed points which acted as customs posts. An Order of the Privy Council in 1611 provided that no merchant or trader passing between Scotland and England should take his goods by the ' West groundis or washes,' [2] and in the following year complaints that the King is prejudiced by loss of customs dues on cattle and sheep led to an Order that all goods passing across the West Border must pay toll at ' the Kirk of Graitnay in Annandale,' those crossing the Middle Border at Jedburgh or Kelso, while those crossing the East Border must go by way of Duns, all on pain of confiscation.[3] The tolls were fixed at high levels both to limit the traffic and to ensure that the public revenues profited to the full by such as did

[1] *A.P.S.*, IV, 366   [2] *R.P.C.*, 1st series, IX, 267-8   [3] *R.P.C.*, 1st series, IX, 394

persist. In the autumn of 1612 the customs dues on cattle leaving the country were fixed at £10 Scots a head and on calves at £5, while barrelled beef paid £10 a barrel or carcase.[1] In 1644 the Customs Officers were directed to keep a record of the number of cattle, the names of the drovers and the dates when they passed, records which, if kept, have not survived.[2] An Order of 1635, aimed at the suppression of bad coinage in circulation, provides that drovers of cattle be compelled to pay customs dues in good coin,[3] and in 1661 the dues on cattle exported were fixed at 2 oz. bullion for every four cows or three oxen [4]; but the art of evading tolls was one with which the drovers had long been familiar. Across the grassy hills of the Border country they had a wide choice of routes, and much of the traffic crossed the Border unobserved and untaxed. An application in 1611 for a tack or lease of the right of collecting customs on cattle and other goods passing over the West Marches was refused on the ground that the probable yield of the customs dues was unknown,[5] and when the annual value of exports from Scotland in 1614 was estimated at £736,986 Scots this excluded 'greit quantetie of lynning claythe, lynning yairne, sheip, nolt, etc. that is transpoirrted by land dalie.' [6]

While the authorities sought to regulate and tax the cattle traffic to England, there is no lack of evidence that they fought a losing battle and that, harassed and hampered as it might be, the droving trade went on little deterred or controlled. This led during the first quarter of the seventeenth century to continued complaints of shortage of food and high prices in Scotland. In 1615, owing to the scarcity of meat, export was banned and the eating of beef during Lent was once again prohibited. The preamble of the ordinance refers to ' suche a continewing storme of froist, snaw, rayne, and wind that the most pairt of the bestiall and goodis of the cuntrey ar outher deade or become so feble and waik that thay ar not able ony lang tyme to indure.' [7] In 1627 the Justices of the Peace for the Counties of Fife and Stirling tried to prevent the export of hides from the country, the droving of cattle to England having caused a shortage of supplies for the tanning industry,[8] while two years before Commissioners had been appointed in Nithsdale, Annandale and Roxburghshire to

[1] *R.P.C.*, 1st series, IX, lxix   [2] *A.P.S.*, VI, Pt. 1, 242
[3] *R.P.C.*, 2nd series, VI, 94   [4] *A.P.S.*, VII, 252, 253
[5] *R.P.C.*, 1st series, IX, 608
[6] *Hist. Manuscripts Commission, Mar and Kellie Papers*, 1904, 74
[7] *R.P.C.*, 1st series, X, 312, 313   [8] *R.P.C.*, 2nd series, I, 684

prevent the export of cattle.[1] A complaint to the Privy Council in 1626 described how ' the most pairt of the nolt within this Kingdom ar ather alreadie boght to be transportit or els some conditioun or bargane is maid for the same afoirhand, sua that now the poore labouraris of the ground can haif no nolt to buy, and, if some few ar to be had, the pryceis thairof ar so extra-ordinair and heigh as thay can not be boght to the grite hurt . . . of all . . . within this Kingdome.' [2] So serious was the rise in prices that the Justices of the Peace were ordered to make annual reports on the position in the light of which export policy could be reviewed, an Order which seems to have been only very partially obeyed.[3] The customs dues paid by cattle exporters or the fines levied on those who sought to evade them were sometimes ear-marked for specific purposes. In 1628, fines exacted from drovers were allocated for the building of the King's castle at Lochmaben,[4] and when in 1646 General Leslie was granted a sum of 50,000 merks Scots in recognition of his services at the Battle of Philip-haugh, £10,000 Scots of this was to be paid from dues on exported cattle.[5] It seems probable that Leslie may have had to wait for his money, for as late as 1683 the total customs including those on cattle collected at Kelso for the half year to November, amounted only to £1,683 Scots, while those collected at Ayton for the same period totalled only £806 Scots, of which cattle dues made up only a small proportion.[6]

By the middle of the seventeenth century the cattle trade to England had, despite all its handicaps, grown to such proportions that Scotland was described as little more than a grazing field for England. The number of beasts passing through the town and paying toll at Carlisle in 1663 reached the considerable total of 18,574,[7] and in the following year the House of Commons

---

[1] *R.P.C.*, 2nd series, I, 138   [2] *R.P.C.*, 2nd series, I, 300
[3] The Justices of Kincardineshire appear to have been among those who sent in reports on prices, for in 1627 they complained that the price of cattle at 50 merks for oxen and 40 merks for cows is even higher than in the previous year. ' If remeid be nocht provydit speidalie ' they declare ' puir men laboraris salbe forcit to quyte their tillage of the ground.' From this it seems clear that the hardship lay in the price of working cattle rather than in the price of beef. (*R.P.C.*, 2nd series, II, 554 and 2nd series, I, Introduction lxxxv–lxxxvii)
[4] *R.P.C.*, 2nd series II, 473   [5] *A.P.S.*, VI, Part 1, 627
[6] *Record of Customs Dues collected at Kelso in 1683*. H.M. Register House
[7] *State Papers. Domestic.* Charles II. 1663–64, 226. ' 1663. August 1. Account of cattle brought in from Scotland to the port of Carlisle since August 1662 ; total number 18,574.' The toll dues were 8d a head. It may be noted that the number of beasts has been misquoted in various publications as 318,574.

complained of the under-selling of English cattle by Scots and Irish beasts. A Petition by Yorkshire graziers for heavier duties against Scots cattle entering England complains that ' the cattle being fed, maintained and fatted with farre less charge than can possibly be done in England they filled and quitte the markets and undersell those of English breed.' [1]

The second half of the century saw a marked change in the attitude of the authorities towards the droving industry, and an unwilling but growing realisation of the benefits of freer trade with England. An Order of 1663 aimed at the improvement of pasture and of the breed of cattle provided that exports by sea should be subject to no customs for nineteen years, [2] and in 1672, to encourage trade, the export of cattle by land or sea was made open to all. [3] The drovers too were coming to be recognised as part of the commercial life of the country and as forming a body of men engaged in an honourable trade. Orders of 1671 and 1674 aimed against those who passing as drovers ' commit severall thiftes and abuses ' provide that drovers shall carry certificates of respectability and passes giving the names of all in their company. [4]

The scarcity of money in Scotland led in 1680 to the appointment of a Commission to encourage the export of cattle and other goods, [5] and the following year brought a complaint that the growing practice among English cattle dealers of giving bills in payment lessened the value of the traffic as a balancing item in the import and export trade of the country. [6] So, in the course of two centuries, the Scottish export cattle trade had passed from active opposition, through grudging tolerance, to emerge at last into an era in which full recognition and active encouragement were given to a trade now acknowledged as an essential part of the economy of Scotland.

[1] *Journal of British Archaelogical Assoc.*, Vol. 87, 1932, 172–83
[2] *A.P.S.*, VII, 476   [3] *A.P.S.*, VIII, 63
[4] *R.P.C.*, 3rd series, III, 312 and IV, 280, 281. Steps to ensure the reliability of drovers seem to have been taken in England earlier than in Scotland, for by Statutes of Edward VI and Elizabeth it was enacted that a drover must be licensed annually by the Quarter Sessions of the county in which he had lived for three years and that he must be a married householder, over 30 years of age. No licence was to be granted to a servant or retainer. (5 and 6 Edw. VI, Chap. 14 Section 13. *Statutes of the Realm*, Vol. 4, part I, 150, and 5 Elizabeth Chap. 12, *Statutes of the Realm*, Vol. 4, part 1, 440)
[5] *R.P.C.*, 3rd series, VI, 431, 432   [6] *R.P.C.*, 3rd series, VII, 669

2

THE LIFE AND WORK OF A DROVER

THE development of the droving trade in Scotland and the important part which it came to play in the life of the country between the start of the sixteenth and the middle of the nineteenth centuries, was the outcome of a combination of circumstances leading logically and almost inevitably to this end. The climate and physical nature of the Highlands in comparison with the Lowland part of Scotland made them a natural grazing area, a division of function further emphasised at first by the turbulent history and later by the agricultural and industrial development of the Lowlands which, increasingly as time went on, confined cattle breeding to the hill country. Here the system of land tenure, encouraging a large tenant population all with grazing rights, led to over-stocking of the land with cattle. These were for long almost the sole form of realisable wealth, while the primitive farming methods practised throughout the Highlands up till the middle of the eighteenth century made a reduction of stock with the approach of autumn a matter of necessity. When there is added the fact that cattle supplied their own transport to market and could gather their own livelihood on the way, droving from the Highlands was the natural outcome.[1] There was, however, one more factor which, if any were needed, helped to bring the droving industry to the important place which for nearly four centuries it occupied.

The literature, the poetry and the whole history of the Scottish people show them to have been a people to whom raids and forays, often taking them over long distances and through great hardships, have for centuries possessed an almost irresistible attraction. Whether it tells of descents from Border hills on the rich pasture lands of Northumberland and the Tweed Valley, of raids from Highland glens to despoil farm lands in Lennox

---

[1] 'Live cattle' wrote Adam Smith, 'are, perhaps, the only commodity of which transportation is more expensive by sea than by land. By land they carry themselves to market. By sea, not only the cattle, but their food and their water too must be carried at no small expense and inconveniency.'—*Wealth of Nations* (Bohn's Standard Lib., 1887, I, 460)

and Strathearn, or of expeditions from Badenoch and Atholl to take toll of the Angus glens, the story of the early raiders seldom varies in its main theme, and everywhere cattle are the pawns in the game. A study of the Acts of the Scots Parliament or any attempt to reckon the time and energy devoted by the Privy Council in the sixteenth and seventeenth centuries to checking these activities, can leave no doubt that cattle raiding was one of the main preoccupations of large numbers of the people and one of the chief sources of worry to those set in authority.

Marks of their heredity remained deeply imprinted on the descendants of these old raiders long after the arrival of more settled times in Scotland, and to this was attributed much of the adventurous and turbulent spirit which remained in vigorous life till 1745 and lingered on into the second half of the eighteenth century. A ' Memorandum concerning the Highlands ' of 1746 speaks of cattle thieving among the Highlanders as ' the principal source of all their barbarity, cruelty, cunning and revenge ' (which) ' trains them up to the use of arms, love of plunder, thirst for revenge. . . .' [1] To a Highlander of the eighteenth century, divided at the most by one generation from such a way of life and possessing beyond a long lineage of cattle-reiving ancestors, it was but a short step to a more legitimate and only slightly less adventurous form of cattle driving. ' He has felt from his early youth,' wrote Sir John Sinclair of the Highlander in his Analysis of the Statistical Account, ' all the privations to which he can be exposed in almost any circumstances of war. He has been accustomed to scanty fare, to rude and often wet clothing, to cold and damp houses, to sleep often in the open air or in the most uncomfortable beds, to cross dangerous rivers, to march a number of miles without stopping and with but little nourishment, and to be perpetually exposed to the attacks of a stormy atmosphere. A warrior, thus trained, suffers no inconvenience from what others would consider to be the greatest possible hardships, and has an evident superiority over the native of a delicious climate, bred to every indulgence of food, dress and habitation and who is unaccustomed to marching and fatigue.' [2] So heredity, aptitude and inclination, re-inforced economic necessity and produced by an easy transition the drovers of the eighteenth and nineteenth centuries.

[1] *Breadalbane Papers (Roads)*, Box 4, H.M. Register House
[2] Sinclair, *Analysis of O.S.A.*, I, 106-7

Of the men who brought the cattle from the Highlands to the markets of the Lowlands or ' trysts ' as some of these were called, there were, as in other walks of life, many grades. There were those, often great landowners, nobles or chieftains, who bred the cattle on their wide estates or received them from their tenants and sub-tenants in payment of rent or other dues. Cattle dealing in the seventeenth and eighteenth centuries was considered a trade in no way unsuited to a gentleman, and during this period the records of the droving industry show how deeply concerned in it were not only the humble folk but some of the highest in the land. Some there were who did little more than send the beasts to market in the care of others and some, like Rob Roy's one time associate the Duke of Montrose, merely acted as sleeping partners or provided the capital needed for cattle dealing enterprises.[1] Others, smaller lairds, tacksmen or monied dealers, attended the markets themselves but entrusted the care and transport of their droves to subordinates. Others again, smaller men of little substance, combined the functions of dealer and drover, buying cattle in the North and themselves driving them to the Lowlands either on commission or, staking their all, as a private and perilous speculation. Finally, there were the drivers of the cattle on whom fell the day to day dangers, hardships and responsibilities of the long journeys from Kintail to Crieff, from Caithness to Falkirk and often from the Highlands of Scotland to the meadows of Norfolk. Of this last class, some were men who had small parcels of land to cultivate, and for them the driving south of a drove in the summer or early autumn meant welcome employment between seed time and harvest ; but many who had no ties at home stayed in the low country, helping to shear the harvest after the droving was finished, and some stayed on through the autumn and early winter, smearing the sheep with the mixture of tar and butter which, in the eighteenth century, was looked on as essential before the winter

---

[1] At the start of his career in the latter years of the seventeenth century, Rob Roy appears to have carried on business as an honest cattle dealer. During this period, he enjoyed the support of the Duke of Montrose who made loans to him for speculations in cattle, but latterly Rob fell on evil times owing to bad markets and finally absconded with, it is said, £1,000 belonging either to the Duke or to other creditors. His estate was attached for the debt and thereafter Rob lived the life of an outlaw, supporting himself by theft and the thinly disguised blackmail of a cattle ' Protector.' Despite his mode of life he avoided capture in the hill country west of Lochearn and died in his bed near Balquhidder about 1738. (Sir Walter Scott, Introduction to *Rob Roy*)

storms.[1] All these are in contemporary records referred to indiscriminately as ' drovers,' but though each played his essential part in the drama, it is mainly with the actual drivers of the cattle that we are here concerned in this attempt to reconstruct something of the life and work of the men who walked the drove roads of Scotland.

The characteristics and qualities required of a successful drover were many. Knowledge of the country had to be extensive and intimate, while endurance and ability to face great hardships were essential. The larger and more prosperous drovers owned ponies which they used either for riding on their long journeys to the Lowlands or for carrying supplies for use on the way, or home-made goods which were often taken for sale ; but most of the drovers did the whole journey on foot. Resource and enterprise were called for with knowledge of men and tact tempered at times with absence of too fine scruple. Knowledge of cattle was needed and good judgment wherewith to balance the varying factors on which depended the successful completion of the journey to the Lowlands. Finally, honesty and reliability were needed in a drover for the responsible work entrusted to him. The list is a formidable one, but for the most part these qualities were attributes inherent in the men from their heredity, their upbringing and their way of life. It may indeed be doubted whether the civil or military authorities in Scotland would have credited with any high degree of honesty the Highlander of the first half of the eighteenth century, but even they would not have questioned his fidelity to his chieftain, a fidelity which, when commerce took the place of war, he transferred to the interest of his employer and the welfare of the beasts entrusted to him which he drove ' with something of the pride of his ancestors when carrying off the fat oxen of the Sassenach.' [2] ' The Highlanders in particular,' wrote Sir Walter Scott in *The Two Drovers*, ' are masters of this difficult trade of driving, which seems to suit them as well as the trade of war. It affords exercise for all their habits of patient endurance and active exertion. They are required to know perfectly the drove roads which lie

---

[1] The cutting of the harvest in the central and southern districts of Scotland gave employment to large numbers from the Highlands each year. An item in the Inverness *Courier* of 26th August 1824 records that over 2,500 shearers from Skye, Mull and the Outer Isles had recently passed through the Crinan Canal bound for the Lowlands.

[2] McIan and Logan, *Highlanders at Home* (1848), 32 et seq.

over the wildest tracts of the country, and to avoid as much as possible the highways which distress the feet of the bullocks, and the turnpikes which annoy the spirit of the drover ; whereas on the broad green or grey track, which leads across the pathless moor, the herd not only move at ease and without taxation, but, if they mind their business, may pick up a mouthful of food by the way.' The need for these qualities of head, heart and body and the varying circumstances which called for them may best be shown if an attempt is made to follow in the footsteps of a drover from the glens of Ross-shire or Kintail to the markets of Central Scotland.

The dress and appearance of a drover of the early part of the eighteenth century have been described by Macky who wrote of the scene at Crieff Tryst in 1723. ' The Highland gentlemen were mighty civil, dressed in their slashed waistcoats, a trousing (which is breeches and stocking of one piece of striped stuff) with a plaid for a cloak and a blue bonnet. They have a poinard, knife and fork in one sheath hanging at one side of their belt, their pistol at the other and their snuff mull before with a great broadsword at their side. Their attendance [following] was very numerous all in belted plaids, girt, like women's petticoats down to the knee ; their thighs and half of the leg all bare. They had also each a broadsword and poinard.' [1] The New Statistical Account for the Parish of Monzie tells that people old enough to remember the Highland drovers at Crieff described them as having been ' bare-kneed and bare-headed, though many of them old men.' A century later, the drover's dress included ' a coarse plaid of a plain brown and white chequer,' [2] and towards the end of the droving period in the latter half of last century he is described as ' dressed usually in homespun tweeds which smelt of heather and peat smoke and which was so thick that those who wore them look like bears as they lounge heavily along ' ; [3] ' great stalwart, hirsute men ' they were, ' shaggy and uncultured and wild,' their clothing and physique alike suited to the hardship of their lives.

The arms carried by the drovers at Crieff Tryst in 1723 were no mere ornament. The Privy Council Records of the sixteenth and seventeenth centuries amply demonstrate their use and

[1] Macky, *Journey through Scotland*, 1723. Quoted in Bishop Forbes' *Journal*, 235.
[2] Macculloch, *Highlands and Western Isles*, 1824, I, 179
[3] R. B. Cunninghame Graham, *A Hatchment*, 1913, 212 et seq.

necessity, particularly for drovers from the north and west whose route through Lochaber, Badenoch, Rannoch and Atholl took them through the wildest part of the country. A drover from Skye in the first half of the eighteenth century, crossing the hills on the way to Glen Garry, must pass uncomfortably close to the wild country to the south of Loch Hourn where, despite the Bernera Garrison, Colin MacDonell of Barrisdale levied blackmail of about £500 per annum as 'cattle protector' of his neighbours, or stole the beasts of those who grudged this primitive insurance premium.[1] Rob Roy too in his later and less reputable days engaged in transactions of a like character, as Sir Walter Scott has described in the forceful language of Bailie Nicol Jarvie : ' Troth I wad advise ony friends o' mine to gree wi' Rob ; for watch as they like and do what they like, they are sair apt to be harried when the lang nights come on. Some o' the Grahame and Cohoon gentry stood out ; but what then—they lost their haill stock the same winter ; sae maist folk now think it best to come into Rob's terms. He's easy wi' a'body that will be easy wi' him, but if ye thraw him ye had better thraw the deevil.' Drovers were exempt from the Disarming Acts of 1716 and 1748. In 1725, General Wade issued 230 licences to ' the forresters, drovers and dealers in cattle and other merchandise belonging to the several Clans who have surrendered their arms ' permitting them to carry arms. The licences were valid for two years and the weapons to be carried were gun, sword and pistol.[2] Even during the Rising of 1745 the exemption in favour of the drovers continued, and a safe-conduct granted by the Sheriff-Depute of Argyll dated 11 December 1746 permits James Macnab, drover in Craig of Glenorchy, going with two servants to buy cattle in Kintail and Skye, ' to pass to and from these countries with their arms alwise behaving themselves as Loyall subjects of His Majesty.'[3] Arms were indeed necessary for the drovers of these times, for cattle raiding was still common, and in the years immediately before and after the Rising of 1745 the task of checking the activities of raiders living in Lochaber and Badenoch was one of the main problems which faced the Hanoverian Government. General Wade reporting to George I in 1724 on the condition of the Highlands drew attention to the prevalence

---

[1] Chambers, *Domestic Annals of Scotland*, III, 616
[2] New Spalding Club, *Historical Papers, 1699–1750*, I, 160, 161
[3] *Celtic Magazine*, VIII, 586

of cattle raiding. ' The Clans in the Highlands most addicted to rapine and plunder are the Camerons in West of the Shire of Inverness, the MacKenzies and others in the Shire of Ross who were vassals to the late Earl of Seaforth, the McDonalds of Keppoch, the Broadalbin men and the Macgregors on the borders of Argileshire. They go out in parties from 10 to 30 men, traverse large tracks of mountains till they arrive at the Low Lands, where they design to commit their depredations which they choose to do in places distant from the glens which they inhabit. They drive the stolen cattle in the night time, and in the day remain in the tops of the mountains or in the woods (with which the Highlands abound) and take the first occasion to sell them at the fairs and markets that are annually held in many parts of the country.' [1] William Mackintosh of Borlum in 1742 describes the part of the country most inhabited by cattle thieves as being the west corners of Inverness, Perth and Stirlingshire and the north part of Argyll.[2]

Scott has described a drover's food as ' a few handfuls of oatmeal and two or three onions renewed from time to time and a ram's horn filled with whiskey which he used sparingly every night and morning,' [3] while R. L. Stevenson adds ' ewe milk cheese and bannock.' [4] Enough oatmeal was carried for a few days and this was replenished on the journey as opportunity offered. The oatmeal was not for the drover's use alone. Dogs were extensively used in droving, and although there is curiously little mention of them in contemporary records, their function must have been an important one on routes which crossed long stretches of open country. Those who can still remember the last years of the droving period recall that the first concern of drovers on arrival at houses or inns was food for the dogs.[5] Sometimes the drover would have his oatmeal made into porridge at

---

[1] *An Authentic Narrative of Marshal Wade's Proceedings in the Highlands of Scotland*, printed as an Appendix in Jamieson's edition of Burt's *Letters from a Gentleman in the North of Scotland* (5th ed. 1822), II, 273.

[2] Mackintosh, *A Short Scheme . . . to stop Depredations . . . so destructive to the Northern Counties of Scotland* (1742).

[3] Scott, *The Two Drovers*, Ch. I   [4] Stevenson, *St Ives*, Ch. 10

[5] Some years ago the late Miss Stewart Mackenzie of Brahan, Ross-shire, informed a friend that in the course of journeys by coach in the late autumn from Brahan to the South during her childhood about the year 1840 she used frequently to see collie dogs making their way north unaccompanied. On inquiring of her parents why these dogs were alone, Miss Stewart Mackenzie was informed that these were dogs belonging to drovers who had taken cattle to England and that when the droving was finished the drovers returned by boat to Scotland. To save the trouble and

inns or cottages beside which the cattle rested for the night, but where the resting-place was in a remote part of the hills far from fuel or shelter the drover must be content with oatmeal mixed with cold water, relying for warmth on his plaid and the contents of the ram's horn. One other item may occasionally have lent variety to the drover's diet. The bleeding of cattle by farmers during a hard winter or spring was an established practice in eighteenth-century Scotland. Writing of Gairloch in 1772 Pennant says that the cattle were blooded in spring and autumn, the blood being preserved to be eaten cold, and according to local tradition the practice continued till the beginning of the nineteenth century. It seems not unlikely that drovers short of food may on rare occasions have bled cattle on the way to the Trysts. The blood, with the oatmeal and onions which they carried, would supply the main ingredients required for the 'black puddings' which were a traditional Scottish food.

Much preliminary work by the dealers and the drovers employed by them had to be done before the cattle were collected and ready for the road to the South. The agriculture of the Highlands of Scotland and the Hebrides in the eighteenth and early nineteenth centuries rested on a complex system of tacksmen, tenants and sub-tenants, broadening out in the lower strata of the social scale to the occupiers of what came to be known as the penny, halfpenny and farthing lands, among whom the country was divided and sub-divided. Each of these classes owned cattle. In many cases small tenants with a single beast or a very small parcel of beasts, sold to the chieftain or the tacksman from whom he held his land, in payment of rent, but though common this was not an invariable practice, and the drove which finally started on the long cross-country journey to the Trysts was generally made up of beasts from many grazings. The onerous 'casualties' or services which the smaller tenants owed to the tacksmen or the chieftain sometimes included, too, an obligation

expense of their transport the dogs were turned loose to find their own way north. It was explained that the dogs followed the route taken on the southward journey being fed at Inns or Farms where the drove had 'stanced' and that in the following year when the drovers were again on the way south, they paid for the food given to the dogs. No evidence has come to light that drovers returned from the South by boat, and it would seem that a possible alternative explanation is that the dogs belonged to drovers who had remained in the South through the autumn for the harvest when the dogs would not be needed.

to sell only to a particular drover who paid the chieftain for this privilege,[1] and in Lewis as late as the last quarter of the eighteenth century the Seaforth Factor, who leased his office ' with all its appendages,' forced the tenants, on the pretext that rents were in arrears, to sell their beasts only through him.[2] Such devices would to some extent simplify the cattle dealer's task, but the collection of the drove for market remained a formidable undertaking, and all through the summer and early autumn months the Highland glens and grazing lands were filled with busy dealers and anxious sellers.

The method by which these local sales were arranged has been so described by James Robertson in his *General View of the Agriculture of Inverness-shire*, of 1813 : ' The manner of disposing of their dry cows or young bullocks is somewhat curious. When the drovers from the South and interior of Scotland make their appearance in the Highlands, which always happens during the latter end of April or the beginning of May, they give intimation at the Churches that upon a particular day and in a central place of the district they are ready to purchase cattle from any who offer them for sale. This is a most important and anxious time to both buyers and sellers. The price of this commodity, like all others, is regulated by the demand. The farmers have only two ways of judging of the demand, first by the number of drovers that appear in the country and, secondly, by epistolary correspondence with persons in the South who have their confidence. The drovers are of two descriptions, either those who buy on commission for persons of capital who, being diffident of their own skill or averse from fatigue, choose to remain at home, or those who purchase cattle on their own account. Much address is used on both sides to feel the pulse of the market at these parochial meetings before the price for the season be mutually settled and it may happen that many such small Trysts or meetings take place in different parts of the Highlands before the price be finally determined. Their anxiety on both sides is sometimes so great that the cattle are given away upon a conditional contract ; that if the price rises within a limited time the seller will receive so much more ; but if the lean cattle fall in value the drover will get a deduction. Ready money is generally given for the cattle ; and this is the season for the Banks to

[1] Walker, *Economical History of the Hebrides and Highlands*, I, 78
[2] Knox, *Tour through the Highlands of Scotland and the Hebride Isles in 1786*, 191-3

circulate their paper money. These petty markets in the Highlands commence at the period above mentioned and the cattle are moved as soon as they can bear the fatigue of travelling that they may be put as early as possible on the Southern pastures. When the demand from the South continues brisk, this sort of trade is carried on with little or no interruption from May to October.' The writer of the Statistical Account for the Parish of Abernethy in Inverness-shire, complaining of these casual markets called by dealers, urged that markets should be fewer and more central, and that the estate factors should get the best information possible as to current prices and the solvency of the dealers. ' Considering what a fatiguing, hazardous business droving is,' he writes, ' men that pay should be much sought after and much encouraged.' [1]

The beasts were generally brought for delivery to some convenient spot where the purchases were gradually collected into a drove and where the real work of the drovers began. The drove might consist of 100, 200 or 300 beasts, with one drover to each 50 or 60 animals, but much larger droves were often collected by the dealers at the more important local Trysts like the Lawrence and Aikey fairs in the Garioch and Buchan districts of Aberdeenshire or the Muir of Ord Tryst in Ross-shire, and the droves belonging to the great dealers of the early nineteenth century were numbered in thousands and stretched for several miles. The profit on a drove of beasts brought from the Highlands to the Lowland markets was often little more than 2s 6d to 5s a head, and a drove of less than 200 animals, unless one of several owned by the same dealer, was thus hardly an economic undertaking. It was to eke out his small wage or his uncertain profit on the enterprise that some drovers, particularly those in a large enough way to have ponies, carried with them home-made goods for sale in the Lowlands. It is probable that this practice was most common among the drovers from the north-east, for the knitted goods and coarse cloth of Aberdeenshire and Morayshire found a ready market in the South. As late as 1876, one who remembers the last days of the droving trade in the south of Scotland recalls having seen droves passing through Liddesdale, the drovers knitting stockings as they went.

Besides the actual drivers of the cattle, a drove of 200 to 300 animals might have a ' topsman ' whose duty it was to go

[1] *O.S.A.*, Abernethy, XIII, 147

on ahead, usually on horseback, to arrange for grazing for the night and generally to plan the route ; but often the drovers relied on their own knowledge of the country and on their own judgment and initiative. In this lay an important part of the drover's art, for the planning and execution of a journey with stock across 150 miles of eighteenth-century Scotland called for ability of no mean order to reckon with and balance a variety of complex factors peculiar to the operation, the country and the period. It was not without reason that a writer of last century compared favourably the skill and organising ability of a drover to that of the Duke of Wellington.[1] ' To purchase 1,000 cattle from a multitude of individuals,' observes a writer of the early nineteenth century, ' and march them, in one or more great battalions, from the extremity of Scotland, into the centre of England, at the expense of only a few shillings on each, is an undertaking that requires genius, exertion and a provision for many contingent circumstances, besides the knowledge which is requisite for their disposal to such advantage, as may encourage the continuance of the trade.' [2]

Maps were, of course, during the greater part of the droving period, not available, and a drover had to rely on knowledge gained from former journeys or perhaps from other drovers. At least till 1750 the state of the country had to be taken into account, for it was not till the middle of the century that drovers traversing the hills of Lochaber, Badenoch and Rannoch could do so with confidence and security. Wet weather might make the passage of rivers dangerous or impossible, while a dry autumn might make certain hill passes less attractive for feeding cattle on the move. Tolls on roads or bridges, or customs dues payable at certain points like Crieff or Dumbarton would reduce the slender margin of profit. These factors and many more must be balanced one with another, and all in the knowledge that Crieff or Falkirk must be reached without hurry by a given date.

The tracks followed by the drovers up to the middle of the eighteenth century were for the most part ill-defined, marked principally by the passage of that very traffic for which they themselves were responsible. The duty of maintaining the roads of rural Scotland, which had been laid on the Justices of the

[1] McLeod, *Reminiscences of a Highland Parish*, 1871, 192–3
[2] Leslie, *General View of the Agriculture of Nairn and Moray, 1811*, 303–4

Peace in 1609, was largely ignored, and the system of Statute Labour introduced in 1669 for the same purpose brought little improvement. Matters improved after the Union of the Parliaments in 1707, but trade in the rural districts was carried on mainly by pack-horse throughout the greater part of the eighteenth century. In 1723, the roads of Scotland outside the main towns were little more than tracks quite unsuited for wheel traffic which was, in consequence, practically non-existent. Between 1723 and 1740, General Wade built nearly 250 miles of military roads in the Highlands. Though these, the first properly constructed roads to be made in the Highlands, were of considerable importance, they did little more than touch the fringe of the problem of Highland transport, and it was not till the military roads were taken over by the Commissioners for Highland Roads and Bridges after 1803 that the work of Highland road construction was seriously taken in hand. Telford in his first survey of Highland roads made for the Commissioners in 1803 reported that ' previous to the year 1742 the roads were merely the tracks of black cattle and horses intersected by numerous rapid streams which being frequently swollen into torrents by heavy rains rendered them dangerous or impassable.' [1] Wade, indeed, in laying out the routes of his roads appears to have followed in some places the routes of older traffic of which cattle formed the bulk, but for the most part the routes of the droves passed unrestricted over open country. Only in those parts where droving traffic passed through Lowland areas, or where the land was considerably cultivated as in parts of Angus and Dumfriesshire, were attempts made to define and restrict its route by the construction of ' raiks ' as they were called 50 to 100 feet wide with turf dykes on either side. One of the earliest examples of this was in the south-west of Scotland, where in 1619 James Murray of Cockpool reported to the Privy Council that on their instructions he had laid out a drove road from Annan to Gretna, the people through whose lands the road led being ordered, with the help of the constables, to build dykes on either side to protect their corn.[2] Again in 1697 the Privy Council as a result of disputes between drovers and local landowners, appointed a Commission to mark out a drove road between New Galloway and Dumfries.[3] In the main, however, it seems clear that during much of the droving period

[1] Telford, *A Survey and Report of the Coasts and Central Highlands of Scotland*, 1803
[2] *R.P.C.*, 3rd series, XI, 633–4　　　　　[3] Chambers, op. cit., III, 153

and over great stretches of the Highlands the droves moved as they chose through a country unmarked by tracks other than their own.

While the general lines followed by the main droving traffic in Scotland can be determined with fair accuracy from contemporary records, local recollection or tradition, the identification on the ground of the actual line of march is in many cases a matter of great difficulty. As has been seen, droving traffic was in general unrestricted, free to cross a wide area or to change its route according to the weather, the season, or the many other factors which influenced that uncertain trade. This must often have prevented the formation of a track sufficiently well defined to remain visible to this day. In some parts of the Highlands, too, the routes followed by the drovers were routes used also by pack-horse, sledge and foot traffic, often dating from a very early period, and it is in many cases now hardly possible with any certainty to distinguish the marks made by one type of traffic from those made by another. Where, however, as in parts of the Highlands, the Southern Uplands and the Cheviots are still to be seen tracks, the predominant use of which by cattle traffic alone is reasonably certain, these are characterised by a number of roughly parallel paths. Where the ground is open and level these paths may in places cover a breadth of twenty to thirty yards and often much more, a type of track which would be left by beasts moving in parallel lines or perhaps by successive droves following the same route and choosing fresh ground to avoid that cut and trampled by the passage of those before. Where the configuration of the ground has concentrated the traffic, the breadth of the track narrows with a corresponding increase in its depth and clarity. The traffic which has left these traces is often referred to as consisting of 'streams' of beasts, and indeed the characteristic marks of a drove road are very similar to those left by the passage of a stream, alternately flowing in broad shallows or narrow deeps and rapids.[1]

The use which Wade and the road-makers who followed him made of the old traditional cattle routes in laying out the new roads, and the steady development and improvement of Highland roads after Wade's time, led to increasing complaints from the

---

[1] In the recent film *The Overlanders* which describes cattle droving in Northern Australia, it is noticeable that the photographs of the droves show the animals moving in parallel strings or streams now broadening and now contracting according to the nature of the ground.

drovers. The gravel of the new roads, they said, hurt the feet of the cattle while the hard surfaces wore down their hooves.[1] To meet these difficulties, many drovers adopted the practice, particularly in autumn or in bad weather, of shoeing the beasts, at least for that part of their journey which took them over made roads. The shoeing of cattle appears to date back to very ancient times. There is some evidence that working cattle were shod in Britain as early as the days of the Romans, and while it is not clear whether shoeing continued to be practised all through the centuries following their occupation, it is known that cattle were regularly shod in England in the seventeenth century. The Welsh drovers also shod their cattle on the way to the English markets, while in parts of England, notably in Sussex, the shoeing of cattle both for working and for travelling to market appears not to have entirely died out until about the beginning of the

---

[1] It seems doubtful whether complaints by drovers about the effect of made roads on the feet of the cattle can have had much justification until well on in the second half of the eighteenth century when the system of military roads had become fairly extensive. Wade's roads in many cases followed routes not extensively used by cattle droves which, in any event, did not keep to a narrow track. The surfaces of Wade's roads appear to have been composed of gravel. It is questionable whether cattle passing over them would suffer as much damage as they caused, and it is hardly surprising to find that in an Essay by William Mackintosh of Borlum in 1742 advocating the use of Wade's roads for stopping cattle-raiding, he recommends that the soldiers to be stationed at intervals on the roads should not allow their use by cattle droves on the way to the south-country markets. ' For these fairs and markets serve only in the latter end of the year when frequent rains fall which must by the cattle's feet potch and break the solidest structure can be made : nor is there any injury done them in this since the muirs on each side of the road affords their cattle as good footing as ever former droves had before that road was made.' The relatively soft nature of the surface of Wade's roads and the effect on them of the passing of cattle may be judged by a further passage in Mackintosh's essay, which emphasises the value of the roads for showing the marks of stolen beasts driven across them. The tracks of pasturing cattle, he states, can be easily distinguished from those of stolen cattle which are being hard driven. In the case of the former, the marks of the hooves are close together, while in the latter the hoof marks are far apart, while the marks of the pasterns appear like little dimples behind the hooves. (*A Short Scheme . . . to stop depradations . . . so destructive to the Northern Counties of Scotland*, Edinburgh 1742.) The progress which had been made by the early years of the nineteenth century in the technique of road construction, is shown by an extract from Telford's Report on the eastern end of the Glen Garry Road quoted in the *5th Report of the Commissioners for Highland Roads and Bridges* in 1811. ' This being a great extent of road,' he reported, ' through a country where much rain falls and a considerable portion of it having been now for three years used by Drovers of Black Cattle and of Sheep, of carts in carrying timber sold by Glengarry and for the conveyance of material for the bridge-building, it affords a very good specimen of the durability of Highland roads made according to the specification of our contracts. I saw it after a month of very heavy and constant rain . . . yet under all these circumstances the road has sustained no serious injury . . .' In 1813, however, the Commissioners referred in their *6th Report* to continued repairs needed on the Arisaig Road as a result of timber and cattle traffic.

present century.[1] The shoeing of animals travelling long distances to market was not confined to cattle, for during the early eighteenth and nineteenth centuries when numbers of geese and turkeys were driven by road from Norfolk to the London market, the birds were ' shod ' by the simple process of smearing the feet with pitch and covering the surface with sand.[2] The method of shoeing cattle was rough, for the beasts had to be thrown on their backs, often with serious damage to the horns, the head being held down and the feet tied while the shoeing was being done. The shoes used by the drovers for their cattle were thin metal plates, crescent-shaped and nailed on the outer edge of the two hooves of each foot with fine metal nails the heads of which were formed of cross pieces giving the nail the appearance of a small hammer. A beast fully shod thus required eight metal plates, but it seems that often only the outer hoof of each foot was shod, as the most wear came on this outer edge.

At what points in Scotland on the journey to the trysts shoes were first fitted cannot be exactly determined, but it seems unlikely that shoes would be fitted for the first part of the journey through the Highlands where much of the way lay over mountain tracks and moorland. Till within recent years there still lived men who could remember the shoeing of cattle at a smiddy at Trinafour on the main drove road to Crieff from the North, and at Tyndrum, and a Ross-shire drover, whose memories of the droving trade go back to 1868, recalls the shoeing of cattle from Wester Ross-shire when they reached hard well-made roads in the neighbourhood of Muir of Ord and Dingwall.

While the shoes used for the Highland droves were no doubt largely made by local smiths, an Aberdeenshire cattle breeder of last century has recorded that many were made by a smith at Crossgates in Fife, who specialised in the craft and produced such good shoes and nails for fixing them that some drovers refused to drive the cattle unless Crossgates shoes were used.[3] The shoeing of half-wild cattle fresh from Highland grazings and unused to handling must have been difficult work, but the same

---

[1] Johnson, *Byways in British Archaeology*, 1912; and Skeel, *Cattle Trade between England and Wales from the 15th to the 19th centuries*. Royal Hist. Society's Transactions 4th series, IX, 1926, 143–4 and 149.

[2] Defoe estimated that about 150,000 turkeys were driven to London each year from East Anglia. The journey of approximately 100 miles started in August, and took about three months.

[3] McCombie, *Cattle and Cattle Breeders*, 1867, 113

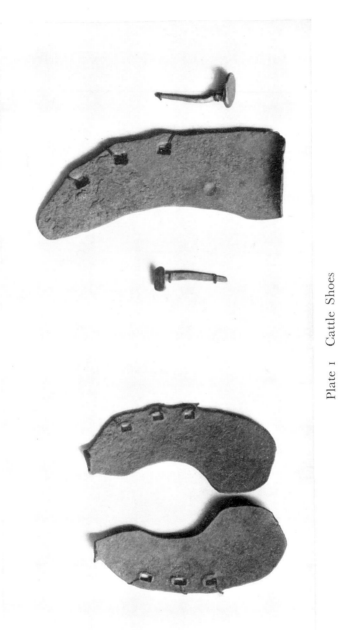

Plate 1   Cattle Shoes

(*left*) Shoes made by the family of Kennedy, smiths at Trinafour, Perthshire, about 1865 (length 2⅞ in.).   (*right*) Shoe and nails made at the village of Grassington, in Wharfedale, in the second half of the 19th century (length 3⅜ in. ; nails 1⅛ in.)

(*Photos by C. S. Minto of shoes in the Author's possession*)

writer has described how Robert Gall of Kennethmont in Aberdeenshire once shod as many as seventy cattle in a day, probably shoeing only the outer edge of each hoof. As the droves moved south to the harder roads of England, the shoes had to be renewed at intervals either at local smiddies where stores of shoes were made and accumulated during the winter months, or with spare shoes carried by the drovers for the purpose.[1] Donald Mackenzie, a crofter living near Broadford in Skye, states that in his youth he repeatedly took cattle from the Islands to Falkirk Tryst. These beasts were not regularly shod, but if any went lame on the journey pieces of leather were attached to the foot to protect the hooves.

Leaving the gathering-point in the northern hills the drove ' crept slowly southward day after day.' The beasts must not be hurried, especially during the first days of the march, and the usual day's journey was ten to twelve miles. At midday the drovers halted to allow the cattle to graze, and when evening came they stopped in some suitable spot where the beasts could rest, graze and drink, while the men passed the night wrapped in their plaids in such shelter as the place afforded, but always on the watch to guard the drove or to do such herding as the tired beasts needed. A party of drovers from Skye whom Bishop Forbes met at Dalwhinnie on the way to Crieff in 1723 were rather better equipped than was usual, and one of the men so described the drovers' work : ' They had four or five horses with provisions for themselves by the way, particularly blankets to wrap themselves in when sleeping in the open air, as they rest on the bleak mountains, the heathy moors, or the verdant glens, just as it happens, towards the evening. They tend their flocks

---

[1] The cattle shoes used by the Welsh drovers were known as ' ciw.' These, like the shoes of the Scots cattle, were in two parts and the method of shoeing the beasts appears to have been very similar to that employed in the North. Shoes for Welsh cattle bound for England were made in large quantities by local smiths, particularly at Bala in Merionethshire. (P. G. Hughes, *Wales and the Drovers ; the Historic Background of an Epoch*, 1943.) On the English drove roads, shoes were made at Langthorpe, near Boroughbridge, at Grassington in Wharfedale and at other points on the routes to the great cattle markets. (William Thompson, *Cattle Droving between Scotland and England. Journal of Archaeological Association*, Vol. 87, 1932.) The smiths appear to have been paid about 10d for each beast shod. In an unpublished manuscript written about 1818 Arthur Young deals at some length with the shoeing of working cattle. He reports that in Sussex cattle are shod where their work takes them frequently on hard roads. His conclusion is that except for road work or on very stony ground shoeing is not advisable because of the trouble and risk of throwing the animal in the process and the difficulty of fixing the shoes securely. (Unpublished Manuscript, *The Elements and Practice of Agriculture*, Vol. 28, 355 et seq. British Museum)

by night and never move till about eight in the morning and then march the cattle at leisure that they may feed a little as they go along. They rest a while at midday to take some dinner and so let the cattle feed and rest as they please. The proprietor does not travel with the cattle but has one for his deputy to command the whole and he goes to the place appointed against the day fixed for the fair. When the flock is very large as the present, they divide it, though belonging to one, into several droves that they may not hurt one another in narrow passes, particularly on bridges many of which they go along. Each drove has a particular number of men with some boys to look after the cattle.' [1]

The factor on which beyond all others depended the success of a droving venture from the Highlands to the trysts was the care of the drover to see to it that wayside grazing was provided for the beasts, with opportunity to profit by it, and that undisturbed rest, food and water were theirs at night. The stopping-places for the night were known as ' stances.' ' These stances are essential to the use of the drove roads as such. The physical powers of sheep and cattle will not suffer them to be constantly in motion, and periodical rests are indispensable for their safety on journeys continuing from day to day for weeks together. Hence the existence of stances without which the drove road would be useless. The stances may therefore be truly said to be part and parcel of the drove road just as much as any other portion of the surface trodden by cattle in the course of their transit.' [2] The choice of these stopping-places to rest and graze the cattle was dictated by the existence of pasture and water for the beasts, and by the limited day's march which the cattle could cover. While ten to twelve miles was the distance generally recognised in Scotland by the careful drover as the most the cattle could do in a day if they were to be in good condition on reaching Crieff or Falkirk, it was sometimes necessary to exceed this limit. In the Hebrides, where the route of cattle bound for the mainland entailed crossings from one island to another dependant on tides, the beasts might have to be driven farther and faster than the drovers liked. A drove starting late from Broadford in Skye might be hurried to catch the slackest of the tide at the crossing to the mainland, or bad weather at an exposed

[1] *Bishop Forbes' Journal*, 235–6
[2] *Macgregor and Others* v. *Breadalbane*, Court of Session Cases, 1846, 9 Dunlop's Reports, 210

part of the route might mean a forced march to cross a high pass ; but these were exceptions, and the good drover was loth to hurry his beasts or to cheat them of their midday grazing and their full night's rest.

Until the second half of the eighteenth century the drovers' stances were in most cases used without payment. As an old drover of last century said of them in giving evidence in support of the drovers' rights : ' The beasts were allowed to feed where they stopped. There was no charge made for that. They were all made welcome—a free table for man and beast.' [1] In many parts of the Highlands, indeed, until changing conditions led to a different outlook, droves were probably not unwelcome, for the passage and pasturage of large droves of cattle meant valuable manuring of the ground, and even to this day the routes of the old drove roads and the sites of the stances remain in many places appreciably greener than the surrounding hill. As the droves moved towards the lower country, however, where enclosure of land was more frequent, payment for grazing and stance rights became, as time went on, more common, especially where cottages or inns beside the stances offered, if they wished it, shelter for the drovers as well as grass for the beasts.

On arrival at a stance, which was seldom enclosed save by the sides of glen or corrie, the beasts were allowed to graze freely. The men ate their simple meal and later lay down to rest, one of their number by turns keeping watch through the night while the others slept. The beasts were usually too tired and hungry to wander far, but old men still (1948) living who in their young days took beasts to the Trysts, have told that sometimes if the moon rose late after the beasts had fed and rested they would wander and must be herded. A writer of the nineteenth century mentions the acuteness of hearing of many of the drovers which enabled them to detect the movements of an animal straying from the stance during the dark hours.[2] During the first few days of the journey, the homing instinct, strong in sheep and cattle, lingered on, and during this period there was the risk of beasts making off the way they had come. Soon the memory of the familiar pastures faded, and from then on the nights were seldom disturbed. Night marches were avoided at all costs, for,

[1] *Scottish Rights of Way Society* v. *MacPherson*, Court of Session Cases, 1887, 14 Rettie's Reports, 875 and Notes of Evidence
[2] McIan and Logan, op. cit., 37

like Candlish and Sym, the drovers who led St Ives over the hills
of the Southern Uplands, they knew that such forced marches
were 'fair ruin on the bestial.' [1] When morning came the beasts
were quietly roused and collected again for the road, for cattle
startled and hurried after a night's rest were liable to scatter and
stampede. The degree of skill and care required of the drovers
in the management of the beasts depended partly on the com-
position of the drove. Beasts newly come from summer grazing
could be more easily spoiled by over-driving than a drove in the
spring which had had no rich feeding, while a mixed drove of
heifers and bullocks or one composed of beasts from several
different grazings was more restless and difficult to drive than
a drove of one sex or from one locality.

The movement of thousands of cattle by ten mile stages from
all parts of north and west Scotland to Crieff or Falkirk by
many and varying routes meant the existence of great numbers
of stances throughout the Highlands. Some of these are still
known by the local people and are on occasion used as stances ;
some are now only fast-fading traditions, while countless others
have passed far beyond the limits of memory or tradition. To
attempt to enumerate them all, even if it were now possible, would
lead into profitless paths of speculation and controversy. It is
sufficient to know that all through the Highlands, in glens and
corries or on open moorland, are grassy hollows or stretches of
open grazing which once offered rest to tired beasts and wearied
men. [2]

Many water hazards lay between the drovers and the Trysts.
The absence of bridges over the rivers of the Highlands was one
of the main obstacles to inland communication in Scotland in
the seventeenth and eighteenth centuries. Wade's work indeed
included the building of between thirty and forty bridges, but
though he bridged the Tay, the Spean, the Tummel and the
Perthshire Garry the total number was made up largely of small

---

[1] R. L. Stevenson, op. cit., Ch. 10

[2] While, for the reason given, no complete list of the stances on the main drove
routes has been attempted, information based on local recollection or tradition
indicates that on the drove routes from Skye to Central Perthshire stances which
were regularly used included Kyle Rhea, Shiel Bridge, Clunie, Torgyle, Fort Augustus,
Meallgarbh, Garvamore, Drumgask, Dalwhinnie, Dalnaspidal, Dalnacardoch and
Trinafour. On one of the alternative routes stances appear to have been in use at
Loch Loyne, Fedden in Glen Cia-aig, Spean Bridge, Blarmachfoldach in Glen
Kiachnish, Kinlochleven, Altnafeadh, Inveroran, Bridge of Orchy, Clifton, Luib
and Balquhidder.

bridges. In the latter part of the eighteenth century a number of new bridges were built over some of the larger rivers, but when Telford started his work as Engineer to the Commissioners for Highland Roads and Bridges in 1803 the absence of bridges at key points was still one of the main weaknesses in the road system of the Highlands.[1] The Conon, the Beauly, the Spey and the Lyon were still unbridged. The only crossing of the Don except by ford appears to have been at the old Bridge of Balgownie near its mouth. On the Dee there were, till 1800, only four bridges, one of these at Aberdeen, while on the Tweed the only bridges available for cattle before 1766 appear to have been at Berwick and Peebles. Of the bridges which did exist, most were naturally at the most populous parts which the drovers sought to avoid, and over countless Highland streams and burns no bridges of any sort existed. There were good reasons, too, why such bridges as existed were not popular with the drovers. Many of the early bridges were narrow wooden structures. To cattle being driven for the first time, and unused as many of them were to anything but their native hills, the crossing of a narrow bridge was a terrifying experience, while the unaccustomed sound of their feet on the timbers was liable to make them panic. Even on the larger bridges the danger was considerable. A note in a Dumfriesshire paper records that while a large drove was on its way south from Dumfriesshire in the early part of last century, it was met by the mail coach while crossing the bridge over the Eden near Carlisle. The cattle took fright and so great was the rush of beasts that the parapet of the bridge gave way, and both men and cattle were thrown into the river.[2]

In these conditions the crossing of rivers by ford or by swimming was the common lot of the beasts and part of the familiar technique of the drovers.[3] Edward Burt has so described the crossing of a river by a drove of cattle in the first half of the eighteenth century : 'It was in a time of rain by a wide river where there was a boat to ferry over the drovers. The cows were about fifty in number and took the water like spaniels, and when

[1] Telford, *Survey and Report of the Coasts and Central Highlands of Scotland*, 1803
[2] *Dumfries and Galloway Courier.* 'Notes and Queries', 1913. Note 439
[3] In this the drovers may well have profited by the traditions and teaching of their less reputable ancestors. Mackintosh of Borlum has described the crossing of the Tay near Kenmore by cattle thieves. 'Each man takes hold in his one hand of horse, bullock or cow's tail, he drove into the water and extends out his other hand with his fusee and his pistol in his teeth, and so is drawn with his firearms dry to the other side.' Mackintosh of Borlum, op. cit.

they were in, their drivers made a hideous cry to urge them forwards : this, they told me, they did to keep the foremost of them from turning about, for in that case, the rest would do the like and then they would be in danger, especially the weakest of them, to be swept away and drowned by the torrent.' [1] Except in time of flood the larger rivers, such as Burt described, would offer relatively little difficulty, for cattle are strong swimmers. Even so, there must have been times when the crossing of rivers such as the Dee or the Spey would be a work of great hazard, and it is hardly surprising that in the *General View of the Agriculture of Elgin* in 1794 the writer reports that drovers from the South do not attend the local sales for lack of a bridge over the Spey at Fochabers.[2] William McCombie the Aberdeenshire cattle dealer already quoted, has described how in the early years of last century, his father, in bringing a drove from Caithness to Aberdeenshire, lost seventeen beasts in the crossing of the Spey, a severe frost having come on shortly after the cattle had swum the river.[3] Difficult as the crossing of the larger rivers might be, however, the smaller ones and many a hill stream would at times present almost greater problems. Too shallow to swim and too rapid to ford, they must at times of flood have proved formidable obstacles involving detours or delays wearisome alike to tired beasts and their harassed drivers.

The period of the year during which droving from the Highlands went on lasted from May or early June, when some of the beasts had recovered from the hungry winter, till the end of October. Little or no droving took place in the winter or early spring, a season which even the old cattle raiders recognised as one during which the beasts were too weak for long journeys ; but even during the droving months, storms of wind and driving mist and rain were to be looked for on high passes or open moorland, while early snows might well come before the last beasts were delivered to the October Tryst at Falkirk. Yet, cold and wet as they must constantly have been, these hardy men the drovers, seldom sought the shelter of houses. Many, it is said, never slept under a roof between Lochaber and Lincolnshire, and those still (1948) alive can recall meeting in their youth with old drovers who, when in charge of cattle, were loth to enter a house

---

[1] Burt, *Letters from a Gentleman in the North of Scotland*, II, 33
[2] Donaldson, J., *General View of the Agriculture of Elgin*, 1794, 27-8
[3] McCombie, op. cit., 100

even to eat. The constant vigilance called for from the drovers no doubt made it necessary for them to rest beside their cattle, a need perhaps all the greater in the vicinity of men and habitations. A writer of the first half of last century has so described the work of the smaller type of cattle dealer in the south of Scotland : ' A mountaineer will travel from fair to fair for thirty miles round with no other food than the oaten cake which he carries with him, and what requires neither fire, table, knife nor any instrument to use. He will lay out the whole, or perhaps treble of all he is worth (to which the facility of the country banks is a great encouragement) in the purchase of 30 or 100 head of cattle, with which, when collected, he sets out for England, a country with the roads, manners and inhabitants of which he is probably unacquainted. In this journey, he scarcely ever goes into a house, sleeps but little, and then generally in the open air, and lives chiefly upon his favourite oaten bread.' [1]

While the hardiness of these men is remarkable, it may be doubted whether they were greatly the losers in shunning the inn of the period. With the great increase in road building in the Highlands during the first half of the nineteenth century some improvement took place in both the supply and the standard of Highland inn accommodation, but at no time earlier than the middle of that century did the inns of Scotland stand in good repute. ' The Band and Statutes of Icolmkill ' by which James VI sought to reduce the Western Isles to order had provided for the setting up of inns in convenient places ; but Thomas Kirke, writing in 1669, says, ' The Scots have not inns, but change-houses as they call them, poor small cottages where you must be content to take what you find,' [2] and it was the existence of too many of these primitive inns kept by lawless people that the Privy Council in 1618 blamed for much of the unrest of the Border.[3] A writer of the first half of the eighteenth century says of the inns in his youth : ' Few were to be met with in which the traveller could either eat or sleep with comfort,' [4] perhaps because the Scot of the period travelled little, and when he did, enjoyed the hospitality of friends or relations which was amply repaid

---

[1] Youatt, *Cattle, their Breeds, Management and Diseases*. Library of Useful Knowledge, 1834, 163
[2] Hume Brown, *Early Travellers*, 264   [3] *R.P.C.*, 1st series, XI, 445–6
[4] Somerville, *My Own Life and Times 1741–1814*, 356

by the relief of the tedium and monotony of the hosts' daily life. The passing of the eighteenth century saw little change in the standard of accommodation provided for the wayfarer, and at the end of the century travellers from the South coming to Scotland in increasing numbers have all the same complaint. Many of the inns of the Highlands of this period were still only wayside cottages providing little more than the rough spirit, illicitly distilled, which, with the small black cattle and the kelp of the Islands and coastal districts, were the only products with which the Highlander of the time could eke out his meagre livelihood. Kingshouse on the Moor of Rannoch was a key point on the drove roads. Here the need for an inn and the lack of incentive to keep one was early recognised by the Government, and travellers of the eighteenth and early nineteenth centuries record that the innkeeper sat rent free and had an annual Government grant. Despite this, the description of the place given by travellers during the droving period shows it to have been rough and cheerless. It is described by a traveller of 1791 as having ' not a bed fit for a decent person to sleep in nor any provisions but what are absolutely necessary for the family,' [1] and in 1802 James Donaldson, Surveyor of the Military Roads, complains that it ' has more the appearance of a hog stye than an Inn.' [2] Dorothy Wordsworth in the following year found it ' a wretched place—as dirty as a house after a sale on a rainy day,' but of the inn at Inveroran ten miles across the moor, she has left a more cheerful picture. Here, on 4 September 1803, she found the inn filled with ' seven or eight travellers probably drovers, with as many dogs, sitting in a complete circle round a large peat fire in the middle of the floor, each with a mess of porridge in a wooden vessel on his knee.' [3] As the nineteenth century wore on, and the routes of the drovers became more defined and restricted, wayside inns came to be increasingly used by them, and those inns with facilities for resting cattle started to advertise the fact in the local papers. Despite this, many drovers remained to the end true to their calling and their traditions, resting at night with their cattle, where ' wrapped in their plaids on which the frost showed white or the dew shone just as it does upon

---

[1] Newte, *Tour of England and Scotland in 1785* (1791 edn.), 120
[2] Letter to John Campbell, Esq., W.S., Edinburgh, dated 9th June 1802 : *Breadalbane Papers (Roads)*, Box 4, H.M. Register House
[3] Dorothy Wordsworth, *Journals*, 1798–1828 (Ed. William Knight), 318, 323

a spider's web, their sticks near their hands, they slumbered peacefully.' [1]

That the connection between the Church in Scotland and the life and work of the drovers was close, is apparent from the early records of the droving trade. The local fairs which in many cases developed into the cattle trysts of the seventeenth and eighteenth centuries commemorate the names of St Lawrence, St Serf, St Faith, St Andrew, St Palladius and a score of others, and as has been seen, the help of the Church was enlisted by cattle dealers in calling together their customers ; but the Church was concerned to see to it that their help and patronage of the droving trade was not abused. In 1503 the holding of markets or fairs on Holy Days had been prohibited by statute ; but drovers were rough folk to whom it seemed that the Sabbath was made for man, and all through the seventeenth century the Register of the Privy Council and the later records of the Presbyteries and Kirk Sessions throughout the country contain constant complaints of Sunday droving and efforts to prevent it. Many of the local fairs had originally been fixed on a Monday, and as this inevitably led to the driving of cattle on the previous day, the dates were gradually changed. In 1640 the great market at Dumfries was changed from Monday to Wednesday,[2] and nearly fifty years later the date of the important fair of St Lawrence in Aberdeenshire was changed for the same reason.[3] The Minutes of the Kirk Session of Peebles in July 1764 record the punishment of drovers passing through the town on a Sunday for neglecting to attend church.[4] Sunday droving, however, continued to be practised, and particularly in the south-west of Scotland the

---

[1] Cunninghame Graham, *A Hatchment*, 212

Sir Walter Scott mentions an incident described to him by one of those who took part in it as a boy. A small number of cattle which had been stolen by Highland cattle thieves had been recovered with the help of Rob Roy acting in the capacity of ' cattle protector.' The beasts were being driven homewards by a small party including the narrator, and when darkness fell they lay down for the night in an exposed place. The season was late October and the night exceedingly cold. The narrator in a desperate attempt to get warm lay down beside one of the Highlanders, and by degrees pulled over himself part of the plaid in which the latter was wrapped. In the morning, he was alarmed to see that the Highlander's neck and shoulders which had been uncovered were white with hoar frost, but the Highlander suffered little inconvenience, merely shaking himself on awakening and rubbing the hoar frost off with his plaid while he muttered that it had been a ' cauld nicht.' (Scott, *Rob Roy*, Introduction, lxxii, Border edn., Waverley Novels)

[2] *A.P.S.*, V, 297-8   [3] *R.P.C.*, 3rd series, VIII, 380

[4] Johnman, *Highways and Byways*, Transactions of Hawick Archaeological Society, 1917, 21

matter was constantly before the local Church authorities during the eighteenth century and at least as late as 1840.[1] Whether in the remoter parts of the Highlands drovers observed the Sabbath may be doubted, but Dorothy Wordsworth's description of Glendochart on a Sunday in September 1803 seems to indicate that perhaps even here men and beasts may have had their Sunday rest : ' On the side of a sunny hill a knot of men and women were gathered together at a preaching. We passed by many droves of cattle and Shetland ponies, which accident stamped a character upon places—else unremembered—not an individual character but the soul, the spirit and solitary simplicity of many a Highland region.' [2]

While the hazards and hardships of his calling must fill much of the canvas of any picture of the drover's life, there were some patches of brightness to alleviate the sombre colouring. His wayfaring life taking him far afield, did more than satisfy the love of movement and adventure handed down to him from the generations before. Gossip and talk with other travellers and drovers at inns and wayside meetings cheered his lonely journeys, and with the packsman, the pedlar and the tramp he shared the function of news carrier so dear to country people at a time when news was scarce. His was the excitement of the Tryst, of the bustle and the bargaining ; his too, the pride of recounting its every detail to eager listeners back in his Highland glen. If at times these advantages may have seemed to the drover small recompense for his life of hardship, and if he were sometimes tempted to turn his back on the drove road and to prefer his poor croft and scanty holding in Uist, Skye or Lochaber, some other thought may have come to him. Perhaps rough hard men though the drovers were, their memories brought to them as they sat by their peat fires pictures which made them forget their hardships and their sufferings : sunlight and cloud-shadow on the hills of Kintail ; gold of the birches in Glen Garry or along the Dee as they took a drove south to the October Trysts ; green of lush grass and flags set against the yellow of seaweed as the Islay cattle moved up the shores of Loch Sween ; Cruachan with an early powdering of snow ; Loch Awe and Loch Lubnaig still on a September morning, or countless other scenes of loch, river, meadow and mountain as they and their cattle passed in the autumn days on their slow journeys through the Highlands of Scotland.

[1] *Dumfries Courier,* 29 January 1840   [2] Dorothy Wordsworth, op. cit., 325

THE ECONOMICS OF DROVING

THE natural barriers of sea, mountain and river which faced the early drovers on their journeys from Highlands to Lowlands, formed part only of the difficulties which lay between them and the success of their hazardous enterprise. To these were added problems of finance and economics so great that it can only be a matter for wonder that trade was carried on in conditions which to a trader of later times must seem well-nigh impossible. Of the complex factors which a cattle drover had to take into account during the centuries preceding the Union of 1603, the most important were probably the political state of the country and particularly of the Border areas, the policy of the Government towards the internal trade of the country and the commercial relations of Scotland and England. By the middle of the seventeenth century, the advantages of freer trading across the Border had come to be more generally recognised, and the years which followed the Union of 1707 brought a gradual realisation that for better or for worse the fortunes of the two countries were indeed finally linked. The changing and opportunist policy which had hitherto hampered the trade of Scotland settled at last on a more fixed course, and from the early years of the eighteenth century it becomes possible to attempt to construct a clear picture of the economic and financial problems which faced the drovers and the methods by which they plied their trade.

The rapid development of droving throughout the eighteenth century was, as has been seen, the natural outcome of the state of rural Scotland at that period. In the early years of the century, road communications between Highlands and Lowlands were still almost non-existent. Markets for cattle were distant, and to reach them involved a journey over large tracts of little-known and disturbed country where, as late as 1747, it was estimated that the total annual loss suffered directly or indirectly from cattle thieving was £37,000 sterling.[1] Yet cattle constituted almost

---

[1] *An Inquiry into the Causes . . . of Rebellions . . . in the Highlands of Scotland,* 1747; Gartmore MS. printed as Appendix in Jamieson's (5th) Edition of Burt's *Letters from a Gentleman in the North of Scotland,* II, 359.

the only form of readily realisable wealth, and were in many cases the principal method of paying rents. Since dealers from the south would not face the risks of journeys to and from the Highlands, there arose this class of hardy and adventurous men —the drovers—to barter knowledge of the country and acceptance of hazard and hardship in return for a meagre daily wage, a small commission on the price realised for the beasts sold, or in the case of some, for the difference between the price paid to the Highland grazier and that realised in the markets of the Lowlands.[1]

Money was scarce in Scotland in the eighteenth century, and at the time of the Union of 1707 the total amount in circulation was reckoned to be not more than £200,000 Sterling.[2] Though the Bank of Scotland had been founded in 1695, nearly half a century was to pass before banking became an active part of the commercial life of Scotland, and even longer before banking facilities became widely available in the rural districts ; but while money was short credit was long, and the written promise to pay or bill of exchange was in active circulation. Many of these bills remained for long unpaid before they could be cashed, and meantime passed from hand to hand, fulfilling to some extent the function of the banknotes of later years. This credit

[1] ' It is alledged that much of the Highlands lye at a great distance from publick Fairs, mercates and places of commerce and that the access to these places is both difficult and dangerous ; by reason of all which, trading people decline to go into the country in order to traffick and deal with the people. It is on this account that the farmers, having no way to turn the produce of their farms, which is mostly cattle, into money are obliged to pay their rents in cattle which the landlord takes at his own price, in regairde that he must either grase them himself, send them to distant markets, or credite some person with them to be againe at a certaine profit disposed of by him. This introduced the business of that sort of people commonly known by the name of Drovers. These men have little or no substance, they must know the language, the different places and consequently be of that country. The farmers, then, do either sell their cattle to these drovers upon credite, at the drover's price (for ready money they seldom have) or to the landlord at his price, for payment of his rent. If this last is the case, the landlord does again dispose of them to the drover upon credite, and these drovers make what profites they can by selling them to grasiers or at markets. These drovers make payments, and keep credite for a few years and then they either in reality become bankrupts, or pretend to be so. The last is most frequently the case and then the subject of which they have cheated is privately transferred to a confident person in whose name, upon that reall stock, a trade is sometimes carried on for their behoof, till the Trustee gett into credite and prepaire *his* affairs for a bankruptcy. Thus the farmers are still kept poor ; they first sell at an under rate and then they often loose altogether. The landlords, too, must either turn traders and take their cattle to markets, or give these people credite, and by the same means suffer.' (ibid., 364–5)

[2] Hume Brown estimates it at only £60,000 in copper, £60,000 in silver and £30,000 in gold. (*History of Scotland*, III, 69)

system was one of which the cattle drovers of the eighteenth century took full advantage, and without which the financing of their operations would have been impossible. For some years before the start of the earliest Scots banks, there had been in existence mercantile houses whose business lay largely in the financing of trade. From them, a drover bound for the Highlands to buy cattle for sale at Crieff Tryst obtained a letter of credit and a slender stock of cash.[1] Armed with these, he made his appearance in the late spring or early summer among the needy tenants, tacksmen and landlords of the north and west. To men short of money and distant from markets, the temptation of a few pounds of cash and the prospect of a further payment on the sale of their beasts proved irresistible. Such scraps of information as had filtered through from the South, or the number and urgency of the drovers in the North were their only means of judging as to the fair market value of their animals. So the scales were weighted and after such bargaining as was possible in the circumstances, the cattle passed to the new owners, these 'little extorting money holders,' as Sir John Sinclair called them, 'who for affording a little supply of money when any distress occurs take the cattle at their own price.'[2] The proportion of the price paid in cash appears to have varied greatly, but probably in few cases was it more than a fraction of the value of the animals.[3] The balance was met by bills or promissory notes which the drovers gave, payable usually at the end of three months, by which time they might reasonably hope to have sold their beasts at the Trysts. Sometimes necessity drove the owners to part with their beasts for bills alone. The needs of the sellers, the optimism and ready wit of the buyers, led to great variations in the type of bargain to suit varying circumstances, but all rested on credit given and risks taken.

[1] In a case which came before the Court of Session in 1767 on the Petition of a Yorkshire cattle dealer, the 'Answers' lodged in reply described how drovers from the South about to proceed to the remoter parts of Scotland procure in Edinburgh promissory notes for different sums payable at some distance of time, when they expect to have finished their round and picked up all the cattle they mean to purchase, the bankers in Edinburgh being re-imbursed by bills drawn on the drovers' correspondents in London. (*Old Session Papers*, Signet Library, 150, 24)

[2] Sinclair, *General View of the Agriculture of the Northern Counties*, 1795, 160

[3] In a case which came before the Court of Session in 1779 the price agreed for a sale of cattle between a Sutherlandshire farmer and a local drover was fixed at 8s to 15s a head below the normal figure because the drover undertook to pay cash when the cattle were delivered at a fixed rendezvous—an undertaking which was in fact not fulfilled. (*Old Session Papers*, Signet Library, 191, 25)

The sale effected and the drovers started on their long journey South, the bills they had signed passed quickly into circulation as part of the currency of the district. When James Boswell and Samuel Johnson visited Skye in 1772 they found that the rents due to the Lairds were paid in drovers' bills.[1] A system of finance based largely on bills of exchange seems to have been general throughout the Highlands at that time, and the Letter-book of Bailie John Steuart, an Inverness merchant of the early eighteenth century, shows such bills to have been in circulation helping to finance a wonderfully active trade not only in such home products as Easdale slate, Morayshire grain and Findhorn salmon, but in coffee beans from Rotterdam, wines from Bordeaux and olives of the Mediterranean shore.[2] Many of these Highland bills were made payable at Crieff, for during the first half of the century Crieff cattle market was probably the greatest centre of money circulation in the country, and Steuart was often represented there to try to get payment of bills held by him from the proceeds of cattle sales. After the turn of the century, the Edinburgh banks were for the same reason represented at Falkirk Tryst, which was then rapidly supplanting Crieff as the centre of the droving trade.

During the first thirty years of the eighteenth century, the financing of trade in Scotland had been done mainly by merchants and goldsmiths in Edinburgh, and by commercial houses, of which Coutts and Company, founded in 1723, was one of the most important. The years which followed the founding of the Royal Bank of Scotland in 1727, however, saw a rapid extension of the cash credit system by means of which any reputable person with two guarantors could get credit. While much of this financing was, so far as concerned the cattle trade, probably in most cases on a small scale, considerable advances were sometimes made, and a record of the British Linen Bank shows that in 1767 the cashier of the bank was sent to Falkirk with instructions to get payment on bills due by drovers and to finance John Birtwhistle, a well-known drover from Yorkshire, to the extent of £2,000 if he required it, while Robert Scott of Shelphill and James Grieve of Todshawhaugh were authorised to get advances of £500 each. The system of cash credit was popular with traders and bankers

---

[1] Boswell, *Tour to the Hebrides*, Isham Collection, 172
[2] *Steuart's Letter-book 1715/1752*. Scot. Hist. Soc,. 2nd series, Vol. 9. Introd. xxii, xxiv.

alike, for while it greatly helped the rapid growth of trade and industry from 1730 onwards, it provided the new banks with an opportunity of getting their notes into circulation. By the middle of the century branch banks had been opened in many of the larger towns, and soon small independent banks started business in many country districts, encouraged by the dangerous but convenient system then in fashion which enabled them to pay cash for their notes, or at their own option to make payment with interest at the end of six months. The dangers arising from the widespread use of this option and the multiplication of small banking companies all over the country which it facilitated soon became apparent, and an Act of 1767 prohibited the issue of notes of less than £1 and provided that all notes should be immediately convertible into cash ; but this alone was insufficient to restore stability to the country's banking system. In the face of rapidly expanding industry and rising prices, ignorance or disregard of sound banking principles produced all the conditions making for the disaster which overtook many of the smaller banks and some of the larger in 1772.

Of the abundant credit so readily available none took fuller advantage than the cattle drovers and dealers. The chance of large profits and the rising demand for cattle in the markets of England in the latter years of the eighteenth and early nineteenth centuries, induced many to go into the business with little or no capital other than their hardiness, their spirit of adventure and their boundless assurance. Though many of them would have found difficulty in raising a few hundred pounds, these men thought little of buying from the Highlands in a single autumn cattle to the value of £10,000 to £12,000, giving in return a little cash and the balance in the customary bills. The existence of the new small banks each vying with its neighbours to extend its business and its note circulation, enabled the cattle owners to discount the bills in disregard, or possibly in ignorance, of the fact that by so doing they themselves became, with the drovers, jointly responsible to the banks which cashed the bills. So long as prices at the Trysts kept up, all went well, but no trade was more vulnerable than the droving trade to the chances of fortune, and losses were frequent and heavy. Few of the drovers were men of any substance, and the Banks which had advanced money to them, or had later discounted their bills for the farmers, saw to it that when repayments were made their advances to the drovers, which were in most cases the least secure, were the first to be cancelled. ' A drover at starting,' writes Webster in his agricultural survey of Galloway in 1794, ' agrees with a banker for money or credit which the latter knows how to make safe and profitable. With some money and this credit he attacks the country and grants his own acceptance at such date as may be agreed upon, not exceeding three months for what he purchases. These acceptances being discounted by the farmer, the banker gets the country as a further security for their own property on the drover's bills, provided the banker sees how to clear his own private account, and the bills are taken up as they fall due of which he takes care to get clear of the worst as early as possible. If the trade is brisk, people get all paid, and the drover obtains the further confidence of the country.' [1] So the farmers carried the main risk of the industry on which perforce they depended, bearing the losses if times were bad and reaping few of the rewards.

A Parliamentary Committee in 1826 considered among other matters measures which might be adopted to reduce the risk of the large-scale failures among cattle dealers and the severe losses to cattle breeders which had been experienced in the previous few years. The evidence of the Agent to the British Linen Bank at Dumfries following the lines of suggestions already made by writers in the Statistical Account went to show that the only solution lay in the drovers themselves finding security for the accommodation which they got from the bankers, so enabling them to pay cash to the farmers who would not then require to resort to the discounting of bills which so frequently led to trouble. It was pointed out, however, that such a system would certainly mean lower prices for the farmers, and consequently lower rents with much disorganisation and distress while the trade was changing from a credit to a cash basis.[2]

In such a system of trading, the solvency and honesty of the drovers were clearly of first importance. Here, too, the cattle owners were at a great disadvantage, for while some drovers were men of known reliability, in many cases the cattle owners were dealing with men whom they did not know and at whose substance and honesty they could only guess. ' Necessity, ignorance or

---

[1] Webster, *General View of the Agriculture of Galloway*, 1794, 25
[2] *Report of Select Committee on Promissory Notes in Scotland and Ireland 1826.* Notes of Evidence.

Plate 2   Driving Cattle
(*From an early print*)

greed of the farmers,' says a writer of the eighteenth century, ' induce them to venture their cattle at 1/- to 2/- more per head to a man who would be ruined if he lost 5/- a head at Falkirk '[1]; but necessity and ignorance at least prevailed, and neither bitter experience nor cruel and frequent loss sufficed to prevent the continuance of the system until the decline of the droving industry in the second half of last century.

The Statistical Account of 1791–99 and the Agricultural Surveys of various parts of Scotland prepared during the last years of the eighteenth and the first years of the nineteenth centuries show the serious effects of the system on the cattle-breeding areas of Scotland. From all parts come the same complaints. The writer of the Statistical Account of the Parish of Assynt estimates that failure among the drovers brings distress to the district one year in every ten.[2] From Morayshire and Sutherland come accounts of heavy losses from the same causes. In his account of the northern counties Sir John Sinclair writes in 1795 that heavy losses have been sustained in recent years and recommends that cattle be sold only for ready money or good letters of credit.[3] The writer of the Agricultural Survey of Dumfriesshire complains of the losses suffered by the farmers and of the stimulus given to an unsound system of finance by the existence of small worthless local banks. He suggests that the remedy lies in the sale by the farmers direct to England or to English graziers in the North, so eliminating the drovers altogether. ' In view of the intelligence needed and the fact that he has the management of property of the value of £10,000 to £12,000,' says a writer on the Agriculture of Galloway in 1794, ' it is surprising that the drovers are often men who could not muster £500 or men who have perhaps only 2 years back paid 10/- in the £ to their creditors. The annual loss to Galloway is immense. In the present year several drovers in charge of large droves had compounded with their creditors not six months before or had narrowly escaped doing so. But possession of confidence and a ready tongue may serve instead of great intelligence. Of these the drovers have their full share. Formerly landed proprietors used to take cattle to England, but latterly they stopped and the drovers took their place. These could not buy except on credit and the country was induced to trust them

[1] *O.S.A.*, Abernethy, XIII, 147   [2] *O.S.A.*, Assynt, XVI, 193
[3] Sinclair, op. cit., 160

and instead of real security to rest content with a shadow.'[1] 'For almost a century,' says a Survey from the same district in 1813, 'there has not perhaps been more than one out of ten among the drovers who have not been at least once insolvent.'[2]

While a cattle owner of the eighteenth century might well complain of what seemed to him the one-sided nature of the bargain by which he parted with his beasts, the drover for his part had cause for grave thought and anxious calculation ; for his was a complex budget in which many of the items were unpredictable and imponderable. A drover bringing beasts from the Outer Islands had in the first place to reckon with the cost and risk of ferrying them to the mainland. Feeding on the cross-country journey cost him little or nothing in the hill country, but in the Lowland districts and near the Trysts he was forced, increasingly as the eighteenth century wore on, to pay for his rights of stance and nightly grazing. The rate of payment appears to have varied considerably, depending on the district and the quality of grazing available, but certainly tending to increase as time passed. When the Common Land at Sheriffmuir was divided in 1772, witnesses in the court proceedings, whose duty it had been to collect the stance money from the drovers who used the grazing on the way to Falkirk, spoke of the ' grass mail ' being 6d a score per night for cattle or 6s a drove. In one case a witness's memory was sharpened by the fact that he had been forced to follow to ' the Gowan Hills of Stirling ' a drover who had gone off in the early hours leaving the bill unpaid.[3] At Inveroran on the Moor of Rannoch the traditional rates were 1s 6d per score for cattle and the same for 100 sheep,[4] but old drovers still (1948) alive, who brought cattle from the Highlands in the last quarter of the nineteenth century, remember the rates having risen to between 3s and 4s 6d a score for cattle and 2s 6d or 3s for 100 sheep.

Bridges or stretches of road under the charge of Turnpike Trustees might cost a drover 2d a beast, and while these were avoided where possible, some, like the bridge at Stirling, might have to be crossed. Market dues at Crieff were around 2d a

---

[1] Webster, op. cit., 24–5

[2] Smith, *Survey of Agriculture of Galloway*, 1813, 251

[3] Division of Commonty of Sheriffmuir, *Durie Decreets*, 2/12/1772. H.M. Register House.

[4] *MacGregor and Others* v. *Breadalbane*, Court of Session Cases, 1846, 9 Dunlop's Reports, 210

beast for cattle, and at Falkirk in 1834 they were 8d a score for cattle and 3d a score for sheep payable to Sir Michael Bruce, the owner of the Tryst ground who let the right of collecting the tolls to a Tacksman at a rent of £120 per annum.[1] In the absence of auctioneers at the Trysts, no commission on the sale price had to be paid, but it was not infrequent for a drover to call in a friend to act, no doubt for a consideration, as a go-between with a prospective buyer, while quite substantial payments in the form of luck-pennies, or at least extensive refreshment on the conclusion of a bargain, were almost the established practice.

Sir Walter Scott speaks of the drovers being paid 'very highly.' The wages of the leading drovers or 'topsmen' may have been considerable and commission on the outcome of a successful drove was not uncommon, but from such information as is available it seems that the ordinary working drover was not highly paid, though the much greater value of money in the droving period must be kept in mind. Early in the eighteenth century the pay of a working drover appears to have amounted to only 1s a day,[2] but gradually this increased, reaching 3s or 4s a day in the first half of the nineteenth century. Even this latter rate left little margin for any but the barest living for men who had to pay for their own food on the outward journey and return entirely at their own charges. Beyond these items, a cattle dealer who sent beasts to the markets of the South might be involved in a variety of miscellaneous costs, and the agricultural writer of 1813 already quoted, complaining of losses sustained by the drovers of Galloway, puts part of the blame on high costs incurred to bankers, lawyers, messengers and innkeepers.[3]

The total expense of a drove from the North has been variously estimated, but the cost of bringing a drove from Caithness to Carlisle, a journey of about twenty-eight days, was reckoned in the early nineteenth century at 7s 6d a head.[4] Such droving as took place in winter or early spring when the cattle required to be fed on hay was much more costly. Contemporary estimates put the cost at 10s to 15s more per head than the summer and autumn droving costs. In England costs were higher, and Youatt writing in 1834 puts the expense of the three weeks' journey from Falkirk to Norfolk at £1 to £1 4s a head. Sir Alexander Maxwell

[1] Youatt, *Cattle, their breeds, management and diseases.* Library of Useful Knowledge, 1834, 121. [2] Macky, *Journey through Scotland,* 1723, 190
[3] Smith. op. cit., 253. [4] Youatt, op. cit., 90

of Monreith in Wigtownshire carried on a large droving trade
with England in the first quarter of the eighteenth century, and
his cash book records the varying success of his transactions.[1]
In 1711 he pays the modest sum of fifty guineas to Pat Maxwell
as droving expenses of beasts which ultimately sold for £2,372
sterling. In 1728, however, Sir Alexander incurred a big loss on
a drove to England. The drove that year consisted of 746 beasts
entered in his accounts as costing just over £2,677. The amount
realised by the sale of the beasts as shown by the bill of sale of
William Dunn the drover, was £2,711 4s 6d ' whereof to reduce
of charges he gives in ain account £250 9s 11d which is a most
extravagant account there being 18 of them died by the way
going to the mercat of murrain which was a ly invented by him
for they were killed by over-driving and all the fat heavy nolt
died being driven till 10 at night and got neither water nor grasse,
he constantlie drunk and never came near them and under-
charged the prices he got. Soe there remains only to bear charges
702 which makes them above 7 shillings 3 half-pence per beast
which must be grosse mismanadgment or dishonestie which is the
same as to my losse. Losse on drove £172 2s 2d sterling which
is £2,065 6/- Scots or 3,098 merks. . . .' Arthur Young, writing
about 1818, quotes the same figure of 7s 1½d per head as the
expense of taking cattle 112 miles from Norfolk to Smithfield.
For a journey of 450 miles from Dumfries to the South he puts
the cost of droving fat cattle travelling fifteen miles a day at 18s
to 24s per head for the journey. The figure is quoted from
Wight's *Husbandry* and corresponds fairly closely with the 1834
estimate, though the time taken for the journey is longer.[2] The
popular belief in the eighteenth century that bleeding was a cure
for most ills was applied to animals as well as to human beings,
and one of the items noted in Sir Alexander Maxwell's account
book as part of the expense of sending a drove to England is the
cost of having the animals bled in preparation for the journey.[3]

In addition to the cash outlay in which the journey involved
him, a drover of cattle from the Highlands had to reckon with
the loss in condition which his beasts might suffer. It seems
probable that this increased as the drove moved south into

---

[1] Maxwell, *Memories of the Months*, 5th series, 278
[2] Arthur Young, Unpublished Manuscript, *The Elements and Practice of Agriculture*,
XXVIII, 355 et seq. British Museum
[3] Maxwell, op. cit.

country where facilities for wayside grazing or nightly resting-places were fewer, and where their increasing cost might tempt the drover to longer marches. The writer of an agricultural survey of Galloway in 1794 has estimated that the loss incurred through deterioration in condition, fatigue, accident or disease on the journey from Galloway to Norfolk cost the drover as much as £1 2s a head,[1] while the Statistical Account of the Parish of Sorbie puts the loss in condition suffered by a beast on the same journey at one-eighth of its original weight [2] ; but in the Highlands where the drove was moving through hill country and grazing was plentiful the loss would be much less. Some drovers even reckoned on an improvement in the condition of their beasts on the journey, and it is told of an Aberdeenshire farmer of last century that having a drove of sheep for which he had no grazing he sent them and their shepherd to travel the drove roads of the district, from which they returned a month later, the beasts in improved condition for the Tryst.

If the end of the seventeenth century brought to the drover relief from some of the political uncertainties which had harassed him, the political sky was still filled with the clouds of gathering storms. For good or ill these were to affect him no less than storms in the Minch or mists on Rannoch. The eighteenth century was hardly well begun before the first of these political storms arose. The volume of south-bound cattle traffic crossing the Borders had, as has been seen, despite all its difficulties grown by the end of the seventeenth century to large proportions. This traffic, with linen and coal, made up the bulk of Scotland's exports, and three-quarters of the total was trade to England, the Navigation Act of 1660 and Britain's foreign policy having cut Scotland off from much of her Continental trade. Scotland's growing dependence on the English markets, and the conviction among men of foresight in both countries that the welfare of each urgently demanded their complete union, had done little to offset the dislike and suspicion with which, in Scotland particularly, the idea was regarded. It was in these circumstances that the English Parliament in 1704 decided to use the threat of exclusion from England of trade in three of Scotland's most important products as a lever with which to force her to accept the Act of Union. By an Act of that year, it was provided that if before Christmas Day 1705 the Scots Parliament had not settled the

[1] Webster, op. cit., 29   [2] O.S.A., Sorbie, I, 248

succession to the Crown of Scotland in like manner to the succession to the Crown of England, all ' great cattle and sheep ' exported from Scotland to England should be forfeited.[1] The measure, which had threatened to prove quite as harmful to England as to Scotland, did not come into operation and was repealed before Christmas 1705. Its threat, however, had been disastrous to drovers and cattle dealers alike. The price of cattle at the West Port of Edinburgh fell in 1705 to £8 Scots, a fall of $33\frac{1}{3}$ per cent which brought great loss to McLaren of Bridge of Turk, a notable drover of the time [2]; but one at least profited by it, for Peter Heron, a far-sighted drover of Galloway, having learned of the impending removal of the restriction, bought large numbers of cattle at Crieff Tryst at the price of £4 Scots to which they had fallen, subsequently selling them in England when the restriction had been removed for £4 sterling —a profit of 1100 per cent.[3]

The impetus given to the Scots cattle trade by the passing of the Act of Union of 1707 and the events at home and abroad in the years which immediately followed was considerable, and from then onwards a gradual increase in the trade took place ; but politics were still to be a source of worry to the drovers, and the effect of the Rising of 1715 is shown in a Petition presented to the Bailies of Dumfries for compensation for the loss of customs dues suffered by the closing of the cattle markets. ' Unto the Honble, the Provest, Baillies and Counsell of Dumfries . . . that where it being evident to all and alsoe verrie weill known to your Honors that since the beginning of August last at which tyme was read the first news of the Pretender's intended invasione, all people were soe surprysed therewith that the fears of intestine troubles did not onlie during the space of those two months of August and September put such a stope to Trades and business that all Publick Mercats did verrie much faill, but lykewise, and more particularly in the beginning of October, the news of the Rebells rising in the North and the threatening of the Rebells in our own country parts to attack our Towne of Dumfries did soe arouse and alarm both Town and Countrie that all Mercats were shut and Traid laid asyde, that during the month of October

[1] Hume Brown, *The Legislative Union of Scotland and England*, 19 and 80. *Statutes at Large*, 4 Anne cap. 3 section 4.
[2] Ramsay, *Scotland and Scotsmen in the 18th Century*, II, 222, note
[3] Walker, *Economical History of the Hebrides and Highlands*, 1808, II, 308n

and first ten days of November, in which your petitioner was wont to collect a great deal of custom, it being the principal tyme of my Cattle Markets, no markets were or could be held by reason of the whole country being obliged to be in arms and the whole passages and entries to the town being shut up.' [1]

The Rising of 1745 seems to have had less immediate effect on the trade than might have been expected. The safe conduct granted to the Glenorchy drover in 1746 shows that even then cattle were being brought south from Kintail, and despite the Rising, Crieff Tryst was in active operation. In that same year a drover from Ross-shire took cattle to Craven in Yorkshire,[2] while a Dumfriesshire drover had nearly 1,500 beasts for sale in East Anglia. Both speculations proved unprofitable however, for in Yorkshire shortage of hay had lowered the price to 35s a head, while the drove in East Anglia fell victim to the widespread cattle disease which, combined with the shortage of beasts in the Highlands after the Rising, led to an increase in the price in the years immediately following.[3]

From 1727 till 1815 the droving trade to England benefited by the almost continuous series of wars in which Great Britain was involved, and with some minor fluctuations the price of cattle showed a gradual increase. In this the demand for salted beef for the navy played a considerable part.[4] The salting of cattle was throughout almost the whole of the droving period an English industry, for only fat cattle were suitable for salting and only England could fatten them. The agriculture of those parts of Scotland capable of fattening stock was till the early years of the nineteenth century largely an agriculture of crop cultivation, and not till then did new farming methods, based on the growing of artificial grasses and turnips, turn the attention of Scottish farmers towards stock fattening. Until that time came, the cattle of the Hebrides, the Highlands and the South Western Counties driven to market lean or at best half fattened, must seek richer grazings for the increased growth and condition which the salters demanded. Only in the South could these be found, and so from the Trysts at Crieff, Falkirk and Dumfries the Scots drovers travelled on across the Border to the grass lands of Northumberland

---

[1] Quoted by Corrie, *The Droving Days in the South-West District of Scotland*, 7–8
[2] MacGill, *Old Ross-shire and Scotland*, I, 177
[3] Letters of Thomas Bell, Dumfries (contained in Reid's *Calendar of Documents found at Dumfries*, H.M. Register House)
[4] See Appendix A (p. 225)

and the limestone dales of Yorkshire, to the pastures of North-amptonshire, Buckinghamshire and Hertfordshire, or the marshes of East Anglia. Thus the drovers profited first by the wars with Spain, Austria and France, then by the American War and most of all by the Napoleonic Wars when prices rose to high levels, reaching in the last years of the struggle a peak from which for a time they quickly fell. As the church bells of Perth rang out in 1815 to greet the peace, George Williamson, a great Aberdeenshire breeder and dealer, passing south with a big drove, heard them with dismay, ' It was a sorrowful peace for me,' he said, ' for it cost me £4,000.' [1]

The variations in the method and condition of sale and the complexity of factors which from time to time affected the cattle trade, make it impossible to do more than indicate over a period the trend of cattle prices in Scotland. When the Records of the Lords of Council and the Register of the Privy Council first start to place a value on the cattle stolen in the sixteenth and seventeenth centuries the figure appears to have been about £20 Scots (or £1 13s 4d sterling), and in 1627 the Justices of the Peace for Kincardineshire complaining of the abnormally high prices then in force quoted figures of 50 merks (£2 15s 7d sterling) for oxen and 40 merks (£2 5s 8d sterling) for cows.[2] About the time of the Union of 1707 the average price of cows in Scotland appears to have been 20s to 27s sterling,[3] and Pennant mentions that the price of cattle in Colonsay in 1736 was even then only 25s.[4] In a case before the Court of Session in 1737 reference is made to a purchase by a Yorkshire drover in Colonsay and Jura of 300 cattle at a total price of £505 sterling.[5]

By the middle of the eighteenth century an appreciable increase had taken place. In 1763 a Yorkshire drover bought Skye cattle for 2 guineas delivered at Falkirk, though 10 years later the Barra beasts only fetched £1 7s 6d.[6] Pennant in 1772 gives the price for the cattle of Skye, Islay and Colonsay as being £2 to £3 each, but those of Mull 30s to 50s,[7] and in 1786 the average price of beasts crossing from Skye was £2 to £3.[8] With the Statistical Account and the Agricultural Surveys of the end

[1] McCombie, *Cattle and Cattle Breeders*, 57   [2] *R.P.C.*, 2nd series, II, 554
[3] Ramsay, op. cit., II, 222 et seq.
[4] Pennant, *Tour in Scotland*, 1772 (1790 edn.), Part I, 274
[5] *Old Session Papers*, Signet Library, F. 24.30. 1737
[6] *Farmer's Magazine*, 1804, 393   [7] Pennant, op. cit., Part I, 263, 357, etc.
[8] Knox, *Tour through the Highlands of Scotland and the Hebride Isles in 1786*

of the eighteenth century, a host of statistics of cattle prices became available ; £2 to £3 in Wick and Caithness[1] ; £2 10s in Uist[2] ; £3 3s about Lochalsh[3] and £3 15s in Islay and Aberdeenshire,[4] while the average price of beasts sold at Falkirk Tryst in 1794 was £4.[5] The lower droving costs to England from the south-west of Scotland are no doubt reflected in the prices given for cattle from Dumfriesshire and Galloway which in 1794 varied from £2 10s to 8 guineas.[6] During the next twenty years the course of Scots cattle prices was directly affected by the French Wars. Evidence given in 1826 before the Parliamentary Committee which inquired into conditions prevailing in the cattle trade during the war period, showed average prices rising to as much as £18 a head, and William McCombie, the Aberdeenshire breeder, quoting from records of his father's transactions during the wars mentions sales of Aberdeenshire cattle at £22, £23 10s and even £25 per head.[7]

A farmer of today may pertinently ask the ages at which these beasts were sold. To this question no certain answer can be given, for circumstances and practice appear to have varied at different times and in different parts of the country ; but many of the beasts were old cows and working animals past their useful life, while of the younger cattle it is probable that at least till near the end of the eighteenth century in view of the slow growth of beasts to whom each winter meant starvation, few were sold before three years and most at four years or older. Arthur Young, in his *Elements and Practice of Agriculture*, quotes from Marshall's *Norfolk* (Vol. I, p. 326). 'A Scot does not fat kindly even at three years old much less at two at which age many hundred head of cattle are annually fatted in Norfolk,' but in another passage Marshall speaks of four years as being the most common age of cattle sold in the South from Skye and the

---

[1] *O.S.A.*, Wick, X, 22   [2] *O.S.A.*, North and South Uist, XIII, 294, 306
[3] *O.S.A.*, Lochalsh, XI, 424
[4] *O.S.A.*, Kilchoman, XI, 278 and King Edward, XI, 405
[5] *O.S.A.*, Falkirk, XIX, 83

[6] Giving evidence in 1826 before the Select Committee already quoted the manager of the Renfrewshire Banking Company referred to the prices for Highland cattle being £2, £3 or £4 a head. His evidence showed that the proportion of £5 notes to smaller notes sent by the Banks to their Highland branches largely for the financing of the cattle dealing industry was one £5 note for every £100 in smaller notes. (*Report of Select Committee on Promissory Notes in Scotland and Ireland, 1826.* Notes of Evidence)

[6] *O.S.A.*, Sorbie, I, 248

[7] *Select Committee on Promissory Notes in Scotland and Ireland 1826.* McCombie, op. cit. 101.

Highlands, some being older than this and some being old working cattle. An Agricultural Survey of Aberdeenshire in 1811 gives a table showing a calculation of the age of various classes of cattle sold from the county about the year 1770. This shows that few beasts were sold under twelve years old and many older. Most of the animals had been used in the plough for from one to four years before being put to grass.[1]

While the high purchasing power of money must be remembered in considering the relatively small prices quoted in the records of the Scots cattle trade, at least up to the end of the eighteenth century, the size of the beasts of these days must also be borne in mind. In his Analysis of the Statistical Account written about 1825 Sir John Sinclair quotes Bakewell the great English breeder as having said that he wished he had laid the foundations of his breed of cattle with Kyloes or West Highland cattle as being perfect in all but size [2] ; and all the evidence goes to show that the animals driven from the Highlands to England throughout the eighteenth century were indeed small.[3] An early commentary on the weight of cattle is contained in an eighteenth-century contract for the supply of meat for the Navy, in which it was stipulated that the carcasses should weigh not less than 5 cwt., and it should be noted that this referred to animals already fattened for killing. Even as late as 1816 a contract for meat for ships in the Downs stipulated only for a weight of 4 cwt., while a provision in a contract of 1823 requiring a weight of 6–7 cwt. is noted as unusual. Culley in 1786 says that the weight of West Highland cattle in general is from 20 to 35 stone, and an Agricultural Survey of Dumbartonshire made about 1794 refers to the cattle in the north of the county as weighing only 11–14 st. fat.[4] Sir John Sinclair in his Survey of the Northern Counties in 1795 refers to a Highland bull weighing 250 lb. as compared with a Bakewell bull of 400 lb. The cattle of South-west Scotland appear to have reached higher weights, at least by the end of the eighteenth century. The Statistical Account for Kirkcudbright mentions weights of only 20–30 st., but Webster in 1794 speaks

[1] Keith, *Agricultural Survey of Aberdeenshire*, 1811, 467   [2] See Appendix C (p. 235)
[3] In considering the figures given for the weight of cattle driven from the Highlands in the eighteenth and early nineteenth centuries, it may be assumed for purposes of comparison that today an average Cross-Highland bullock sold off the hills at 3–4 years old for fattening weighs approximately 8 cwt., and that the same animal when fattened for the butcher will weigh approximately 11 cwt.
[4] Ure, *General View of the Agriculture of Dumbarton*, 1794, 58

of Galloway cattle at five years old weighing 40–50 st., and Arthur Young writing about 1818 puts the average weight in the same district as 40–60 st., with some up to 70 st. Contemporary estimates of the weight of cattle must, however, at least till well into the nineteenth century be accepted with caution, for in some cases this was reckoned in Dutch stone of 22 lb. It appears also that in parts of Central Scotland the stone used contained 16 lb. of 22 oz. each, while at Smithfield a stone of 8 lb. appears to have been at one time in use.[1] The average weight of cattle sold at Smithfield is reported as having increased by more than 100 per cent between 1710 and 1775, and the Aberdeenshire cattle breeder Williamson stated in the early years of last century that during his time the average weight of cattle produced in Aberdeenshire had, from better feeding, more than doubled.[2] While the figures available clearly do not make it possible to determine with any certainty the rate of increase over a period in the average weight of Scots cattle, it seems probable that until the early years of the nineteenth century only a small proportion reached a size which, by modern standards, would entitle them to be described as more than ' stirks.'

If these figures seem in some respects to detract from the achievements of the drovers, they do indeed go some way to explain how the eighteenth-century drover solved problems of driving and transport which, with beasts of modern size and weight, would defy solution. They go far to explain, too, the revolution in the cattle trade which took place during the first half of the nineteenth century when new and better methods of farming were so greatly increasing the size and quality of livestock, a revolution which was to prove fatal to the droving industry.

Despite the credit so readily given by banks and financial houses, and the light-hearted enthusiasm with which they entered into commitments sometimes involving tens of thousands of pounds, the cattle dealers of the eighteenth century often found it necessary to ' engage a co-adventurer in an intended speculation.'[3] The names of Highland chieftains and Lowland lairds

---

[1] Robertson, *Rural Recollections*, 1829, 120

[2] Alexander, *Northern Rural Life in the 18th Century*. Youatt, writing in 1834, stated that after careful inquiry he had arrived at the conclusion that the average weight of a fat bullock sold at Smithfield at that time was approximately 6 cwt. (Youatt, op. cit.)

[3] *Old Session Papers*, Signet Library, 413.8. 1800

appear little less frequently than those of graziers, cattle dealers, merchants and business-men of the cities in the story of this hazardous trade. Many of these partnerships were of the loosest and most casual nature. Accurate book-keeping was unknown, and records of transactions between drover and drover, or between partners, were kept, if kept at all, in the form of scribbled notes, intelligible at the time to none but the parties themselves, their meaning and content soon to be inextricably mixed in a maze of complex dealing. Failure to keep clear and accurate accounts was not, however, confined to the drovers of the eighteenth century. One of the leading Aberdeenshire dealers, writing in 1867, described how in the early part of the century he had at one time taken for a short time a co-partner. 'As co-partners,' he writes, ' we were not very regular book-keepers and our accounts got confused. At the wind up at Hallow fair (Edinburgh) as we had accounts of the Falkirk Trysts likewise to settle, we worked at them for days and the longer we worked the more confused they became. To this day I do not know in whose favour the balance was.' [1] In such conditions it was inevitable that disputes and quarrels should arise, and that finally the aid of the courts should be sought to unravel or, in the last resort, to cut knots in the tangled skein. That the process was slow and involved is amply shown by the records of cases decided by the Court of Session during the eighteenth century. Dishonoured bills, bankruptcies—real and assumed—liability of partners, claims by sellers and purchasers, banks and landlords, all found their way to the courts.[2] These were no easy cases. Agents and counsel too often waited in vain for instructions of clients or evidence of witnesses scattered from May to October over the length and breadth of Scotland, though as contemporary law reports show this did not always prevent the premature argument of a case in court by puzzled and ill-briefed counsel before a bewildered Bench. The drovers, for their part, ' precluded from personal interview with their Law Agents by frequent absences from home, are unable to comprehend the numerous windings and intricacies of a complicated and long protracted process.' Men who could thread their way through mountain passes and

---

[1] McCombie, op. cit., 6
[2] An English Act of Parliament passed in the reign of Queen Anne made it unlawful for drovers to evade their obligations by becoming bankrupt (1706, 6 Anne Cap. 22, sec. 8, *Statutes of the Realm*, Vol. 8, 602).

over the hill tracks of the remotest Highlands were lost among the Petitions, Answers and Objections, the Replies, Duplies and Triplies of an eighteenth-century lawsuit. Little wonder if, faced at last with the hurry and bustle of the courts in the Parliament Hall of Edinburgh, they longed for the quiet hills and the fresh uplands, for the friendly presence of their placid and slow-moving cattle.

An excellent example of the complexity of droving finance and of the litigation to which it so often gave rise occurs in a case which came before the Court of Session in 1741. The case concerns the dealings of two drovers, one from Argyllshire and the other from Dumbartonshire, who had become insolvent. With a view to recovering sums owed by them, a creditor was induced in partnership with an Argyllshire laird to lend them money to enable them to purchase a drove of 300 cattle from McNeill of Colonsay. The transaction was coupled with the most elaborate precautions to ensure the repayment of the loan from the proceeds of the cattle when sold, precautions which, as the outcome was to prove, were most fully justified. The drovers having obtained possession of the cattle, the subsequent story of their dealings soon became obscured in a fog of bills and sub-sales in which drink played no small part, an obscurity deepened by the fact that the drove became mingled with another, and that while some beasts were sold at Crieff, some were taken to Falkirk and the rest to Carlisle. The case, which did not reach the courts until three years after the events with which it was concerned, dragged on before them for at least six years, and reading today the closely printed pages which contain the pleadings of the parties, even a lawyer must feel the liveliest sympathy for the law agents who marshalled the facts, the counsel who argued the case and Lord Elchies who tried it. It was little wonder that at the end of the third year of litigation he ' made great avizandum ' [deferred judgment for further consideration] and ' circumduced the Term quoad ultra ' [declared the term for bringing further evidence to have elapsed]. It is hardly surprising to read that when nearly eighteen months later, by which time one of the parties had died, the decision of the Court was given, the unsuccessful party appealed against it. The case dragged on till March 1749, when, more than ten years after the events which gave rise to it, it was finally disposed of by a decision of the House of Lords.[1]

[1] *Arbuthnot* v. *Macfarlane*. *Old Session Papers*, Signet Library. F. 24:30. 1749.

Were an assessment of the work and character of the drovers of Scotland and of the part played by them in the commercial life of the country to be based solely on the material available in the Register of the Privy Council, the records of the Court of Session or the evidence of those who wrote of agricultural conditions at the close of the eighteenth century, the judgment must indeed go hard with the drovers ; but to base judgment on this evidence alone would be to ignore a great part of the picture. Privy Council and Law Courts saw little but the sombre side of the drover's trade, for to them fell the task of unravelling threads tangled through ignorance, misfortune or dishonesty. The parish ministers, from whom was gathered a great part of the material in the Statistical Accounts, were mainly concerned with the welfare of their parishes, and misfortunes which aggravated the hard lot of their people bulked large in their eyes. To those who wrote of Scottish agriculture in the first years of the nineteenth century, the hardships and grievances of the farmers also took first place. When Sir Walter Scott wrote in the introduction to *The Two Drovers*—' An oyster may be crossed in love . . . and a drover may be touched on a point of honour,' he was no doubt reflecting the contemporary view of the standard of a drover's honesty, and few there were to champion the drover's cause or to tell of the honest endeavour of those who successfully faced the difficulties, the risks and the hardships of the droving trade. Yet when it is considered that a system of commercial dealing calling for skill, courage and honesty of the highest order continued in Scotland through nearly three centuries marked by so much of social change and political disturbance, it is impossible not to recognise the merits and qualities of the men whose work it was. Hardship and toil were the common lot of most of Scotland's people in the droving period, and it may well be that the physical hardships faced by those who drove the cattle to the Trysts were no greater than those of the men and women who fought to win a bare existence from the soil in days before knowledge, skill and capital had made the farmer's life tolerable ; but physical hardship was perhaps the least which the drovers had to face. To them fell all the risks of accident, loss and delay on the journey, of fluctuating and uncertain prices governed by social, political and economic factors beyond their knowledge or control. Shortage of ready money but a growing abundance of credit had led to the growth of a system which put on them a heavy burden of responsibility. For many the test was too severe, and it is of those and of the distress and ruin caused by their failure that the records mainly tell ; but many kept faith whether to the men who hired their services to take their beasts to the Tryst, or to the farmers who had parted with their cattle for only the written or the spoken promise of future payment.

In the early records of these dealings few names appear, and with one or two exceptions it is not till the nineteenth century that the fuller records of the Trysts note the recurrence, year after year, of the same names showing a continuous course of honest dealing. A class of professional cattle-dealers was then arising, ' Trusty factors,' as a contemporary writer has called them,[1] whose reputation for honesty and fair dealing came to be widely recognised throughout the country. In Aberdeenshire and Galloway, names such as those of Williamson and McTurk and many another were known and respected, while in the West, Cameron of Corriechoillie in Lochaber, perhaps the greatest of all the drovers, held in the cattle-dealing world a place un-challenged for the scale of his dealings and the degree of his integrity. Cameron of Corriechoillie died in February 1856. In the year of his death he claimed that he had ' stood ' the three yearly trysts at Falkirk and the two yearly ones at Doune for fifty-five years without missing one. Mr Joseph Mitchell, the Road Engineer, has left the following description of Cameron of Corriechoillie : ' One whom I used to know and meet was a remarkable man and deserves to be noticed—Mr Cameron of Corriechoillie in Lochaber. He was the son of a crofter, who died early in very poor circumstances his only stock being a few goats. (Corriechoillie, from early association and long habit, till his death kept a stock of goats.) When quite a lad he was employed by the principal dealers to drive their sheep and cattle to market. He was so poor that his first journeys south were made without shoes, he wearing only a pair of footless stockings. Being very careful, he was soon enabled to buy a few stirks (half grown cattle), which he took to market with his employer's stock. He soon acquired a character for acuteness in the buying and selling of stock as well as being the largest sheep-farmer in the Highlands. At one time he was tenant of 11 farms and the reputed possessor of 60,000 sheep.

' He was a badly dressed little man, about five feet six inches

[1] Logan, *The Scottish Gael*, 1831, II, 65

in height, of thin make, with a sharp hooked nose and lynx eyes. A man of great energy, he frequently rode night and day on a wiry pony from Falkirk to the Muir of Ord, 120 miles, carrying for himself some bread and cheese in his pocket and giving his pony now and then a bottle of porter. As may be supposed, he possessed a wonderful power of organisation. . . . Corrie-choillie was in the height of his influence about 1840, but after that period, what with cautionary obligations, said to amount to £20,000, and heavy losses, he did not die a rich man. . . .'[1]

' Now such dealers are indeed a blessing to a country,' said a writer of the early years of last century, ' while a King of Prussia wilfully breaks his word, while a Monarch of Austria pays even his ally, England, with compromise and instalments, here are three companies of drovers, exposed to all the vicissitudes of a most various trade, yet paying their way for thirty, forty or fifty years without one insolvency.'[2]

The drovers of England appear to have been equally honest. Marshall describing the scene at Smithfield in 1782 when the drovers were settling accounts with the graziers writes : ' The room was full of graziers who had sent up bullocks last week and were come to-day to receive their accounts and money. What a trust ! A man perhaps not worth a hundred pounds brings down twelve or fifteen hundred or perhaps two thousand pounds to be distributed among 20 or 30 persons who have no other security than his honesty for their money ;—nay even the servant of this man is entrusted with the same charge, the master going one week, the man the others ; but so it has been for a Century past and I do not learn that one breach has been committed. The business was conducted with great ease, regularity and dispatch. He had each man's account and a pair of saddle-bags with the money and bills lying upon the table and the farmers in their turns took their seat at his elbow. Having examined the salesman's account, received their money, drank a glass or two of liquor and thrown down sixpence towards the reckoning, they severally returned to the market.'[3]

But honesty and fair dealing in the face of difficulty existed long before the nineteenth century, as is shown by the letters of Thomas Bell, a drover of 1745, addressed to his partner Bryce

[1] Mitchell, *Reminiscences of my Life in the Highlands*, I, 335 et seq.
[2] Cincinnatus Caledonius, *Lights and Shadows of Scottish Character and Scenery*, 2nd series
[3] Marshall, *Rural Economy of Norfolk*, 1785, 2nd edn., II, 267-8

Blair of Annan on whom he had drawn three bills totalling £1,449 for cattle purchased. Bell had taken over 1,000 cattle south to the East Anglian markets, paying for them with the usual three months' bills. There, the cattle disease which raged that autumn throughout England attacked them, and his drove died first in scores and then in hundreds. 'God knows what we shall do,' he writes from Norfolk on 20 December. 'We cannot get money to bear pocket expenses; all manner of sale is over . . . our conditions are such that several drovers have run from their beasts and left them dying in the lanes and highways and nobody to own them.' So bad was the disease that the drovers had been forced to guarantee the beasts for a certain time in the hands of the purchasers, and Bell reports that beasts already sold by him had died within the period of guarantee. Ten days later, the position is worse. 'All is over now. We can neither pay London bills nor nothing else. We have over £1,000 charges to pay in this country and not a shilling to pay it with.' By 7 January 1746 the disaster is complete. 'I am positive we have lost £3,000 by [the distemper] already. I shall be home at Candlemas and people may do with me as they will. They shall get every groat we have and we can do no more.' [1]

---

[1] Letters of Thomas Bell, op. cit., H.M. Register House

In a Note to an Article by Mr R. C. Reid describing this incident which appeared in the *Transactions of the Dumfriesshire and Galloway Natural History and Antiquarian Society* (3rd series, Vol. XXII), Sir Arthur Olver, Principal of the Royal (Dick) Veterinary College writes: 'A serious outbreak of cattle plague (Rinderpest) occurred in Great Britain in 1745 following its extension throughout the greater part of the Continent. The outbreak was so serious that the Privy Council was compelled to take prompt action by control of movement, slaughter and provision for the disposal of carcases. It is of interest that even in those early days compensation was allowed for animals slaughtered—40s for grown beasts and 10s for calves. In all about £135,000 was paid in compensation. The outbreak lasted till 1757 and there is no record of any other major outbreak of cattle plague in this country till 1865. The mortality was exceedingly high, probably running to 90 per cent in badly affected herds. . . . This stamping out policy was effective though cattle plague existed in some parts of this country up to 1770.'

THE DROVE ROAD FROM SKYE AND THE WESTERN ISLES

THE descriptions of Scotland which have come down from early travellers through the country make it clear that Scotland was from very early times a cattle-producing country, the main area of supply being the mass of high ground intersected by mountain valleys lying to the north and west of that line from Dunbartonshire to the Angus glens, which later came to be known as the 'Highland Line.' This was an area little suited to any other type of farming, while the glens and the lower slopes of the hills afforded, at least in summer, ample grazing for cattle. The primitive but intensive type of cultivation practised in those limited areas of lowland country sufficiently drained for any form of agriculture, restricted stock grazing on any considerable scale to the higher ground. The Lowland areas, too, lay open to the ravages of the Civil Wars which scourged Scotland for nearly three hundred years from the end of the thirteenth century, while that part of the country lying south of the Forth and including the rich areas of East Lothian and Berwickshire were in addition at the mercy of invasion from England or raids from the unsettled districts immediately north and south of the Cheviots. For these reasons it was inevitable that the Highlands should, till more peaceful times came, be the main area of supply of cattle needed to meet the modest home demand for meat, the needs of the tanning industry for hides, or the small export demands from England and the Continent.

While these circumstances may explain why the Highlands as a whole produced Scotland's cattle in early days, it is not so clear why one of the most important supplies of cattle came originally from the remote areas of western and north-western Scotland, and particularly from the Island of Skye. The reason may lie partly in their very remoteness which, while ensuring that those areas remained for centuries the 'peccant' parts of the country so often complained of, meant that they were victims mainly of their own local troubles and were to some extent insulated by their geographical position from the troubles of their neighbours and of the country as a whole. In this, Skye and the Western Isles were peculiarly favoured, the Minch and the narrow strait between Skye and the mainland doing for them the service which for centuries the English Channel has rendered to Great Britain. The nearness of the sea gave them a freedom from frost and snow which the mainland did not enjoy, with better and earlier grass. Skye possessed much low moorland and many small glens running in from the sea, well suited for cattle to supplement the small patches of arable land, while in the Hebrides was some upland grazing and much low ' machair ' land, too sandy and windswept for crops, but land where close-growing grass afforded grazing for cattle in numbers which, even by modern standards, appear to have been surprisingly large. These Western Isles had little to export, and so soon as the country passed from the most primitive stage, the need arose to send their cattle to the mainland in return for such simple products as were available, to provide money for the payment of such part of the small rents as was not paid in services, and for the landowners to pay the taxes which were levied on, and with difficulty extracted from, them. Whatever the reasons, and those suggested surely played their part, the fact is clearly established by such records as exist that behind their barriers of sea and hills, Skye, Kintail and the Western Isles from early times bred and exported in growing numbers cattle of a type peculiar to those districts and for long widely recognised as being superior to those of the rest of Scotland. ' It is in the northern and western Highlands and all the Islands and particularly the Isle of Skye and that tract of country near Kintail,' wrote George Culley in the last quarter of the eighteenth century, ' that you meet with the native breed of kyloes ; a hardy, industrious and excellent breed of cattle, calculated in every respect to thrive in a cold, exposed, mountainous country.' [1]

How early this island traffic in cattle began it is not possible with any certainty to determine, but it is known that as early as 1502 the district of Troutterness (Trotternish) in Skye was already exporting ' marts '—the surplus beasts sold off in the autumn—to the Lowlands.[2] The records of the Privy Council

---

[1] Culley, *Observations on Live Stock*, 1807, 70
[2] *Exchequer Rolls*, XII, 56

It is probable that these formed part of the produce rent paid by the tacksmen to the chieftain in addition to the money rent and other dues. In the first half of the sixteenth century ' marts ' handed over in part payment to the Crown of dues on tacksmen's holdings in Kintyre were driven each year to Stirling Castle, but in Morven in 1541 the ' marts ' and other produce payments were apparently resold to the tenants. (McKerral, ' The Tacksman and his Holding in the South-West Highlands.' *Scottish Historical Review*, Vol. XXVI, 10–25)

for the last years of the sixteenth century contain repeated references to thefts by men of Badenoch of cattle sent by Mackenzie
from Kintail to ' Elycht (Alyth) in the Bray of Angus ' and other
markets in the east of Scotland,[1] and the number of stock already
being reared in the north may be judged by a complaint of
Alexander Bane of Tulloch in 1594 that the Laird of Raasay had
stolen 2,400 cattle from his land.[2] One of the first to engage in
the cattle trade between Uist, Skye and the mainland is believed
to have been Donald MacDonald Third of Castle Camus, Skye,
who at the end of the sixteenth and the beginning of the seventeenth centuries established a regular trade in ponies and cattle.
About 1601 he is reported to have defeated an attempt by the
MacLeods of Dunvegan and Harris to round up and ship to
Skye the cattle of North Uist.[3]

By the end of the seventeenth century, a regular trade in
cattle had grown up between Skye and the north-west districts
on the one hand and the markets of east and central Scotland
on the other. ' The Highlanders,' wrote Thomas Morer in 1689,
' are not without considerable quantities of corn, yet have not
enough to satisfy their numbers, and therefore yearly come down
with their cattle of which they have greater plenty and so traffick
with the Lowlanders for such proportion of oats and barley as
their families or necessities call for.' [4] One of the best of
the contemporary descriptions of the early drovers is contained
in Bishop Forbes' account, already quoted, of a meeting in
Drumochter Pass in 1723 with droves from Flodigarry in Skye
belonging to Macdonald of Kingsburgh on their way to Crieff
Tryst.[5] Five years later, during the short period when the
Bank of Scotland ceased payment, the Royal Bank of Scotland
cashed notes of the old Bank for a drover on his way to Skye to
buy cattle,[6] and by the middle of the eighteenth century English
cattle dealers from Yorkshire were already visiting Skye for the
same purpose. Despite the risks of the overland journey, the cattle
trade from Skye continued all through the seventeenth and
eighteenth centuries as droving traffic which only finally came to
an end in the latter part of the nineteenth century.

During the droving period Skye sent to the mainland not

[1] R.P.C., 1st series, VI, 184, 459   [2] R.P.C., 1st series, V, 204
[3] Angus and Archibald MacDonald, Clan Donald, III, 42–5
[4] Hume Brown, Early Travellers, 268   [5] Bishop Forbes' Journal, 235–7
[6] Munro, History of the Royal Bank of Scotland 1727–1927, 58–9

Plate 3   Loading Cattle at Kyleakin

(From an early print)

only cattle bred on the island but beasts from other parts of the Hebrides. Skye was a gathering point for cattle from North and South Uist, and in the last years of the eighteenth century the number of beasts sold annually from these islands were 300 and 450 respectively.[1] Barra sent cattle to Skye, though sometimes also to Ardnamurchan, at a transport cost of 2s 6d per head,[2] as being the nearest point on the 'continent,' and to the Ross of Mull.[3] Some Harris cattle were also landed in Skye, some being shipped direct and some going to Lochmaddy in North Uist for trans-shipment to Skye. The Statistical Account estimates the total number sold annually from Harris at only about 200. These, with kelp, are reported as being almost the only source of money to pay rents, the beasts being ferried to Skye in July.[4] Drovers from Skye sometimes went in search of beasts to the islands of Soay and Canna, but it seems that the cattle of Rum and Eigg and part of Sleat were generally shipped to the mainland near Mallaig or Arisaig, bound for Fort William and the South.

This island cattle trade was a risky and troublesome business, and the services owed by the smaller tenants to the chieftains or tacksmen in the eighteenth century often included the ferrying of cattle from island to island.[5] Between the islands of South and North Uist lies the low island of Benbecula, separated from South Uist by the South Ford and from North Uist by the North Ford. These shallow arms of the sea were till recently negotiable only at low tide, but while the South Ford could then be crossed almost dry-shod and has lately been bridged, the North Ford, which is four miles across, is intersected by deep channels which even at low tide are never dry. The main gathering-points for the cattle of the Outer Hebrides appear to have been at Ormiclate in South Uist, at Griminish in Benbecula and at Lochmaddy in North Uist, the markets taking place twice a year in late July and early September, dates which suited the Skye markets and the larger trysts at Crieff and Falkirk. When a drover attending the Ormiclate market had bought all the cattle he wanted, the beasts were rounded up and sent off on the eighteen-mile journey to the

---

[1] *O.S.A.*, North and South Uist, XIII, 294, 306
[2] According to information supplied by Mr Angus McLeod, Achgarve, Ross-shire, who started droving cattle from the Islands about 1868, the charge for bringing cattle by sailing boat from Stornoway to Lochewe at that time was 2s 6d a head.
[3] *O.S.A.*, Barra, XIII, 331   [4] *O.S.A.*, Harris, X, 356–7
[5] Buchanan, *Travels in the Western Hebrides, 1782–1790*, 53

South Ford where they crossed at low tide to Griminish. Here the same procedure was followed, the beasts from Ormiclate and the new purchases being driven across Benbecula and so over the North Ford to North Uist and Lochmaddy. The way across the North Ford is treacherous, with quicksands ready to trap men or beasts straying from the winding track. Any delay or miscalculation might mean that the inflowing tide would catch a drove in the crossing, when men and cattle would have to swim for their lives. The crossing was thus a hazardous adventure, the recollection of which lives vivid in the memories of those still (1948) alive who shared in it during the last days of the droving industry.

Lochmaddy was the main point of shipment for Skye, but Lochboisdale and Loch Skipport in South Uist and Loch Eport in North Uist were also used. In the Bay of Lochmaddy smacks from the other islands of the Hebrides had been collecting for several days before the market. It may be that the sea transport had in some cases been arranged in advance, particularly in the case of the larger drovers who were regular buyers of the Island cattle, but it seems that in many cases the owners of the boats came at their own risk, knowing the dates of the Island markets and anticipating demand for their services. These boats varied in size from ten to fifty tons, and came from Barra, Harris and Berneray, perhaps bringing additional cattle to join the Uist beasts, while some came from as far as Coll and Tiree, for as the records of the Statistical Accounts show, in the eighteenth and early nineteenth centuries few parishes in the Islands were without their boat builders. These sailing boats were strongly built for this rough trade and for the transport at other times of slates from Easdale and Ballachulish, lime from Lismore or kelp from the Outer Isles. Some were open from end to end except for a small covered portion in the stern. Others were decked or half-decked with an open hatch-way for loading. A few were boats of forty to fifty tons, schooner rigged, and in some of these larger boats were fitted barriers at intervals to prevent the cattle falling in the rough seas of the Minch, for a fallen beast in a crowded boat seldom got up. The larger boats held up to fifty cattle and the tighter packed they were the better, for so there was less chance of beasts falling, while the drovers' profit was the greater. The method of loading was rough and ready. The boats were brought to a pier or to a convenient rock—in Gaelic a ' laimhrig '—and the cattle were driven aboard. To lessen the strain on the timbers of the boats, the stones with which they were ballasted were covered with birch branches, heather or bracken—in Gaelic a ' farradh '—which served the double purpose of protecting the timbers and affording the cattle a foothold during the voyage. According to information received from Tiree, osier twigs were also sometimes used as a covering for the floor-boards of the boats. It is suggested that this type of floor-covering served a further purpose, in acting as a filter to the dung of the beasts and so preventing it from clogging the pumps in the larger boats. The New Statistical Account of South Uist records that there were at that time (1842) four small decked vessels in the parish, chiefly employed in ferrying cattle to Skye and the mainland and in taking kelp to Liverpool and Glasgow.[1] The chief harbours then in use were Lochboisdale, Loch Eynort and Loch Skipport. The number of the crew seems to have been usually three or four. A wherry wrecked on Hyskier in 1808 while bringing cattle across from North Uist contained four men. The number of cattle on board is not stated, but all were drowned except one, on the blood of which the sole survivor of the crew kept himself alive till he was rescued.[2]

The landings in Skye were made chiefly on the shores of Loch Dunvegan, but some cattle, particularly those from Harris, were landed in Uig Bay at the north end of the island and some at Loch Pooltiel in Duirinish. When the Commissioners for Highland Roads and Bridges were considering the making of new roads in Skye in 1806, a Petition presented to them by the local people asked for a road from Dunvegan to Snizort, as ' being also the line by which the cattle from the Long Island are driven to the market at Portree.' [3] The method of landing was as rough as had been the shipment. Piers were scarce and primitive, and landing dues played little part in a drover's budget. Most of the cattle were forced overboard into the water. A rough block and tackle rigged on a yard from the mast was sometimes used to hoist them out of the larger boats, and this method was also occasionally employed for loading the cattle on to the boats, the beasts being slung aboard by means of slings attached to their horns. The practice of making the beasts swim ashore had a double merit, for it washed the cattle after what was often a rough journey,

---

[1] *N.S.A.*, South Uist, XIV, 194   [2] *Inverness Courier*, 1808
[3] *H.R & B.*, 3rd Report 1807, Appendix F
Writing in 1695, Martin mentions two Cattle Fairs held annually at Portree in mid-June and early September. (Martin, *Description of the Western Islands*, ed. D. J. McLeod, 244–5)

while the salt water would be good for any gored by their neighbours in the crossing of the Minch. Some drovers carried with them Archangel tar which was useful for the rough doctoring of injured animals and also served to mark beasts bought at local markets. Various other methods were adopted by the drovers to mark their animals. Some beasts were marked on the horn, some by clipping part of the hair and some were branded. When a beast changed hands at the trysts, the new owner's mark was put on top of the old or substituted for it. This sometimes led to trouble when, as often happened, a beast strayed from one drove into another, and disputes arising between drovers from this cause found their way to the Court of Session in the eighteenth century.[1]

From Portree the cattle were driven on south, some by the route of the present road which climbs through Glenvaragill and over the moor to Sligachan, but the majority by the coast following the shores of the Sound of Raasay to Loch Sligachan and along the north side of that Loch to its head. Here at Sligachan they were joined by cattle from the grazing lands on the shores of Loch Bracadale and the glens which lie immediately to the north of the Cuillins. Midway between Sligachan and Broadford, the next important stage on the journey, the road to the South passes round the head of Loch Ainort, and here the cattle rested. It may be that the spot was chosen as a convenient half-way house between Sligachan and Broadford, but more probably because of the rich grass of the saltings at the head of the Loch. Whatever the reason, the drovers of two hundred years ago chose for their halting-place one of the most beautiful spots in the whole island. Here, sheltered from the west by the slopes of Marsco and Bheinn Dearg and from the east by the island of Scalpay, the waters of Loch Ainort mirror hills which look down on the cup of the glen into which the short River Ainort falls from the corries above. On a still September day the view of the calm loch, reflecting surrounding hills still hung with the shreds of early mist, may have gone some way to reconcile to his hard life a drover resting beside his cattle or emerging from the little change house on the north shore of the Loch, the ruins of which are to be seen today.

At Broadford, cattle from parts of Sleat and the grazings on the shores of Loch Eishort joined those from the North for the

---

[1] *Old Session Papers*, Signet Library, 134:36. 1766

market which was held where today the road from Armadale joins the main road to Kyleakin, a mile to the east of the scattered houses of the village. Here, too, would come cattle from the meadow ground at Torrin on Loch Slapin and the corries at the back of Blaven. From Broadford the drovers skirted the sandy inlets and rocky promontories of Broadford Bay. Then climbing southward through Glen Arroch they got from the watershed their last wide view back to the Bay and the Skye hills and forward to the hills of Glenelg across the Sound of Sleat.

Kyle Rhea, the narrowest point between Skye and the mainland, appears from earliest times to have been the principal crossing-place from the island. It was, no doubt, for this reason that Glenelg was chosen as a site for the barracks built at Bernera after the troubles of 1715. Telford in a report to the Commissioners for Highland Roads and Bridges in 1811 considered that Kyle Rhea would ' always remain the usual ferry for the Black Cattle of Skye,' [1] and it continued to be the main crossing-place till the construction of the railway to Strome Ferry and subsequently to Kyle of Lochalsh diverted the main traffic to the wider but easier crossing at Kyleakin. The transport of cattle across the narrow Strait of Kyle Rhea has been written of by many travellers who toured Scotland in the last years of the seventeenth and throughout the eighteenth centuries. Martin, Defoe, Knox and Pennant have all described it in some detail, and all agree substantially on the methods employed, but the most detailed account is given in an Agricultural Survey of Inverness-shire dated 1813 : ' All the cattle reared in the Isle of Skye which are sent to the Southern markets pass from that Island to the mainland by the ferry of Caol Rea. Their numbers are very considerable, by some supposed to be 5,000 but by others 8,000 annually, and the method of ferrying them is not in boats as is done from the Long Island where the passage is broad, but they are forced to swim over Caol Rea. For this purpose the drovers purchase ropes which are cut at the length of 3 feet having a noose at one end. This noose is put round the under jaw of every cow, taking care to have the tongue free. The reason given for leaving the tongue loose is that the animal may be able to keep the salt water from going down its throat in such a quantity as to fill all the cavities in the body which would prevent the action of the lungs ; for every beast is found dead and said to be drowned at the landing

[1] *H.R. & B.*, 5th Report, 1811, Appendix K

place to which this mark of attention has not been paid. Whenever the noose is put under the jaw, all the beasts destined to be ferried together are led by the ferryman into the water until they are afloat, which puts an end to their resistance. Then every cow is tied to the tail of the cow before until a string of 6 or 8 be joined. A man in the stern of the boat holds the rope of the foremost cow. The rowers then ply their oars immediately. During the time of high water or soon before or after full tide is the most favourable passage because the current is then least violent. The ferrymen are so dexterous that very few beasts are lost.' [1]

Methods similar to those employed at Kyle Rhea appear to have been used in other parts of the Hebrides, and the Reverend James Hall, writing of Barra in 1807, refers to ' the abominably cruel method ' of tying cattle and sheep to one another's tails and swimming them across a ferry often more than a mile broad, though the beasts were sometimes drowned or their tails pulled off. He speaks of this practice being then not quite abolished owing to the indolence of the people in conveying the beasts from one island to another or from the island to the ' continent,' though he adds that the shipping of half-wild cattle is certainly difficult and dangerous. [2]

Estimates vary of the number of cattle crossing Kyle Rhea annually from Skye and the Outer Islands. Pennant, who toured Scotland in 1772, puts the number at 4,000,[3] and Knox a few years later gives the same estimate. [4] Daniel Defoe in his *Tour in Great Britain*, written about 1726, gives no estimate of the total number crossing Kyle Rhea each year, but in describing the methods employed, similarly to other contemporary writers, he adds that 300 to 400 cattle can be taken across in a few hours. [5] The Statistical Account of the Parish of Glenelg puts the number at only 2,000,[6] but Youatt writing in 1834 puts it at 6,000 to 7,000. [7] A writer of the very early nineteenth century estimates that 22,000 cattle—one-fifth of the total cattle population—were

[1] Robertson, *General View of the Agriculture of the County of Inverness*, 1813, xxxviii–ix
[2] Hall, *Travels in Scotland*, 1807, II, 545
[3] Pennant, *Tour in Scotland*, 1772, I, 358
[4] Knox, *Tour through the Highlands of Scotland and the Hebride Isles in 1786*, 150
[5] Defoe, *Tour through Great Britain in 1724* (1762 edn.), IV, 294
[6] *O.S.A.*, Glenelg, XVI, 270
[7] Youatt, *Cattle, their Breeds, Management and Diseases*. Library of Useful Knowledge, 1834, 81.

exported annually from the whole of the Hebrides,[1] and as the cattle population of the parish of Snizort alone was reckoned in 1794 at over 2,500,[2] it seems clear that the numbers crossing Kyle Rhea each autumn for the southern markets must have been very considerable. As late as 1821, the cattle traffic crossing the Kyle was of such importance that when new piers were erected on both sides of the strait at Kyle Rhea, a sloping cobbled slipway which can still be seen was provided beside the main pier on the south side for cattle leaving the water.[3] The crossing of cattle at Kyle Rhea continued till the end of the nineteenth century, though by then the traffic had shrunk to a mere fraction of what it once had been, and latterly beasts were brought across by boat. The freedom from accident noted in the 1813 description, seems to have marked the crossing throughout, and even on one of the rare occasions when the ferry boat capsized, most of the cattle are believed to have come in the end safely to shore, though some as far away as Eileanreach on the mainland side more than a mile across the bay of Glenelg.

The difficulties of the crossing of Kyle Rhea, one of the most formidable of all the narrow straits around the Scottish coast, are to some extent reduced by a natural accident of which the boats of the local fishermen to this day take full advantage and of which the drovers no doubt availed themselves. At nearly all stages of the tide an eddy flows close inshore on either side of the Kyle, in a direction opposite to that in which the tide is flowing, and by skilful use of this a boat in the crossing may to some extent defeat the great force of the main current. For all that, the crossing of Kyle Rhea even in modern times is no light undertaking. At few stages of the tide does the current flow at less than three knots, while there are periods at each tide when the speed is seven to eight knots.[4] To one watching from the hill overlooking the Kyle how the tide sweeps like a great river northward to the junction of Loch Duich and Lochalsh, or how when the current sets south, tide and wind meet in Glenelg Bay in a welter of white and angry water, it may well seem that this crossing of the Kyle marks, as little else could do, the hardihood, the courage and the skill of the drovers of Scotland.

A drover who had successfully brought his cattle from Uist

[1] Macdonald, *General View of the Agriculture of the Hebrides*, 1811, 422
[2] *O.S.A.*, Snizort, XVIII, 184   [3] *H.R. & B.*, 9th Report, 1821. Appendix Y
[4] *Nautical Survey*, 1901. Lochalsh and Kyle Rhea (New Edn. 4th December 1912)

or the north of Skye across the island and over Kyle Rhea, had before him a choice of alternative routes for the next stage of his journey south. Though the military road from Bernera to Fort Augustus by Mam Rattachan and Glen Shiel was not made till 1771, a track of some sort no doubt existed before that date if only to serve the barracks at Bernera. When James Boswell and Samuel Johnson crossed the Mam Rattachan ridge on their way to Skye in 1772 soldiers were still working on the road. It was kept in repair by military labour till 1776, after which according to the Statistical Account it was allowed to fall into disrepair. Telford reported in 1802 that ' there are just the vestiges remaining of what was once a military road to Bernera opposite the back of the Isle of Skye,' and this was one of the roads reconstructed by him for the Commissioners for Highland Roads and Bridges [1] ; but made roads had in any event little to commend them to a drover of the eighteenth century, and as he rested beside his cattle on the Skye shore before the crossing or on the mainland side with the passage of the Kyle behind him, his mind would be filled with doubts and perplexities unknown to a traveller of today. Some drovers certainly went over Mam Rattachan and up Glen Shiel, continuing down Glen Moriston and so to Fort Augustus bound for the Pass of Corrieyairack, Dalnacardoch and Crieff. A Memorial to the Commissioners for Highland Roads and Bridges in 1805 refers to the practice of sending cattle—the main source of revenue—south from Skye, Uist, Harris, Glenelg and Loch Alsh via Kyle Rhea and Fort Augustus.[2] Others, after climbing through Glen Shiel, turned southward at Cluanie, or Rhiebuie as it was then called, across the hill to reach Glen Garry and Tomdoun by way of Loch Loyne. The route by Loch Loyne and Tomdoun was chosen by Telford in 1811 for a new road to serve cattle and other traffic coming from Skye.[3] This was part of a great project, never completed, for the construction of a road from Kyle Rhea through Lochaber and across the Moor of Rannoch to Killin. The scheme was to cost about £34,500, and it was hoped that it would shorten the journey of a drove of cattle from Skye by two to three days, saving about £12,000 per annum largely in the better condition of the beasts on arrival at the Tryst ; but Telford only made his choice of this route from Glenelg after carefully weighing another alternative which may well have

---

[1] Telford, *A Survey and Report of the Coasts and Central Highlands of Scotland*, 1803
[2] *H.R. & B.*, 2nd Report, 1805, Appendix C   [3] See Appendix B (p. 227)

Plate 4   Looking to Glenelg from Skye

(Photo by Robert M. Adam)

been in the minds of the Skye drovers as they waited with their beasts beside the Kyle.

Behind Glenelg, leading east into the high hills, lie the parallel glens of Glenmore and Glen Beg. The two glens are connected near their head by a low pass, and near the point of connection a higher pass known as Gleann Aoidhdailean leads south-east to the head of Glen Arnisdale and so to Kinloch Hourn. This route over the Glenelg hills was one of those which Telford surveyed as an alternative to that by Glen Loyne and Glen Shiel.[1] It was a route of no great difficulty to a drove of cattle, offering the advantage of upland pasture and quiet resting-places for the night, and in his first report to the Commissioners in 1804, Telford refers to the Glen Garry road connecting with Bernera through Glenelg or Glen Shiel as a drove road ' of the utmost importance.'[2] It seems highly probable therefore that some of the cattle driven from Skye reached Kinloch Hourn by these tracks over the Glenelg hills which continued to be marked on maps at least as late as 1842.

Martin, in his *Description of the Western Islands of Scotland,* speaks of cattle sold from Skye crossing one of the *two* ferries, and while the almost unanimous evidence of other contemporary writers shows that till the railway came to Strome Ferry the great bulk of the traffic used the Kyle Rhea crossing, local recollection and tradition confirm that some droving traffic went by way of Kyleakin. The drove road on the mainland side from Kyle of Lochalsh appears to have gone by Glen Elchaig into Glen Cannich or by Glen Lichet into Glen Affric making for Beauly and Muir of Ord.

Of the drovers who reached Glen Garry by Glen Shiel and Glen Loyne or by Kinloch Hourn and Glen Quoich, it appears that many continued with their beasts down Glen Garry for only a few miles before turning south at Inchlaggan, a short distance to the west of the head of Loch Garry. Here the cattle forded the river or swam the narrow head of the Loch if the river were in flood. Then they climbed the hills on its south side, crossed the watershed and, resting at Fedden near the ridge, came by Glen Ci-aig to the east end of Loch Arkaig. This was a stage of their journey which formed part of Telford's projected road from Skye, saving nearly ten miles compared with the alternative route by Invergarry, ' nearly equal to a day's journey of a drove of cattle

---

[1] See Appendix B (p. 227) [2] *H.R. & B.,* 1st Report, 1805, Appendix G

or sheep.' Though Telford's project failed, the route from Inchlaggan to Achnacarry appears to have been in common use until well on in the nineteenth century. It was the route followed by James Hogg when he visited the North-west Highlands in 1803, and in the map of Highland Roads printed in 1811 with the 5th Report of the Commissioners it is marked as ' made or under contract.' It is marked as a road in James Knox's map of 1839, and appears to have been in partial use for droving traffic till well on in the nineteenth century. From Loch Arkaig, joined by cattle from Glen Dessarry and Loch Nevis, the route of the Skye drovers was easy to the crossing of the Spean, which Wade recognised as the key-point for traffic passing at the west end of the Great Glen when he built the High Bridge of Spean in 1723.

At Spean Bridge the drovers were again faced with a choice of routes which, on the journey to Crieff and Falkirk, was so often to call for that intimate knowledge of country, of weather or of political conditions, which made their calling so difficult and so responsible. Three routes were open to them. Some drovers passed to the east of the Ben Nevis group of hills, and so to the southern end of Loch Treig, crossing the flat moorland where the Blackwater Reservoir now lies and coming down to Kingshouse at the head of Glencoe on the western edge of the Moor of Rannoch. Some might prefer the route by Fort William and Glen Kiachnish which led over the pass known as the Lairigmore to Kinlochleven, and on by the military road and the Devil's Staircase to Altnafeadh at the head of Glencoe. Others went down the east side of Loch Linnhe, crossing Loch Leven and climbing through Glencoe to Kingshouse.[1]

The first of these routes, by Loch Treig, was that considered by Telford as a continuation of his projected road from Skye to Loch Tay, though he proposed, instead of going by Kingshouse, to take his road from Loch Treig by the east end of Loch Laidon. From here it was to cross the Moor of Rannoch, passing by Glen Meran into Glen Lyon and on over the hills to Glen Lochay and Killin. It is probable that this route had long been used by droving and other less legitimate traffic. The military commander of the post at Tummel Bridge, reporting on a theft of cattle in 1749, reports that watch was kept for the thieves at the head of Glen Lyon, ' a very remarkable pass to and from the Isle of Skye.' In the following year a report from the military station at the

[1] See Appendix B (p. 227)

head of Loch Rannoch refers to the practice of ' drovers returning from Crieff Fare stealing cattle from the Low Country, which they were accustomed to drive to the Highlands by the head of Loch Tay and Lion, and by the important Pass at Carn half-way between this and Augh-Chalada, a large village near Dillebegg.' [1] In General Roy's Survey 1747–55, Dillebegg (spelt Derrybeg) is marked at the east end of Loch Tulla. Telford's proposed road was never made, and in a report to the Commissioners for High-land Roads and Bridges in 1811 he refers bitterly to the failure of the project because ' the personal convenience of the proprietors is not immediately concerned.' Though his plan failed there is evidence to show that this route from Rannoch into the head of Glen Lyon continued to be used by droving traffic till the early part of the nineteenth century, the droves crossing from Glen Lyon to Glen Lochay or joining at the eastern end of Glen Lyon the drove road by Kenmore and Amulree to Crieff.

With the exception of any which went from Loch Treig across the Moor of Rannoch into Glen Lyon, it seems that by far the greater part of the droving traffic from Spean Bridge to the Trysts congregated at the head of Glencoe, the cattle resting at Altnafeadh where the military road from Kinlochleven joins the Glencoe road, or two miles farther on at Kingshouse. Here under the shadow of Buchaille Etive Mor, at the meeting-place of Glen Etive and Glencoe, of the road from Kinlochleven and of older tracks leading eastward across the moor, an inn has stood for centuries, offering such poor shelter or refreshment as it could afford to drovers, pedlars, soldiers and travellers of every sort about to face the long bleak stage southward, skirting the western edge of ' that thorofare of thieves,' the Moor of Rannoch.[2]

From Kingshouse, the next stage for the drovers was to Inveroran. Here among the woods at the head of Loch Tulla Dorothy and William Wordsworth in 1803 came on a drove southward bound, ' a stream coursing the road with off stragglers to the borders of the Lake and under the trees on the sloping ground,' [3] and a traveller in the autumn of 1818 has described the scene on this western fringe of the moor : ' Notwithstanding the wild and desolate general aspect of a great part of the tract,' he writes, ' the road at this time from the 23rd September to the

[1] *Historical Papers.* New Spalding Club (1699–1750), II, 540 and 582
[2] *Breadalbane Papers (Roads),* Box 4, H.M. Register House
[3] Dorothy Wordsworth, *Journals, 1798–1828,* Ed. Knight (1924), 322

4th October was far from being solitary. After passing on the 23rd of September the point where the road from Lochearnhead and Crief joins that from Killin to Tyandrum, the King's House and Fort William, large flocks of sheep with their drivers were met on their way to the Falkirk Tryste (Fair) ; and on the 3rd of October a considerable extent of the road through Glenurchay was almost covered with flocks of sheep and droves of cattle proceeding to the same destination from the district of Morven in Argyllshire and the Western coast and islands of Rossshire. The flocks and droves from these quarters pass the Invernessshire Lochy at the head of Loch Linnhe, or are ferried across that Lake about 10 miles further west at the Ferry of Corran and are then driven round the head of the Argyllshire Loch Leven through Glenurchay and Braidalbane by Lochearnhead to Crief and Falkirk.' [1] At Inveroran the droves rested, traditional rights of pasturage existing till 1846 when these were successfully challenged. South-east of Inveroran the route of the drovers led by the head of Glenorchy to Tyndrum. At Bridge of Orchy, or at Clifton near Tyndrum the Skye and Lochaber droves might be joined by some of the beasts from the Argyllshire coast and Loch Awe side, though it seems probable that the greater part of the Argyllshire cattle reached the markets of Central Scotland by routes farther to the south.

Till the middle of the eighteenth century Crieff Tryst was the great centre for cattle trade from the Highlands. The droves which had reached the Perthshire county boundary near Tyndrum moved on down the long glen of the Dochart, many of them reaching Crieff by way of Glen Ogle and the side of Lochearn, though according to local tradition a route from Ledchary in Glen Dochart over the hills to Balquhidder was also used. Some may have chosen the route by Loch Tay. For these, the route led along the south side of the Loch to Ardeonaig where they climbed southward through the hills and so came into Glenlednock. When Telford planned his road to the South, his description of the lines of communication from Killin contains a reference to ' the new road through Glen Lednaig to Comrie.' [2] The road through the hills from Ardeonaig to Comrie, which Telford planned, was never completed, and the route remains to this day a rough though well defined hill track, but there seems little doubt that it was much used in the eighteenth and early nineteenth

---

[1] Larkin, *A Tour in the Highlands, 1818*, 140–1 [2] See Appendix B (p. 227)

centuries. Local tradition tells of a considerable cattle traffic coming from the Loch Tay end of the Pass, crossing near Invergeldie from Glen Lednock into Glen Boltachan and so reaching the valley of the Earn. While Crieff Tryst still flourished, these droves would turn east down the river, but at a later date when Falkirk had become the main destination, the local evidence available shows that part at least of the droving traffic crossed the Earn and climbed the high ground on its south bank, reaching Doune through the hills on the south side of Glenartney.

In the second half of the eighteenth century, Crieff Tryst began to diminish in importance for reasons which will appear at a later stage, and by 1770 Falkirk had taken its place as the greatest cattle market in Scotland. From this date till the end of the droving days the principal route of the Skye and Western Isles cattle from Glen Dochart appears to have followed very much the line of the present road by Glen Ogle, Balquhidder and Loch Lubnaig to Callander and Doune. So they came to the Bridge of Stirling, though some, if the autumn were dry, avoided the toll on Stirling Bridge by crossing the Forth at the Ford of Frew six miles west of Stirling, where Prince Charles Edward's army crossed in September 1745 on their way to Carlisle and Derby. Evidence given before the Court of Session in 1783 shows the Ford to have been then in frequent use by drovers.[1]

At Stirling the Skye droves met those from the North of Scotland and from the Central and Eastern Highlands; so here at the crossing of the Forth is a suitable point to leave them, now part of a great composite stream of beasts, plodding slowly on towards Falkirk and their unknown fate.

[1] *Old Session Papers*, Signet Library, 351:6

THE DROVE ROADS OF ARGYLL

WHILE the stream of cattle from Skye and the Outer Hebrides moved through the autumn days by Kintail and Lochaber to Rannoch and Central Scotland, parallel streams were flowing from the Argyllshire coast. These too had their springs in the Islands. The geographical and political isolation, mild climate and good grazing which have been suggested as reasons for the early growth in importance of the Skye trade, characterised in equal measure this more southerly district where moist airs from the Atlantic sweep across the islands and over the grass lands along the coast and bordering the sea lochs.

A trade in cattle from Argyll existed at least as early as the time of Mary Queen of Scots, and in 1565 and 1566 the inhabitants of ' Ergile, Lorne, Braidalbane, Kintyre and the Ilis,' having complained that they were afraid to come to the Lowlands for trading purposes for fear of the confiscation of their cattle, the Privy Council ordered that loyal subjects bringing cattle from Argyll to the Lowlands were not to be molested, provided, however, that goods were not taken back to Argyll.[1] Despite this, the trade remained precarious, and in 1609 the Privy Council annulled a recent Proclamation prohibiting all trade with Mull or any of the Western Isles, Maclean of Duart having protested that the sale of ' mairtis,' horses and other goods was the only method of paying taxes to the Crown[2]; but the troubles of the Mull cattle dealers were not yet at an end, and a few years later they are again complaining, this time against tolls unlawfully exacted by Macdougall of Dunollie on cattle landed from the Mull ferries.[3]

The hazardous nature of this early cattle trade from Argyll may be judged by the amount of time which during the sixteenth and seventeenth centuries the Privy Council had to devote to dealing with complaints of cattle thefts, and the key to the diffi-culties of which the local landowners complained may perhaps be found partly in the frequency with which these same land-

---

[1] *R.P.C.*, 1st series, I, 401, 470–1   [2] *R.P.C.*, 1st series, VIII, 757
[3] Transactions of Iona Club, *Collectanea de rebus albanicis*, I, 154

owners are cited as the guilty parties. Stewarts of Appin, Macgregors of Loch Awe side and Campbells of Glen Orchy and Inverawe come and go through the records, their raids taking them as far east as Glen Isla and Strath Bran, and in 1602 the Privy Council had before it a complaint against the Earl of Argyll for theft by certain of his men, including Duncan Campbell of Inverawe, of cattle from various places, including Strathbran and Snaigow in East Perthshire.[1] In 1667 the Earl of Argyll faced charges of theft by his tenants as far afield as Ruthven in Strathspey, Wester Coull and Tarland in Aberdeenshire. Acknowledging that stolen cattle had been brought to the ' wyld rockish country of Glencoe,' he observed that ' neither the Earl nor any landlord in the Highlands in these large mountainous countries is able to prevent this.'[2] As late as 1682, when measures were taken for securing ferries against the passage at night of goods stolen from the Lowlands, the list included ' the boats on the Watter of Aw ' and ' the ferry boats of Carranarngour, Kyllsich Phatrick, Ardchattane and Connell.'[3]

These first references to the cattle trade of Argyll have shown that from early times the island of Mull exported cattle to the mainland, and throughout the main droving period of the eighteenth and early nineteenth centuries the island continued to be one of the principal sources of the Argyllshire droving traffic. In this, Mull played a part rather similar to that which Skye played in the trade from the north-west, supplying not only cattle bred on the island, but sending to the mainland those collected from the neighbouring islands. The rich grazings of Coll and Tiree fed considerable numbers of cattle, and it was natural that cattle breeders there should choose routes offering the greatest chance of grazing by the way and the shortest sea passage for the small sailing boats then in use.

Few estimates of the number of cattle ferried to Mull from Coll and Tiree are available till the last years of the eighteenth century. At that time a traveller in Scotland estimates the number sent from Coll each year at 400,[4] while a few years later the Statistical Account puts the number ferried from Coll and Tiree at over 500.[5] The New Statistical Account for Coll and

[1] *R.P.C.*, 1st series, VI, 442   [2] *R.P.C.*, 3rd series, II, 330–1
[3] *R.P.C.*, 3rd series, VII, 646. ' Caolas' ic Phatric ' was the local name of the Ferry across Loch Leven near Ballachulish.
[4] Knox, *Tour through the Highlands of Scotland and the Hebride Isles in 1786*, 74
[5] *O.S.A.* Coll and Tiree, X, 411

Tiree records that in Tiree there were four decked vessels of 20–40 tons sometimes used for carrying country produce to market but generally looking for employment elsewhere, and 20 open or half-decked boats of 6–20 tons chiefly employed in ferrying cattle.[1]   The landing place for the cattle of Coll and Tiree is vaguely described as 'at the back of Mull,' but local tradition puts the landing point at the little Bay of Kintra at the north-west corner of the Ross of Mull, and the Second Report of the Commissioners for Highland Roads and Bridges in 1805 refers to a proposed extension of the Mull road to Kintra to which Iona cattle and very frequently those from Tiree, Barra and South Uist were brought.[2]   From Kintra the cattle travelled along the side of Loch Scridain and through Glen More and the Parish of Torosay where, by the second half of the eighteenth century, the birch, ash and oak woods were already being cut and burned for charcoal by the Lorne Furnace Company on Loch Etive.[3]

The Mull cattle, numbering with those from the neighbouring islands as many as 2,000 per annum, were shipped from the island at Grass Point at the mouth of Loch Don.   Oban as late as the end of the eighteenth century was still, as Dr Johnson described it in 1772, 'only a small village if a few houses can be so described,'[4] and the cattle were landed on the island of Kerrera from which they swam across the narrow sound which separates the island from the mainland.   According to local tradition the point on the west side of Kerrera at which the Mull cattle landed was the Bay of Barr nam Boc.   This continued to be the main route till the middle of last century, but by the time the New Statistical Account of Scotland for the Parish of Torosay was compiled in 1843, the traffic was already declining, for by then many of the Outer Island cattle were being taken direct to the mainland, though the dates of the Tiree cattle markets were still fixed with reference to those of Mull. [5]

Besides the route from Grass Point, Mull possessed in the eighteenth and early nineteenth centuries another ferry of some importance to the drovers.   Salen on the Sound of Mull had for long been a considerable cattle market for beasts from the north

---

[1] *N.S.A.*, Tiree and Coll, VII, 216–7
[2] *H.R. & B.*, 2nd Report, 1805, Appendix B   [3] *O.S.A.*, Torosay, III, 267
[4] Boswell, *Tour to the Hebrides*, Isham Collection, 346
[5] *N.S.A.*, Torosay, VII, 292

of the island and from the islands of Ulva and Gometra, and
drovers attending that market sometimes found it of advantage
to ferry their beasts from Fishnish, opposite Lochaline, to the
Morven shore. There is a local tradition that the Lochaline
Ferry was also used to take beasts from the Morven shore to Mull
and so to the South by way of the Kerrera crossing. The fact that
the local cattle sales in Morven were fixed for a date *before* the
sale at Salen in Mull indicates that part of the cattle traffic went
this way. Drovers who used the route to Lochaline took their
beasts from Morven to the shores of Loch Sunart. At Strontian
where, besides the lead mine developed by the York Buildings
Company in 1730, there was a cattle market, they would be
joined by droves which were sometimes landed from the Outer
Isles at Kilchoan in Ardnamurchan and ' the Creek of Salen '
on Loch Sunart, or at the western end of Loch Shiel by boats
from the islands which entered the loch by the River Shiel for
return cargoes of timber.[1] From Strontian the drove route led
through Glen Tarbert in Ardgour to Corran where they were
ferried, or, if weather and tide were favourable, possibly swam
across the ' current of Lochaber,' as it was then called, to join
the road to Ballachulish and Glencoe used by some of the Skye
cattle.[2]

While the route from Mull through Morvern was of some
importance, the records available to us make it clear that by far
the greater part of the cattle from Mull and the neighbouring
islands reached the mainland opposite the island of Kerrera.
There they would be joined by beasts sent to the trysts from the
district immediately south of Oban, while cattle from Appin,
Benderloch and Loch Etive side swelled their numbers. In
tracing the paths by which these beasts reached their destinations,
it is well to bear in mind the difference between the outlook of a
drover of the times and that of a traveller of today. The hills
and the lochs of Argyll run roughly from north-east to south-west,
and to follow the shortest line from the shores of the Firth of
Lorn to Crieff, Falkirk or the towns of the Clyde involves a
crossing of successive barriers of hill, sea and inland lochs. To a
drover these presented few obstacles, for the hills offered firm
going, good grazing and resting-places for beasts at night, while
the lochs could be easily crossed by ferries or privately owned
boats, which contemporary records show to have been much more

[1] *N.S.A.*, Ardnamurchan, VII, 130, 155–6   [2] ibid.

numerous than today. In times when roads were still unmade the lochs of the Highlands were no doubt largely used for inland transport, and the shipping of beasts by boat or ferry was then a rough but familiar art. The list of boats and ferries from which bonds were taken in 1682 included the private boats on Loch Etive and the coast of Appin and Lorn. Others included in Privy Council measures of 1682 and 1684 to check cattle thieving included boats on Loch Lyon, Loch Rannoch, Loch Tay and Loch Lomond.[1]

To determine with any certainty the exact routes taken by the early cattle traffic from Argyll is now hardly possible. There is a sixteenth-century record of cattle being driven from Kintyre to Stirling,[2] and there is evidence that at least some of the Argyll cattle traffic passed regularly through or near Dumbarton in the seventeenth century ; but the exact routes at this early period must be a matter of conjecture, and it is not till the eighteenth and nineteenth centuries that the routes followed can be traced with any confidence.

For the Mull cattle which came ashore from the island of Kerrera and those from the grazings by the shores of Loch Etive and the Firth of Lorn, two possible alternative roads to Central Scotland lay open. Of these the first led through the Pass of Brander and so by Dalmally and Glen Lochy to Tyndrum, Killin and Crieff. The second led over the high ground south of Loch Etive, across Loch Awe and so to Inveraray, Loch Lomond and the markets of Stirlingshire. On the Dalmally route the River Awe was a formidable obstacle. No bridge appears to have existed till after 1755,[3] but on the large-scale survey of Scotland, associated

---

[1] *R.P.C.*, 3rd series, VII, 646 and VIII, 532

[2] McKerral, 'The Tacksman and his Holding in the South-West Highlands.' *Scottish Historical Review*, Vol. XXVI, 10–25.

[3] While it seems fairly certain that no bridge capable of carrying a drove of cattle over the River Awe existed before 1755, there is reason to think that a bridge of some sort may have been in existence at a much earlier date. In his poem *The Bruce*, written about 1487, John Barbour, Archdeacon of Aberdeen, described the skirmish between Bruce and John Macdougal of Lorn in 1308. The poem tells how the men of Lorn after failing to stop Bruce's advance through the Pass of Brander retreated down the pass :

'. . . till ane wattir held thair way
that ran down by the hillis syde
and was rycht styth bath deip and wyde
that men in na place mycht it pas
bot at ane brig beneth thaim was.'

The Lorn men attempted unsuccessfully to break down the bridge to stop Bruce's advance. In a note to his edition of the text published in 1909, Mr W. M. Mackenzie

with the name of General Roy which was drawn between 1747 and 1755,[1] a ferry is shown near the point where the river leaves Loch Awe, and the route of an old road leading to this point, though not marked on General Roy's survey, can to this day be clearly traced on the west side of the river. According to local tradition fords over the Awe were at one time in use, including one just below the loch, but this must almost certainly have been destroyed when the level of the loch was lowered in the early years of last century for the benefit of the low-lying ground around Dalmally.[2] These fords can in any event only have been passable at infrequent intervals, and it seems probable that at least before 1755 the cattle traffic which went by this route was on a small scale. After the building of the Bridge of Awe the Dalmally route would be greatly simplified, but by then Falkirk Tryst was displacing Crieff, so tending to divert the traffic farther to the south, to the crossing of Loch Awe and to Inveraray.[3]

It seems then that it was rather to the alternative route to the south-east that the drovers from Mull and Lorn turned their eyes, to the great stretches of hill country which lie between the Firth of Lorn, Loch Awe and Loch Fyne. Through these hills run tracks traditionally believed to have been in use from the early days of Scotland's history by kings and nobles, monks and pilgrims in days when Iona was still the spiritual centre of Scotland and the burial-place of her kings. There is some evidence and much local tradition to support the view that these same tracks were extensively used by droving traffic during the eighteenth and the first half of the nineteenth centuries.

One of the chief crossing-places on Loch Awe for droving traffic was at Taychreggan. To reach this point some of the

[1] See Appendix D (p. 237)   [2] *N.S.A.*, Glenorchy, VII, 99
[3] See Appendix E (p. 339)

---

writes : ' The bridge was, of course, made of wood. It was probably beyond the lower extremity of the Pass, somewhere near the present bridge.'

Groome's Ordnance Gazetteer of Scotland after describing the difficult nature of the Pass of Brander adds : ' It always, nevertheless, was a point of transit or thoroughfare between the regions of Glenorchy and West Lorn ; and it is believed to have anciently had some sort of rude bridge ; yet even with aid of either bridge or boat or other contrivance, it never could be traversed without much danger, or by any but a sure-footed mountaineer ; for it was barred by a mural ascent still called the Ladder Rock and long commanded by a fortalice on the crown of the ascent.' (*The Bruce* by John Barbour, Archdeacon of Aberdeen ; ed. W. M. Mackenzie, 1909, 171 and 423. Groome's *Ordnance Gazetteer of Scotland*, new edn. 1893, Vol. I, 96) droves may have passed through Glen Lonan into Glen Nant and so by way of Loch Tromlee to the shore of Loch Awe, but the main route was more probably by way of Glen Feochan and so east through the hills to Taychreggan. This route across the hills is now deserted except for the shepherd's house at Midmuir, but it is probable that over it has passed the traffic of centuries, and at least as late as 1747–55 it appeared on General Roy's survey.

A parallel track leaving the coast near the mouth of Loch Feochan, climbs through Glen Euchar by Loch Scamadale and over the stretch of low hills known as the Sreinge of Lorn to reach Loch Awe near Dalavich. By this route would go not only some cattle from the Hebrides, but those from the pasture grounds on the south side of Loch Feochan and from the islands of Seil and Luing. Other tracks led east from Kilmelfort and from the head of Loch Craignish up the Barbreck River, both making for Loch Avich and reaching the side of Loch Awe at the narrow part of the loch near Dalavich. All these are shown on General Roy's survey, and in a Memorial to the Commissioners for Highland Roads and Bridges in 1811, the local people urged that the route from Glen Euchar to Dalavich should be improved as being necessary to develop the traffic from the coastal district to Inveraray and the South.[1]

On the south-east side of Loch Awe many tracks crossed the hills making for the south ; from Dalmally into Glenshira or into the glen of the Dubh Eas which leads to Glen Falloch ; from Cladich to Inveraray on the line of the present road ; from the farm of Braevallich, six miles east of Ford, to near Furnace on Loch Fyne, while perhaps the most important started from where the little ruined chapel of Kilneuair still stands two miles east of Ford, leading south-east across the hills through the stretch of country known at one time as the Leckan Muir to Auchendrain three miles north of Furnace on Loch Fyne. Local tradition speaks of other tracks, and others no doubt existed, for the hills between Loch Awe and Loch Fyne presented no great obstacle to a drove, and offered good going and ample pasture to travelling beasts.

On this stage of their journey, the droves were not the only traffic on the move. The woods around Loch Awe and Loch Etive supplied the fuel and the charcoal for the local smelting

[1] *H.R. & B.*, 5th Report, 1811, Appendix D (1)

industry. Furnaces had been established before the middle of the eighteenth century to smelt iron ore brought from Ulverston in Lancashire, first at Glen Kinglass on Loch Etive side, and latterly at Bonawe. Timber cut in the woods of Glen Orchy, Glen Strae and Glen Lochy was floated down the River Orchy and through Loch Awe to the Pass of Brander,[1] and when Coleridge and the Wordsworths came down the side of Loch Awe in 1803 they found a sailing-boat in the Pass loaded with charcoal for the Bonawe Works.[2] A furnace had also been started at Goatfield on Loch Fyne in 1754, and until well on in the nineteenth century strings of ponies loaded with charcoal were to be seen crossing the hills to the south of Loch Awe.[3]

As the cattle from Mull and Lorn crossed the watershed south of Loch Awe and started the descent to the oak and hazel woods of the Loch Fyne shore, they were met by other droves coming from the west. These too were largely cattle from the islands. Off the coasts of Kintyre and Knapdale lie the large islands of Islay and Jura, with the smaller islands of Colonsay and Oronsay ten miles farther out in the Atlantic, and the nearer island of Gigha off the mouth of West Loch Tarbert. To Islay, the most southerly and one of the most westerly of the Scottish islands, nature has given a climate and a soil which have placed her from early times among the rich grazing and farming lands of Scotland. The island is described in 1549 as ' fertile, fruitful and full of natural grassing, with many great deer, many woods with fair games of hunting beside every town,' [4] and it was to bring this rich but remote part of his lands under the control of the Crown that James the Sixth in the early years of the seventeenth century directed his repeated and finally successful efforts. The grasslands of these islands fed, even in these early times, large numbers of stock. A raid by Maclean of Duart on the small island of Gigha in 1579 resulted in the theft of no less than 500 cattle and 2,000 sheep and goats.[5] As early as the latter part of the seventeenth century the sale of cattle from Islay for droving to the south appears to have been on a considerable scale. In the

---

[1] *N.S.A.*, Glenorchy, VII, 92
[2] Dorothy Wordsworth, op. cit., 288 et seq. The cargo would be landed in the Pass and carted to Bonawe.
[3] Macadam, *Notes on the Ancient Iron Industry of Scotland.* Proceedings of Society of Antiquaries of Scotland, 1886, Vol. 9, New Series, 130.
[4] Hume Brown, *Scotland in the Time of Queen Mary,* 30
[5] *R.P.C.*, 1st series, III, 135

spring of 1680 Sir Hugh Campbell sold to Walter Scott of Langhope ' 1,000 stots and cowes of the ile of Ila,' and a few years later he writes to his factor that owing to disturbed conditions having interfered with the normal marketing of his tenants' beasts, he will ' raise a drov on (his) own wentur and giv the tennents a resonable pryce,' though he has ' noe assurance nor probability of pryces in Ingland.' [1]

The abundance of summer grass, but the absence of hay-making, which did not become common in the islands till after 1754, made it almost inevitable that much stock should be disposed of on the approach of autumn, and it is not surprising that when the latter part of the eighteenth century brought an awakening of interest in agricultural knowledge and statistics, the export of cattle from these favoured islands was found to be large. Pennant in 1772 estimates that 1,700 cattle were then exported annually from Islay, though despite this many died in the spring from lack of food, while Colonsay and Oronsay sent 300 to market.[2] At the time of the Statistical Account, the number sold each year from the parish of Kilchoman in the south-west corner of Islay was alone estimated at 800.[3] In his *General View of the Agriculture of the Hebrides* published in 1811, James Macdonald gives figures showing the average number of black cattle ferried from Islay to Jura in each year from 1801 to 1807. These figures, kept by the tenant of the ferry at Port Askaig show that during this period the average number of beasts ferried annually was 2,640. On the conservative assumption that only one quarter of the total stock was sold off each year Macdonald estimates that this indicates a cattle population in Islay of over 10,000 head. The average price was stated to be £7 a head.[4] The *Falkirk Herald* of 27 June 1900 refers to a notice published in the *Edinburgh Advertiser* of May 1779 by the Lairds of the Island of Islay to the effect that they have in hand ' for disposal by small lots of 8 or 10, between 2,000 and 3,000 of the largest and best of the true Highland breed which have never been housed in winter or summer ; that being strangers to the gentlemen graziers of England they do not expect to be furnished with money or credit from them, but will at their own expense execute the

[1] *The Book of Islay*, 414 and 419
[2] Pennant, *Tour in Scotland*, 1772, I, 263 and 273-4
[3] *O.S.A.*, Kilchoman, XI, 278
[4] Macdonald, *General View of the Agriculture of the Hebrides*, 1811, 623

commissions given and find careful drivers with the cattle and deliver them at Glasgow or Dumfries upon receiving payment of the original purchase money, 3% commission and the net expense incurred in ferrying and driving.' The price of the cattle is not stated.[1]

The cattle owners of Islay, Colonsay and Oronsay followed the same principle as guided those of Coll and Tiree in sending their cattle to the mainland by the routes which offered the most grazing on the way and the shortest sea crossing. Colonsay and Oronsay cattle would cross to North Jura, while those of Islay were ferried from Port Askaig over the narrow Sound of Islay to Feolin at the south end of the island.[2] The *Stent Book of Islay* records the activities of the committee on the island which during the last quarter of the eighteenth and the first half of the nineteenth centuries raised and administered local assessments before the modern system of rating was established, and in it occur many references to droving from the island. In 1787, drovers coming from Islay complained of the lack of a fank for enclosing their beasts while waiting for the ferry at Port Askaig, and in that year it was decided to establish one on a site of 60 to 80 acres, an extent which shows that the droves must have been of considerable size. A few years later, James Hill in charge of the ferry was ordered to keep the paving of the slipway in good order to prevent damage to the cattle, and to regulate disputes which had arisen among the drovers about priority in ferrying their beasts to Jura.[3] John Macculloch, who toured the Western Isles in 1824, has described the scene at the crossing of the Sound of Islay : ' The shore was covered with cattle ; and while some were collected in groups under the trees and rocks, crowding to avoid the hot rays of a July evening, others were wading in the sea to shun the flies, some embarking, and another set swimming onshore from the ferry boats ; while the noise of the drovers and the boatmen, and all the bustle and vociferation which whisky did not tend to diminish, were re-echoed from hill to hill, contrasting strangely with the silence and solitude of the surrounding mountains.'[4] Macculloch's description of the noise at the

---

[1] On referring to the files of the *Edinburgh Advertiser* for 1779, the notice in question cannot be found. It is probable that a mistake has been made in the date but there seems little reason to doubt the accuracy of the reference in other respects.
[2] *H.R. & B.*, 5th Report, 1811, Appendix B
[3] *The Stent Book of Islay*, 121, 151 and 219
[4] Macculloch, *Highlands and Western Islands*, 1824, IV, 420

ferry would seem to be well-founded, for only six years earlier the local Stent Committee had found it necessary to give their attention to this very matter. Hitherto the allowance of whisky for the ferrymen had been unlimited, but a ' surplus quantity being often found injurious to the cattle and the proprietors thereof,' the allowance was in future to be fixed at one mutchkin [an English pint] for every thirty cattle ferried.[1]

After crossing to Jura, the route of the Islay cattle lay up the eastern shore of the island, some following the coast to Kinuachdrach at the extreme northern point.[2] In a note to his *General View of the Agriculture of the Hebrides* in 1811, James Macdonald wrote as follows : ' In former times the cattle exported from Islay for the mainland markets were never strong enough for the journey until the middle of June, the driest and best season of the year. They were then driven by herdsmen thro' Jura by a hill road (the shortest possible way) which went between the back of the farms, which are all on the Eastern shore, and the mountainous ridge which occupies the middle and western parts of the Island. They had freedom of pasturage, gratis, during the journey. In consequence however of the late improvements carried on in Islay, the cattle of its proprietors and tenants are much earlier ready for the market than June and indeed are exported all the year round ; and they are also much heavier and more unwieldy than they were in former time, and consequently cannot travel along the hill road. The road now making, and of which one half is made by Government, is carried along the Eastern shore, and Mr Campbell of Shawfield maintains that he is entitled to the use of it for the cattle of Islay in their passage through Jura, while Mr Campbell of Jura alledges that Islay is limited to the hill road only, which is practicable, as already mentioned, during the summer months.' [3]

From the north end of Jura the cattle crossed to the mouth of Loch Craignish, and moving up the north shore of the loch either continued up the Barbreck River towards Loch Avich and the crossing of Loch Awe, or more probably turned south-east at the head of Loch Craignish towards the west end of Loch Awe and the road over the Leckan Muir on the direct route to Inveraray. The cattle which crossed from this northern point of

[1] *The Stent Book of Islay*, 213
[2] H.R. & B., 5th Report, 1811, Appendix B and *N.S.A.*, Jura, VII, 543
[3] Macdonald, op. cit., 618/9. Note.

Jura to Craignish faced a passage little less hazardous than that at Kyle Rhea between Skye and the Inverness-shire coast. On the Jura shore they were dangerously close to the tides and eddies of the Sound of Corrievrechan, while their route to Craignish took them past the north end of the perilous waters of the Dorus Mor, where the tide sweeps round the end of Craignish Point. The number of cattle which crossed by this route cannot be accurately determined, but as late as 1843 when the New Statistical Account of the Parish of Craignish was compiled, it was recorded that the parish still possessed a small vessel, chiefly employed in ferrying beasts from Jura. At that time, it was estimated that each year, 3,000 sheep and 1,000 cattle, including some from Colonsay, were ferried there on their way to the trysts,[1] and in the New Statistical Account for Jura the number of black cattle ' annually sold out of the Island ' is estimated at 1,000 to 1,200.[2]

While some drovers chose this route from North Jura, the greater part of the Islay and Jura cattle crossed to the mainland from Lagg half-way up the east coast of Jura to Keills, which lies on the north side of the mouth of Loch Sween on the coast of Knapdale. The landing jetty at Keills still stands in a little bay facing south-westward down the Sound of Jura. Sea-thrift growing among the stones and the rust of its ironwork tell of a vanished traffic ; but here on a September day of the late eighteenth century was a busy scene, and old men still (1948) living in Knapdale remember in their youth the last remnants of the traffic already shrunk to a mere shadow of what it once had been. The boats appear to have been mainly open, not decked or half-decked like some of those on the crossing of the Minch, single-masted but with heavy oars to help in calm weather. The bottom and sides were thickly lined with birch branches. These according to local evidence were often tied in bundles, the whole being secured by chains. As on the crossing from Uist to Skye, many of the beasts were thrown overboard in deep water as the ferry boats neared the mainland shore. In some of the larger boats it seems that a section of the gunwale hinged outwards to help the unloading, but cattle wearied with hours in the boat and smelling the grass of the shore would seldom linger, and once the leader took the plunge the rest would follow easily. Sometimes in calm weather the five miles crossing would take

---

[1] *N.S.A.*, Craignish, VII, 57   [2] ibid., Jura, 541

the full day, while the boats drifted with the strong currents of the Sound, the men laboured at the oars and the morning mist lingered on the Jura hills. In the days when the traffic was at its height, many boats would be employed and here, where the most part of the cattle of Islay, Jura and Colonsay crossed, the ferrying took several days, the cattle already landed on the mainland resting and feeding in the rich pasture along the Knapdale shore till the ferrying was completed and the drove ready to continue its long journey. Mr Joseph Mitchell, Engineer to the Commissioners for Highland Roads and Bridges from 1825 to 1853, has recorded the following description of the crossing from Lagg to the mainland :

' On arriving at the Ferry, we found every corner of the Inn crowded with drovers who had been detained by the weather for several days, and were passing their time, as was their wont, in riotous and continuous drinking.

' We felt it was no agreeable sojourn to stay in the inn with these half-intoxicated and noisy people, for the very air was impregnated with an odour of whisky.

' We appealed to the ferrymen to take us across. At first they positively refused on account of the storm, but with some persuasion, and a handsome douceur, their scruples were overcome, and they prepared for the voyage.

' No sooner had the drovers, who had been so long detained, heard that the boat was to cross at our instigation, than they got excessively angry, talked in Gaelic long and loud, and insisted that we should take at the same time a cargo of their cattle. This the boatmen could not refuse, and eighteen cattle were put on board.

' The boat was of great width of beam, and the cattle were fastened with their heads to rings on the gunwale on each side. We had also the chief drover's pony, which stood in the middle of the boat.

' The wind was quite in our favour, but it blew furiously, and the sea was high, but its severity we did not so much notice in the shelter of the harbour.

' At last we cleared the land, and got into the channel. How the wind did roar, and how the cattle struggled to get their heads free ! The extent of sail we carried was forcing the bow of the boat too deep into the sea, and there was fear of being swamped.

96

'The men tried to lower the sail, which, in their agitation, they could not effect, and all looked helpless.

'On this the drover seized the helm, and with sharp and decisive words took the command of the boat. By his admirable steering he relieved her a good deal, and enabled the men to lessen sail. Still the boat flew before the wind and rolled heavily ; every moment we expected would be our last. I grasped the stirrup of the saddle on the pony, in the hope that if we did go the creature might swim ashore. On we ploughed our way in the midst of this furious storm.

'How admirably the drover steered ! We had to take the narrow and rocky entrance of Lagg harbour, a most difficult navigation ; but the drover's sharp and distinct orders were promptly obeyed, and in no time he landed us in shelter within the little bay.' [1]

From Keills, ' the boating place at Keills ' as it is called in the Reports of the Commissioners for Highland Roads and Bridges, the droves made their way up the north-west side of Loch Sween, skirting the little inlets and arms of the sea which are the peculiar characteristics of that loch, and past the wooded promontories where the oak and hazel grow to the water's edge. Then skirting the flat moss of Crinan they made for Kilmichael-Glassary in the valley of the River Add, a cattle tryst of considerable importance in those droving days, the memory of which is now preserved only by a pool in the river still known as the ' Stance Pool.' To Kilmichael-Glassary came also the cattle of Kintyre and Gigha, travelling up the Kintyre peninsula to West Loch Tarbert and on by routes marked in the survey of 1747–55 over the Knapdale hills by Loch Killisport and the head of Loch Sween. Those still (1948) living in Kintyre can recall the landing on the west coast of beasts brought in from Islay, Jura and Gigha for grazing in Kintyre and subsequent sale at the Tryst at Kilmichael-Glassary. The cattle were brought from the islands to near the Kintyre coast by sailing-boat and were then flung overboard to swim ashore, shepherded by rowboats which headed them off if they tried to swim in the wrong direction.

The Kilmichael market over and their cattle rested, the Kintyre, Knapdale and Islay drovers faced the first stage up

---

[1] Mitchell, *Reminiscences of my Life in the Highlands*, I, 302–3, 1883–4
Though Mitchell's description suggests that the landing was made at Lagg, it appears from the context that the crossing was from Lagg to Keills.

Loch Fyne of their long march to Falkirk.[1] Roy's map, already referred to, marks the route they followed up the valley of the Add to its head waters to join the track which crosses the Leckan Muir from Kilneuair making for Inveraray. ' By this route,' says a Memorial of 1807 urging the improvement of the road, ' the inhabitants of Knapdale, Jura, Islay, Colonsay, North Lorne and the adjacent islands take their cattle to the Low Country with hardly a single exception,' and while the statement of the Memorialists may have been coloured by a desire to prove their case, there seems small reason to doubt its substantial truth.[2] The old track, part of which is still on the list of the country roads of Argyll, is now deserted and grass-grown, and as long ago as the time of the New Statistical Account the writer of the Account for the Parish of Glassary complained of its upkeep at public expense, though it ' scarcely deserves the name of road ' ; but to follow the track as it winds uphill from the Loch Awe shore, marking how deep it has cut, is to realise that here the latter-day drovers followed in the footsteps of droves of earlier times, of pack-horse and foot traffic, perhaps dating back to a very early period in the history of the country. It was on this road among the hills above Loch Fyne, that the cattle from South Argyll and the islands met the Mull droves as they crossed from Loch Awe by the routes of the old charcoal burners.

Loch Fyne in the eighteenth and early nineteenth centuries, like many another Scottish loch, had crossing-places now gone out of use. Crossings at Otter opposite Ardrishaig, at Strachur and at St. Catherine's certainly existed, and while all the routes across the loch used by the drovers cannot now be known, it seems highly probable that the Strachur route at least was used by cattle on their way to the Clyde coast at Ardentinny and Dunoon.[3] In an action in the Court of Session in 1777, droving rights and stances were successfully claimed in North Cowal for cattle in transit from the Western Isles,[4] and in 1810 the inhabitants of

---

[1] According to information supplied by Mr McDougal, Minard, Loch Fyne, formerly tenant of Barmolloch Farm near Kilmichael-Glassary, the journey from there to Falkirk took from seven to eight days but usually a little longer was allowed for contingencies. In his early days Mr McDougal frequently drove cattle from Knapdale to Falkirk. [2] *H.R. & B.*, 3rd Report, 1807, Appendix L

[3] The cattle traffic from the north-west side of the loch was not the only traffic using the Strachur Ferry for the *O.S.A.* reports that the birch, alder and hazel woods above Strachur were made into charcoal for the use of the smelting works across the loch (*O.S.A.*, Strachur, IV, 563).

[4] *Campbell* v. *Campbell*, 1777, 5 Brown's Supplement, 599

Plate 5   Looking towards Kingshouse from Altnafeadh

(Photo by Robert M. Adam)

Dunoon complained to the Commissioners for Highland Roads and Bridges of the lack of a good harbour to serve the roads which brought several thousands of cattle to be shipped to the southern markets.[1]

While these routes across Loch Fyne were certainly used, the greater part of the droves from the west appear to have continued up the north-west side of the loch to Inveraray, some perhaps turning up Glen Shira bound for Dalmally and Tyndrum, while others continued eastward to the head of Loch Fyne. Till the coast road was made round the head of the loch, the route of the latter traffic probably led up Glen Shira as far as the Kilblaan Burn. Then crossing the hills by a track to the north of Dunderave, used according to tradition by pilgrims on their way to Iona and marked on Elphinstone's map of 1745, they came down into Glen Fyne at the old chapel of Kilmorich. General Roy's survey marks a route from the head of Loch Fyne to Loch Long by way of Glen Croe, following very much the line of the present road. It seems probable that this route was used by part of the early droving traffic from south and west Argyll, and the evidence of those who took part in the trade in the latter part of last century shows that by then this route to Loch Lomondside was in regular use. The 1747-55 survey, however, shows that there was an alternative route which according to local tradition was used by some drovers. This route led up Glen Fyne for several miles, crossing by the Allt-na-lairige into Dumbartonshire at the top of Glen Arnan and so reaching Glen Falloch at the head of Loch Lomond.

The north end of Loch Lomond was the meeting-place of three drovers' routes. While Crieff Tryst flourished, the quickest route for any cattle making for Crieff lay up Glen Falloch to join the route from Skye at the top of Glendochart, but after 1770 when Falkirk Tryst had taken the place of Crieff, it is probable that this route saw little traffic. A second route crossed the Falloch at the head of Loch Lomond and climbed the hills to the east of Ardlui to come into the head of Glen Gyle. James Hogg used this route in 1791 for droving sheep,[2] and those still (1948) living on Loch Lomondside remember seeing droves from Argyll climbing to the watershed from Glen Falloch. By Glen Gyle the

---

[1] *H.R. & B.*, 5th Report, 1811, Appendix R
[2] Hogg, *A Tour in the Highlands in 1803*, 15

droves passed along the side of Loch Katrine and were driven over the hill to Aberfoyle, and crossing the flat ground at the head of the Forth came by Gartmoren into the valley of the Endrick Water and so to Falkirk.[1]

The third route from the head of Loch Lomond led down the west side of the loch to Balloch and Dumbarton. The town of Dumbarton occurs early in the records of the cattle trade. In 1661 the Duke of Lennox as hereditary Keeper of Dumbarton Castle petitioned the Privy Council for an Order compelling drivers of cattle from Argyll passing Dumbarton Castle to pay a toll of 4s Scots on each beast as in the past, complaining that lately the drovers had taken a new route avoiding the castle, ' whereby his Majesty's garisons in the said castle is mightilie prejudged.' The Order was granted, but three years later the drovers protested that it was invalid and that they had a right to the road without payment ' past memory of man.' The dispute continued till 1684, when the drovers were finally successful and the tolls were abolished.[2] Four years earlier the magistrates of Dumbarton had petitioned the Privy Council for a bridge over the Leven. They claimed that ' this lying in the mouth of the Highlands and being the passe and inlett of all trade betwixt them and the Lowlands, the want of a bridge in that place does very much prejudge the trade of cowes which is one of the most considerable commodities of the nation, and which cowes are either stopt when the storme is great and so starved or in swimming over are extreamlie weakned and ofttimes drowned or in hazard thereof . . . so that they are forced to goe about by the bridge of Striveling, which is twenty-four myles of unsecure and rough gate where there is neither meat nor safety for the passingers nor cowes.'[3]

Throughout the entire droving period Dumbarton remained a cattle market of some importance for the supply of the growing population of the Clydeside towns, but from 1770 onwards an increasing proportion of the droves which came down the side of Loch Lomond crossed the Leven at Balloch, and from this point to Falkirk Tryst the route followed can be established in some detail, for it was still used in living memory by drovers from

[1] Information as to the use of this route has been supplied by Mr Donald McNicol whose family have for several generations been tenants of the Doune Farm, Ardlui, and by others living on Loch Lomondside.

[2] *R.P.C.*, 3rd series, I, 100, 101, 553–4 and 654 ; *R.P.C.*, 3rd series, IX, 86, 87, 90–3

[3] *R.P.C.*, 3rd series, VI, 498

Knapdale and Kintyre. From Balloch the route led by Gartocharn to Drymen or Killearn and then climbed the valley of the Endrick. The beasts then crossed the south shoulder of the Fintry Hills and came into the valley of the Carron Water, and so at last to Stenhousemuir and the Falkirk Tryst ; for some of them the end of all their journeyings ; for most the start of fresh travels to strange places and pastures new.

6

THE DROVE ROAD FROM THE NORTH

To one who watched from the hills behind Crieff the gathering
of the cattle for the Tryst on an autumn day of the early eighteenth
century, it would have been apparent that two main streams of
beasts were converging from different directions on the town.
While some droves were coming from the north-west down the
valley of the Earn or across the hills from Loch Tay, a second
stream was moving through the Sma' Glen from the direction of
Amulree and the valley of the Tay. Half a century later, when
Crieff Tryst had given way before the rising importance of
Falkirk, a watcher from the Castle Rock at Stirling might have
observed a similar meeting of traffic. While many droves were
approaching the crossing of the Forth from the direction of Doune
and the north-west, many more were slowly winding their way
down the track which led from Sheriffmuir into the Forth valley.

A study of the history of the cattle trade between the Highlands
and the Lowlands shows that, broadly, there were two main
routes by which droving traffic came from the north, north-west
and central Highlands to the Lowland Trysts. Of these main
streams one, and possibly the larger, had its origin in Skye, the
Outer Islands and part of the north-western districts. The other
had its source in the far north and the eastern half of the counties
of Ross and Inverness, and each was fed by tributary streams
from the country through which it passed on its way to the south.
The separate existence of these two streams of beasts is accounted
for largely by the mass of high ground lying across Scotland both
north and south of the Great Glen, which made it necessary for
much of the traffic to pass at the west or at the east end of what is
now the Caledonian Canal.[1] There were important lateral con-
nections between the streams, but in the main they remained
distinct till the markets of Southern Perthshire and Stirlingshire
and the barrier of the Forth brought them together. It is with
the stream of animal traffic which had its source in the far north,
which moved through Easter Ross-shire, Badenoch and Atholl,
and which came at last to Crieff by way of the Sma' Glen, that
we are here concerned.

[1] See Appendix B (p. 227)

Plate 6   A drove route in Wester Ross-shire : in Strathnashellag

(*Photo by Robert M. Adam*)

It has been seen that the earliest evidence of legitimate cattle traffic comes from the west and north-west where droving to the Lowlands can be traced back to the start of the sixteenth century. The reason for this would, as has been suggested, seem to lie partly in the need of the poorer north-west districts to export their beasts in the absence of feeding to carry them through the winter. In the flatter and richer districts of the east side of Scotland arable farming provided some sort of winter feeding, poor as it no doubt was, and made it perhaps less essential to market beasts on the approach of winter, while the cattle raised in the eastern half of the country seem on the whole to have been less suited for droving than those of the hardier west coast breed. Larger population and the possibility of some coastwise or export trade from the north-eastern counties meant more local demand, while it may be that the character and way of life of the people of these rather more developed areas were also less suited to the droving trade. None the less the volume of cattle traffic which used the more easterly route was by no means negligible, and the evidence available indicates that the stream of beasts which started in the far north had, with its tributary streams, reached a size rivalling the droves from the west by the time it passed through the Sma' Glen to reach the Perthshire lowlands.

In the extreme north of the country, Caithness had, at least as early as the start of the eighteenth century, an outlet for her cattle readier to hand than the markets of Central Scotland. John Brand, writing of Orkney, Shetland and Caithness in 1701 speaks of a considerable export trade with Leith in barrelled beef, tallow, skins and hides,[1] while the Dutch herring boats which came in large numbers each summer to Orkney and Shetland meant a local demand for beef ; but not all the Caithness beasts were marketed at home, and the letters of Sir James Sinclair of Mey show that before the middle of the eighteenth century cattle were being sold from the county for droving to the South.[2] Defoe writing about 1726 refers to many black cattle being bred in Caithness and sold to drovers, mainly for droving to Norfolk, Suffolk and Essex,[3] and Pennant in 1772 estimated that in good years the county sold to the drovers

---

[1] Brand, *A Brief Description of Orkney, Zetland, etc.*, 1701, 149
[2] *Manuscript Letters of Sir James Sinclair of Mey*, Box xviii, 1738–43, H.M. Register House   [3] Defoe, *Tour through Great Britain in 1724* (1762 edn.), IV, 253

as many as 2,200.[1] By the end of the century, the annual number driven south had risen to about 3,000,[2] and the writer of the Statistical Account for Wick speaks of the parish being full of black cattle which are sold to drovers for Falkirk and England at a price of 40s to 50s.[3] He maintains that these cattle from the north-east coastal districts drive as well as those from the Highland districts. The general view of many contemporary writers was, however, that cattle of the true Highland breed from Skye and the West Highlands were better in quality and more suitable for droving, and the relatively poor quality of Caithness cattle for droving may well explain the important place which barrelled beef and hides occupied in the list of exports from the district. The beasts from Caithness moreover, faced a four weeks journey to the South of Scotland, and a letter from James Gunn of Braemore to Sir James Sinclair, whose beasts he had bought in 1743 suggests that drovers of Caithness cattle were fortunate if all their beasts ' held out to travill.'[4] An account of a recent Falkirk Tryst contained in a letter written from Edinburgh in October 1805 makes the following comment on Caithness cattle : ' Large cattle from Caithness will not answer. Sir John Sinclair's Galloway oxen, worth £14 each in Caithness, only fetched £7 3 6d at Falkirk. The true breed for droving to be established in Caithness is either the pure Sky or the Argyle breed or a cross between the Argyle or Sky Bull and the best sort of Caithness Cows. That kind of stock would always fetch a fair price . . .'[5]

As the stream of cattle from the far north moved down the East Coast by Helmsdale and Brora, it was augmented by droves coming from Strath-Naver and Strath Halladale and the glens immediately to the westward and by other cattle driven across the hills from the north-west coast. Here in the upland glens and on the Atlantic seaboard of Sutherland cattle rearing had for long been the main, if not the only, industry of the country. In the district of Reay the breeding of cattle and the inevitable accompaniment of cattle thieving had figured in the Privy Council records of the seventeenth century,[6] and when the Statistical

[1] Pennant, *Tour in Scotland, 1772*, III, 202
[2] *O.S.A.*, Caithness, XX, 519   [3] *O.S.A.*, Wick, X, 22
[4] *Manuscript Letters of Sir James Sinclair of Mey*, Box xviii, 22nd Oct. 1743, H.M. Register House
[5] *Sutherland Estate Papers*. Letter from John Sinclair, 12th Oct. 1805
[6] *R.P.C.*, 3rd series, II, 566, 567

Account was compiled at the close of the eighteenth century the parishes of Reay and Eddrachillis had a combined cattle population of close on 6,000 beasts.[1] Sales to the drovers at a price of £2 10s to £4 a head were, says the Account, the main support of the people. Cattle were evidently being regularly driven to the South from the Sutherland Estates at the beginning of the century, for in a letter written from Edinburgh on 31 August 1703 addressed to the Earl of Sutherland, Mr Charles Ross asks that ' Your Lordship will be pleased to order one of your drovers to give me two fat cows to be my winter beef.' [2]

For those cattle from Caithness and East Sutherland, the Kyle of Sutherland and the Dornoch Firth were formidable obstacles on the route to the South. Some of the beasts may have been taken across at the Meikle Ferry near Skibo, but many of the drovers appear to have preferred to cross the Kyle at Creich. The minister of that parish writing in the Statistical Account in 1794 reports that this crossing is necessary for all the cattle of Caithness and Sutherland and also for those coming from Lord Reay's country except the Assynt district. The cattle swam the Kyle, he writes, or if necessary were ferried across, the readiness with which the beasts took to the water foretelling, according to a local supersitition, whether the prices at the Trysts would be good or bad.[3]

Until the beginning of the nineteenth century there existed north of Inverness little in the way of roads save the tracks of pack-horses and cattle. There were no bridges over the large rivers, and though some of the smaller ones appear to have been bridged, Telford in his Survey and Report to the Commissioners for Highlands Roads and Bridges in 1803 reported that the lack of bridges over the Conon and the Beauly was one of the chief weaknesses of communication in the north.[4] These water barriers were a deterrent to dealers coming from the south in search of cattle, and a further discouragement appears to have been the difficulty of droving through and finding stances for their beasts in the relatively rich cultivated farming lands of Easter Ross-shire. As late as 1831 drovers were refusing to go north of Bridge

[1] O.S.A., Eddrachillis, VI, 283
[2] Sutherland Estate Papers, Bundle 19, Nos. 619-44
[3] O.S.A., Creich, VIII, 372
[4] So rapidly did the work of the Commissioners open up the country that in 1818 the Inverness Courier was able to report that ' From Inverness to John o' Groats it is now possible to travel without crossing a ferry or fording a river.'

of Conon because of the action of local landowners in confiscating cattle straying from the drove roads, particularly on that part of the route which led from Kincardine on the Dornoch Firth to Strathrusdale.[1] From the reference to this route it seems that the drovers after passing the Kyle of Sutherland crossed the high ground between the Dornoch and Cromarty Firths by the hill road past Aultnamain Inn, or possibly by tracks farther to the westward.

At intervals on the drove route from the northern counties, small local trysts had been established, at least by the mid-eighteenth century, for the sale of cattle brought from the glens and the grazings lying to the westward. Contemporary records of the cattle trade contain scattered references to Trysts at Georgemas and in the Strath of Dunbeath in Caithness, at Clashmore, Monibuie and Dornoch in Sutherland and at Kildary in Ross-shire. Some of these were certainly in existence in the first half of the eighteenth century, but the most important tryst for the droves from the north dates only from the first quarter of last century.

Midway across the narrow neck of low land which lies between the head of the Cromarty Firth and the Beauly Firth and in the direct path of traffic from north to south, the position of Muir of Ord gives to it many of the advantages which made Falkirk the great cattle market of Central Scotland. For traffic from the north and north-east reaching the Cromarty Firth about Alness the only route to the south was by the crossing of the Conon at the head of the Firth. To the west and north-west of Muir of Ord radiated Strath Garve, Strath Bran, Strath Conon and Glen Orrin, the first two affording to this day the main overland communication with the seaboard of Wester Ross. A few miles to the south lay the valley of the Beauly leading inland to Strath Glass, Glen Strathfarrar, Glen Cannich and Glen Affric. All these glens sent their quota of cattle to the Muir of Ord market. The valley of the Beauly and the road up Strath Glass offered, moreover, a route to the south by way of Fort Augustus, while the road to Inverness gave an alternative route to Crieff and Central Scotland. The Tryst at Muir of Ord was established about 1820. At first it was held near the village of Beauly and was known as ' Feill-na-manachainn.' Later it was moved to a better site about a mile to the north, and though it never rivalled

[1] *Inverness Courier*, 1st November 1821

in size the great Trysts at Crieff, Falkirk and Dumfries, ' Blair dubh ' as it was then called remained until near the end of last century the greatest market in the north for cattle from Caithness, Sutherland and Ross-shire.

Before the development of Oban, Mallaig and Kyle of Lochalsh, Poolewe on the West Ross-shire coast was the main port of entry for traffic from a considerable part of the Western Islands. The cattle of Skye and many of the Outer Hebrides crossed to the mainland, as has been seen, at Kyle Rhea, but for sea-borne traffic from the islands to the mainland, Poolewe was almost the only port. It seems probable that the use of Poolewe for island traffic dates back to comparatively early times. John Knox who toured in the Highlands and Islands in 1786 reported that he sailed from Stornoway to Poolewe in a small unseaworthy vessel used for the transport of cattle to the Ross-shire coast.[1] Evander MacIver, for many years factor on the Sutherland Estates, has described how as a boy he sailed from Stornoway to Poolewe about the year 1818 in a sloop laden with cattle which had been purchased at the Lewis cattle tryst. The beasts were thrown overboard in Loch Ewe and made to swim ashore.[2] At least as early as the end of the eighteenth century the route between Poolewe and Dingwall appears to have been in frequent use. James Hogg, describing a tour in the Highlands in 1803, refers to the Inn at Kinlochewe as having been built to accommodate those travelling from Dingwall to Gairloch or towards the ferry of Poolewe ' where there is a packet once each week to Lewis,' and in the same year George Brown, reporting to the Commissioners for Highland Roads and Bridges, refers to the route from Poolewe by Loch Maree and Kinlochewe to Achnasheen, Strath Bran and Garve as ' the great line of communication ' from Lewis and the West Coast to Dingwall and Inverness.

To Poolewe or to points on the nearby coast came the cattle of Lewis. The New Statistical Account for Stornoway records that near the town ' there is a square mile of moor enclosed for a cattle tryst where several thousand head are exposed for sale and 2,000 at least change hands in 2 days. From 20 to 30 drovers come from the Mainland and some from England.' [3] Some cattle from Harris also landed at Poolewe, and evidence given in

[1] Knox, *Tour through the Highlands of Scotland and the Hebride Isles in 1786*, 192-3
[2] *Reminiscences of Evander MacIver*, 1905, 6
[3] *N.S.A.*, Stornoway, Ross and Cromarty, XIV, 140

the course of litigation in 1868 by those who had taken part in the droving trade in the early years of the century tells of landings of cattle from the Outer Isles at Gairloch, Aultbea and Gruinard.[1] From Poolewe these island cattle together with those of the parish of Gairloch of which as many as 500 were sold off each year, appear to have followed the north shore of Loch Maree to Kinlochewe and Achnasheen, while many of those which landed at Aultbea and Gruinard went up the valley of the Gruinard River past Loch-na-Shellag near the head of the river and so by hill tracks to join either the road from Ullapool to Dingwall or that from Achnasheen to Garve.[2] The landing of cattle from Lewis at Poolewe and near Aultbea as late as 1880 is confirmed by Mr Angus McLeod, a retired drover now (1948) in his 100th year living near Gruinard who started droving about the year 1868. The beasts which came ashore near Aultbea at that time were, it seems, driven to Muir of Ord by way of Gruinard, Dundonnell and Braemore as being shorter than the route by Kinlochewe and Achnasheen. The hill route by Loch-na-Shellag which had been upheld as a drove road in the litigation of 1868, was apparently by that time no longer in regular use. From Braemore the beasts were driven east to Garve and Dingwall but two deviations from the main road were used by the drovers, and it appears from local information that these are still in occasional use. One of these turned due south from the main road near Altguish and crossed the forest of Corriemoillie to Garve, so shortening the distance and keeping the beasts on soft ground where grazing was available. The other short cut left the Ullapool-Garve road near Inchbrae Lodge and crossing the saddle between Ben Wyvis and Little Wyvis rejoined at Auchterneed the road to Dingwall.[3]

The Statistical Account records that in 1794 the parish of Applecross in Wester Ross-shire contained about 3,000 cattle, the annual sales of cattle being the chief means of support of the people.[4] For these, the natural route would be by Strathcarron

---

[1] *Mackenzie* v. *Bankes*. Court of Session Cases, 1868, 6 Macpherson's Reports, 936 and Notes of Evidence in *Session Papers*, Signet Library.   [2] ibid.

[3] From information collected in the Ullapool district it appears that cattle from Lewis were regularly landed at Ullapool within living memory. It is also reported that cattle from the Ullapool area were at times driven through Glen Achall into Glen Einig and so to Strathoykell by a branch road turning off at Craggan in Glen Einig which leads into Strathcarron and so to Ardgay. These routes, it seems, were regularly used for taking beasts to the late autumn sale at Ardgay.

[4] *O.S.A.*, Applecross, III, 371

and Strath Bran to the East Coast, and local tradition tells also of the regular use of droving tracks from the districts of Lochalsh and North Kintail to Glen Cannich and Glen Affric bound for the Muir of Ord market.

Many of these tracks across the North of Scotland are certainly of very early origin ; how early cannot now be determined, but when General Roy surveyed the Highlands in the years between 1747 and 1755 some of the routes, such as that from Loch Broom to Dingwall by Strath Garve were marked on the large-scale map of Scotland which was at that time prepared, and Pennant in 1772 noted that in the Loch Broom district the sale of black cattle to drovers from as far south as Craven in Yorkshire was the chief support of the people.[1] For these the only practicable route to the South was by Strath Garve to Muir of Ord and Beauly.

While the accident of a nineteenth-century litigation has established beyond all doubt the existence of droving traffic from the Poolewe area and one of the routes by which these droves crossed the country from the West Coast, it is hardly possible at this distance of time to establish with equal certainty the routes of all the other cross-country traffic in this great area of hills and glens and lochs. But if the exact routes cannot be determined the general trend of the traffic is not in doubt, and it would seem to be beyond question that to Muir of Ord came cattle not only from Caithness and Sutherland and from the many glens which drain to the Beauly and Cromarty Firths, but also from the whole seaboard of Wester Ross lying between Loch Broom and Loch Alsh.

To the south of Muir of Ord two alternative routes lay open to drovers bound for the Trysts at Crieff or Falkirk. Some part of the droving traffic from the north went by Beauly and the Aird of Lovat to Inverness, and after 1817 Inverness became the great centre for the wool and sheep trade in the North of Scotland. For cattle traffic from the north, however, Inverness appears to have been of minor importance. The town never figured in the list of important cattle markets. The *Inverness Courier* for 28 October 1824 reports that the tryst recently established at Muir of Ord has almost superseded that at Inverness, but it is on record that in the third week of May 1818 as many as 1,500 cattle purchased at the Ross-shire Trysts passed through the town.[2]

---

[1] Pennant, *Tour in Scotland, 1772*, I, 364   [2] *Inverness Courier*, 21 May 1818

The route by Inverness reaching the Spey Valley about Nethy Bridge or Aviemore passed south through the Pass of Drumochter, while it also gave access to the high passes through the Cairngorm Mountains to Deeside and the Angus glens. A Survey of the Agriculture of Inverness-shire in 1813 mentions the existence of a periodical cattle market at Kingussie and a new one established in 1804 on a date fixed to suit drovers for the South passing through Badenoch,[1] while in 1814 a Tryst was in existence at Pitmain near Kingussie for the sale to drovers of cattle for Falkirk.[2]

The alternative route to the South chosen by many drovers from Muir of Ord illustrates their preference for the less frequented ways leading them through hill country which offered greater freedom of movement with more abundant and cheaper wayside grazing for their cattle. A few miles south of Muir of Ord, the valley of the Beauly leads south-westward into Strath Glass and the hills of the Forests of Fasnakyle and Guisachan. What proportion of the droving traffic from the north chose this route cannot be accurately estimated, but it is known that many and probably most drovers preferred it. An article which appeared in the *Inverness Courier* for 26 September 1827 contains the following passage : ' We believe the great Northern Drove Road begins somewhere about the Kyle of Sutherland (at which place a number of important cattle markets are held throughout the year) and runs nearly parallel with one of the Parliamentary roads for a considerable distance, through the lands of Ardross, by Fowlis, and Dingwall to the Muir of Ord (another great market)—then branching away through the mountains towards Fort Augustus and from thence southwards—avoiding the public lines of road throughout the whole distance till it touches occasionally on the turnpike roads in Perthshire. There are other branch drove-roads leading from various points of the country into this line, but this is unquestionably the principal one as proceeding direct from two of the greatest market stances in the North of Scotland.' From the point where Guisachan House now stands near the head of Strath Glass, an easy route leads across the hills of the Guisachan Forest to Torgyle in Glen Moriston, connecting with the old military road leading to Fort Augustus, and when in 1888 a right of way past Guisachan was unsuccessfully challenged, the evidence brought in its support revealed the steady use by drovers

---

[1] Robertson, *General View of the Agriculture of the County of Inverness*, 1813, 302
[2] Elizabeth Grant of Rothiemurchus, *Memoirs of a Highland Lady*, 1898 ed., 248–9

Plate 7   A drove route from Kintail to Glen Affric : in Glen Lichet

(Photo by Robert M. Adam)

of this and other cross-country routes throughout the preceding half-century. The traffic at that time recorded was mainly a traffic in sheep, but cattle traffic too used these roads and there seems little reason to doubt that this route had long been in use for cattle droving.[1]

As these droves from Strath Glass and Guisachan descended into Glen Moriston they joined one of the routes used by the cattle which had crossed from Skye at Kyle Rhea. A Memorial of 1805 presented to the Commissioners for Highland Roads and Bridges refers to the use by cattle from Skye and the Outer Isles of the military road to Fort Augustus, and a Memorandum of about the same date among the *Breadalbane Papers* speaks of this as the alternative line for the droves which did not use the route by Glen Garry.[2] South of Fort Augustus the droves from Skye or from Muir of Ord crossed the hills to the Upper Spey Valley by the Pass of Corrieyairack, the route which Wade chose for the construction of his military road in 1731, and over which Prince Charles Edward passed in 1745. This route from the North of Scotland to the trysts was evidently in active use by stock in the early nineteenth century, for the *Inverness Courier* of 24 July 1823 reports that in the course of discussions over the Bill for the Maintenance of Highland Roads and Bridges then before Parliament, a concession had been made whereby cattle might travel from Strath Halladale in Sutherlandshire westward and southward to Fort Augustus, and so over the Corrieyairack road to Perthshire without payment of toll except 10d per score of black cattle and 5d per score of sheep and lambs payable once at the Pitmain Bridge over the Spey. This route over the Pass of Corrieyairack was almost certainly the route used by the large droves from Skye which Bishop Forbes met at Drumochter in 1723, and references to it in contemporary records show the Pass to have remained in extensive use by drovers till the second half of the nineteenth century.

At Dalwhinnie the droves which had crossed the Monadhliath Mountains from Fort Augustus joined those which had come from Inverness and the North by the more easterly route, and it seems probable that during the droving days the hills which enclose the Pass of Drumochter looked down on a concentration

---

[1] *Winans and Chisholm* v. *Lord Tweedmouth*, Court of Session Cases, 1888, 15 Rettie's Reports, 540 and Notes of Evidence in *Session Papers*, Signet Library, No. 98, 1888.

[2] *Breadalbane Papers (Roads)*, Box 4, H.M. Register House

of droving traffic as great as was to be seen at that time in any part of the Highlands. At Dalwhinnie on 31 August 1723 Bishop Forbes found eight droves—1,200 beasts in all—bound for Crieff, and in the Drumochter Pass a drove a mile in length, with 300 more resting at the head of Loch Garry.[1] A few miles south of Drumochter Pass the drove road from the North left the valley of the Garry at Dalnacardoch, and crossing the hills by Trinafour and the head waters of the Errochty on the line of General Wade's military road, came to Tummel Bridge and the borders of the Rannoch country. Passing to the east of Schiehallion the route of the cattle then led to Coshieville near the junction of Lyon and Tay. In the 14th Report to the Commissioners for Highland Roads and Bridges in 1828 the route from Dalnacardoch to the valley of the Tay is referred to as the route by which go to Falkirk, Doune and other trysts ' almost all the cattle and sheep of the North and North-West Highlands.' [2]

From the foot of Glen Lyon part of the cattle traffic appears to have gone by Aberfeldy and Wade's Tay Bridge, while part forded the Lyon and the Upper Tay, crossing the hills to the south of Kenmore into Glen Quaich and so to Amulree on the road to Crieff. Here, at the crossing of the Tay, the drovers were on ground trodden by the feet of their less reputable ancestors. Mackintosh of Borlum, writing in 1742, refers to Kenmore as ' a very frequent and beaten Pass for driving stolen cattle from Perthshire, Stirlingshire, Kinross and Clackmannan into Glenlyon, Rannoch, Breadalbane, Glencoe, Appin and Lorn.' [3]

Until the middle of the eighteenth century Crieff remained, as has been seen, the main centre of trade for the cattle from the North of Scotland and for many of those from the West Coast and the Hebrides, but shortly after 1750 various factors undermined the importance of Crieff as a cattle market and led ultimately to the transference of the main trade to Falkirk Tryst. By the last decade of the century when the Statistical Account was compiled, though many thousands of cattle were still using the route through the Sma' Glen to Crieff, they passed the town on the day before the date fixed for the Tryst, so avoiding the market dues which were still levied.[4] By that time Crieff Tryst

---

[1] *Bishop Forbes' Journal*, 235   [2] *H.R. & B.*, 14th Report, 1828, Appendix D
[3] Mackintosh, *A Short Scheme . . . to stop depredations . . . to the Northern Counties of Scotland*, 1742
[4] *O.S.A.*, Crieff, IX, 596

had shrunk to a mere shadow of what it once had been, and a description of the cattle route from the North must follow the beasts a short distance farther to their destination at Falkirk Tryst.

A little way down-stream from Crieff the old ford of Dalpatrick crosses the River Earn. The ford is on the direct line from Gilmerton where the Sma' Glen road emerges from the hills, and the name of ' Highlandman ' which the nearby railway station still bears is locally believed to date back to the days when Highland drovers in large numbers came that way. At Dalpatrick Ford the droves crossed the Earn and, coming into Strathallan by way of Muthill and the Muir of Orchil, they crossed the Allan Water about Greenloaning, and came to Sheriffmuir. Here on the north-west slopes of the Ochils, at a point immediately to the east of the site of the battle of 1715, extensive common rights of grazing for long existed. The area was a favourite stance ground, and when the common was divided in 1771 the evidence of local witnesses agrees as to its frequent use by drovers bound for Falkirk. The situation of Sheriffmuir made it peculiarly well suited for the purpose, for this was the last hill grazing available for beasts from the North on their way to Falkirk, and here drovers who were not pressed for time could rest their droves perhaps for a day or more before taking them on to the Tryst. From Sheriffmuir the droves moved down the south-west slopes of the Ochils to Bridge of Allan and the valley of the Forth, on the last miles of the long road to Falkirk Tryst.

While the extensive use of this route by Sheriffmuir is well established by a variety of contemporary evidence, it seems that some of the cattle from Crieff and a portion of those which passed through Perth from the north-eastern counties reached Falkirk by a different route. Due south of Crieff across Strathearn, Gleneagles and Glendevon provided a ready way through the low range of grassy hills which a contemporary writer called ' those verdant Downs the Ochil Hills,' [1] while to the east of Gleneagles other tracks offered an easy crossing of the Ochils and the best of upland grazing. In his *Memorial respecting the Road from Yetts of Muckhart through Glendevon and Gleneagles into Strathearn*, Sir Patrick Murray of Ochtertyre records that between July 1812 and July 1813 at the side bar on the Hillfoots road giving access

[1] Knox, op. cit. 11

to the Glendevon road at Yetts of Muckhart the following tolls were collected :

Cattle, 863 at 1s a score
Sheep, 13,219 at 5d a score

but it is not clear from the context whether these beasts were going south or north or both. The numbers are small, but Gleneagles and Glendevon comprised only one of several routes through the Ochils, and it must be borne in mind that drovers were adepts at avoiding tolls. For droves crossing the Ochils by any of these routes bound for Falkirk, the natural crossings of the Forth were at Alloa and Kincardine-on-Forth, and the Minute Book of the Justices of the Peace for Stirlingshire for the year 1827 shows the two ferries in active use by the drovers. In May of that year the Justices had before them a complaint that the existing rates for ferrying black cattle at Alloa were too high, and that for this reason many droves took other routes to the South. New rates were fixed at 4d. a beast up to six and 3d a beast for more, or 5s a score. In the spring of the following year a steam ferry boat was put on at Higginsneuk (Kincardine) Ferry in addition to the sailing boats used for black cattle, the ferrying rate being fixed at 6s 8d a score. The cattle traffic at the Higginsneuk Ferry appears to have interfered with the ferrying of passengers, for in the autumn of the same year it was found necessary to make special rules for dealing with the ferrying of cattle droves. It was provided that a drover coming to the ferry should have the right of using the first boat to cross, but that passengers should have the right of the next boat even if they had arrived after the arrival of the drove, and so on alternately till the whole drove had been ferried. No passengers were to cross with cattle except those in charge of them, and extra men were to be available to help with the ferrying at times of Fairs or Trysts.[1]

The crossing of the Forth behind them, a few more miles brought the tired cattle from the North to the tryst ground at Stenhousemuir, there to merge in the vast assembly of men and beasts which was gathering from every part of the Highlands and Islands of Scotland.

[1] *Minute Book of Quarter Sessions, of J.P.'s for Stirlingshire*, 6th December 1819

Plate 8   A drove route from Deeside to Angus : in Glen Doll

(Photo by Robert M. Adam)

THE DROVE ROADS OF MORAYSHIRE, ABERDEENSHIRE AND ANGUS

THE great agricultural developments which brought into the forefront of Scotland's cattle-breeding industry that part of the country which contains the valleys of Dee, Don, Deveron and Spey and the glens of Angus belong to the last years of the eighteenth and the first half of the nineteenth centuries, but long before then this north-eastern area of Scotland had figured in the story of Scotland's cattle. The long valleys of the Dee and the Don, with the passes north and south of the Cairngorm Mountains, gave ready access to the area from the wild hilly country which stretched from Badenoch to Lochaber and the West Coast, while the streams which feed the Dee on its right bank provided easy routes across the hills into the glens of Angus. The natural barrier of hills which stand round the head waters of the two rivers was thus less of a protection than a source of danger, and it was over paths trodden by centuries of raiding traffic that, when more peaceful times came, the drovers of north-east Scotland passed on their way to the trysts and their lawful occasions.

The sites chosen for the castles built at various dates on the banks of the Dee and the Don in the stormy days of Scotland's history, show how greatly the life of this area in early times was conditioned by the ready access offered by the hill passes and the valleys of the two rivers. On the Don the Castle of Corgarff guarded the upper valley of the river and the pass which leads from its head waters through the Forest of Glenavon to Speyside. A few miles down-stream Glenbucket Castle kept watch on tracks leading north-westward across the hills into Glenlivet and Lower Speyside, or northwards to the Deveron valley. Lower again the ancient Castle of Kildrummy dominated the low pass giving access to Strathbogie and the Moray coast. On Deeside, the site of Kindrochit Castle near Braemar controlled both the route leading from Badenoch and the West into the valley of the Dee and also the Cairnwell Pass which led from the Dee to the South, while down-stream the Castle of Aboyne guarded the crossings of the Dee, which gave access by hill passes to the glens of Angus.[1]

The historical records available do not make it possible to determine how early cattle breeding in this part of Scotland began, but there is no reason to doubt that on the pasture lands of what is now Morayshire, Banffshire, Aberdeenshire and Angus, cattle grazed from very early times. Certainly, by the middle of the fifteenth century, the cattle on the borders of Angus and Perthshire were of sufficient importance to attract unwelcome attention from their neighbours, and in 1454 a raid by the Munros of Foulis on Strathardle led to a fight near Inverness between them and the Mackintoshes of Moy, who had demanded a tribute or ' Road Collop ' for the right of passage through their land of a large booty of cattle which the Munros were driving north.[2] By the sixteenth century, cattle trading in this area of eastern Scotland was evidently well established, for when at the end of the century the men of Skye and Kintail started to sell cattle, it was, as has been seen, to the markets of Glamis, Brechin and ' Ellit [Alyth] in the Bray of Angus ' that they sent them. It was a precarious trade attended by heavy loss, for the route of the beasts took them through wild country whose inhabitants no doubt demanded some return for the right of passage, and if need be, took it by summary methods. Complaints of these cattle thefts found their way in due course to the Privy Council in Edinburgh, in common with similar tales of loss suffered by the people of Strathardle, Glen Isla and Glen Shee, for the eyes of the men of Atholl and Badenoch turned for their prey to these eastern glens.

Farther to the north, in Aberdeenshire, a regular trade in cattle had been established at least as early as the first quarter of the seventeenth century. An Order of the Privy Council in 1628 granted a weekly market a few miles north-west of Inverurie, and a further Order of the same year fixed the prices for goods, including cattle, at three fairs in the Aberdeenshire districts of Garioch and Strathbogie.[3] A description of Aberdeenshire and Banffshire compiled about the year 1662 notes the existence of a number of fairs covering the area, including fairs at Turriff on

[1] Simpson, *Early Castles of Mar.* Proceedings of Society of Scottish Antiquaries, 1928, LXIII, 102
[2] Mackenzie, *History of the Munros*, 25–6
[3] *R.P.C.*, 2nd series, II, 409, 616

Deveronside, Rayne in Garioch, Kincardine and Birse on Deeside and Deer in Buchan.[1] The contemporary description shows that horses, cattle and sheep were sold at these fairs, as well as home products and especially the webs of coarse woollen cloth in which the Aberdeenshire hand-loom weavers had established an early and prosperous trade.

While the amount of trade crossing the hills between Deeside and the South was at that time a mere fraction of what it was to become, a regular traffic over the passes certainly existed in the first half of the seventeenth century, and when about 1630 Sir James Balfour of Denmylne described ' the Chief Passages from the River Tay to the River Dee over the Mountains ' his list covered no less than eleven routes, including ' the Carnavalay [Cairnwell] from Glenshee to Castle Town in the Brae of Mar,' the Cairn-o-Mount Pass from Fettercairn to Kincardine o'Neil and routes from Glen Clova and Glen Esk to Glen Muick and Glen Tanar.[2] Sir James also listed the ' Passages over the River Dee by Boate,' and this shows thirteen crossing-places on the river between Braemar and the mouth including ferries at Braemar, Crathie, Abergeldie, Kincardine o'Neil, Banchory and Drum. Of the passes in use over the hills, the Cairn-o-Mount route was probably the most important, and in 1664 the Privy Council granted a Petition of Douglas, the Laird of Tilliquhillie near Banchory for a national contribution for the repair of the Bridge of Dee which had been destroyed by flood.[3] The Petition claimed that the bridge is the only ' hie passage mercat way ' for beasts and other traffic from north to south by way of Cairn-o-Mount, except by going twenty-four miles out of the ordinary way to Aberdeen. The use of the Cairn-o-Mount route for cattle traffic at this time is confirmed by a reference in the Acts of the Scots Parliament in 1681 to a toll on cattle passing over the Bridge of Dye.[4]

Throughout the first half of the eighteenth century, cattle breeding in the north-eastern counties of Scotland remained on a comparatively small scale. The agricultural developments which brought such big changes to the district were still to come, and in Aberdeenshire and along the coasts of Morayshire and Angus

---

[1] *Macfarlane's Geographical Collections*, II, 305
[2] National Library of Scotland, MS., 33.2.27
[3] *R.P.C.*, 3rd series, I, 519
[4] Fraser, *The Old Deeside Road*, 78–80

the farmers laboured on in a struggle to win a livelihood from land cultivated under a system whose only merit lay in its antiquity. Infield and outfield persisted, the infield in constant crop, enriched only by the manure of cattle which struggled half-starved through the winter, the outfield left fallow till the lapse of time should store enough fertility to grow a few successive crops of indifferent barley before it reverted to its fallow state. In Aberdeenshire, Banffshire and Kincardineshire, fields growing ten, fifteen or even more successive crops of grain were not uncommon as late as the closing years of the eighteenth century, and it is told of a Kincardineshire farmer that on being complimented on the good appearance of his crop he replied that it was no wonder seeing it was only the eighteenth crop since the field got dung.[1] Arable farming remained the chief activity, and with the six-, eight- and even ten-ox plough the universal method of cultivation, cattle were valued chiefly for their use as draught animals. As late as the end of the eighteenth century the minister of an Aberdeenshire parish recorded that of 953 cattle in the parish 346 were oxen for its 65 ploughs.[2] In the upland parts of these north-eastern counties some cattle breeding was carried on, and a small droving traffic passed over the old routes from Donside to Deeside and on across the hills to the markets of the Angus coast, to Crieff and the South ; but this was on a small scale. Until well into the second half of the eighteenth century, though the payment of rents in money was becoming more common,[3] these continued to be paid largely in produce, a practice which forced the farmers to keep much of their land under cultivation. Moreover the risks of cattle breeding near the hills or cattle droving through them were great. Morayshire, Aberdeenshire and the Angus glens were still the hunting-ground of the cattle thieves in the country to the westward—' those wild scurrilous people among quhom ther is bot small fear or knowledge of God,' as Sir James Balfour called them, and when after 1746 the authorities set their minds to the task of bringing peace and security to the Highlands, the protection of this area from cattle raiding was one of their main preoccupations. The key to the problem lay in the guarding of a line running from Blair Atholl up the valley of the Perthshire Garry through the Pass of Drumochter to the Upper Spey, and

---

[1] Alexander, *Northern Rural Life in the 18th Century*, 23
[2] Alexander, op. cit., 71. Graham, *Social Life in Scotland in the 18th Century*, 156
[3] *O.S.A.*, King Edward, XI, 405

Plate 9   A drove route from Braemar : looking north from the Cairnwell Pass

(Photo by Robert M. Adam)

the securing of the glens and passes leading east of that line through the hills to the valleys of the Don and the Dee and the glens of Angus and Kincardineshire. Memoranda of 1744 and 1747 detail the measures proposed to check cattle thieving.[1] Small military detachments were to be posted at various points on a line between Blair Atholl in the south and Ruthven in the north, and at key-points to control such passes and inlets through which ' the thievish sett used to make their incursions.' [2] These points included Dalnacardoch and Dalwhinnie on either side of the Drumochter Pass, Glenfeshie and Glenclunie in the hills near the top of the Dee, Corgarff and Inchrory at the head waters of the Don, and Glenmuick and Glen Clova on the passes leading to Angus. In the Memorandum of 1747 the routes by which cattle were driven to the raiders' strongholds are described. From Angus and Kincardineshire the raiders passed with their stolen beasts, through Glen Clova, Glencallater and Glenclunie to Deeside and so up the south side of the Dee to the hills of the Atholl Forest, or crossing the Dee below Invercauld, they went by Glen Lui through the passes of the Cairngorms. Cattle stolen in the country between the Dee and the Don were driven through the Forest of Morven, up the valley of the Gairn and by way of Loch Builg into the valley of the Avon, and so to Speyside. The report of an officer in charge of the garrison at Corgarff in the years immediately following the Rising of 1745 described the route followed by raiders driving cattle from Banffshire.[3] Crossing the hills of the Cabrach at the head of the Deveron, they came by Glenbucket, Glen Nochty or Glen Ernan into Strathdon, then following the Don up-stream to its head waters, they passed by Inchrory into Glen Avon and so westward to the hills of Speyside and beyond. These routes which a hundred years earlier had known the hurried tread of the Macdonalds of Clanranald and Glen Garry, men from the Western Isles and men of Ulster who followed Montrose, led through high and rugged hill country calling for long forced marches with little rest or fodder for men or beasts till they reached uneasy sanctuary in the hills of Badenoch or Lochaber ; but the men who plied this trade were well accustomed to long marches and dangerous living, and it may be

---

[1] Spalding Club Miscellany II (1842), 85 ; New Spalding Club, *Historical Papers*, II, 490 et seq.
[2] Spalding Club Miscellany II (1842), 88
[3] New Spalding Club, *Historical Papers*, II, 506–8

doubted whether they found their lot more hard than did the English garrisons stationed after 1745 in remote outposts in the hills, and linked only by weekly patrols with other garrisons isolated in a wild and hostile countryside.[1]

The years which followed the Union of the Parliaments marked the beginning of great changes for Scotland's agriculture, and by the second half of the century an agricultural revolution was in full progress, the effects of which were nowhere more apparent than in these north-eastern counties. Hitherto arable farming had been their main activity, and even the cattle required for the heavy cumbrous ploughs which were then in use were largely imported from the counties south of the Tay. On the higher ground sheep were bred to supply the Aberdeenshire trade in woollen cloth and stockings, but cattle seem to have played a small part, and the droving traffic which crossed the hills south of the Dee remained of small proportions. ' Mr Hamilton, a steward of the Duke of Gordon's Estate of Strathbogie,' says a writer of 1811, ' was the first, it is believed, who attempted this adventurous expedition, which while then perhaps attended by advantages which exist not now, was counterbalanced also by corresponding inconveniences. The speculation was unprofitable to Mr Hamilton. He joined in the ruinous adventure with Prince Charles and in the rank of Governor of Carlisle exhibited a mournful example of the evils of revolution.' [2]

The mid years of the eighteenth century saw a great change. Improved methods of agriculture in Berwickshire and the Lothians turned the attention of the Lowland farmers from stock-raising to intensive crop-farming as a more profitable use of their rich soil, and this tended to push stock and particularly cattle-breeding farther and farther north. The trade in cloth and woollen goods which had hitherto been of importance to the north-east coast had suffered from the loss of Scotland's continental markets in which British foreign policy now involved her. The only markets now open to it were in England in direct competition with the growing English cloth industry which was

[1] A ' Memorandum concerning the Highlands,' dated 1746 pointed out that the difficulty of checking cattle thieving or of tracing those responsible lay partly in the unwillingness of witnesses to give evidence which would lay them and their goods open to the revenge of the raiders, and partly in the cost of criminal prosecution. This was estimated at £25, few of those seeking justice being themselves possessed of goods or property exceeding £40. (*Breadalbane Papers* (*Roads*), Box 4, H.M. Register House)

[2] Leslie, *General View of the Agriculture of Nairn and Moray*, 1811, 303–4

stimulated by the settlement in East Anglia of immigrant workers from the Netherlands. Britain's foreign wars meant a growing demand for cattle, while the settlement of the Highlands after 1745 and the end of the long tradition of cattle thieving meant that now stock-breeding and the traffic in beasts through the hills had at last been rid of one of its main risks and deterrents. The improved methods of farming which were to spread so rapidly during the next half-century were already having their effect. The sowing of rye grass and clover was being practised in Kincardineshire by 1752,[1] and with the increase in the enclosing of pasture ground, stock-raising took a great step forward. The Rebellion of 1745 caused a shortage of cattle in the Highlands. It is said that after the Battle of Culloden the Duke of Cumberland's soldiers drove in a herd of 20,000 cattle from the surrounding districts,[2] and this, aided by serious cattle disease in England in 1746 and 1762, caused a steady rise in price, a rise which with minor fluctuations, was to continue all through the Napoleonic Wars. English cattle dealers started to come to the markets of Central Scotland in search of beasts in 1766, and Scottish drovers and dealers soon entered the trade in competition with them. This date may be taken as marking the beginning of droving on a large scale not only from the north-eastern counties but from all the cattle-breeding areas of Scotland, and from that time on the demand for Scottish cattle was steady and urgent.[3] So the farmers of the north-eastern counties came more and more to be drawn into the cattle trade, and from then on each year saw increasing numbers of their beasts brought for sale to the Tryst at Falkirk.

The north-eastern corner of Scotland now under consideration can be divided roughly into three sections. Of these, the most easterly consists of a relatively flat coastal plain stretching south from Banff and Fraserburgh on the Moray Firth to Stonehaven and the coast of Angus. To the west of this Lowland section a belt of hilly but not mountainous country extends south from Banff and the mouth of the Spey to Kirriemuir and Brechin in Angus, including in its area the valleys of the Deveron and its tributaries and the middle courses of the Don and the Dee. Westward again, from Elgin and Forres in the Morayshire plain

---

[1] Donaldson, *General View of the Agriculture of Kincardine*, 1795, 21
[2] McIan and Logan, *Highlanders at Home*, 1848, 72
[3] Keith, *General View of the Agriculture of Aberdeenshire*, 1811, 460–1

a belt of high and mountainous land stretches south to Blair-gowrie, Dunkeld and the valley of the lower Tay. Within this area are included the middle reaches of the Spey, the Cairngorm Mountains, the forests of Glenavon, Mar and Atholl and the high hills which stand round the head waters of the Don and the Dee.

The difficulties of the task of tracing today the drove roads of these several areas is determined largely by the nature of the country through which they passed. On the coastal plain the routes which linked the cattle grazings and markets of north Aberdeenshire with the markets of Central Scotland, were influenced less by the physical difficulties of the ground than by the need to avoid enclosed land. Many alternative routes were open, but with the steady growth of cultivation and enclosing in the latter part of the eighteenth century the cattle traffic came more and more to be confined to the recognised roads. Here, as the years went by, the traces and finally the memory of its passing became increasingly overlaid and obliterated by the growing traffic of a later age. In the hilly area immediately to the westward, the routes of the droves were determined to some extent by the nature of the country, by the glens and the low upland passes, but here the hills were not so high that alternative routes over them could not in places be chosen, and many of these, untouched by changing times and more recent traffic, retain the tradition and the clear record of the droving age. Only in the mountainous country on the extreme west of the area were the routes of the drovers strictly confined to mountain glens and passes, routes which remain to this day the only practicable ways through the region, used through successive centuries by raiders and soldiers, by pedlars and merchants and now by shepherds and hill walkers of a more peaceful age.

The establishment of local fairs in Aberdeenshire, which had begun to receive statutory recognition as early as 1628, continued all through the seventeenth century, and a list of fairs in the county in 1727 contains over fifty names.[1] The names, most of which commemorate festivals of the Church, cover the whole county,[2] but many were in the Lowland districts of Buchan, Garioch and Formartine ; at Fraserburgh and Old Deer in Buchan ; at Tarves, Methlick and Ellon in the valley of the Ythan, and at

[1] Smith, *The Exact Dealer's Companion*, 1727
[2] *Macfarlane's Geographical Collections*, II, 305

Rayne, Inverurie and Monymusk, where the Don and its tributaries emerge from the hills into the rich pasture land of the coastal plain. By the end of the century, a great network of small markets covered the county for the sale of cattle which were collected by the dealers into droves for the markets of the South. Of all these, the Fair of St Lawrence at Rayne dating back to the early seventeenth century was probably one of the oldest, while the market known as Aikey Fair at Old Deer in Buchan was, by the end of the eighteenth century, one of the largest in the north of Scotland. The exact routes followed on the north side of the Dee by these cattle from north and east Aberdeenshire on their way to Angus and the South, are for reasons already suggested now difficult to determine, but it is certain that these were influenced largely by the crossings of the Dee and the passes through the hills on its south bank. A bridge over the Dee had existed at Aberdeen since the end of the first quarter of the sixteenth century, and a ferry at about the same point was still in use in the seventeenth century.[1] Some cattle no doubt crossed at or near Aberdeen and followed the coast making for Stonehaven ; but dislike of tolls and thickly populated parts and a preference for hill routes no doubt influenced the drovers in Aberdeenshire as elsewhere, and all the indications are that the bulk of the cattle crossed the river farther to the west. A bridge at Banchory existed at least as early as 1664, and near Drum, ten miles down-stream, were important crossing-places either by ford or by the ferry mentioned in Sir James Balfour's list of 1630.[2] To reach these points, the route of the north and east Aberdeenshire cattle was probably by Inverurie and Kintore on the Lower Don and so south to Deeside. Cattle crossing the Dee about Drum would cross the hills on the south side of the river by the route known as the Slug Road to Stonehaven or by the old route known as the Cryne's Cross Mounth,[3] the route by which Montrose went north to Deeside in September 1644 after the Battle of Tippermuir. This route led from near Durris over the hills to Fordoun in Kincardineshire, where a tryst of some importance —the Fair of St Palladeous or ' Paldy Fair '—had long been established. Donaldson in his *General View of the Agriculture of Kincardineshire* in 1795, describes the Fordoun cattle fair as the most important in the county, as many as 3,000 cattle

[1] Fraser, *The Old Deeside Road*, 61n and 69   [2] ibid., 66
[3] Simpson, *Early Castles of Mar*, 123-4, 133

being sold here in July each year, mostly from the North. Traffic crossing at Banchory used the important Cairn-o-Mount Pass to Fettercairn, Edzell and Brechin, while a subsidiary route, the Stock Mounth, branched off the Cairn-o-Mount Road at the village of Strachan, and crossed into Glenbervie giving further access to Fordoun and the coast.

While a substantial part of the droving traffic from the north-east thus found its way to the South by routes crossing the Dee between Banchory and the mouth of the river, it seems probable that many, if not most, of the important drove roads passed through the belt of hilly country immediately to the west. The description of Aberdeenshire and Banffshire about 1662 already referred to and the 1727 list of Fairs in Scotland [1] show the existence at these dates of cattle fairs in Strathisla, Strathbogie and Strathdon, and in the hilly country lying between Don and Dee, and with the stimulus to cattle-breeding which came to Aberdeenshire in the second half of the eighteenth century, the rich grazing of these districts became of increasing importance. This upland country, grassy, well watered and largely unenclosed was ideal for droving, and during the years from 1750 to 1830 when droving from the north-east was at its height, a large and steady stream of cattle found its way to the South by routes which crossed the Dee at points between Braemar and Kincardine o'Neil. Till the middle of the eighteenth century, the chief crossings on this stretch of the river appear to have been ferries at Braemar, Crathie, Abergeldie, Ballater, Glentanar Church and at Kincardine o'Neil. [2] Bridges were added at Invercauld in 1752 and Ballater in 1783, while in 1814 the important bridge at Potarch, near Kincardine o'Neil, was built by the Commissioners for Highland Roads and Bridges. [3] These crossings of

[1] Smith, op. cit.   [2] Fraser, op. cit., 60–5
[3] H.R. & B., 6th Report, 1813

The building of the bridge at Potarch met with considerable difficulties. Two of the arches had already been completed and the central arch was nearing completion when a large part of the work was swept away by cut timber which was being floated down from the upper reaches of the Dee. The loss to the contractor was reduced by public subscription and a contribution from the Commissioners, and the accident resulted in the passing in 1813 of an Act for regulating the floating of timber during the spring and summer months. The large rivers of Scotland appear to have been extensively used for the floating of timber during the eighteenth century. The York Buildings Company who purchased woods on Speyside in 1728 are said to have introduced the practice of floating cut timber on that river in the form of rafts, and Mrs Grant of Rothiemurchus has described the floating of timber on tributaries of the Upper Spey. According to the New Statistical Account for Glenorchy, an Irish Company which leased the woods in Glen Strae, Glen Orchy and Glen Lochy in

the river all gave easy access to passes over the hills to Kincardine-shire and Angus, and it was on these points that the drove roads on the north side of the Dee concentrated.

The crossings of the Dee at Kincardine o'Neil and Potarch were important ones, giving access to the Cairn-o-Mount Pass through which the Banchory traffic also passed. To Kincardine o'Neil came cattle from the Alford district of Strathdon and the country to the north, crossing the Don at the Boat of Forbes at Alford. For cattle from Strathisla in Banffshire and much of the Deveron Valley, the route to the South was easy and direct. Ascending the valley of the Bogie from Huntly to Auchindoir, the site of an early eighteenth-century fair, they crossed the low uplands which lie between Strathbogie and Strathdon and came by Kildrummy to Donside, making for Ballater, Dinnet or Aboyne.

In the twelve miles of the Don which lie immediately up-stream from the old castle of Kildrummy were the crossing-places for a large volume of droving traffic from the North. As the river winds among the steep rounded shoulders of the surrounding hills, it receives on the north side the waters of three considerable tributaries, the Bucket, the Nochty and the Ernan. Down Glenbucket came cattle from the Cabrach and the upper valley of the Deveron.[1] The route is shown on Roy's map of 1747. It was used by eighteenth-century cattle raiders returning from Banff-shire, and it was not till the second half of the century that the glen knew more peaceful times, for here was the home of ' Old Glenbuchat ' whose implication in the troubles of 1715 and 1745 cost him his lands, his whole estate and all but his life. By Glenbucket, too, came drovers from the Lower Spey valley, ascending Glen Livet and crossing into Aberdeenshire over the high ridge known as The Ladder. These latter drovers had a choice of alternative routes down to the banks of the Don, for from the ridge they could reach the river by Glen Nochty or by Glen-Ernan, in each case following tracks marked out by the raiding traffic of other days.

---

[1] *The Book of Glenbuchat*, Third Spalding Club, 1942, 39–40

the eighteenth century floated the timber down the River Orchy to Loch Awe where it was sawn and made into rafts for floating to the Pass of Brander. From there it was carted to Bonawe on Loch Etive. (Murray, *The York Buildings Company*, 60–1. Larkin, *A Tour in the Highlands*, 1818, 330. Mrs Grant of Rothiemurchus, *Memoirs of a Highland Lady*, 1807, 1898 edn., 200–5)

The immediate destinations of these drovers from Banffshire and East Morayshire were the crossings of the Dee at or between Aboyne and Ballater. To reach these points on Deeside their route lay up the glen of the Deskry Water, crossing the ridge into Deeside in the Parish of Logie Coldstone to the north of Dinnet. This, one of the busiest of the drove roads between Don and Dee, remained in active use till well on in the second half of last century, and there are those still (1948) living on Donside who remember seeing the cattle climbing to the watershed and resting at the stance at Badnogoach near the top of the Deskry Water, some distance to the west of the present road. At the top of the ridge, some may have chosen the route through Tarland to Aboyne, but it seems that many skirted the east shoulder of the hill of Morven by the old drove road, traces of which are still to be seen on the side of Culblean Hill, making for Milton of Tullich and the crossing of the Dee at Ballater.[1]

For the droves which reached the Dee at Aboyne several alternative routes were open through the hills to Angus. The old tracks known as the Fungle Road and the Firmounth Road linked Deeside with Glen Esk by way of the Forest of Birse, while farther to the west an important route led up Glen Tanar, crossing the west shoulder of Mount Keen before descending into Glen Mark at the head of the North Esk. A writer of this century has recorded that within living memory this road was much used by bands of men and women going to the south country for the harvesting.

For the droves which crossed the Dee at Ballater the main route was through Glen Muick, and so over the pass known as the Capel Mount to the top of Glen Clova and the valley of the South Esk. Glen Muick, as has been seen, was chosen in 1747 as a point for one of the military posts stationed in the hills. It seems therefore probable that this was one of the routes of the eighteenth-century cattle raiders, and the testimony of old drovers and shepherds giving evidence before the Courts in 1887 shows it in active use in the first half of the nineteenth century for droves of cattle bound for Falkirk Tryst.[2]

The survey of the drove roads from the north-east which has

---

[1] Fraser, *An Old Drove Road over Culblean*. Aberdeen Free Press, 7 June 1921.

[2] *Scottish Rights of Way Society* v. *Macpherson*, Court of Session Cases, 1887, 14 Rettie's Reports, 875 and Notes of Evidence in *Session Papers*, Signet Library, 730, 165–89.

Plate 10   A drove route from the North-east : in Glen Fernate

(Photo by Robert M. Adam)

been attempted has covered the lowland part of the district and the upland country immediately to the west. It remains to trace the cattle routes which threaded their way through the great hills surrounding the head waters of the two rivers and the high ground lying to the south. For all this traffic the key-point was the crossing of the Dee at or about Braemar. Here was the meeting-point of the droving routes through the high hills now to be considered.

It has been seen that cattle from that part of Speyside which lies between Grantown and Craigellachie had access to the south by way of Glenavon, and that many went up Glenlivet crossing the hills to Strathdon on their way to Ballater and Aboyne ; but for these Speyside cattle a more direct route was open to the South, and there is evidence to show that, at least in the later years of the droving period, a part of the droving traffic preferred it. This route continued up the Avon to Tomintoul where, turning to the south-east, it followed the line of the military road built by the Hanoverian Government in 1754 and crossed the Don near the old castle of Corgarff, making for Crathie and Braemar. Some drovers might prefer to follow up the Avon to Inchrory, where the river turns to the west, continuing south by Loch Builg and Monaltrie Moss to Invercauld. This latter route was one of those mentioned in 1747 as in use by cattle thieves returning from raids farther to the east,[1] and an old drover still living (1948) on Donside remembers it in active use for sheep traffic, the beasts resting for the night beside Loch Builg. From the higher reaches of the Spey, about Nethy Bridge and Aviemore, led the high passes through the Cairngorms known as the Lairig Ghru and the Lairig an Laoigh, leading to the Dee by Glen Dee and Glen Lui and so to Braemar. These also are mentioned as in use by the cattle thieves of the mid-eighteenth century.[2] The Glen Dee route was in use in 1846 for bringing sheep which had come from Skye by way of Fort Augustus and Corrieyairack. According to local evidence the route through the Lairig Ghru continued to be used for cattle bound for Braemar and the South till about 1873, and people now living in the Rothiemurchus district of Speyside can recall that, until that date, men were sent up the Cairngorm passes each spring to clear from the tracks boulders moved by the winter frosts.

[1] New Spalding Club, *Historical Papers*, II, 493-4
[2] New Spalding Club, op. cit., 507

One more completes the tale of the main routes by which the droving traffic converged on Braemar. A few miles up-stream from Aviemore, the Spey receives the waters of the River Feshie running through the long glen which drains the south-west slopes of the Cairngorm Mountains. Twelve miles up the glen, where the burn divides, a low pass leads over the Aberdeenshire border into Glen Geldie and so to Braemar and the valley of the Dee, while to the south lie open the routes through Glen Tilt to Blair Atholl or by Glen Fernate to Kirkmichael. Wade planned a road through Glen Feshie after 1734 to link the barracks at Ruthven with Braemar, though this was never made,[1] and the establishment of a garrison in Glen Feshie in 1747 shows it to have been recognised at that date as a raider's route. A cattle tryst at the head of Glen Geldie is traditionally believed to have been an early forerunner of the great trysts of the eighteenth and nineteenth centuries.[2] According to local tradition the market was held on the extensive and flat top of An Sgarsoch, a grassy hill of over three thousand feet which stands about three miles to the south of the upper reaches of the Geldie Burn. The evidence of those who have visited the site bears out the existence of clear traces that the top of the hill was once used for some human purpose, though the site appears never to have been examined in detail. The position of An Sgarsoch suggests that its use for the assembling of livestock may date back to a period when freedom from surprise or attack was an important consideration.[3]

In the 1887 litigation already referred to, the evidence of drovers who appeared before the Court suggests that the route through Glen Feshie and Glen Geldie was in regular use till the middle of last century. It is probable that some droving traffic bound from Upper Speyside for Crieff and Falkirk also used the route leading from Glentromie over the Minigeig Pass into Glenbruar. In the second half of the eighteenth century this route was frequently urged as suitable for the construction of a military road. It is marked on a map of 1733 as ' The summer road to Ruthven ' and was probably one of the routes surveyed by Wade between 1723 and 1740. Evidence as to the use of the Glen Tilt route by droving traffic is not so clear. In an action which was brought before the Court of Session in 1849 to have

[1] Salmond, *Wade in Scotland*, 252
[2] Fraser, op. cit., 93. Salmond, op. cit., 253
[3] *Cairngorm Club Journal*, VIII, 166–9, 215–6 and 262–5

this route to Blair Atholl established as a right of way, the Pursuer's case was based partly on the use of the route by droving traffic. No hearing of evidence before the Court appears to have followed, while the statements of witnesses which were at that time taken and subsequently lodged with the Court are now missing.[1] Such local evidence as is available seems to indicate, however, that the Glen Tilt route, perhaps owing to the narrowness and difficulty of the glen, was not extensively used for droving traffic, the route by Glen Fernate being preferred.

From Braemar the routes to the South were easy. The route up Glen Clunie and over the Cairnwell Pass to Glen Shee and Strathardle had for centuries been one of the main links between Deeside and the South, and a long chain of evidence stretching from the Register of the Privy Council, through the Statistical Accounts and the records of early nineteenth-century travellers, shows it to have been in constant use by the varied traffic of four centuries. A subsidiary, but for the drovers an important route, branches off the Cairnwell road in Glenclunie and leads by Glen-callater into Glen Clova and Angus, while near the summit of the Cairnwell road a further route branches off to the south-east and crosses the hills at an altitude of over 3,000 feet to reach the head-waters of the Isla. Though not mentioned in Sir James Balfour's list of roads over the hills to Deeside, the Glencallater route, or the Tolmount route as it was later called, was in use by cattle raiders in the early eighteenth century, and in the litigation of 1887 which finally established it as a right of way, the evidence of witnesses drawn from personal recollection stretching back to the early years of the century, shows it then carrying a steady traffic of cattle and sheep from Aberdeenshire, from Ross-shire and even from Skye.[2]

The comparative scarcity of detail available as to the routes followed by the cattle of the north-eastern counties after crossing the hills south of the Dee again illustrates the difficulty of tracing the routes of such traffic in populous or well-cultivated country. For those beasts which crossed into Perthshire by the Cairnwell Pass, it seems probable that the route most commonly used, instead of continuing down Glen Shee to Blairgowrie, branched south-west at the Spittal of Glen Shee and crossed the hills to

[1] *Torrie* v. *Duke of Athol*, Court of Session Cases, 1849, 12 Dunlop's Report, 328
[2] *Scottish Rights of Way Society* v. *Macpherson*, Court of Session Cases, 1887, 14 Rettie's Reports

Enochdhu and Kirkmichael in Strathardle. In the Statistical Account for the Parish of Kirkmichael, the writer of the Account refers to two fairs held annually at the Spittal of Glen Shee and one at Kirkmichael, of which the latter was, in the middle of the eighteenth century, one of the principal cattle markets in the kingdom, lasting for several days and sometimes a week.[1] Sir J. D. Marwick in his *List of Fairs and Markets held in Scotland*, refers to Kirkmichael as the meeting-place of two routes over the hills—the route over the Cairnwell Pass from Braemar and that through Glen Fernate.[2] Some further confirmation that this route by Kirkmichael was commonly used by beasts from the north and north-east comes from the Reports of the Commissioners for Highland Roads and Bridges. A Memorial addressed to the Commissioners had urged the construction of a road from Dunkeld to Kirkmichael, and in their Fifth Report published in 1811, the Commissioners recommended that this road should be extended to join the road from Braemar near the Spittal of Glen Shee. This proposed route would give the drovers of Aberdeenshire and the north-east direct access to Crieff through open grazing country, so saving in distance and avoiding the inconvenience of passing through enclosed and populous country.[3]

As to the route of cattle after passing Kirkmichael, the local evidence available shows general agreement that the bulk of the traffic went south-west up Glen Derby and, crossing the hills by way of Loch Broom, came into the valley of the Tummel a short distance north of its junction with the Tay. The droves are believed to have crossed the Tummel just north of Ballinluig, and the Tay by a ford called 'Stair Cham' or 'Crooked Stepping Stones' near Logierait, continuing in a south-westerly direction across the hills by Loch Skaich to the top of Strath Bran and Amulree. Whether many of the droves which reached the Tay at Ballinluig continued down the river is not quite certain, but Larkin, writing in 1818, speaks of six annual fairs at Dunkeld, of which the one held at Martinmas was a great market for cattle.[4]

Of the beasts which crossed into Angus and Kincardineshire by

---

[1] *O.S.A.*, Kirkmichael, XV, 514
[2] Marwick, *List of Fairs and Markets held in Scotland*, 77
[3] *H.R. & B.*, 5th Report, 16
[4] Larkin, *A Tour in the Highlands in 1818*, 350

passes farther to the east and by the great Cairn-o-mount route, some no doubt moved west by Kirriemuir and Blairgowrie, crossing the Tay at Dunkeld on their way to Crieff and Falkirk by way of Strath Bran and the Sma' Glen, but it seems probable that many, like the Aberdeenshire drover so hard hit by the Peace in 1815, continued south to Perth, entering Strathearn at its eastern end.[1] From here, those bound for Falkirk would take the route by Sheriffmuir and Stirling, or the short cut by Gleneagles and Glendevon and other routes across the Ochils used by some of the cattle from Crieff and the Sma' Glen. It may be that part of the traffic from the north-eastern counties bypassed the Falkirk Tryst, going direct to the markets of Edinburgh. For these beasts the crossing of the Ochils would be made by Glen Farg on the road to North Queensferry, and descriptions of the Forth crossing in the first half of last century refer to the number of cattle which were at times shipped across, not without accident. The Statistical Account of Inverkeithing refers to the loss of a ferry boat loaded with black cattle,[2] and a traveller in 1802 describing the crossing of the Forth recommends that 'when the boats are loaded with black cattle passengers ought to avoid them lest any sudden squall should upset them and endanger their lives.'[3]

All through the latter part of the eighteenth century, the cattle trade from the north-eastern counties grew steadily and in the early years of last century reached very large proportions. The improvement in agricultural methods which brought this about brought with it, however, other changes which were to mean the ultimate decay of the droving trade, and the first half of the nineteenth century saw in the north-east a change from cattle breeding to cattle fattening, a change which called for the

[1] About a mile to the north of Brechin in the neighbourhood of the village of Little Brechin wide trackways or 'raiks' of turf with a ditch on either side are still to be seen. These are the remnants of drove roads leading to Trinity Tryst, an ancient tryst still held annually, which was at one time an important market on the drove road from Kincardineshire to Perth. 'This unique track, which averages a hundred feet in width, stretches for over a mile, between Findowrie and Little Brechin, and for centuries was part of the great drove road for Highland cattle coming over the Cairn o' Mounth. The once famous Trinity Tryst, on the Muir of Brechin, was the first lowland market for the distribution of these cattle, which were driven south annually in immense herds. Fifty years ago, I have seen the entire roadway of ten miles, between Fettercairn and Brechin, literally blocked for some days before the Tryst with thousands of black horned cattle, which were driven by unkempt Celts, who shouted and swore in Gaelic.' (Don, *Archaeological Notes on Early Scotland*, 42)
[2] O.S.A., Inverkeithing, X, 506
[3] Campbell, *Journey from Edinburgh through parts of North Britain*, 1802, II, 82

quicker and easier forms of transport which were by then becoming available ; but consideration of the factors which meant the end of droving belongs to another chapter. It has no place in the story of how, by routes trodden in times past by Roman legions and English armies, by Highland raiders and by Montrose's men, the cattle of the north-east came to the Lowland trysts.

THE TRYSTS

THE holding of fairs and markets has from a very early stage in the development of civilised life been a necessity common to all countries and all peoples. In every part of the world so soon as civilisation passed beyond the most primitive stage of isolation and self-sufficiency, demand arose for goods not produced locally or for others calling for division of labour, and with that demand came the need for means of distribution. In an age long before the development of adequate communication by road, the only solution lay in the establishment by custom of convenient and central points where local products could be disposed of, and those from surrounding districts acquired. The development of such a system among the early peoples of China, India, Egypt, Africa and South America shows it to have been in every land the outcome of fundamental needs and conditions, in no way influenced by the customs of others, but common to all. In Europe, as elsewhere, such a development took place and the great fairs of Nijni Novgorod, Leipzig and Frankfurt, which have continued in flourishing existence up to modern times, trace their direct descent through many centuries. The sites of these great fairs were chosen for their ease of access for buyers and sellers, by the sides of large rivers, or at the meeting place of caravan and trading routes. The dates, too, were determined by common needs. Many of the great fairs were held in the late summer or in autumn when the products of harvest were available, when livestock nourished by the summer grazing were in a fit state to travel, and when men must lay in goods and stores for the winter.[1]

To the fairs and markets established in these islands from early times, the same general characteristics apply. The dates for the holding of fairs seem at first to have been fixed where possible to coincide with local or national festivals, but as the influence of the Church increased fairs became more and more associated with religious festivals and the Feast Days of the Patron Saints, the protection and patronage of the Church being shown in the names by which many of these fairs for long were known.

Nowhere were fairs more sorely needed than in Scotland

---

[1] Marwick, *List of Fairs and Markets held in Scotland*, Introd.

where mountain, river and sea and the absence of roads divided the country into isolated regions. The holding of fairs and markets had long been a monopoly of the burghs. This was a privilege jealously guarded, and the establishment of markets outside the burgh and in the remoter districts where they were most needed was achieved only gradually in the face of the bitter opposition of the burghal interests.[1] Till well on in the eighteenth century, cattle, hides, timber and salmon were the main exportable products of the Highlands, and to the cattle breeder the existence of fairs at times suited to the needs of his trade and at points convenient alike to buyer and seller, was of supreme importance. Local markets were needed where cattle from the glens, the coastal pasture lands and the hills could be collected for transport to the Lowlands, while larger markets were needed at central points nearer more populous areas.

While the origin of many of these local fairs lies far back in Scottish history, for the purpose of tracing the growth of the droving trade it is hardly necessary to attempt to follow their development back further than the latter part of the sixteenth century, when clear records of regular cattle droving make what is probably their earliest appearance. By that date, cattle from northern and western districts were already being driven to markets in the eastern half of Scotland. Fairs for their sale were then, as has been seen, in existence at Elycht [Alyth], Brechin and Forfar, while at least as early as the first half of the seventeenth century cattle fairs also existed in the Garioch and Buchan districts of Aberdeenshire [2] and at Dumfries.

In the early grants by the Crown or Privy Council conferring rights to hold annual or periodical sales, these are generally described as 'fairs' or 'markets,' and it seems that the name 'tryst,' derived probably from the old word 'triste' or 'trust,' only at a later date came into general use. The name was appropriate for the meeting-place of merchants and customers, and particularly for cattle dealers who 'trysted' the owners of beasts to meet them at an agreed place for the sale of their cattle. What is possibly the earliest known use of the word as meaning a fair occurs in a verse attributed to Thomas the Rhymer :

> 'I neither dought to buy or sell
> At fair or tryst where I may be.' [3]

---

[1] Mackenzie, *The Scottish Burghs*, 88–95   [2] *R.P.C.*, 2nd series, II, 409, 616
[3] Scott, *Minstrelsy of the Scottish Border*, 1st edn., 1802–3, I, xviii

While the words 'tryst,' 'market' and 'fair' were used somewhat indiscriminately by contemporary writers, it would seem that as a general, though not invariable rule, 'tryst' indicated a market established by agreement between buyers and sellers, while 'fair' meant one established by public authority or Crown grant, 'market' probably applying to both. At least as early as the beginning of the eighteenth century the word 'tryst' came into fairly general use to describe these meeting-places, and from then on though some continued to be known merely as 'markets' or 'fairs' many, and particularly the larger ones, were commonly known as 'trysts.'

The early cattle markets were scattered and probably of no great size, but till near the end of the seventeenth century they sufficed. The Union of the Crowns in 1603 had had little immediate effect in improving the political or commercial relations of Scotland and England, and the trade passing between the two countries continued to be regulated by few considerations other than the individual and immediate needs of each. In 1669, however, all export and import duties on cattle going to England were abolished,[1] and the appointment in 1680 of a Commission for the encouragement of trade between the two countries marked the approach of new and better times.[2]

The change in the commercial relations of Scotland and England coincides very closely with the confirmation by Act of Parliament of 1672 to James, Earl of Perth, of the right to hold 'ane yeirlie fair and weiklie mercat' at Crieff, a coincidence in which it is probable that mere chance played little part.[3] For with the steady increase of cattle traffic to the South, the need had arisen for the concentration of the trade at some central point where buyers and sellers could easily come together, a need which the scattered local markets hitherto in existence could not meet. Crieff, like Perth, lies at the gateway of the Highlands, where the Grampians fall to the valley of Strathearn, and at the northern edge of one of the richest and most populous parts of Scotland. For the cattle trade Crieff possessed advantages which Perth did not offer. The traditional route for cattle from the North lay, as has been seen, by Dalnacardoch to Tummel Bridge and Kenmore and so through the Sma' Glen, while cattle from parts of Morayshire and Aberdeenshire had easy access by the

[1] R.P.C., 3rd series, III, 16   [2] R.P.C., 3rd series, VI, 431, 432
[3] A.P.S., VIII, 65

passes south of the Dee to the valley of the Tay and thence, avoiding the more populous districts, through Strath Bran to join the same route at Amulree. For cattle from Skye and most of the Outer Isles the route across the western edge of the Moor of Rannoch led them easily to Crieff by Loch Tay and Loch Earn, while drovers from Argyll could, if they wished, reach the same point by way of Glen Dochart and Loch Earn. Here, then, was a natural gathering point for beasts from the Highlands, while affording easy access to dealers coming from the South or to those returning with stock for the markets of England. It was for these reasons that at the end of the seventeenth century Crieff became the greatest cattle market in Scotland, a position which it retained for well over half a century.[1]

The growth of the Crieff Cattle Tryst must have been rapid, for when Macky visited it in 1723 the number of cattle reported by him as having been sold there that autumn was 30,000, the total price being about 30,000 guineas,[2] many of the beasts being driven on to England by Highland drovers who, according to Macky's description, hired themselves at 1s a day for the southward journey, returning at their own expense. The market took place in the second week of October each year, a date which forced those bringing cattle from the north and west to dispose of them or face the hazardous alternative of driving them on, so late in the year, to seek other markets farther south. The market was under the control and patronage of the Earl of Perth, who held a court for the purpose of regulating disputes which might arise and for keeping order. Certain of his feuars were bound by their charters to act as guards for policing the market, and as late as the time of the New Statistical Account, though Crieff Tryst had come to an end nearly eighty years earlier, these services had not long since ceased to be exacted.[3] While the Earl of Perth's court may have been effective in preventing trouble on the tryst ground itself, it appears to have had a very limited jurisdiction. The writer of the New Statistical Account of the Parish of Monzie, describing the past glories of Crieff Tryst, reported that when the market was at its height the inhabitants

[1] The position of Crieff at the border of Highlands and Lowlands which made it so suitable as a centre for the cattle trade in the early eighteenth century made it also a potential centre of political trouble and intrigue. Despite the presence of Hanoverian troops at the Autumn Tryst of 1714 quarrels occurred which only the close of the market prevented from anticipating by one year the troubles which were so soon to overtake Strathearn. (Millar, *History of Rob Roy*)

[2] Macky, *Journey through Scotland*, 1723, 190   [3] *N.S.A.*, Crieff, X, 525

of the surrounding country went in fear of their lives from the Highland drovers who broke into their houses, forcibly billeting themselves, and often carried off part of the household goods.[1] Yet despite this, the passing of Crieff Tryst was a cause of local regret, and the Rev. Robert Taylor, who compiled the Statistical Account of Crieff in 1794, reported that ' The old people here sometimes speak with deep regret of the glorious scene displayed to view when 30,000 black cattle in different droves overspread the whole adjacent country for several miles round the town.' [2] In return for his patronage of the market, the Earl of Perth was entitled to the market dues amounting to 2d per beast, but the right of collecting these was let by him for a yearly sum of £600 Scots (£50 sterling) to a tenant who made what he could on the transaction.[3] Much of the trade was done by means of bills, and during the second quarter of the century Crieff came to be regarded as one of the main financial centres of Scotland. Considerable sums, however, also changed hands in the form of gold as Macky has described, and an entry in the Minute Book of the Royal Bank of Scotland in 1730 shows that tellers were that year sent from Edinburgh to Crieff with £3,000 in notes to put into circulation in return for cash.[4]

The Rising of 1745 seems not to have affected Crieff Tryst seriously, for a Dumfriesshire cattle dealer writing to his partner in 1746 refers to a rival having gone to Crieff to buy several thousand beasts,[5] and references by the commanders of English garrisons stationed in the Highlands immediately after the Rising to thefts of cattle on their way to Crieff show that the troubles of the times had not deterred some at least of the drovers.[6] The Rising had, however, a more serious if less immediate effect on Crieff Tryst. Hitherto the trade with England in Scots cattle had been largely in the hands of Scotsmen. The more peaceful times and the higher cattle prices which followed the failure of the Rising brought English dealers increasingly to the Scots cattle markets after the middle of the century to share directly in the trade. This in turn meant the need for a market more convenient to them, and in conjunction with the increasing cost of droving and the need to adopt the quickest routes to market, led to the

[1] N.S.A., Monzie, X, 270   [2] O.S.A., Crieff, IX, 596   [3] ibid.
[4] Munro, History of the Royal Bank of Scotland, 1727–1927, 105
[5] Letters of Thomas Bell, in Reid's Calendar of Documents found at Dumfries, H.M. Register House
[6] New Spalding Club, Historical Papers, (1699–1750), II, 524, 540 and 582

eventual eclipse of Crieff by Falkirk, which remained till the end of the cattle-droving industry the greatest cattle tryst in Scotland.

The early history of the cattle market which came to be known as the ' Falkirk Tryst ' is obscure, but in the complex legal proceedings between 1761 and 1772 which led up to the division of the Commonties of Whitesiderigg and Reddingsrigg near Falkirk, where the market was originally held, the evidence of witnesses traced it back to the years immediately following the Union of 1707.[1] The Tryst at Falkirk was never a statutory fair. The process in connection with the division of the commonties states that it ' was originally constituted and has since been kept up by advertisements in the newspapers or other notices given to the public that a tryst was to be held at Falkirk upon such a day to which all dealers in cattle, buyers and sellers, are invited, the proprietors of the land to give a proper stand for the cattle, security and protection as far as they can and that all comers will have entertainment at reasonable rates. . . . It stands confessed and is proved that these trysts have uniformly been kept upon these muirs immediately above the town of Falkirk at least from 1716.' The documents in connection with the division also show from 1717 the names of the tacksmen who collected on behalf of the Duke of Hamilton tolls from cattle coming to the market, and in writing of his tour of Scotland in 1747 Pococke tells of having been turned off the road by droves on their way to Falkirk.[2]

Shortly after the division of the commonties the market was moved to a site called Rough Castle to the west of Falkirk. ' From time immemorial,' wrote Nimmo in 1777, ' the Highlands of Scotland which in few places are capable of culture have produced great quantities of cattle ; these though of a small size when fattened upon richer pastures are reckoned superior to English beef. By transporting them into England large sums of money were brought back in return, insomuch that before the establishment of manufactures this was almost the only branch of trade which conveyed specie into the country. After the Union, the Scots had still greater advantages for carrying on this article of commerce ; and in order to settle a regular method of transacting it the dealers of both Kingdoms agreed to fix certain convenient places where at proper seasons they should meet for

---

[1] Division of Commonties, Reddingsrigg and Whitesiderigg. Signet Library, *Old Session Papers*, 135, No. 30, 1768 ; and *Durie Decreets*, 19/12/1807, H.M. Register House   [2] Pococke, *Tours in Scotland, 1747, 1750 and 1760*, 295

the purpose of buying and selling the cattle. A large muir called Reddingridge a mile southward of Falkirk was pitched upon for that purpose. This continued to be the place where these stated markets were held till a few years ago when on account of the division of that Muir which was formerly a commonty they have been removed to another Muir westward of that town. At one of these trysts which usually last two days, sometimes above 50,000 head of cattle have been assembled and all sold off.' [1] The site at Rough Castle continued to be used till 1785 when, possibly in consequence of the construction of the Forth and Clyde Canal which interfered with easy access from the north, the market was again moved, this time to an extensive site at Stenhousemuir near Larbert, where, still known as Falkirk Tryst, it remained till its final disappearance in the last years of the nineteenth century.

Originally the market appears to have been held twice a year, but in consequence of the decline of Crieff between 1760 and 1770, the Falkirk Tryst came to be held three times a year—in August, September and October—the October Tryst being possibly the largest as offering practically the last chance for Highland drovers to dispose of their beasts. By 1770, though market dues were still levied at Crieff, to the annoyance of the drovers from the north, Crieff had almost come to an end as a cattle market, all the business being done at the Falkirk Tryst [2]; and Pennant,

---

[1] Nimmo, *History of Stirlingshire*, 1st edn., 1777, 456–8

[2] In October 1770 a Petition signed by twenty-seven ' dealers in black cattle from the North of Scotland for themselves and in name of all the other dealers ' was presented to the Commissioners for the Annexed Estates in Scotland. It narrates that ' whereas in former years the Michaelmas mercat at Crieff was annualy the Great Mercat for black cattle and the meeting place for that purpose betwixt the English buyers and the Petitioners, yet that now too true it is that for several years past this mercat hath been dwindling away ; and that this year the Petitioners and others are laid under the necessity of carrying on their cattle at great expense to Falkirk, there to meet with the English buyers, few or none of them have at this time appeared at this place. That by this means the Village of Crieff hath now become and probably will continue to be only a resting place for the Petitioners and their cattle.' They complained that customs were still levied at Crieff though they had no opportunity of selling their cattle there, the market stance having been almost wholly enclosed and that a further toll was exacted from them at Stirling Bridge ; that if the customs dues at Crieff were continued they would be forced ' to take some proper method for elideing the payment thereof by taking another road with their cattle ' to the prejudice of Crieff which ' would suffer greatly through the loss of money that would be there necessarily spent during their stay.' (*Forfeited Estates Papers*, Perth, Ptfo. 21F, 21 January 1771, H.M. Register House.) It appears that the customs dues complained of were not then abolished, for the writer of the *O.S.A.* for the Parish of Crieff reports that in 1792 cattle from the North were forced to pass through the town before midday on the day preceding the market to avoid the dues, though by that time the sales of cattle had fallen to only about 1,000. (*O.S.A.*, Crieff, IX, 596)

writing in 1772, estimates the number of cattle sold there that year at 24,000.[1] At the time of the Statistical Account the numbers had reached 20,000 to 30,000 at the October sale alone,[2] and the writer of the Agricultural Report for Stirlingshire of 1812 puts the numbers sold at the October Tryst at between 25,000 and 40,000.

' The central situation of Stirlingshire,' he writes, ' with regard to the breeders of cattle in the northern and western counties on the one hand and the buyers or dealers from the southern and eastern parts of the island on the other, has for a long period rendered it the theatre of the principal fairs or cattle markets in Scotland. Of these, the Falkirk Trysts, as they are called, are the most distinguished. These trysts were originally held upon a large common in the vicinity of Falkirk which is at present in the course of being brought under cultivation ; they are now held on that account upon a field in the Parish of Larbert, but though the site be changed the ancient name remains. They were formerly held upon a fixed day of certain months but on account of the inconvenience which often arose from these days falling too early or too late in the week they have been lately fixed to a certain Tuesday of these months. The first Falkirk Tryst is held upon the second Tuesday of August. There are generally exhibited there from 5,000 to 6,000 black cattle. The second tryst is held upon the second Tuesday of September. There are generally exhibited about 15,000 black cattle and 15,000 sheep. The third tryst is held upon the second Tuesday of October when there are generally exhibited from 25,000 to 30,000 black cattle ; even 40,000 have been known to have been exhibited at this tryst. There are also at an average 25,000 sheep exposed to sale.' [3]

The original selection of Falkirk for a cattle market and its subsequent removal to the site at Stenhousemuir may have been a matter of accident and expediency rather than of conscious judgment, but however it came about, the outcome proved it to be a fortunate choice, and for over a century this broom-covered field near Larbert and the land immediately around it was to be the scene of one of the most important yearly events in the commercial life of Scotland. For here, midway between the rich

[1] Pennant, *Tour in Scotland, 1772*, II, 230
[2] *O.S.A.*, Larbert and Dunipace, III, 335
[3] Graham, *General View of the Agriculture of Stirlingshire*, 1812, 332-3

areas of the eastern Lowlands and the fast-growing population of Clydeside was a natural centre for cattle traffic from the north, already concentrated by the passage of the Forth, while it was a convenient centre for the drove roads from the west which passed to the north and south of Loch Lomond. For the cattle dealers of Southern Scotland and of England, too, it was a convenient point, saving them from arduous and often hazardous journeys into the Highland districts, while to the south led easy routes across the Southern Uplands to Dumfriesshire, to the Border and to England.[1]

Contemporary descriptions of Falkirk Tryst show it to have presented a scene of rare animation.[2] Here came dealers from Yorkshire, the north of England and the Border counties to meet the drovers of Uist, Skye, Lochaber, Ross-shire, Angus and Argyll. The Gaelic of the west and the speech of Aberdeenshire mingled with the dialects of Yorkshire, Cumberland and the Borders as men strove and argued over the merits of black and dun, red and brindled, collected from every district of Highland Scotland. The numbers of beasts brought to the tryst were such that the tryst ground itself was quite inadequate to hold them. As the tryst days approached, the gathering droves spread over a large area of the surrounding country, moving into the tryst ground for the actual sale. Here the cattle congregated in the centre of the ground. On the outskirts were the tents of those who provided ' the elements of conviviality in immense abundance,' while fires lit in the open cooked huge pots of broth for men chilled by autumn rains or flagging markets. There were, of course, during the greater period of the tryst's existence no auctioneers, and though a friend might intervene to break the deadlock between a Skye drover and a Yorkshire dealer arguing over the merits of Highland stirks, business at the tryst was done largely by the dealers threading their perilous path among the parcels of cattle and striking their own bargains direct

---

[1] The view that the choice of Stenhousemuir may have been arbitrary is rather strengthened by a passage which appears in the *O.S.A.* for the Stirlingshire Parish of Kippen: ' It is the opinion of many of the graziers and dealers in cattle that Kippen is one of the most convenient places perhaps in Scotland for a cattle market ; and that in the late fluctuating state of the trysts it might not have been difficult to transfer to it a great part of the spring and autumn markets. There is a spacious moor near the village which lies very convenient for that purpose. With a view to encouraging their resort to it Mr Graham of Gartmore, the proprietor, offered it to the dealers in cattle free of custom for 90 years.' (*O.S.A.*, Kippen, XVIII, 351)

[2] See Appendix F (p. 240)

with the owners. The deal made, the two parties retired to a refreshment tent to seal the bargain, or to the booths set up by the Royal Bank of Scotland, the British Linen Company, the Commercial Bank or the Falkirk Bank for the benefit of those who wished to deposit money, or to get notes of the Scottish banks in return for the Letters of Credit from English banking houses with which the dealers from the South had supplied themselves. Through the motley crowd went sharpers, thimblers and gamblers, ballad singers, fiddlers and beggars, to make up a concourse which for variety, bustle and noise must have been almost without parallel in contemporary Scotland. The number of beasts for sale was such that the business was not completed in one day, the October Tryst in particular lasting for several days, while the drovers fought to get the last penny of price from dealers equally determined to get bargains of beasts which they knew must, so late in the year, ultimately be sold.

'At times,' writes a contributor to the *Stirling Journal* of 27 September 1844, 'when the market is densely crowded and there is danger of the separate lots being mixed, the Celt is seen in all his fury and excitement ; his Highland blood is up and he screams himself hoarse in shouting to his dogs, ordering his neighbours or assistants and threatening with the infliction of his cudgel those who show a disposition to encroach upon his stance or throw his lot into confusion. The maledictions between the herdsmen are exchanged in Gaelic and as the colleys seem to catch the spirit of their masters the contention is generally wound up by a regular worry, presenting altogether a scene of the most admired disorder and of no little amusement to those who have nothing else to do than to look on and enjoy it.'

The constant vigilance of the drovers was nowhere more necessary than in the neighbourhood of the tryst ground, and here, as in the northern hills they slept beside their beasts. A writer of the early part of last century [1] has so described the scene :

'In the latter part of the day when the tryst is over, to see every spot not only of the flat muir but of the beautifully undulating ground above, covered with cattle asleep and herdsmen in their characteristic Scottish dress either stretched in their plaids or resting for a while their wearied limbs—but still watchful —or gathered in groups and telling of the occurrences and bargains

---

[1] Youatt, *Cattle, their Breeds, Management and Diseases.* Library of Useful Knowledge, 1834, 121n

of the day ; this is a scene which the agriculturist will not soon forget and to which no one can be insensible.'

All through the first quarter of the nineteenth century the importance and popularity of Falkirk Tryst steadily increased. Each autumn saw more and larger droves coming from the Highlands across the old bridge leading to Stirling, where a dispute with the tollsman once held up the traffic till the whole road back to Bridge of Allan was ' one dense mass of cattle, sheep and ponies.' Before the middle of the century the total number of cattle sold each year at Falkirk Tryst is reported in the local Press to have risen to close on 150,000 besides sheep in great and increasing quantities.[1]   But the years after 1860 saw a rapid change, and railways, steamships and auctioneers combined with changing methods of agriculture to rob the trysts of their former glory.

The streams of beasts which fed the great Trysts of Crieff and Falkirk had, like the Highland rivers which they crossed, passed through pools and eddies before reaching their final destination. On most of the cattle routes from north, east and west were smaller local markets, where droves on the main routes swelled by tributary streams from the surrounding hills changed hands, some to local graziers in need of fresh stock, but most to dealers collecting their purchases into composite and larger droves for the great markets.   A list of fairs covering the whole of Scotland in 1727 contains over 500 names spread over the whole year.[2] Not all of these are described as cattle fairs, but the list includes the names of almost all those fairs known to have been cattle fairs, and from an examination of the districts and the dates of the remainder, it seems clear that the great majority were at least partially for the sale of cattle.   Despite the number of these local markets, however, it appears that few of them offered the local cattle proprietors an opportunity of selling to big dealers from the South, not many of whom came far north.   Marshall, writing in 1794, urged the establishment of regular cattle markets in the Central Highlands,[3] while Hogg considered that markets should be set up along the line of the proposed Caledonian Canal for the benefit of the farmers of the North who were forced to take what price was offered by the drovers at their

[1] *Stirling Journal*, Sept. and Oct. 1827
[2] Smith, *The Exact Dealer's Companion*, 1727
[3] Marshall, *General View of the Agriculture of the Central Highlands*, 1794, 68

doors or face the long drove to Falkirk perhaps with only a few beasts.[1]

The route from Skye and the Islands had its markets at Portree, Sligachan and Broadford. Robertson reports that ' at Portree there is an annual fair but in other places of the Isle of Skye some fluctuating meetings are held by concert among the dealers which are called " trysts ".' [2] The Portree Market had from its origin, probably in the early seventeenth century, grown to such proportions that John Macculloch, who visited it in 1824, found the place too crowded for his liking. ' Do not pay it a visit,' he writes, ' when all sorts of cattle come to be bought and sold ; when horn is entangled in horn, and drover with drover.' The inn that year was little better. ' Have I not sat over the fumes of tobacco amid the steam of hot whiskey to listen to prices and bone and rib and weight and pedigree till I could almost have bought and sold a stot myself. . . . And therefore I took refuge from the Lairds and Chiefs in the opener element of the Fair itself. And then the cows and the queys and the stots and the stirks began to bellow and roar and whisk their tails, and the sellers of cows and the buyers of cows began to compete for the mastery and all the town began to look like a stable, and I had nothing to do but to leave them to poke about their horns and bellow down the Highland drovers if they could, or remain to be daubed by the whisking of cows' tails in Portree itself.' [3] In a map of Portree in 1766 the tryst ground is marked slightly to the north-west of the town, and the Statistical Account complains of the damage done to grass and corn by cattle brought to the tryst.[4]

At Broadford, cattle from Dunvegan and the Outer Isles, their numbers swelled by many from the south of Skye, passed through their second market on the journey to the Lowlands. Though not so old as Portree Market, that of Broadford was of some importance, and as late as the third quarter of last century a traveller in Skye found the scene a busy one.[5] Here too were the noise of cattle and the shouting of drovers, the quarrelling, bargaining and courting of the crowd, the tents in the hollow where food was cooking for weary drovers, and in the background the steep stony sides of Ben-na-Cailich looking down on the

---

[1] Hogg, *A Tour of the Highlands in 1803*, 48
[2] Robertson, *General View of the Agriculture of Inverness-shire*, 1812, 302
[3] Macculloch, *Highlands and Western Isles*, 1824, III, 366 et seq.
[4] *O.S.A.*, XVI, 159   [5] Smith, *A Summer in Skye*, 138

bay and the river and the old farm buildings at Coirechatachan where Dr Johnson stayed in 1772. In his *Tour to the Hebrides* Boswell has recorded that MacKinnon of Coirechatachan had made so much money by droving and selling meal in his earlier days that the interest on the money sufficed to meet the rent of £50 which he paid for the holding.[1]

'These markets,' wrote Joseph Mitchell in his Journal for September 1837, 'are of much importance in Skye. They are held at Portree, Sligachan and Broadford at stated periods. The south-country drovers attend and purchase from the breeders and farmers. The large farmer here generally disposes of his stock, the cottar his cow and stirk, or two or three sheep. The debts that are contracted at other periods of the year are here generally discharged and there is thus a most heterogeneous collection of people—tacksmen, farmers, drovers, cottars, factors, shopkeepers, innkeepers, many women and gillies great and small. There are besides the extensive droves of cattle and sheep that are driven to these places to be sold and sent forward to the South.'

'At Sligachan the road was lined with tents. It was about 11 o'clock of the second day and the tent-keepers were engaged in cooking broth, mutton and potatoes for the country people inside with the only drink, mountain dew. The tents, if they could be called such, were temporary, formed of blankets and most miserable. The whole aspect of the place—a lone and barren mountainside—was wild and savage. It had been raining all night, and as most of the people had been either up drinking or sleeping on the bare ground during the night, they had a dirty and dishevelled appearance. The gentlemen had a bleary, unshaven aspect, the horses were ungroomed, and there being no stables little gillies with kilts, bare heads and bare legs were mounted and with much glee were riding backwards and forwards along the road.'

'The cattle and sheep extending over an immense space were standing quietly looking at each other while the gillies, their drovers, were leaning on their sticks or lying on the damp ground, their faithful collies at their feet, panting for employment. Such was the fair at Sligachan which I viewed with no very favourable impression of the civilisation of the people.'[2]

---

[1] Boswell, *Tour to the Hebrides*, Isham edn., 125
[2] Mitchell, *Reminiscences of my Life in the Highlands*, 219-20

The drove road from the north of Scotland also had its local markets. Those of Caithness, like that held in the Strath of Dunbeath, were probably little more than gathering places for cattle bought locally for driving to the South, but Muir of Ord in Ross-shire was an important market, and in the second quarter of last century was probably the largest tryst in the north of Scotland. South of the Great Glen on the moor near Kingussie a cattle market was, by long-standing custom, held each September to suit the convenience of drovers coming from the North. This was something of a social gathering, and Mrs Grant of Rothiemurchus in 1814 described the gathering of drovers, lairds and farmers for this 'Tryst of Pitmain' where Lord Huntly presided after the morning market at a dinner for which he provided a stag from his Forest of Gaick.[1]

Of the Aberdeenshire trysts, some were of very long standing. A weekly fair at 'The Chapel of Garioch' near Inverurie had been granted by the Privy Council in 1628,[2] and St Lawrence cattle market in the same district was, as early as 1684, of such a size that the Privy Council changed the market day from Monday to Tuesday to avoid Sabbath-breaking by drovers coming to it.[3] Aikey Fair, held on Aikey Brae in the parish of Old Deer in Buchan, was one of the largest of the Aberdeenshire fairs, and at the beginning of last century was probably the most important in the north-eastern counties. At that time beasts in their thousands were to be seen moving south in one continuous drove after the fair ended, and Aikey was said to be one of the only cattle fairs in the North to which English buyers regularly came.[4] The fair continued to be held till the last quarter of the century, though by then the cattle sales had shrunk to a mere shadow and the main business was in horses. Besides the fairs which existed in the eastern and north-eastern parts of the county, important fairs were also held each year in Strath Isla, Strath Bogie and on Deeside at least as early as 1662,[5] and it is estimated that by the early years of the nineteenth century no fewer than 180 fairs and markets took place annually in various parts of Aberdeenshire.[6]

[1] Elizabeth Grant of Rothiemurchus, *Memoirs of a Highland Lady*, 1807 (1911 edn.), 273 and 300
[2] *R.P.C.*, 2nd series, II, 409
[3] *R.P.C.*, 3rd series, VIII, 380
[4] Alexander, *Northern Rural Life in the 18th Century*, 79–82
[5] *Macfarlane's Geographical Collections*, II, 305–6
[6] Fraser, *The Old Deeside Road*, 100

Plate 11   All-Hallow Fair, Grassmarket, Edinburgh—about 1800

(From a print in Edinburgh Central Library)

At most of these the main trade was in cattle to be driven across the Don and the Dee and through the hill passes to Angus and the South. Those drovers who took their beasts south by Braemar and the passes at the head of the Dee might make further purchases at Kirkmichael in Strathardle, where a market was held each autumn a few days before the September Tryst at Falkirk. The Kirkmichael market is described in the Statistical Account as one of the main cattle markets of the kingdom.[1] Here, says a traveller of the early nineteenth century, used to come not only sellers of black cattle but shoemakers from Atholl and sellers of bog-oak from Badenoch.[2]

Argyll had its local markets at Salen in Mull and Strontian in Ardnamurchan, at Duror in Appin and Kilmore and Kilchrennan in Lorn, while to the large tryst at Kilmichael-Glassary near Lochgilphead came dealers and drovers from all parts of Scotland to buy the cattle of Islay, Jura, Kintyre and Knapdale.

Farther to the east, Doune in Perthshire was the scene of an important cattle market for beasts coming from Skye and north-west Scotland, and it was from Doune Tryst that Robin Oig set out on the ill-fated journey to England described in Sir Walter Scott's tale *The Two Drovers*. This market long remained of considerable importance, and at the time of the Statistical Account, though Falkirk Tryst was steadily growing in size, 10,000 cattle were sold here at the Autumn Tryst. In the course of the proceedings in 1768 leading up to the Division of the Commonties of Whitesiderigg and Reddingsrigg, reference was made to ' the tryst lately set up at Down . . . which is now in a flourishing way. . . . The town of Stirling, judging this tryst would be hurtful not only to its fairs and markets but also to duty upon black cattle passing along their bridge, as by coming to the Tryst at Down they could have passage (over the Forth) duty free by the other fords,' took legal advice as to their right to stop Doune Tryst but were advised they could not do so.[3] ' Snowy Doune,' as it was called, had the distinction of being the last important cattle sale of the year, and here in November, drovers late for Falkirk or disappointed with prices there found a last chance of selling before approaching winter put a stop to cattle trade. Cattle brought to the Tryst at Doune appear not to have been

---

[1] *O.S.A.*, Kirkmichael, XV, 514
[2] Larkin, *A Tour in the Highlands in 1818*, 35
[3] Signet Library, *Old Session Papers*, 135, No. 30, 1768, 24

subject to the customs dues levied on those sold at Crieff or Falkirk, and as late as 1845 the New Statistical Account refers to cattle for Doune Tryst being allowed to graze free for a week before it. Nimmo, writing in 1777, describes how at Stirling too in the month of November another of these trysts was formerly held, but of late the drovers had ' relinquished that station on account of the enclosures which now everywhere surround the town and assemble with their cattle at Down in Menteith where they have more room and are likewise exempted from sundry tolls and customs which they were obliged to pay at the former place.' [1] Despite these advantages, Doune Tryst seems to have been unpopular with the drovers, probably because the weather was often bad and the tryst ground cut up by the trampling of the beasts, while the late date resulted in forced sales and bargain prices in a buyer's market.

Dumbarton was an old and important market for cattle from Argyllshire, while in the uplands of southern Scotland, a market which met with only moderate success, replacing one of much earlier date, was set up at Hawick in 1785 near one of the main drove roads to England, on a date between Falkirk Tryst and St Luke's Fair at Newcastle.[2] In the south-western counties a number of cattle markets existed for the sale of animals locally bred or imported from Ireland. Of these the market held on the White Sands at Dumfries was by far the largest, rivalling in importance all but Falkirk Tryst itself.[3]

So over the whole of Scotland spread a network of fairs, markets and trysts, where the local people sold the homely products of farm and hand-loom, buying in return the goods of pedlar and packsman. To nearly all came cattle from the surrounding hills and grazing lands for sale to the dealers and drovers, and for many of these fairs in the Highland areas it was the cattle sales chiefly which justified the existence and ensured the continuance of the market. Geography had determined the sites, custom and convenience the dates ; but Crieff and, later, Falkirk Trysts were the central points in the cattle dealer's year, and as the local cattle markets developed, they came less by conscious design than by necessity to form integral parts of one great continuous enterprise, by means of which cattle collected

---

[1] Nimmo, op. cit., 458   [2] *N.S.A.*, III, Hawick, 402
[3] For a fuller account of the cattle trade of the south-western counties, see Chapter 9

in early summer from the Outer Islands, the far North, Aberdeen-shire and the Central and Western Highlands came at last to the markets of Perthshire, Stirlingshire and southern Scotland. To serve this end, from May to October in all parts of the country men met, argued, quarrelled and bargained, for, as a writer of last century has said : ' If there's ocht in this warl' the farmer breed prides itself in, its in ha'en ta'en in somebuddy most desperately wi' a beast.'

THE DROVE ROADS OF SOUTHERN SCOTLAND

In the attempt which has been made to trace in some detail the routes through the Highlands used in the eighteenth and nineteenth centuries by the drovers of Scotland's cattle, it will be seen that the task has been made possible by the existence of certain sources peculiar to the district and to the period. The years which followed the Union of the Parliaments saw a steady growth in England of interest in Scottish affairs and an increasing realisation of the urgency of solving the many problems affecting Scotland, of which those relating to the Highlands were among the most acute. The political and economic instability of this area had concentrated attention on the question of Highland communications, and the selection of the routes of the military roads and the measures taken to bring order and peace to the Highlands before and after 1745, provides evidence of the routes and methods then in use by cattle drovers both within and without the Law. The task of Highland road construction reached its fullest development in the work of the Commissioners for Highland Roads and Bridges in the first quarter of the nineteenth century. The duties and functions laid on the Commissioners were based largely on the principle of assisted self-help in road-making, and to this is due the considerable body of local evidence in support of applications for assistance brought before the Commissioners, which is contained in their reports and which includes valuable material bearing on the economic life of the country. From the growing interest in Scottish affairs resulted also the increasing popularity among Englishmen of travelling in all parts of the country and particularly in the Highlands. Their experiences and observations have been recorded in detailed journals, some written in the fashion of the times in a verbose and philosophical strain tedious to modern ears, but many containing fine descriptive writing and much valuable information. The last decade of the eighteenth and the early years of the nineteenth centuries saw too in the Statistical Account and the County Agricultural Reports a comprehensive survey of Scotland which provided a wealth of detail relating to the social and economic life of the country, equalling if not surpassing, that available for any other part of these islands.

For the south of Scotland these sources are not available, or where they exist, as in the case of the Statistical Account and the Agricultural Surveys, contain less detail bearing on the work of the cattle breeders and drovers. With the notable exception of the south-western counties, breeding and dealing in black cattle was in the south of Scotland of far less importance than in the north. From a very early date the Lothians and the lower parts of what are now the counties of Berwick and Roxburgh, were among the most highly developed and closely cultivated parts of the country. In the pastoral and upland areas of Peeblesshire, Selkirkshire and Roxburghshire cattle were indeed bred and grazed in substantial numbers, but the emphasis from early times was rather on sheep rearing, an emphasis which became more marked as time went on, encouraged in the eighteenth century by the English demand for wool and mutton and finally by the growth of the cloth industry in the towns of the Southern Uplands. For the southern counties, other than Dumfriesshire, Kirkcudbrightshire and Wigtownshire, the Statistical Account and the Agricultural Surveys contain comparatively small reference to cattle rearing, while the evidence on the subject which is available for the Highlands through the work of the road-makers is largely lacking. The great cattle trysts of Ross-shire, Aberdeenshire, Perthshire and Stirlingshire on which the livelihood and interest of the Highland farmer of the eighteenth century so largely centred, had, save in the south-west, no parallel south of Falkirk, and the material and colour available from this source for reconstructing a picture of the drover's work is to this extent limited. The place of the southern counties of Scotland in the story of Scotland's cattle industry is indeed, with the exceptions mentioned, less that of a breeding and gathering ground than of an area of passage for beasts in transit to markets across the Border.

A further difficulty presents itself in attempting to trace the history and course of the droving trade in southern Scotland. The general trend of the droving routes of the Highlands was towards two fixed points—Crieff and Falkirk. South of Falkirk the course of the animal traffic was subject to no such concentrating influence. Between Falkirk and the Cheviots lay the wide grassy tableland of the Southern Uplands, offering a variety of easy routes with few obstacles of river or hill worthy of the name to men who had brought their cattle from the farthest parts of the Highlands, and such information as is available seems to indicate that for at least part of the journey to the Border a variety of routes were in fact used. Among the Cheviot Hills themselves, there were from Yetholm to Kershopefoot few points at which the crossing could not be made, while the destinations of the cattle on the English side were as yet too distant or too diversified to impart to the traffic more than a general southward trend. It is subject to these difficulties and limitations that the attempt is made to reconstruct the droving routes from Central Scotland to the Border.

The early history of the Scots droving trade has shown that at least as early as the fifteenth century Scots cattle were being driven to England in a traffic which, despite many changes of fortune, grew slowly but fairly steadily in volume in the centuries which followed. The Union of the Parliaments and the political and economic changes of the eighteenth century brought a great expansion of this south-bound trade. It will be recalled that the Tryst at Crieff was rising to importance in the early years of that century and continued in existence till about 1770. While there seems little doubt that many of the cattle which changed hands at Crieff found their way to England, there is little direct evidence as to the extent at this period of the traffic to the South. It seems probable that only a few English buyers at that time ventured even as far as the borders of the Highlands, and while Highland drovers were no doubt regularly taking beasts to the South it was probably not until Falkirk Tryst began to take the place of Crieff after the turn of the century that English buying in Scotland assumed large proportions. By then the demand for beef in Scotland itself was growing. There is evidence of buying in the eighteenth century at Falkirk by Scots graziers who fattened the animals in Stirlingshire and Dumbartonshire for the growing towns of Central Scotland,[1] and as early as 1777 Nimmo had referred to the increase in manufacturing in Scotland and the consequent increasing demand for beef as tending to lessen the export of meat to England.[2] The greater part, however, continued their journey to England by drove routes which led though the Southern Uplands to the Border.

---

[1] Belsches, *General View of the Agriculture of the County of Stirling*, 1796, 45 and 58
[2] Nimmo, *History of Stirlingshire*, 1st edn. 1777, 457-8

In his description of the Parish of Morvenside (Muiravonside), written about 1723, Alexander Johnstoun mentions the crossing of the West Lothian Avon at the Bridge of Dalquhairn by 'the Highland cattle from the markets at Falkirk in their way to the Borders of England.'[1] Johnstoun was, of course, writing at a time when the Falkirk market, as yet in its infancy, was still being held on its original site at Reddingsrigg to the south of Polmont. All the evidence available suggests, however, that even after the tryst had been moved to Rough Castle and later to Stenhousemuir the drove routes from it to the Border continued to lie as Johnstoun had indicated, to the south-east rather than due south, and there is little indication in contemporary sources that cattle from Falkirk used to any large extent the routes leading to the Border by way of Lanark and the valley of the Upper Clyde. The exact route from the crossing of the Avon is uncertain. Some drovers may have preferred to pass by Bathgate on the south-west side of the high ground lying to the south of Linlithgow. Others appear to have chosen the route through Linlithgow itself, and according to an old tradition in the district these drovers after passing through Linlithgow turned south making for Ecclesmachan, Uphall and Mid Calder.[2] Whatever the exact route, and in this cultivated country it can hardly now be definitely established, there is general agreement that the aim of the south-bound droves was the pass known as the Cauldstane Slap which crosses the Pentland Hills between the East and West Cairn Hills.[3] In Armstrong's and Thomson's maps of Peeblesshire drawn in 1775 and 1821 respectively, the pass is shown as a drove road and is still so shown on the maps of today. Both Armstrong's map and Thomson's were prepared at a time when cattle droving to England was in steady operation, and since the marking of drove roads as such in contemporary maps was by no means usual, there seems little reason to doubt that this route through the Pentland Hills was then in active use, and that the continuation of these routes through the Southern Uplands, marked by both these map-makers as drove roads, can be accepted as authentic. To this day the marks of animal traffic through the Cauldstane Slap can be seen in the soft broken ground

---

[1] Macfarlane's *Geographical Collections*, I, 317
[2] Miller, *The Origin of The Falkirk Trysts*. Falkirk Archaeological Society Transactions, 1936
[3] Chalmers, *Caledonia*, IV, 940. The road through the Cauldstane Slap to Peeblesshire is described as having been 'established by custom and continued by use.'

to the east of the small burn which feeds Harper Rigg Reservoir at its south-eastern corner. The tenant of Harper Rigg Farm, whose family have been in the farm for several generations, recalls having seen a few droves using the route by the Cauldstane Slap as late as the end of last century, and of having heard his father and grandfather speaking of heavy droving traffic in their day. According to their account the beasts crossed the Water of Leith a short way to the east of the present reservoir and passed to the east of the farm-house. The farm tenants tried, if possible, to get their meadow hay cut before the arrival of the droves, for the beasts went pretty much as they chose, and the drovers were none too careful in herding them. The cattle ' stanced ' for the night in the meadow or beside the drove road all up the slope of the Pentland Hills towards the pass, the drovers sleeping beside them, the ' topsmen ' or the owners sleeping in the farm-house. The present tenant can remember his father telling him of having seen the snow in an early autumn reddened from the feet of the beasts, presumably worn by the hard roads which they must have used for part of their journey from Falkirk Tryst.

South of the pass the line of the road as indicated by Armstrong followed the Lyne Water to West Linton, and thence to Romanno Bridge from which point it crossed the hills in a south-easterly direction to Peebles. Romanno Bridge was evidently a point of some importance on the drove route to the South, and in 1832 a dispute, which came before the Court of Session, arose between the trustees for the 1st and 2nd Districts of Turnpike Roads for Peeblesshire over the erection of tollbars. A statement to the Court by the Clerk of the 2nd District claimed that the annual revenue of the tollbar at Harestanes, two miles south of Dolphinton, was £262 and of that at Romanno £193, and that a large portion of this revenue and in particular that from the Romanno Tollbar arose from toll ' paid by Highland cattle passing through the County of Peebles from the North, partly by drove and partly by Turnpike roads on their way South to the English and other markets, which cattle have been in use heretofore to enter the County of Peebles at the Cauldstane Slap and to pay the first toll within the County at Romanno Tollbar. That these cattle pass that tollbar on their way South and never return, yielding an annual revenue to the 2nd District varying between £80 and £100.' [1] At Peebles the drovers were liable

[1] *Williamson* v. *Goldie*, Signet Library, *Old Session Papers*, 1832, 236, No. 218, 5

to payment of customs duty but had in return the right of grazing their beasts on a stretch of common land beside the Tweed on a site known as the Kingsmuir, rights of common pasture dating back to a Charter of James IV in 1506.[1]

South of Peebles, Thomson's maps of Peeblesshire (1821) and Selkirkshire (1824), show various alternative routes, all marked as drove roads. Of these one led from Peebles by way of Kirkhopelaw and Stakelaw into the glen of the Douglas Burn and so to Dryhope at the east end of St Mary's Loch. This route, which is still marked on modern maps as a drove road, is easily traced as it climbs the hill to the south of Peebles, enclosed by drystone dykes. Crossing Yarrow the road came by Tushielaw into the Ettrick Valley. From Tushielaw the route led south up the Rankle Burn by Buccleuch, crossed the high ground by Kingsmoor Loch and Girnwood to reach Deanburnhaugh on the Borthwick Water ; and so to the valley of the Teviot. Another route shown on Thomson's maps led south-east from Traquair, crossing the hills by Minch Moor and Broomylaw to the top of Long Philip Burn to reach the Ettrick Valley to the west of Selkirk. This was the route which Montrose's defeated troopers had followed north in September 1645 after the Battle of Philiphaugh, and it was the Minch Moor route which was followed by the droves under the charge of Robin Oig and Harry Wakefield, described in Sir Walter Scott's tale *The Two Drovers*. Yet another route, marked on Thomson's maps as a drove road, branches off the road from Selkirk to Hawick some three miles south of Selkirk and passes by Akermoor Loch and the Shaws Lochs to Gildiesgreen and Buccleuch.

It is clear that droves using these routes to the South would pass within a comparatively short distance of Hawick. The town of Hawick appears to have been of some importance in the cattle trade, at least as early as the second half of the seventeenth century. In 1669 the King and Parliament had before them a Petition of William, Lord of Drumlanrig for himself and the inhabitants of Hawick, which stated that the town and village of Hawick being situated near the English Border ' wherethrow diverse persons doe repair thither for buying and selling of bestiall, victuall and other commodities propper to be bought and sold ther,' the inhabitants are prejudiced ' throw the want

[1] *Charters and Documents relating to Peebles, 1165–1710.* Scottish Burgh Records Society, 38

155

of the liberty of two other frie Fairs . . . besides the Fairs which they presentlie have.' The Petition was granted and by an Act of that year two free fairs were established for the sale of ' horse, nolt, sheip, etc.' to be held on 6 May and 10 September.[1] Till 1777 there existed at Hawick a common where beasts could be rested, but in that year the common was divided, and since at that time, despite the grant of 1669, no cattle market of any size appears to have existed in the town, Hawick ceased to be a point of importance on the drove route to the South. The Burgh Records of Hawick contain the following reference : ' 1777. June 3. The which day the Magistrates and Town Council being convened heard ane advertisement read to be published in the " Edinburgh Courant " against Drovers of Cattle to rest in Hawick Common, now allotted to the Burgesses and Inhabitants of the Town of Hawick, which was approven of and ordained to be published.' [2] The lack of an established resting-place here for their beasts seems to have been felt by the drovers, for in 1785 they proposed to the Hawick authorities that they be allowed to rest their beasts for three days on condition that they offered them for sale. In support of their proposal, the drovers argued that all the cattle that are driven from Crieff and Falkirk to Newcastle and most of those bound for Carlisle passed through Hawick or within twelve miles of the town. This was the year when Falkirk Tryst was moved to its new ground at Stenhousemuir, and it is possible that the Hawick people saw an opportunity of developing their town as a centre of the cattle trade. However this may be the Hawick authorities appear to have welcomed the proposal which was adopted.[3] The Statistical Account for Hawick records that ' there is a weekly market and four Fairs besides a Tryst established within these few years for black cattle, etc. in October between Falkirk Tryst and Newcastle Fair, which promises to succeed,' [4] but the writer of the New Statistical Account for Hawick half a century later referring to the October cattle tryst there mentions that 'it has not been so successful as was expected.' [5]

The doubts thrown by the New Statistical Account on the success of Hawick Tryst lend some support to the view that the route shown on Thomson's map of Selkirkshire (1824) as reaching the Teviot Valley some way to the west of the town, was largely

[1] *A.P.S.*, VII, 661–2
[2] Johnman, Transactions Hawick Archaeological Society, 1917, 33
[3] ibid.   [4] *O.S.A.*, VIII, 527   [5] *N.S.A.*, Hawick, III, 402

used by the drovers. Local tradition, and the evidence of those still living in the district whose memory reaches back to the last days of droving add confirmation.[1] According to this evidence the droves reached the valley of the Teviot below Commonside some seven miles up-stream from Hawick. Here they were on the direct route to Langholm and Carlisle, and it is at least highly probable that some droves went that way. Well defined droving tracks are still plainly visible on the west side of the Limiecleuch Burn, one of the head waters of the Teviot, at a point which suggests that droves bound for Langholm and the Esk Valley may have left the main Carlisle road at Teviothead rejoining it by way of the valley of the Eweslees Burn about three miles south of Mosspaul Inn. Local evidence however leaves little room for doubt that while the route by Langholm was probably used by some of the drovers, it was not the main drove route to England.

Almost opposite the point where the drove road from Dean-burnhaugh reaches the Teviot Valley below Commonside, the Northhouse Burn joins the river from the south side, and the local evidence available is to the effect that this was the route more commonly used. Following a short way up the Northhouse Burn this route crossed the head of the Allan Water and the Dod Burn, making for Peelbraehope. The next point on the route was the shepherd's cottage at Hawkhass, from which, crossing the flat ground at the head of Longside Burn, the droves are believed to have crossed the ridge which lies between Greatmoor Hill and Scaw'd Law. Marks of droving traffic are clearly to be seen near Hawkhass and again on the south slope of the ridge where they may be easily traced on the east side of the Sundhope Burn, and on the first edition of the 6-in. Ordnance Survey of Roxburghshire published in 1863 the route is clearly marked as a drove road. The route crosses the Whitterhope Burn up-stream from the old tollbar near Whitterhope which was thus avoided, and today the tracks are to be seen climbing the low shoulder of the hill known as the Ninestone Rig. Here the tracks divide. One branch leads by Riccarton and Saughtree to the top of the Liddel Water and so to England and the valley of the North Tyne. The other turns due south from the Ninestone Rig and keeping to the east side of the Hermitage Water, where the tracks are still in places to be seen, crosses the Liddel Water some three miles above Newcastleton to reach the English Border at the Kershope Burn.

<hr/>

[1] Curle, *The History of the Berwickshire Naturalists' Club*, XXIX, 195

Of the routes to Carlisle from the North which passed farther to the west or north-west of Hawick, there is evidence that at least the one which led through Annandale was used. The writer of the Statistical Account for the Dumfriesshire Parish of Dryfesdale, referring to the road which led to Lockerbie, reports that ' along this road in the spring, but especially in the end of harvest, vast droves of black cattle from the North and West Highlands pass into England to the number of about 20,000 annually, prices from £3 to £7 each, in order to be fatted in the Norfolk fens and other places and supply the London and other markets, making the most delicious meat, vastly preferable to the large and rancid Irish horned bullocks.' [1] It may well be that some beasts reached Annandale by way of Ettrick and Eskdalemuir or by St Mary's Loch, Birkhill and the Moffat Water. There is little direct evidence, however, that these routes were used, and the reference in the Peeblesshire litigation already quoted, to cattle traffic at the tollbar of Harestanes near Kirkurd, suggests that some of the traffic which crossed the Pentlands at the Cauldstane Slap reached Annandale by Broughton and the head waters of the Tweed.

It will be recalled that the argument used by the drovers in asking for pasturage rights at Hawick in 1785 was that all cattle bound for Newcastle and most of those bound for Carlisle passed through the town or within twelve miles of it. Now if this statement be accepted as approximately correct, it is consistent not only with the use of the route to the west of Hawick by Deanburnhaugh and Commonside which has been described, but with the existence of other routes to the east of the town crossing the Border by way of the Jed Water and Carter Bar, or by the ancient Dere Street and the top of the Kale and Oxnam Waters. The list of routes across the Border which was compiled in 1597 [2] includes many to the east of Hawick, and the use of Duns and Kelso as customs posts for controlling cattle traffic in the sixteenth century would seem to show beyond reasonable doubt that some cattle at that time crossed to England by way of the East as well as the Middle and West Marches. It seemed therefore a reasonable assumption that two centuries later when the cattle traffic to the South had increased so greatly some at least of these routes would still be in use, and when the present inquiry was taken in hand it was anticipated with some confidence,

[1] *O.S.A.*, Dryfesdale, IX, 428   [2] *Border Papers*, II, 1595-1603, 469

that despite the limitation of sources already referred to, clearer evidence to this effect would emerge than has in fact become available.

An examination of the ground at the head of Bowmont Water reveals the existence of a number of well-defined tracks, some of which have very much the appearance of drove roads crossing the Border to the south of Cocklawfoot, and at Windy Rig and Windy Gyle slightly to the west, leading down into the head-waters of the Coquet. On Stobie's map of Roxburghshire which is dated 1770, a road is marked crossing the Border from the head of Bowmont Water. Neither on that map, however, nor on later maps of that area up to and including the first edition of the 6-in. Ordnance Survey in 1863, is there any indication that this route was in fact a drove route, nor does there appear to be in the district any tradition of droving traffic from the North having used the valley of the Bowmont at least during the main droving period in the eighteenth and early nineteenth centuries. It is not possible to determine with any certainty the age or even the exact character of the traffic which caused the tracks now to be seen near the top of Bowmont Water, and all that can be said of them is that they have all the appearance of having been made by animal traffic. It may be that such droving traffic as passed that way was of a purely local character and of comparatively recent date. Some of it may, however, be much older, dating back to the fifteenth, sixteenth or seventeenth centuries, to a time when cattle trade from the North, legal and illegal, was using every byway over the Cheviots, when frequent cattle raiding or stock movement across the Border was causing ' brode waies or rakes ' like those which Sir Robert Bowes and Sir Ralph Elleker observed in this district in 1542.

As to the routes which crossed the Cheviots near the head-waters of the Kale and Oxnam Waters the state of the evidence is rather similar. Here, too, occur many tracks still clearly visible on the ground which appear to have been made by animal traffic. The first edition of the 6-in. Ordnance Survey (Sheet XXXV) shows indeed three routes marked specifically as drove roads crossing the Border immediately to the south of Nether Hindhope Farm and in the vicinity of the Roman camp at Chew Green, but these routes are not continued on the adjoining sheets to the North. There are, indeed, many traces of droving traffic visible on the ground to the north of this point, but it is not possible to say whether these were made by through traffic or merely by the movement of stock from grazings in the neighbourhood. Pennymuir Fair which took place annually near Tow Ford on the Kale Water was an important local sheep market. It continued in existence into the last quarter of the nineteenth century, and from it considerable numbers of stock were regularly driven south across the hills to the top of the Coquet and Redesdale. There is little evidence that droving traffic used the route by Carter Bar, but many traces suggestive of droving traffic are to be seen on the high ground between the Jed and the Rule Waters, possibly making for the Wheelcauseway and the North Tyne. In the absence of direct evidence all that can be said is that while heavy droving traffic by this route within the last two centuries seems unlikely, it is hard to believe that no droves used it, at least during the early years of last century when the total numbers of cattle driven to England are believed to have reached figures in excess of 100,000 per annum.

To attempt to draw, from the scraps of evidence available, any definite conclusion as to the large numbers of tracks across the Cheviots to the south-east of Hawick would clearly be unwise and quite unwarranted. In an upland district of this nature over which has passed the varying traffic of many centuries, it is only possible to guess at the age of the tracks which are still today so plainly visible, or at the precise type of traffic which caused them. There is, however, one consideration which is not without relevance. A study of the map will show, that while the route from the Cauldstane Slap by Peebles and Tushielaw crossing the Teviot west of Hawick, leads almost directly south to the Border from the West Lothian plain, any route to the Border hills passing between Hawick and Coldstream would entail a wide detour to the east of the direct line. Had such a route led through country more attractive for droving than the direct route it might well have been chosen ; but the reverse is the case. Any such route would entail the crossing of the lower part of Teviotdale or the Merse of Berwickshire, districts which from early times were closely cultivated and thus less suitable for droving than the upland country to the westward which offered all the conditions which the drovers sought. When this factor is considered in conjunction with the absence of satisfactory evidence to the contrary from maps or printed sources, local recollection or tradition, it may at least be said to support a tentative but reasoned conclusion that during the eighteenth and nineteenth centuries the bulk of the droving traffic from Falkirk to the Border passed to the west rather than to the east of Hawick.

If the part played in the story of Scotland's cattle trade by the south-eastern counties would seem to have been rather that of a passage-way to England than of a breeding ground, the role of the south-western counties was very different. Here from an early date cattle breeding had been of prime importance. In the reign of William the Lion (1165–1214) the penalties fixed by the justices of Galloway for breaking the King's Peace was 12 score cows and 3 bulls, a fine which could only have been paid in districts where the cattle population was considerable.[1] Hector Boece in 1527 wrote of Annandale, Nithsdale and Galloway as having ' store of bestiall '[2] grazing in a countryside which half a century later Bishop Leslie described as abounding in ' nobill pastorall,'[3] and it seems probable that cattle breeding in this south-west district on a scale of some importance dates back at least as early as in any other part of the country. The unsettled state of the Border up to 1603 no doubt acted as a severe check on the activities of the earlier cattle breeders of the south-west, but there is little reason to doubt that at least a part of such cattle trade with England as persisted during the two or three centuries preceding the Union of the Parliaments came from Wigtownshire, Kirkcudbrightshire and Dumfriesshire. The choice in 1612 of Gretna as a customs post for taxing livestock traffic crossing the Border[4] was no doubt made partly with a view to traffic from these south-western counties, while the construction of a drove road from Annan to Gretna in 1619,[5] and the appointment in 1625 of Commissioners in Nithsdale and Annandale to prevent the export of cattle to England,[6] seem conclusive evidence that an appreciable droving traffic from these districts already existed. Taylor ' The Water Poet ' reported having seen numerous herds grazing in south-west Dumfriesshire in 1618, and in Annandale alone he counted 1,100 beasts on ' as good grasse as ever man did mowe.'[7]

The full extent of this seventeenth-century livestock traffic from the south-west is uncertain. Customs dues levied on

[1] *A.P.S.*, I, 378
[2] Hume Brown, *Scotland before 1700 ; from Contemporary Documents*, 70
[3] Hume Brown, op. cit., 117   [4] *R.P.C.*, 1st series, IX, 267 and 394
[5] *R.P.C.*, 1st series, XI, 633–4   [6] *R.P.C.*, 2nd series, I, 138
[7] Taylor, *Works*, 1630, 128

livestock crossing Dumfries Bridge in 1655 only amounted to £573 6s 8d Scots,[1] so the numbers paying toll can hardly have been large, but the changing attitude of Crown and Parliament towards the cattle trade to England, which marked the latter part of the seventeenth century, no doubt benefited the drovers of the south-west. When in 1697 a drove road from New Galloway to Dumfries was marked out on the instructions of the Privy Council, the route was described as ' the line of passage taken by immense herds of cattle which were continually passing from the green pastures of the Galloway Hills into England—a branch of economy held to be the main support of the inhabitants of the district and the grand source of its rents.' [2]

The first attempts at improving the methods of rearing and management of cattle appear to have taken place in south-west Scotland, and in the last quarter of the seventeenth century Sir David Dunbar of Baldoon in Wigtownshire started the practice of enclosing land on a large scale for grazing. The cattle park which he formed is said to have been two and a half miles long by one and a half miles broad capable of holding 1,000 beasts, of which some were bred at Baldoon and some collected from the neighbouring country. From this enclosure it is reported that Dunbar sold yearly to the drovers or sent to the markets of England as many as eighteen to twenty score of cattle. The beasts bred at Baldoon appear to have been so large that in 1683 a number of them were seized in England and slaughtered under the belief that they were Irish cattle, the import of which was at that time, and for many years to come, prohibited. The mistake complained of was perhaps not altogether surprising, for it appears that in 1670 Sir David had been fined for importing Irish cattle for sale in England.[3]

The enclosing of land in Galloway by stone dykes for the improvement of cattle breeding and the enlargement of farms was to lead to serious disorders. Many small tenants who had hitherto enjoyed grazing rights in common over the ground enclosed were evicted in favour of a single farmer renting the enclosed land at an increased rent. In the spring of 1723, when much enclosing had already been completed, many of the evicted

---

[1] *Minutes of Dumfries Town Council.* Quoted in McDowall's *History of Dumfries*, 838 et seq.
[2] Chambers, *Domestic Annals of Scotland*, III, 153
[3] *R.P.C.*, 3rd series, III, 105–6, 129

Plate 12   A drove route south of Peebles
(*above*) Between stone dykes near Kirkhope Law.   (*below*) Climbing from the
Tweed Valley
(*Photos by the Author*)

tenants met at the Fair of Kelton Hill and organising themselves into companies of fifty, set to work systematically to overturn the dykes. The movement soon assumed the aspect of a riot, and troops were sent from Dumfries, Ayr and Edinburgh to deal with it. The authorities appear to have acted with moderation, and of 200 ' levellers ' rounded up and taken to Kirkcudbright, many were allowed to escape and only a few of the ringleaders were imprisoned or sent to the Plantations. The movement is said to have materially retarded the progress of improvement in the south of Scotland, and the factors which gave rise to it are in many ways parallel to those which were to cause distress in the Western Highlands and Islands half a century later.[1]

The part played by these south-western counties in the Scots cattle trade depended not only on their importance as a breeding ground but on the export through them of cattle brought in from overseas. As early as 1627 the Earl of Annandale had obtained from the Privy Council permission to land at Portpatrick and take to England cattle belonging to his Irish tenants, to enable them to pay their rents.[2] The import of Irish cattle appears to have continued, for Thomas Tucker writing of Galloway in 1655 speaks of Portpatrick as having a trade with Ireland in horses and cattle.[3] In 1667 and 1668 the Privy Council made orders prohibiting the landing of Irish cattle,[4] and in 1684 a Commission was appointed with the object of preventing it.[5] There is no evidence to show how successful were these efforts to check the trade, but the import of Irish cattle remained at least in theory illegal till 1765. The ban was then withdrawn, and it is on record that five years later Portpatrick possessed six vessels of fifty tons each which were mainly employed in shipping cattle from Ireland.[6] The Statistical Account for the Parish records that between 1786 and 1790 over 55,000 head of Irish cattle were imported,[7] and in 1812 as many as 20,000 were landed.[8] ' This trade,' says the Statistical Account, ' depends so much upon the quantity of grass, of hay, or of turnips in England, and sometimes even upon the prospect of large crops of these articles that there is much speculation in it. Great gains and great losses

---

[1] Mackenzie, *History of Galloway*, II, 393–403
[2] *R.P.C.*, 2nd series, I, 591   [3] Hume Brown, *Early Travellers*, 180
[4] *R.P.C.*, 3rd series, III, 147   [5] *R.P.C.*, 3rd series, VIII, 411
[6] *N.S.A.*, Portpatrick, IV, 152   [7] *O.S.A.*, I, 43   [8] *N.S.A.*, IV, 153

are therefore sudden and frequent. Hence the import is unequal. Some people suppose the trade is favourable to smuggling and hostile to the revenue. Others object to it, as in a peculiar manner detrimental to those districts in Scotland where black cattle are bred ; and there seems to be rather a hardship in permitting such numbers of cattle to be imported into North Britain or even carried through it in order to rival the productions of that very country in the only market to which it has access. Without entering, however, into these speculations it may be sufficient at present to remark that the import will probably diminish of itself in consequence of the rapid progress which Ireland is now making. The time is fast approaching when that Kingdom will be in the same state in which England is at present, having a market within itself sufficient for the consumption of its own production.' [1]

From the Wigtownshire coast to Dumfries stretched a series of cattle markets or trysts. Some of these appear to date back at least as early as the end of the seventeenth century and owed their existence to the importance of the local cattle-breeding industry, but some, of later date, no doubt owed their rise and growth largely to the Irish trade. The position of these trysts gives a fair indication of the route by which the Irish beasts and those of local breeding passed eastward to Dumfries, to Carlisle and to England. [2] The main trysts appear to have been held at Glenluce, Newton-Stewart, Gatehouse, New Galloway, Kelton Hill, Crocketford and Dumfries. The market at New Galloway dates back to a Royal Charter ratified by an Act of Parliament in June 1633 which conferred on the Provost, Bailies and Council the privilege of holding ' one market on Wednesday weekly with three fairs yearly, each one to last for the space of three days. . . .' [3] In a description of the market in 1778 reference is made to the town as being a gathering place for all the cattle in the Stewartry on their way to England, and Heron in 1792 speaks of it as a stage on the road to Rhonehouse or Gatehouse of Fleet. [4]

The market at Kelton Hill was at one time described as among the largest in the south of Scotland. According to an old tradition its selection as a site for a market came about by an

[1] O.S.A., Portpatrick, I, 43
[2] Further detail regarding the drove routes from Portpatrick to Dumfries is given in J. M. Corrie's The Droving Days in the South-Western District of Scotland, 91 et seq.
[3] Reg. Mag. Sig., 1620–33, 458–9 ; A.P.S., V, 101
[4] Heron, Journey through the Western Counties of Scotland, II, 157

accident somewhat similar to that which is said to have determined the site of Aikey Fair in Aberdeenshire. A passing pedlar had occasion to spread his goods out to dry on the side of the hill. The local folk, attracted by the display, collected, and bought up the whole contents of the pack with a readiness which induced the pedlar to promise to return at the same time in the following year, so giving rise to a custom which continued year after year.[1] Though the date when the Kelton Hill market originated is not known, it seems probable that it was in existence at least as early as the middle of the eighteenth century, for a writer in 1825 describes it as dating back far beyond the reach of any living recollection. Heron gives a description of it which corresponds very much to the contemporary descriptions of Falkirk Tryst : ' From Ireland, from England, and from the most distant parts of North Britain, horse dealers, cattle dealers, sellars of sweet-meats and of spirituous liquors, gypsies, pickpockets, and smugglers are accustomed to resort to this fair. Every house in the village (of Rhonehouse, which owes its origin to the fair) is crowded, and all become on this occasion houses of entertainment.'

' The roads are, for a day or two before, crowded with comers to this fair. On the hill or park where it is held tents are erected in rows so as to form a sort of street. . . . Through the whole fair day one busy tumultuous scene is here exhibited of bustling backwards and forwards, bargaining, wooing, carousing, quarrel-ling, amidst horses, cattle, carriages, mountebanks, the stalls of chapmen, and the tents of the sellers of liquors and of cold victuals. The village also holds high festival during the week, and besides the peasantry, the neighbouring gentry are spectators for a short time of the confusion, the tumult, and the rude festivity which it displays.'[2]

But of all the cattle markets in the south of Scotland none appears to have equalled the Tryst at Dumfries. The natural centre for an extensive and rich grazing area, Dumfries lay on the direct road to Carlisle and the South. Weekly markets and three Autumn Fairs at Dumfries date back at least as early as the seventeenth century, and during the last quarter of the eighteenth and the first half of the nineteenth centuries, the White Sands at the mouth of the Nith saw each year a growing number of cattle exposed for sale. Pennant in 1772 records that ' the great weekly

[1] Alexander, *Northern Rural Life in the 18th Century*, 79
[2] Heron, op. cit., II, 129 et seq.

markets for black cattle are of much advantage to the place and vast droves from Galloway and the Shire of Air pass through on their way to the Fairs in Norfolk and Suffolk.'[1] The fortunes of the Dumfries Market were naturally and directly affected by the demand from the South, and the largest sales appear to have been those in September, which fitted in with the big Fair at Brough Hill in Westmorland later in the same month or the October Market of St Faith's near Norwich, while at the Dumfries sales in the middle of October cattle changed hands on their way to the Market at Hempton Green in West Norfolk held on 16 November. Indeed the importance of the English trade to the Dumfries sales was so great that the market held there in mid-October came to be known as 'Hempton Wednesday,'[2] while the great composite drove collected in September for the Norwich sale was locally known as the 'St Faith's Drove.'[3] An Agricultural Survey of Dumfriesshire in 1794 reports the sale in one year of 20,000 head of cattle to the four main drovers at a price of £130,000.[4] All through the first quarter of the nineteenth century the local Press records a growing trade at the Dumfries Market. In 1829 and 1830 the number sold in the last week of September was reported to have risen as high as 6,000[5]; but by that time changes in farming methods in Scotland were already far advanced, and with the growing diversion of the Irish cattle trade to the direct sea passage to England the droving traffic which passed through Dumfries entered on a period of gradual decline.

For the cattle which crossed the Nith at Dumfries bound for the English markets, the natural routes lay by way of Annan and Gretna, crossing the Esk and the Eden by fords near their mouth. In addition to these routes, fords across the Solway Firth itself were at times also used.[6] The most important were those known as the Dornock Wath and the Stoney Wath or Bowness Wath, and in his life of George Moore, a Cumberland merchant, Samuel Smiles has described the crossing of the Bowness Wath in the first quarter of last century. Moore in his early youth

[1] Pennant, *A Tour in Scotland, 1772*, I, 115
[2] Bryce Johnston, *General View of the Agriculture of the County of Dumfries*, 1794, 11
[3] Signet Library, *Old Session Papers*, 1798, 392, No. 14, 6
[4] Bryce Johnston, op. cit., 19   [5] *N.S.A.*, Dumfries, IV, 20
[6] For a fuller description of the fords of the Esk, the Eden and the Solway Firth, see *The Fords of the Solway*, McIntire. Transactions Cumberland & Westmorland Antiquarian and Archaeological Society, 1939, XXXIX, new series, 152–70

Plate 13   Cattle crossing the Solway Firth
(From the painting by Sam Bough, R.S.A.)

had been sent by a Cumberland banker to take cash to a client who had bought cattle at Dumfries, and had been persuaded to help in driving the cattle south. 'They drove the cattle by unfrequented routes in the direction of Annan. At length they reached the shores of the Solway Firth. The proper route into England was by Gretna, though the road by that way was much longer. But the cattle dealer declared his intention of driving his cattle across the Solway sands. . . . The tide was then at low ebb. The waste of sand stretched as far as the eye could reach. It was gloaming by this time and the line of the English coast— about five miles distant—looked like a fog-bank. Night came on. It was too dark to cross then. They must wait till the moon rose. It was midnight before its glitter shone upon the placid bosom of the Firth. The cattle-dealer then rose, drew his beasts together and drove them in upon the sands. They had proceeded but a short way when they observed that the tide had turned. They pushed the beasts on with as much speed as they could. The sands were becoming softer. They crossed number-less pools of water. Then they saw the sea-waves coming upon them. On, on ! It was too late. The waves which sometimes rush up the Solway three feet abreast were driving in amongst the cattle. They were carried off their feet and took to swimming. The horses upon which George Moore and his companion were mounted also took to swimming. They found it difficult to keep the cattle together—one at one side, and one at the other. Yet they pushed on as well as they could. It was a swim for life. The cattle became separated and were seen in the moonlight, swimming in all directions. At last they reached firmer ground, pushed on and landed near Bowness. But many of the cattle had been swept away and were never afterwards heard of.' [1]

[1] Smiles, *George Moore, Merchant and Philanthropist*, 42 et seq.

10

BEYOND THE BORDER

I will bring you, my kine,
Where there's grass to the knee :
But you'll think of scant croppings
Harsh with salt from the sea.

The Drover

PADRAIC COLUM

THE story of Scotland's cattle trade from its first discernible beginnings in the fourteenth and early fifteenth centuries has shown how closely its varying fortunes were, from the first, bound up with the markets south of the Border. Now encouraged, now restricted, and at times entirely prohibited, the trade was, at least up till the Union of 1603, always conditioned by the political and economic relations between the two countries and by the state of the Border lands ; in short, by the presence or absence of factors which interfered with the free flow of cattle to the English markets. As the seventeenth century drew to a close, the barriers which had divided the two countries began at length to give way. The Union of the Parliaments saw the final end of the customs and tariffs against which the cattle traders had for so long fought by protest or by evasion, and from 1707 dates the steady increase in their trade with England, which gradually brought the volume of south-bound droving traffic to its peak in the second quarter of last century. From first to last the most powerful magnet drawing cattle from the glens of the Highlands lay south of the Border, and as the years passed, buying for England came more and more to determine the prosperity of the markets at Crieff, Falkirk, Dumfries and many smaller trysts. A full account of the cattle trade to England forms no part of the present purpose, but no attempt to describe or understand the droving trade in Scotland can be complete or fully intelligible which ignores the fate of the Scots cattle, their routes and their final destinations south of Berwick and Carlisle, and the watersheds of the streams which drain the Cheviots.

The volume of southbound cattle traffic in the centuries prior to the Union of the Parliaments is hard to gauge. Such references to the trade as are available occur mainly in the complaints of those, on one side of the border or the other, whose object lay in controlling, taxing, or preventing it, in Acts of Parliament or Orders of the Privy Council passed with a similar purpose, the wording of which, to modern ears, suggests exaggeration. 'Vast,' 'universal' and 'in great numbers,' phrases frequently used, give little real indication of the volume of traffic, and it is not till the second half of the seventeenth century that the references become more specific. One of the earliest estimates is that already referred to from the Tax Records of Carlisle in 1662 when it was reported that 18,574 cattle passed through the town paying toll,[1] a total which would, no doubt, include, and may well have been made up largely of, cattle from the important cattle-breeding districts of Galloway and the south-west. Pococke, in a letter dated 6 May 1760 describing his tour in Scotland, wrote : 'I came to the Downs of Wigtown. . . . Here they graze a great number of small oxen which they send to a Fair near Norwich and they are fattened for six months in Norfolk, Suffolk and Essex for the London Markets,'[2] and a Note to Pococke's *Tours in Scotland* quotes Agricultural Reports of 1794-5 for the statement that in 1675, 20,000 to 30,000 cattle went south each year from Galloway.[3] Had the Scots beasts sent to London from Norfolk been as numerous as is indicated by the eighteenth-century writers they would have accounted for a very large part of the total consumption of London, leaving small place for the cattle of Wales and the south-west and Midland counties. It seems probable that the estimates are too high. Nathaniel Kent put the fat bullocks sent from Norfolk to London at 20,000 per annum, three-quarters of which he estimates were Scots cattle.[4] It is known, however, that during the first half of the eighteenth century the number of cattle sold at Smithfield alone for the London market was between 75,000 and 80,000,[5] and that a high proportion of these came fat from the Norfolk grazings. Whatever the true figure of Scots cattle driven to England before 1700, it was certainly considerable. The important part played by the cattle trade in the negotiations for the Union of 1707 shows that cattle were already among Scotland's main exports, and in

---

[1] *State Papers. Domestic.* Charles II, 1663–4, p. 226
[2] Pococke, *Tours in Scotland, 1747, 1750 and 1760*, 18   [3] ibid., note
[4] Fussell and Goodman, *18th Century Traffic in Livestock.* Economic History (Supplement of Economic Journal) Feb. 1936, III, No. 11
[5] McCulloch, *Dictionary of Commerce*, new edn., 1856, 271

contemporary records there seems to be general agreement that by then at least 30,000 Scots cattle crossed the Border each year.

The century which followed the Union of the Parliaments was marked for Scotland and England alike by changes so great that the two countries which then came together in complete, if unwilling, union are hardly to be recognised in the nation which fought Napoleon. England, at the start of the eighteenth century, was still almost entirely an agricultural country. The vast majority of her people lived in districts still completely rural. Roads, their neglect or upkeep a matter of purely local responsibility, were still in a primitive state, and communities divided one from another by difficulties of transport were, of necessity, largely self-supporting. Such industry as existed was carried on mainly in small villages or country cottages, and the larger towns were little more than markets for the products of the country districts which they served. Norwich, Bristol, Leeds and Halifax distributed the cloth and woollen goods of East Anglia, the Cotswolds and the Dales. Newcastle carried on a coastal trade with London and some export trade with the Scandinavian ports, but the great stimulus of the coalfields of the north-east coast was yet to come. Only London, with one-fifth of the entire population of $5\frac{1}{2}$ millions, was already showing clear signs of possessing those magnetic qualities which were to transform her out of all recognition in the coming century.[1] Outside London, the population of the country was fairly evenly spread. The most populous districts lay in a belt extending north-east from the Bristol Channel to Northamptonshire and Buckinghamshire. Over the great part of the remainder of the country the density of population was generally uniform, only Cumberland, Westmorland and the North Riding of Yorkshire falling much below the average.

By 1800 the picture was very different. The London area was still by far the most densely peopled, but outside it the greatest centres of population now lay in Lancashire and the West Riding of Yorkshire, in Staffordshire and the North Midlands, with a lesser degree of concentration along the Bristol Channel and in Durham.[2]

These movements of population are significant of a great social and economic change which, by the end of the century, was already far advanced. At the beginning of the eighteenth

[1] Trevelyan, *English Social History*, 341, 343
[2] Grant Robertson, *England under the Hanoverians*, 337, 338

century as many as four-fifths of the population were engaged in agriculture, tilling by traditional and unscientific methods land little developed and occupied at the will of the landlord, or at best on short tenancies. As the century progressed, increasing wealth seeking profitable investment in a time when opportunities for investment were scarce, and the demands of an expanding population, turned the attention of the landowning classes more and more to the development of their estates, while growing knowledge of scientific methods of farming made available to them the means of turning their land to good account. It is estimated that in the hundred years between 1696 and 1795, two million acres had been added to the agricultural land of England and Wales.[1] Townshend, the retired Secretary of State of George II, Coke on his Norfolk estate at Holkham and Jethro Tull in Berkshire had shown the benefits of crop rotation made possible by the sowing of clover and artificial grasses and the cultivation of the turnip, while Bakewell in Leicestershire had pointed the way to better livestock by improvement in the methods of breeding. The enclosure of land for crop cultivation and the consolidation into economic units of the mosaic of small patches cultivated under the old system, was a necessary outcome of the new agriculture. In the first half of the century enclosure of land by agreement had made substantial progress, and by 1800 a further area of over 4,000,000 acres of land had been enclosed by Act of Parliament,[2] a development partly responsible for and partly facilitated by the drift of population to the growing towns. By the end of the century, though the standard of English livestock and arable farming had enormously improved, the proportion of England's population engaged in agriculture is estimated to have fallen from four-fifths to one-third.

The revolution through which England's agriculture passed in the course of the eighteenth century was, as in Scotland, complementary to the great Industrial Revolution which started about 1760 and gathered momentum all through the remaining years of the century. The rapid growth of Britain's colonial empire and the expansion of her overseas trade supplied for industrial development the necessary markets and raw material, while the discoveries and inventions of the second half of the century provided the means to profit by them. Cargoes from the American plantations fed through Liverpool the growing mills of Lancashire,

[1] Trevelyan, op. cit., 374n   [2] Grant Robertson, op. cit., 331

where Arkwright's invention was transforming the cotton industry, as those of Hargreaves and Compton were transforming the spinning industry of the West Riding. In Staffordshire Wedgwood was laying the foundations of the pottery trade, while perhaps most important of all was the discovery that coal and coke could be used in place of charcoal for smelting iron. This was a development which more than any other influenced the movement of population in Britain, bringing industry and wealth to those areas where coal and iron were to be found close together, to South Wales and South Yorkshire, to Tyneside and the Clyde basin. The end of the century found the Industrial Revolution little more than well under way, but already the movement of population to the new industrial areas had gone far in defining the lines of later development. These changes in eighteenth-century England have a close bearing on the Scots cattle trade, and in their light it is possible to assess with some certainty the factors which, during the century following the Union of 1707, led to the steady increase in the cattle traffic to the South, freed from the burden of tariff restriction or national prejudice.

Throughout the whole of the period of upward of four centuries covered by the records of the droving trade of Britain, a large and steadily growing portion of the traffic made its way to the London market. Here, throughout, was by far the greatest concentration of population and wealth. Meat and bread were the chief foods. Defoe says that as early as the sixteenth century it was the common practice to send beasts to London to have them killed there, and by the time of Queen Elizabeth great cattle fairs in Northamptonshire and Leicestershire were already supplying through Smithfield the needs of the taverns, the coffee-houses and the private households of the capital. As has been seen, no reliable figures are available for the period before 1700, but it is known that long before that time the trend of cattle movement to market was more and more towards south-east England. During the eighteenth century this trend continued and the numbers grew despite the growing demand of the new industrial areas of the Midlands and the North. From Wales, following traditional routes, cattle were driven to the Midlands, to Essex and to Kent for fattening for the London market. From the south-western counties, by way of the Wiltshire Downs and the valley of the Kennet, they crossed the country to Hertfordshire and Buckinghamshire to the same end, while the destination of the Scots cattle was the grass land of the

Home Counties and of East Anglia, which fattened much of London's beef.[1] From 1732 to 1794 the number of cattle sold each year at Smithfield Market alone rose from 76,000 to 109,000.[2] How many of these were Scots beasts cannot be determined, but in view of the high proportion of Scots cattle which found their way to East Anglia for fattening or to the great market at Barnet in Hertfordshire, it would seem beyond doubt that the demand of the London market was throughout of the first importance for the Scots cattle trade. ' Often at great distances of two or three hundred miles or more from the collossal emporium of men, wealth and intellectual power,' wrote de Quincey in the early years of last century, ' have I felt the sublime expression of her enormous magnitude in one simple form of ordinary occurrence, viz. in the vast droves of cattle upon the Great North Road all with their heads directed to London and expounding the size of the attracting body together with the force of its attracting power by the never-ending succession of these droves and the remoteness from the capital of the lines in which they were moving.' [3]

The movement of population and the rise of the industrial towns of the Midlands and the north of England in the second half of the century created new demands, second only to the needs of London. Cattle for the new markets must, like those for Smithfield, be fattened in areas within easy reach of the consumers. Graziers in Northumberland now supplied the growing population of Tyneside and the north-east ports, those in north-east Yorkshire the needs of Whitby, Scarborough, Hull and the Yorkshire coast, while the grass lands of Cumberland, Westmorland and the Craven district of Yorkshire fed the cloth workers of the West Riding and the mill workers of Lancashire.[4]

---

[1] Fussell and Goodman, op. cit.

[2] The Smithfield figures show a marked decline in the totals for the years between 1745 and 1750. As the figures relate to all cattle brought there for sale, it is impossible to tell to what extent this was due to the Rebellion and the unsettled state of the Highlands immediately after it. It may well be that the widespread cattle disease in England in 1746 was a more important factor, though evidence given in the course of the division of the Commonties of Reddingsrigg and Whitesiderigg already quoted referred to few cattle being brought there for sale in 1746. A marked increase in the Smithfield figures after 1760 corresponds closely with other evidence as to the growth of the Scots droving trade. (Macculloch op. cit., 1856, 271. *Report of Select Committee on Cultivation etc. of Waste Lands,* 1795)

[3] Thomas de Quincey, *Autobiographical Sketches,* Vol. XIV of Works (1863 edn.), 179

[4] Fussell and Goodman, op. cit.

While the demands of the English home market were thus steadily growing, the cattle trade was being called on to meet another urgent need. From the early years of the eighteenth century till the Battle of Waterloo the armed forces of Britain were almost continuously on a war footing, engaged first in maintaining the balance of power in Europe and latterly in the growing struggle with France. From first to last the part played by the Navy was of supreme importance, whether in the Narrow Seas, the Baltic, the Mediterranean or on the American coast, and it was on the possession and maintenance of sea power more than on any other factor that the issue throughout depended.

Beef, fresh or salted, was among the traditional foods of the Navy, and agents of the Naval Victualling Board were constant buyers of fat cattle to meet the growing demands of Britain's expanding fleet. From the main victualling depot and ' cutting house ' at Deptford, the smaller depots at Chatham, Dover, Portsmouth and Plymouth were fed, and they in turn supplied ships lying at these ports, in the Downs, and at Margate, New Romney, Falmouth and Weymouth and at other ports of the south and south-east coast.[1] Among the Minutes of the Victualling Board in the Public Record Office are preserved the contracts for the supply of a great variety of naval victualling stores. Here are contracts for the supply of flour, bread and ' bisket stuff'; of rum, beer and lime juice ; of sugar and molasses ; of lemons, onions and vinegar ; and beef was one of the chief items.[2] The main salting season lasted from the end of September to the end of March, and many of the contracts for the supply of H.M. ships required that beef be cured between these dates with a sufficient quantity of Saint Ubes Bay Salt ; ' that it be full of pickle ; good sound, sweet, well fatted and of the best quality.' [3] No ' bull stags ' must be supplied ' nor any ox which dropped upon the road.' Despite the conditions in the Supply Contracts as to the quality of the animals and the methods of salting, complaints about the meat issued to the Fleet were frequent. From the beginning of the eighteenth century to the end of the Napoleonic Wars the records hold many references to inquiries into complaints lodged, but these seem generally to have ended in a finding

[1] *Select Committee on Finance*, June 1798. House of Commons Committees, XIII, 509
[2] *P.R.O.*, Admiralty, 111/73
[3] *Select Committee on Finance*, op. cit., 534. Setubal, a bay on the coast of Portugal was known by British sailors as St Ubes, or St Ives Bay.

Plate 14   Smithfield Market in the early 19th century
(*Drawing by Thomas Rowlandson.   By permission of the Trustees of the British Museum*)

that the meat is ' good, sweet and fit for the service.' [1]   The
small size of the cattle of the eighteenth century, even when
fattened for killing, is shown by a condition in a contract of 1798
that the beasts must weigh not less than 5 cwt. [2]   A contract of
1816 requires a weight of only 4 cwt., [3] while a stipulation in one
of 1823 that the beasts must weight 6 to 7 cwt. is described as
unusual. [4]

The purchases of cattle by the Victualling Board were on a
large scale.   The Board Minutes for the early years of the
eighteenth century frequently record the supply of up to 200 fat
cattle by one contractor in a single transaction, and a Minute
of 1 October 1746 records that this being the day when contracts
were made for the supply of beef, contractors were notified that
the Board would require during the next six weeks 1,600 cattle
for the Deptford stores, 600 for Portsmouth, 500 for Plymouth
and 300 for Dover. [5]   By the closing years of the century the
needs of the Navy had greatly increased.   Victualling Board
Minutes of 1794 show payments in that year totalling close on
£18,000 for the supply of beef, much of it described as ' Scotch
beef,' for ships lying in the Thames, and over £15,000 for fresh
meat supplied for Chatham, [6] while one of October 1804, typical
of many at the time, records the payment to John Grant of over
£1,000 for fresh beef supplied during five months of that year
to ships lying at Norwich. [7]   In the year of Trafalgar payments to
contractors who supplied salted beef to the stores at Deptford,
Chatham, Dover, Portsmouth and Plymouth show that for these
alone the number of cattle slaughtered was over 16,000, [8] while
local purchases of fresh meat were made at every port from
Newcastle to Margate, from Dover Roads to Dartmouth and from
Milford Haven to Greenock. [9]   As the French Wars neared their
end the purchases of cattle for the Navy appear to have reached
still higher levels, and an entry in the Victualling Board's ledger
for the year 1812 shows payments to Wm. Mellish, one of the
principal naval contractors, totalling no less than £455,397 for
beef and suet supplied between 1 October 1811 and 30 September
1812. [10]   The average price appears to have been approximately
£15 a head.

[1] *P.R.O.*, Admiralty, *passim*
[2] *Select Committee on Finance*, op. cit., 509
[3] *P.R.O.*, Admiralty, 112/85
[4] *P.R.O.*, Admiralty, 109/78
[5] *P.R.O.*, Admiralty, 111/32
[6] *P.R.O.*, Admiralty, 112/180
[7] *P.R.O.*, Admiralty, 111/173
[8] *P.R.O.*, Admiralty, 112/191
[9] *P.R.O.*, Admiralty, 112/84
[10] *P.R.O.*, Admiralty, 112/198

The extent to which the naval demand for beef was affected by the political situation is shown by a series of communications between the Victualling Board and the Admiralty in 1771.[1] Fresh as well as salted beef was supplied to the Fleet on certain days in the week, and in the spring of that year when the calls on the victualling stores were heavy, that department asked the Board of Admiralty to direct that fresh meat be issued only twice a week to enable the stores of salted meat to be built up. Two months later they reported to the Admiralty that the Convention with Spain [2] having been ratified, the demand for meat would be much less than had been expected and that a great quantity of salted beef was in store. They asked that salted beef only be issued, the surplus in store being sold to the public, and the records for the next few months show public sales to the extent of over £4,000.[3] The end of the Napoleonic Wars brought a great contraction in the scale of naval buying, and for Plymouth alone the number of cattle supplied fell from over 5,000 in 1812 to less than 700 in 1820.[4]

What proportion of the cattle supplied to the Navy were Scots cattle cannot be exactly determined. It has been seen that some of the beef supplied to the Thames in 1794 was specified as Scots beef and there is no reason to consider this an isolated case, but as a rule the contracts did not distinguish Scots meat or Scots beasts from English. The demand was for fat beasts which had already passed from the hands of the drovers to those

---

[1] *P.R.O.*, Admiralty, 110/25

[2] In 1770 relations between Great Britain and Spain, already strained over the question of Louisiana and complaints of contraband trade with the Spanish colonies, became further embittered by a dispute over the possession of the Falkland Islands, where a Spanish expedition from Buenos Aires had forced the British to evacuate Port Egmont. Great Britain demanded reparation and both countries prepared for war. Spain looked to France for help, but this was refused and, faced with a naval war in which her fleet would be no match for that of Great Britain, Spain gave way. The Spanish forces were withdrawn from the Falkland Islands, and on 22 January 1771 a Convention was signed which provided for the restoration of Port Egmont to Great Britain. (*Recueil de Traités*, Martens, 1st series (2nd edn.), XI, 1)

[3] Confirmation of the fall in cattle prices in England in 1771 may be found in a Petition of William Robertson to the Commissioners on the Forfeited Estates for the tenancy of the farm of Wellhouse in the parish of Kilmorack in Inverness-shire, previously rented by his brother Duncan. Duncan in that year had driven to England some 1,600 or 1,800 cattle from the Trysts at Crieff and Falkirk, but the prices fell and he suffered great loss, spending the whole winter driving the beasts from place to place at great expense in an attempt to market them ' whereby he lost more of his health and effects than he has since that time been able to recover or make up again.' (*Forfeited Estates Papers*, Scot. Hist. Soc., 1st series, 57, 140)

[4] *P.R.O.*, Admiralty, 112/206

of the English graziers. The records show, however, that much of the naval beef supplies came from East Anglia where a large proportion of the Scots beasts found their way, while the total volume of the demand disclosed by the Admiralty Victualling Records shows beyond doubt that during the whole period from 1700 to the end of the French Wars naval buying was a factor of major importance to the droving trade. The War Office Records do not show so clearly the extent of Army purchases of beef as do those of the Admiralty, but some idea of the scale of the purchases of meat for the Army may be got from correspondence which passed between Lord Palmerston, at that time Secretary for War, and the Duke of York in 1812. Lord Palmerston had advocated that in the interests of economy bulk contracts should be made for the supply of the Army's meat. In support of his argument he wrote to the Duke in September 1812 that he estimated from figures available to him that if bulk contracts were entered into the saving alone in the course of one year would amount to between £60,000 and £80,000.[1]

Founded then, at its outset, on a demand from the South, and freed at length from political obstacles, the Scots droving industry derived from 1707 onwards stimulus and growing incentive from many sources ; from the change in farming methods which developed cattle feeding in England nearly half a century earlier than in Scotland ; from the growing wealth of the industrial areas ; from demand for the Navy and the Merchant Fleet and, always and above all, from the growth of London.

The difficulties which until 1707 drovers of cattle from Scotland to England faced in crossing the Border hills were political and economic rather than physical. At few places in the whole stretch of the Cheviots is the ground so rugged or the hills so steep as to present a serious barrier to travelling cattle. The route by the east coast entailing passage of the rich Berwickshire plain would have relatively few attractions, but to the south-west a succession of easy passes lay open across the hills offering to the droves grass, water and quiet stances ; by the valleys of the Bowmont, the Kale and the Jed into the head waters of the streams which feed the Coquet and the Rede ; from the top of Liddesdale to the source of the North Tyne, from Eskdale and Annandale to the valleys of the Eden and the South Tyne. The exact routes followed by the Scots cattle in England up till the

---

[1] *P.R.O.*, War Office, 4/442

time of the Union must remain a matter for conjecture, for few detailed records have survived. The figures given for the Carlisle cattle traffic in 1661 indicate that the west-coast route into England was extensively used, but since London was already by far the greatest market in the South, it is probable that a large proportion of the traffic at that time kept down the east side of the Pennines by Corbridge and Northallerton. That some of the beasts were sold in Yorkshire is apparent from the complaint of the local graziers about 1660 that the Scots were underselling them, but it seems probable that many of the Scots beasts travelled straight on to East Anglia and the Home Counties.

By the middle of the eighteenth century the volume of cattle traffic from Scotland had reached great proportions, one contemporary estimate putting the total as high as 80,000 head each year.[1] By now the movement of population in England was having its effect in changing the routes and destinations of the Scots beasts. More of the traffic now entered England by way of Carlisle, from Eskdale and Liddesdale, or across the shallow estuary of the Solway to the Cumberland shore, a traffic swelled by imported Irish cattle. From Carlisle the routes of the Scots beasts led up the Eden Valley to Appleby and Kirkby Stephen or to Brough Hill near the borders of Westmorland and Yorkshire. At Brough Hill, towards the end of the century, as many as 10,000 Scots beasts were sold annually at the great fair at the end of September.[2] Some of these went to drovers from the South, some to graziers from Yorkshire and Cumberland, and some stayed in Westmorland for fattening.

From Westmorland a variety of routes led to the South. Some crossed the country by Richmond or Ripon to join the eastern drove route at Northallerton or Boroughbridge, while others led south to Kirkby Lonsdale, to Settle or to Skipton. These drovers' routes in the northern counties of England are in many places still to be seen, some as tracks crossing bare and open moorland, some enclosed between dry-stone dykes, but nearly always keeping so far as possible to the higher ground. The period of the main growth of the droving traffic to the South after 1750 corresponded with the period of the greatest extension of the Turnpike Trusts, and the choice of routes for the droves was dictated very largely by the need to avoid the tolls which the Trusts exacted. A

[1] Postlethwaite, *Britain's Commercial Interest Explained and Improved*, 1757, I, 57
[2] Fussell and Goodman, op. cit.

Broadsheet printed in 1753 urging a Turnpike Trust in Craven says : ' It is well known that the graziers in driving cattle from the North and other places where they buy them, keep constantly to the moors and never come on any road at all.' [1]

The Craven district of Yorkshire in which Skipton lies occupies an important place in the story of the Scots droving trade. The rich grazing of this limestone area, well suited to the fattening of cattle, was equally well placed for the supply of the English markets. To the west and south were the growing industrial areas of Lancashire and Yorkshire, while cattle fattened here could be readily driven across the low passes of the Pennines to supply the ports of the Yorkshire coast, or to join the main routes down the east side of the country to Northamptonshire, Buckinghamshire and East Anglia. During the first half of the eighteenth century the cattle trade from Scotland to England was, as has been seen, largely in the hands of Scotsmen, but after the turn of the century English dealers started to go north in increasing numbers. Graziers from Craven were among the first English dealers to come to Scotland in search of cattle. As early as 1745 Birtwhistle, one of the largest and most successful Yorkshire dealers, undeterred by political events around him, travelled through the Hebrides and the Highlands buying lean stock.[2] Moorhouse, another Craven grazier, bought the Skye and Raasay cattle in 1765.[3] A few years later Pennant reports dealers from the same district buying as far north as Ullapool,[4] and soon English dealers were attending the trysts at Crieff and Falkirk and penetrating far to the north and west in search of beasts. In 1767, the same year in which he was financed by the British Linen Bank,[5] Birtwhistle was pursuer in a Petition to the Court of Session against the factor for Mackenzie of Seaforth. The dispute was over a bill given by Birtwhistle for cattle purchased in Lewis. ' Of late years,' says the factor in his ' Answers ' to the Petition, ' it has been usual for the dealers in black cattle in our neighbouring country to come or send to the remotest parts of Scotland to purchase cattle.' [6] Birtwhistle was for many years tenant of the limestone grazing around Malham

---

[1] Brigg, *The King's Highway in Craven*, 59
[2] Hurtley, *Natural Curiosities in the Environs of Malham in Craven, Yorkshire*, 1834
[3] *The Farmer's Magazine*, 1804, 393
[4] Pennant, *Tour in Scotland, 1772*, I, 364
[5] See Chapter III
[6] *Old Session Papers*, Signet Library, 150, No. 24, 2

(861)179   13

Tarn in Upper Wharfdale, ' a prodigious large field of enclosed land, being upwards of 732 acres in one pasture, a great part of which is a fine rich soil and suitable for making cattle both expeditiously and uncommonly fat.' Here ' you might frequently see 5,000 head of Scotch cattle at one time. As soon as these were a little freshened, notice was dispersed among the neighbouring markets and villages that a fair would be held in this field on a particular day. . . . As soon as these were disposed of a fresh drove succeeded, besides sheep and horses frequently in great numbers. Mr B. has had 20,000 head of cattle on this field in one summer. . . . To say the truth, when fattened on these rich old pastures, there is no beef equal to them in fineness either of grain or flavour.' [1]

While the route from Scotland down the west side of the Pennines saw yearly an increasing traffic, the more easterly route continued to be extensively used. Some of the Scots cattle lingered in the grazing lands of Northumberland to supply the needs of the small towns and the shipping of the north-east coast. Others grazed their way down through the hills which drain to the Coquet and the Tyne passing through Northumberland and Durham to North Yorkshire. From Northallerton their road lay by Boroughbridge to Doncaster and on by Gainsborough and Newark to Grantham and Peterborough, following roughly the route of the Great North Road which a traveller of the middle of the eighteenth century described as having wide stretches of turf on either side perpetually roughened by the passage of great droves of cattle.[2] Some, turning east about Grantham, went by Spalding and Wisbech into Norfolk, and a record of 1750 reports 20,000 Scots cattle as passing along the Wisbech road.[3] The routes of the drovers through Yorkshire and Lincolnshire, as in other parts of the north and Midlands of England, are marked by the names of the wayside inns, some of which still survive. The Drover's Inn at Boroughbridge and Wetherby, the Drover's Call between Gainsborough and Lincoln and the Highland Laddie at Nottingham and St Faith's near Norwich, recall the droving traffic to East Anglia and the Home Counties, as the Highland Laddie at Gretna and the Drover's Rest at

---

[1] Hurtley, op. cit.
[2] Fletcher, *The Making of Modern Yorkshire*, 17
[3] Thompson, *Cattle Droving between Scotland and England*. Journal of Archaeological Association, 1932, 87 (new series, 37), 181.

Kirkandrews in Cumberland recall that bound for Cumberland and the West Riding.[1]

In his *Tour through Great Britain 1724* Defoe described the meadow land between Norwich and Yarmouth : ' In this vast track of meadows,' he wrote, ' are fed a prodigious number of black cattle which are said to produce the fattest beef though not the largest in England. . . . The gross of all the Scots cattle which come yearly to England are brought thither, being brought to a small village lying north of the City of Norwich called St. Faiths where the Norfolk graziers go and buy them. These Scots " runts " as they call them, coming out of the cold and barren mountains of the Highlands of Scotland, feed so eagerly on the rich pasture of its marshes that they thus in an unusual manner grow monstrously fat, and the beef is so delicious for taste that the inhabitants prefer them to the English cattle which are much larger and fairer to look at. . . . Some have told me and I believe with truth, that there are about 40,000 of these Scots cattle fed in this country every year and most of them in the said marshes between Norwich, Beccles and Yarmouth.' [2]

Writing of the Norfolk grazings, half a century later, a writer of 1769 says : ' Here besides the cattle of the country numerous herds of starved cattle from the Highlands of Scotland find their way. Here they lick up the grass by mouthfulls, the only con-tention is which can eat the most and grow fat the quickest. When they have gotten smooth coates and swagging sides they continue their journey to the Capital and present themselves to Smithfield where they find many admirers.' [3]

The Fair at St Faith's which Defoe describes had existed since the twelfth century, and throughout the 150 years during which detailed records of Scots cattle droving to England are available this was the principal market for cattle from the North. To it came not only cattle from Skye and the Central Highlands but from Galloway. It started on 17 October each year and seems to have continued so long as there were cattle left for sale —usually a period of several weeks.[4] The woollen industry

---

[1] Thompson, op. cit., 180, 182

For certain of the information regarding the cattle trade and the drove routes in the northern counties of England I am indebted to an unpublished manuscript by Mr Kenneth J. Bonser, Leeds.

[2] Defoe, *Tour through Great Britain in 1724*, 6th edn., 1762, I, 59–60

[3] Gilpin, *Observations on Several Parts of the Counties of Cambridgeshire and Norfolk, etc.*, 1769   [4] Marshall, *Rural Economy of Norfolk*, 1795, I, 340–4, II, 49–52, 361

around Norwich which flourished through the greater part of the eighteenth century provided a local demand for fat cattle, but the greater part having been finished off on turnips after the autumn grazing were driven to the fat market at Smithfield in the following spring. Besides the great market at St Faith's, smaller but important ones existed in other parts of East Anglia, particularly at Hempton Green in West Norfolk, held on 16 November each year, and at Bungay, Hallisworth and Harleston near the borders of Norfolk and Suffolk.[1] Most of these were, like St Faith's, autumn markets, but some were held in the spring and early summer for the sale of stock from Scotland and the north of England for the summer grazing. Farther to the east in Hertfordshire, Barnet was the scene of a great market mainly for the supply of London, and here came cattle from Scotland, from the west of England and from Wales.[2]

The droving traffic from Wales affords a close parallel to the Scots droving traffic with which it must often have been in competition. Droving of Welsh cattle to England appears to be at least as old as the Scots traffic. As early as 1312, 700 cattle from North Wales were sent to Windsor for the supply of the King's household kitchen, and throughout the fourteenth century Welsh cattle were regularly bought for the supply of the Court or the houses of the great nobles. Welsh cattle were used in the fifteenth century for the provisioning of the army in France, and in the reign of Henry V there is a record of the salting of ninety-three Welsh cattle for the supply of the troops at Calais.[3] Disorder on the Welsh marches and the activity of cattle thieves hampered the traffic to England just as the state of the Borders affected the traffic from Scotland, and during the early years of the Civil War Welsh drovers petitioned the King for a safe conduct through the royal armies for the cattle traffic on which they depended for their livelihood and the payment of taxes.

From the records available it seems that the Welsh drovers fulfilled a function for which there is little parallel among the drovers of Scotland. In the seventeenth and early eighteenth centuries, when banking facilities were still unknown and travel was still precarious, the Welsh drovers started to act as agents for

---

[1] Smith, *Survey of the Agriculture of Galloway*, 1813, 249–50
[2] McCombie, *Cattle and Cattle Breeders*, 1867
[3] Skeel, *Cattle Trade between England and Wales from the 15th to the 19th Centuries.* Royal Hist. Soc. Transactions, 1926, 4th series, IX, 137–8

people in Wales who wished to transfer money or pay debts to correspondents in London. In some cases the money appears to have been carried to its destination, and there is a record of the transfer by drovers to London of the Denbighshire ship-money in 1636,[1] but latterly the drovers took to leaving the money at home and discharging the commission from their receipts in England at the end of the drove. This led to a primitive form of banking, and in 1799 the Black Ox Bank of David Jones and Company was started at Llandovery by one of the principal Welsh drovers with a picture of a black ox engraved on its notes, one ox for each pound of the note's value.[2]

Despite the drovers' difficulties, the Welsh cattle trade prospered, and during the seventeenth and eighteenth centuries reached large proportions. An estimate of the number of cattle driven from the three counties of Carmarthenshire, Pembrokeshire and Cardiganshire about the end of the eighteenth century puts the total at 30,000 per annum.[3] The routes from Wales are known with rather more certainty than those from Scotland. From South and Central Wales the main route appears to have taken the drovers across the Radnorshire border into Herefordshire and thence by Ross, Ledbury and Tewkesbury bound for the grazings of Leicestershire and Northamptonshire or as far east as Essex and Kent, but it seems probable that few Welsh drovers went as far east as Norfolk. From North Wales they passed through Kenilworth and Castle Bromwich into Warwickshire making for Barnet Fair and Essex.[4] A substantial part of the North Wales traffic came from Anglesey, and Aikin, in his *Journal of a Tour from North Wales in 1787*, has described the scene at the crossing of the cattle to the mainland in words which might well have been written of the crossing of Kyle Rhea by the Skye drovers :

' They are urged in a body by loud shoutings and blows into the water and as they swim well and fast, usually make their way to the opposite shore. The whole herd proceeds pretty regularly until it arrives within about 150 yards of the landing-place, when, meeting with a very rapid current formed by the tide eddying and rushing with great violence between the rocks that

---

[1] Skeel, op. cit., 151   [2] Skeel, op. cit., 143
[3] Lloyd, *Historical Memoranda of Breconshire*, 1903
[4] Fussell and Goodman, op. cit. Skeel, op. cit. Hughes, *Wales and the Drovers*, 1943

encroach far into the Channel, the herd is thrown into the utmost confusion. Some of the boldest and strongest push directly across and presently reach the land ; the more timorous immediately turn round and endeavour to reach the place from which they set off ; but the greatest part, borne down by the force of the stream, are carried toward Beaumaris Bay and frequently float to a great distance before they are able to reach the Caernarvonshire shore.'

Aikin records that as in the case of the Skye cattle, 'an instance seldom, if ever, occurs of any being lost.'

If the risks of droving from the Highlands to the trysts of the Scottish Lowlands were great, the drover who crossed the Border was launched on an enterprise fraught with risks and uncertainties even more varied and more serious. In the easier country of the South a longer day's march was possible, and stages of fifteen to twenty miles seem to have been not uncommon ; but charges for grazing and stance rights were higher. Shortage of hay or failure of the English turnip crop might spoil markets. Cattle disease, like that which ruined Thomas Bell in 1747, was a constant menace, while the cattle trade was always at the mercy of the issues of peace or war which were never far from men's thoughts in eighteenth-century Europe. As the droving trade developed and competition among the dealers grew more keen, it became the custom for those in charge of southbound droves to maintain with the dealers in Scotland a regular correspondence.[1] Some of these letters were honest appreciations of the situation from which the dealers in the North could judge the state of markets and the prospects for further droves, but some, less honest, were intended to convey to a wider circle such information as the drovers judged it wise and profitable to let them have. On any good news from the South, further droves would be sent off from Scotland with an optimism characteristic of the droving profession, which took little account of the risk that bad weather or political changes might, while the droves were on the long road, produce conditions ruinous to their owners. Evidence given before the Parliamentary Committee in 1826 already quoted, shows that in the autumn of 1801 severe losses were suffered by the drovers owing to the fact that news of the negotiations for the Peace of Amiens was only received

[1] Webster, *General View of the Agriculture of Galloway*, 1794, 25

after the Scots cattle had started on the journey to the English markets.[1]

Part of the droving traffic to England was spring droving. For this there were ready markets and good prices, though the losses among beasts driven in spring were often heavy. The number of beasts marketed in the spring was relatively small, and with the whole of the summer grazing ahead there was little of the autumn pressure to sell ; but most of the traffic took place in autumn when financial losses were more frequent. The writer of the *General View of the Agriculture* of *Galloway in 1794* has described the dangers of the trade to England :

' In September it is chiefly the best cattle that are bought to be fed on turnips and if the crop of turnips in England be plentiful, the prices of cattle in Galloway are generally high. Of consequence they must also be high in the Hempton Market, and if the first sold there are got off to advantage, then instant orders are sent down to hurry up every beast that can be purchased. At the approach of winter it is plain that every person will wish to dispose of all he can. . . . The English dealers, well acquainted with the former practices of the drovers and expecting plenty to be sent up, keep off from buying. Drove follows drove, no sales are made but at losing prices ; keeping gets up to an extravagant rate and perhaps the season becomes late, is rainy, the road becomes bad and numbers of cattle must be left at every stage, the greater part of which pay little more than for their skins. Such a practice as this may seem unaccountable but it must be considered that the drovers are in such a situation that it becomes unavoidable ; for while they are selling in England their bills are running on in the country, and thus their credit is constantly at stake, of which the banker takes care to advertise them.' [2]

In his account of St Faith's Fair in 1781, Marshall observes :

' The drovers do not bring their whole stock upon the " Bullock Hill " at once, but let them remain in the pastures until they are wanted ; nor do they bring any large droves at once into the country, but keep them back in Lincolnshire or

---

[1] *Report of Select Committee on Promissory Notes in Scotland and Ireland, 1826.* Notes of Evidence.
[2] Webster, op, cit., 26

185

perhaps in Scotland until they see how the demand is likely to prove. I did not learn the annual demand on a par of years but was told that Tate (one of the principal drovers) alone brings some thousands every year into this country.' [1]

Despite the risks and constant losses, the trade to England continued on an increasing scale. What they lacked in capital the drovers made up in courage and optimism, some secure in the knowledge that they had in fact little to lose, and that their losses if they failed would fall on others, but many relying in all honesty on their skill, knowledge and fortune. In the course of evidence given before the Select Committee on Promissory Notes in 1826 covering the preceding quarter century and the end of the Napoleonic War, witnesses drawn largely from officials of the Scots banks referred to bankruptcies involving £30,000 to £55,000, and in one case £70,000, on which dividends as low as one shilling in the pound were paid. William McCombie the Aberdeenshire cattle breeder, who was in the trade during the first half of last century, has recorded that when prices were at their height during the French Wars as much as £4 was sometimes made or lost on each beast driven to England. [2] In some cases the loss fell on the farmers, but in others on the bankers who had too readily given advances to the drovers, or had departed from their prudent rule of requiring two good names on a bill before it could be discounted. But such disasters appear to have acted as small deterrent, and the droving trade to England continued to flourish until a change in the farming practice in Scotland and the development of other means of transport led to the rapid decline of the industry in the second half of the nineteenth century.

[1] Marshall, op. cit., 52   [2] McCombie, op. cit., 99

THE COMING OF SHEEP

THE story of the origin and growth of the droving industry in Scotland is to a great extent the story of Scotland's cattle. The traffic which from early times traced out the routes of the drove roads, was largely traffic in the small black cattle of the Highlands with which these roads will always be associated; but sheep too played their part, and in the first decades of the nineteenth century when stock traffic from the Highlands to the Lowland Trysts was at its height, sheep and cattle were equal partners.

The descriptions of Scotland, which have come down to us from travellers through the country in the thirteenth, fourteenth and fifteenth centuries and the records of the Privy Council in the sixteenth and seventeenth centuries, on which in the main must be based our knowledge of the livestock of contemporary Scotland, lay the main emphasis on the cattle rather than the sheep population. In Scotland, as in many other countries in primitive times, the ownership of cattle was the accepted measure of wealth, and cattle rather than sheep formed the common currency of the thieving traffic of the Highlands and upland districts of Scotland, with which so many of the early records are concerned. To men engaged in a perilous trade, the most valuable stock alone could justify the risks they ran, and when success depended on rapid escape with their booty, it was of vital concern to them that only those animals should be taken which could face hard forced marches across hills and rivers and mountain passes. Cattle alone supplied the answer to the reivers' problems, and save in island raids where boats were used or occasionally where large-scale expeditions gave leisure and opportunity for carrying off more cumbrous booty, cattle were the reivers' main prey.

For all that, there is no lack of evidence of the existence in Scotland from early times of a considerable sheep population. John of Fordoun in the fourteenth century, John Major, Hector Boece and Bishop Leslie in the sixteenth century all agree as to the large numbers of sheep in Scotland at the times of which they wrote. The grazing rights from which the early monasteries derived much of their wealth were not confined to cattle alone, and the Chartularies of the Abbeys of Arbroath, Newbattle, Melrose and Kelso fully confirm the descriptions of these early travellers.[1] The Exchequer Rolls for the year 1378 put the number of fleeces exported at 1,473,586.[2] The surprisingly high figure is possibly to be explained by the fact that until the latter part of the sixteenth century export trade from which the Crown derived its revenue was encouraged rather than home industry. It seems probable that for this reason the early export trade in wool was considerably greater than at a later date.[3] Ayala and Perlin writing of Scotland in the sixteenth century refer to large numbers of sheep as well as cattle in the country, and in 1591–92 the Privy Council had before it a complaint against the Scotts of Harden and Quhitslaid for the theft from Drumelzier and Dreva in Upper Tweeddale of 4,000 sheep.[4] Major in 1521 wrote of 10,000 sheep in the ownership of one man,[5] and in the confusion of Orders, Statutes and Regulations which reflect the changing and uncertain policy of the Crown to the livestock traffic of the sixteenth and seventeenth centuries, sheep are mentioned little less frequently than cattle.

At the start of the eighteenth century, the woollen industry in Aberdeenshire was one of the few prosperous industries in the country. Here a trade in rough plaiding had been gradually built up by the farming folk working their hand-looms to eke out the bare livelihood which their small farms or meagre daily wage afforded them. By the early years of the century as much as 400,000 ells of cloth were reported as being exported from Aberdeen each year, and while much of this appears to have been made from wool imported from the south of Scotland, some would no doubt come from the sheep of the North-eastern and Central Highlands. Before the end of the seventeenth century woollen cloth had taken its place with linen yarn and salt among the main exports of Scotland,[6] and the woollen industry was among those which were intended to benefit from the ' equivalent ' payment arranged to compensate Scotland for the joint obligation for the National Debt which the Union of the Parliaments imposed on her.

[1] Cosmo Innes, *Sketches of Early Scottish History*, 99, and *Liber Sancti Marie de Melros*, xiv and xv
[2] *Exchequer Rolls*, II, xc   [3] Davidson and Gray, *The Scottish Staple at Veere*, 87
[4] *R.P.C.*, 1st series, IV, 709
[5] Hume Brown, *Scotland before 1700 : from Contemporary Documents*, 48
[6] Hume Brown, *History of Scotland*, III, 50

Little in the way of contemporary description of the sheep in Scotland before the eighteenth century has come down to us, and it was not till the middle of that century that the introduction of new and better breeds drew comparisons with the old native sheep, which tell what these were like. These eighteenth-century descriptions, while differing in small details, agree in the main that the old breed of sheep in Scotland was small in size, mainly white or dun-faced with wool fine in texture but meagre in quantity, a contemporary writer estimating that the fleeces of the old native sheep weighed no more than from twenty to twenty-eight ounces.[1] One writer described the sheep as having coats of short down, with some long straight hair like the coat of the beaver or other furred animals.[2] The small size of these native sheep is hardly to be wondered at in a breed which, like Scotland's cattle, had seen little change in blood for centuries, while lack of wool would naturally follow from the prevailing practice of keeping the sheep indoors throughout the winter. William Mackintosh of Borlum in 1729, advocating as a means of improving livestock the enclosing of farm land in Scotland by the planting of hedges, pointed out that such enclosing would not only make possible hay for winter food but would give some shelter for sheep in winter. ' Why may they not keep them unhoused,' he writes, ' which housing is certainly an enemy to the sheep and the staple of their wool.'[3]

There was indeed at that time little incentive to improve the breed of sheep in the country. There was little demand for mutton even at 1½d or 2d a pound, and till the great expansion of the woollen cloth trade, which took place after the middle of the eighteenth century, the crop of wool from the native sheep of the old breed would be sufficient to meet home demands or such cloth export trade as had survived the loss of the continental market and the competition of England. It seems, too, that the practice of smearing the skins of the sheep in autumn with a mixture of tar and butter, which was considered necessary to destroy parasites and to protect the sheep against the cold and wet of the winter, not only lowered the value of the wool but raised the cost of home-produced woollen cloth by the added labour which the cleaning of the wool entailed.

[1] Alexander, *Northern Rural Life in the 18th Century*, 71
[2] Marshall, *General View of the Agriculture of the Central Highlands*, 1794, 46
[3] Mackintosh, *Essay on Enclosing*, 1729, 257-8, 263

Until the middle of the eighteenth century the farmers of Scotland continued in the belief that the weather of a Scottish winter would be fatal to sheep in the open, but about 1750 the discovery was made in Perthshire that sheep wintered out of doors not only survived but prospered. The discovery came at a time when the agriculture of Scotland was entering on that long period of change and improvement, which in the course of the next century was to raise it from a static condition of hopeless apathy till it rivalled, if it did not surpass, that of any other part of the British Isles. The defeat of the Rebellion of 1745 had brought with it the final disappearance of the clan system. Hitherto the main feature of land tenure in the Highlands had been the existence of large numbers of tenants and sub-tenants occupying their land with no fixity of tenure under a tacksman, often a relation of the chieftain from whom he held the land at a low or nominal rent. It was a system which had little to commend it, either as a social system or as a method of sound land management. The small tenants, with no security of tenure, struggled under the weight of burdensome services to make a bare living from such grazing rights as they had, or from the tiny patches of land which poverty and traditional methods of bad farming made them unable to improve. The land was over-peopled [1] and much of it over-stocked, and, in the absence of turnips, hay or potatoes, only the most rigid economy, the barest of living and the sale of surplus stock in the autumn, enabled the people to emerge from the winter months with enough starving beasts or sufficient seed to start the weary round when the spring came. The rents in money, in kind or in services paid by the smaller folk to the tacksmen greatly exceeded the nominal rents which the latter paid to the chieftain, and for the tacksmen, often with little real interest in or feeling of obligation towards their land or their tenants, the arrangement was highly profitable. For the chieftains, the main benefit lay in the fact that their lands were peopled by large numbers of tenants owing allegiance to them at a time when the ability to call on the services and loyalty of a strong following carried with it prestige and political advantage.

The years immediately after 1745 brought widespread changes.

---

[1] Sir Walter Scott quoting from the *Gartmore Manuscript* records that in the first half of the eighteenth century in the country round Inversnaid 150 families lived on an area rented at a total of only £90 per annum. (*The Highland Clans*, Sir Walter Scott, 1856, 30)

Of these, some were the direct result of the defeat of the Rebellion, others the outcome of the Union with England, the benefits of which to Scotland were only then coming into full effect. The loss of Scotland's continental markets through England's wars with France and Holland was only slowly made good by the opening of wider markets and trade opportunities in Britain's growing colonial possessions, and, for a time, it seemed to Scotsmen that their country had at the Union surrendered much and received little in exchange ; but when they came the changes and the benefits came quickly. Expanding trade abroad and growing industry at home meant a greater flow of money into circulation, fed by increasing commerce and stimulated by the activities of the growing banks. Nowhere were the changing times more felt than in Scotland's agriculture, and the years which followed the Rebellion saw the beginning of an agricultural revolution which was in its outcome to prove as complete as the Industrial Revolution of the first half of the nineteenth century. The growing towns of the Lowlands and a rising standard of living meant more demand for the products of Scotland's farming lands, and as the lowland areas became steadily more fully developed, the country came more and more to look to the Highland districts for its livestock.

In the Highlands the change was very marked. The growing wealth of the country put into circulation money for the improvement of estates. The enlightened policy of those responsible for the administration of the Forfeited Estates and the legislation which quickly followed showed the benefits of longer leases, and led to the establishment of a class of professional farmers with the knowledge and the desire to improve their farms and security of tenure to make this possible.[1] With the altered conditions had come too a change in the relationship of landlord and tenant. The end of the Rebellion and the abolition in 1748 of the old heritable jurisdictions of the chieftains and great landowners marked the close of a period when the existence of a multitude of small tenants was a desirable object. Amalgamation of holdings

[1] The Forfeited Estates Act of 1752 allowed leases up to twenty-one years to be granted and made provision for tenants receiving compensation for improvements, while the Montgomery Act of 1770 allowed heirs in possession of entailed estates to grant leases up to thirty-one years, the tenants being under obligation to keep the fences in order. Pennant in 1770 noted the effect of the 1752 Act in the increased amount of enclosing and planting. (Hume Brown, op. cit., III, 269. Pennant, *Tour in Scotland, 1772*, II, 92–3)

into larger units was seen to mean more economical working and easier administration, and this in turn led ultimately to the abolition of the tacksmen and the complex system of land tenure of which they formed an essential part. It was in these new conditions that sheep farming on a large scale came to the Highlands ; to a countryside where political and economic change had shaken loose the fetters which had bound it to an old way of life ; to hill grazings stored with the accumulated fertility of centuries of partial and inadequate use.[1]

In the middle of the eighteenth century, sheep farming on a considerable scale was already being carried on in the south of Scotland where, as has been seen, the hills of Tweeddale and the Southern Uplands had fed large flocks in the prosperous days of the monks. Though Scots sheep as a whole were not highly valued either as mutton or for their wool, the sheep of these southern areas, with richer grazing and more readily crossed with the improved breeds in England, were no doubt superior to the old inbred native sheep of the Highlands. A considerable trade already existed with England. By the year 1757 it was estimated that 150,000 sheep were sent each year across the Border,[2] and the demand for mutton in England is shown by the fact that as early as 1745 the number of sheep sold each year at Smithfield had already reached 600,000, though what proportion of these came from Scotland is uncertain.[3] By the middle of the century an increasing demand was arising for wool and mutton from the growing population of Central and Southern Scotland, from the expanding ports of the north-east coast of England and from the wool manufacturers of Yorkshire. Improved arable farming methods, and particularly the introduction of the turnip, greatly increased the possibility of fattening stock, while at the same time limiting the areas available for stock raising in the south of Scotland, and the sheep farmers of the South turned to the Highland hills and glens for new and extended breeding grounds. About 1759, farmers from the Annandale district of Dumfriesshire introduced, near Callander in Perthshire, south-

---

[1] The waste of hill grazing prior to the introduction of large-scale sheep farming had been accentuated by the absence of winter-feeding crops such as hay or turnips on the low ground and the almost complete lack of storage accommodation. This meant that the cattle must be brought down from the hills in time to join the droves to the low-country trysts—probably by the middle of September at latest.

[2] Postlethwaite, *Britain's Commercial Interest Explained and Improved*, 1757, I, 57

[3] *Report of Committee on Cultivation of Waste Lands, etc.*, 1795, Appendix A

country sheep of a kind known as the Linton breed which appear to have differed little in essentials from the black-faced breed of today.[1] From here the new vogue of sheep farming quickly spread, and by 1764 large tracts around the head of Loch Earn, in Glen Dochart, in Glen Falloch and in the Cowal district of Argyll had already been made over to sheep.[2] So quickly had the new system spread that Pennant, writing in 1772 of the growth of sheep farming in the Breadalbane country at the head of Loch Tay, complained : ' The livestock of cattle of this Kingdom decreases ; from whence will our Navy be victualled ? ' [3]

All through the second half of the eighteenth century, the spread of sheep continued through the Central and much of the West and North-west Highlands, and by the time the Statistical Account came to be compiled in the last years of the century a great change had come over the stock farming of Highland Scotland. In a large part of north and west Perthshire, in much of southern Argyllshire and in Morvern, sheep were predominant. So, too, in the Lochaber district of Inverness-shire where James Hogg in 1803 found the whole of Glen Garry made over to sheep, while in the Kintail district Glenshiel had been let to a grazing tenant from Annandale and the houses of the old small tenants were in ruins.[4] Only in Skye, the Outer Islands and parts of Ross-shire and the far north and north-west were cattle still the main stock, though even here much of central Ross-shire was already under sheep. A description of Sutherland and Caithness in the 14th Report of the Commissioners for Highland Roads and Bridges speaks of an annual export of 80,000 fleeces and 20,000 sheep in 1828 as compared with an export in 1809 of a small number of cattle.[5] When in 1803 Telford planned his new road from Kyle Rhea to Killin to serve the droving traffic from Skye and the north-west to the markets of Central Scotland,

---

[1] Campbell, *Journey from Edinburgh through North Britain*, 1802, II, 375-6
[2] ibid.   [3] Pennant, op. cit., II, 17
[4] Hogg, *A Tour in the Highlands in 1803*, 53-4
How very local had been the spread of sheep farming at this time is shown by the fact that, in contrast to Glenshiel, James Hogg found the Dundonnell district ' so crammed full of stout able-bodied men and women that the estate under the present system must have enough to do maintaining them. The valleys are impoverished by perpetual cropping and saving for one farm in the north-east quarter . . . the extensive mountains are all waste ; for the small parcels of diminutive sheep which the natives have are all herded below nearest the dwellings and are housed every night ' (ibid. 92).
[5] *H.R. & B.*, 14th Report, Appendix D, No. 15, 61

he estimated that it would be used by 20,000 cattle and 80,000 sheep each year,[1] and in describing the road through Glencoe in his Survey and Report of 1803 he blamed the sheep, which had supplanted the cattle formerly pastured in the glen, for the frequent falls of stone from the hillside above.[2] 'The sheep farming system in Glencoe,' wrote a traveller in 1818, 'had done the work of extirpation of the inhabitants more effectively than the Massacre of 1692.'[3]

The introduction of the Linton breed of sheep had enormously increased the immediate productive capacity of the Highlands. The new sheep were larger than the old native breed. They were hardier too, while the new method of leaving them on the hills in the winter meant that the hill grazings were stocked throughout the year and not only in the short period when, under the old system, the cattle were herded from the shielings on the high pastures. But the fleece of the Linton breed, though heavier than that of the old sheep, was coarse, and with growing demand for wool as well as mutton, Scots graziers turned their attention to finding a breed which would combine in the fleece weight and quality. The mill owners of Halifax, Wakefield and other Yorkshire cloth-manufacturing towns required wool in increasing quantities and of the best quality, while between 1775 and 1797 the weight of wool made into cloth in the Galashiels district of Scotland had risen from 772 stones to 4,944 stones.[4] To meet this demand the Cheviot breed was, with the active support of Sir John Sinclair the compiler of the Statistical Account, introduced in the far North in the last years of the eighteenth century, and from this time onwards grew steadily in popularity. In his survey of the Northern Counties in 1795 Sir John made a strong plea for the introduction into Ross-shire, Sutherland and Caithness of sheep, and particularly those of the Cheviot breed. He produced detailed figures to show that under cattle the rent of the land was only about 2½d per acre while under sheep it would be 2s per acre. The annual export from the Highlands would, he reckoned, be double the existing figure of £200,000 to £300,000 without taking into account the considerable value of the wool. His arguments had to overcome great opposition owing to

---

[1] See Appendix B (p. 227)
[2] Telford, *A Survey and Report of the Coasts and Central Highlands of Scotland*, 1803
[3] Larkin, *A Tour in the Highlands in 1818*, 221
[4] Hamilton, *The Industrial Revolution in Scotland*, 66

Plate 15   On the Corrieyairack Road

(Photo by Robert M. Adam)

prejudice and the deep-rooted belief that sheep must be housed in winter.[1] So rapidly, however, did the Cheviot breed grow in favour that the *Stirling Journal and Advertiser* for September 1827, describing the Falkirk Tryst of that year, reported : ' Till 20 years ago black-faced sheep was the favourite, but now Cheviots have been introduced all over the Highlands and are prospering. The black-faced breed—the hardy aboriginals—are now only seen on the rugged summits of bare mountains along with the blackcock, the ptarmigan and the eagle.' The arrangements for marketing the wool were also improved. Hitherto sheep and wool had been sold, with cattle, at the local trysts, the manufacturers of Yorkshire and the south of Scotland sending to the farthest parts of the Highlands to buy, but in 1817 a special market for sheep and wool was, with the support of the Yorkshire buyers, established at Inverness, where in the following year as much as 100,000 stones of wool were sold.[2] Writing of his work in the Highlands during the second quarter of the nineteenth century, Mr Joseph Mitchell, the road engineer, has so described the sheep and wool market of Inverness :

' Besides the local fairs throughout the country, there is a great sheep and wool market held annually in the month of July at Inverness. It was established in 1817, and has been for many years an important gathering. Chiefs and country gentlemen, great sheep farmers, factors, and mountain peasants, assemble at this market once a year to meet and transact business with south-country buyers.

' This meeting is unique. Here you see the portly figure of a wool stapler of Huddersfield and Leeds ; beside him the quick and intelligent Liverpool merchant, or the shrewd, broadspeaking woollen manufacturer of Aberdeen or Bannockburn. The burly south-country feeder stands at the street corner in deep conversation, and about to strike a bargain with that sharp, lynx-eyed, red-haired little man, who is the largest farmer in the North, and counts his flocks by 40,000 or 50,000. The greatest agriculturist in the North compares notes of his experience with the celebrated member of the Highland Society, who is also an extensive farmer in the Lothians. That stout man who is talking

---

[1] Sinclair, *General View of the Agriculture of the Northern Counties, etc.*, 1795, 182 and 184 et seq.
[2] Anderson, *The State of Society and Knowledge in the Highlands of Scotland*, 1827, 127–8

with the Highland drover came to the North some thirty-eight years ago a common shepherd. He is now a great farmer and owner of 12,000 or 15,000 sheep.

'You may notice also from their military air the retired colonel and captain, who in the Highland regiments bled on the fields of Spain and Waterloo, and who now as sheep farmers are passing the evening of their days in their native glens, and come here to dispose of their year's stock. That gentleman with sunburnt and weather-beaten visage, who for years cruised around the coasts in His Majesty's service, is now securely moored in a remote valley as the breeder of sheep. There is also the capitalist who has invested £10,000 or £15,000 in sheep and cattle, and who applies to this branch of husbandry all the knowledge and acquirements of agricultural science.

'Besides these there are small farmers, clad in homespun tweed of various colours, the real aborigines of the country, tall, stout, athletic fellows, some in kilts, with their plaids carelessly thrown over their shoulders. There also with their crooks are numerous common shepherds, in whose conversation you may overhear the deep guttural of the Highland brogue, and the broad Scotch of the border counties. The collie dogs must not be forgotten, the constant and vigilant attendants on their masters. Notwithstanding the kicks and ill-usage they encounter in the crowd, they cling to the shepherd's side, and look as if they had as great an interest in the market as the more intelligent bipeds.

'This market is perhaps the most singular in Great Britain. About 1,000 persons attend. No stock or samples are produced ; the buyers know the stock of each farm, and make their purchases without seeing either sheep or wool. They merely agree upon a price and exchange missives as to delivery and payment. Bargains are thus said to be made at the market to the amount some years of £400,000. A casual observer would stare at this motley crowd of well-dressed people on the street, lounging from morning till night for two successive days, without any apparent purpose.

.　　.　　.　　.　　.　　.　　.　　.

'The market still holds, but alas ! the glory of it is gone. Almost all those fine fellows mentioned above, with warm hearts and generous sympathies, have gone to their rest. The frequent wool and sheep sales in the great towns in the South, and the rapidity with which the whole produce of the North is now transported to its destination by railway, have destroyed the interest that once belonged to this commercial and social gathering.' [1]

The revolution in the farming practice of the Highlands which took place in the second half of the eighteenth century and the early years of the nineteenth century was not carried through without great changes in the social system on which the old methods rested, and much distress among the people most closely affected. The new improved methods were directly opposed to the interests and the very existence of the small tenants cultivating their tiny strips of arable ground and exercising their limited rights of grazing in common on the hills. The introduction of artificial grasses brought with it the need for enclosing those arable parts of Highland farms where, up till then, the cattle of small tenants had grazed at large after the harvest. The demand for low-ground grazing and wintering for the stock of the new sheep farms was equally fatal to the old system, while the change in outlook which had come about as a result of the decay of the clan system removed the incentive to Highland landowners to maintain large populations in their glens.

'I have lived to woful days,' said an Argyllshire chieftain in 1788. 'When I was young the only question asked concerning a man's rank was how many men lived on his estate ; then it came to be how many black cattle it could keep ; but now they only ask how many sheep the lands will carry.' [2] The urge for high rents and the attraction of easier land-management and smaller obligations all tended in one direction, offering to Highland landowners the opportunity of compensating themselves for the loss of political power which they had suffered.

The outcome of the changes which were taking place was fully apparent to the men of the time, and the new trend was by no means universally welcomed, even by those to whose immediate advantage it seemed to be. The writer of the Statistical Account for the Parish of Glenshiel reported that a few years before, an offer of a threefold increase in rent from a sheep grazier had been refused by the proprietor on the ground that ' he would never prefer sheep to men,' [3] but James Hogg's description of the glen twenty years later shows that here, too, the pressure of economic change had proved irresistible.[4] James Anderson

---

[1] Mitchell, *Reminiscences of my Life in the Highlands*, I, 336 et seq.
[2] Scott, *The Highland Clans*, 36   [3] *O.S.A.*, Glenshiel, VII, 128
[4] Hogg, op. cit., 53–4, 56

writing in 1785 tells of the reluctance of landlords to disturb the sitting tenants, but foretells that ultimately their dispossession in favour of those offering more rent is inevitable.[1] Marshall ten years later predicted the depopulation of the Highlands,[2] and at the beginning of the nineteenth century Telford foresaw that the change-over to sheep would go too far, that a balance between sheep and cattle must be the ultimate object of Scottish stock-farming, but that before this came about a depopulation of the Highlands would take place which it might be hard to redress.[3]

The troubles which far-sighted men like Telford predicted did indeed come, and the end of the eighteenth and the beginning of the nineteenth centuries saw great distress in a large part of the Highlands. The period was one of rapid and wide-spread change, both economic and social. Growing industry meant a redistribution of population, while growing wealth, increasing knowledge and improved methods brought new ideas of land ownership and estate management. Prices were rising and rents with them, while improved medical knowledge and living conditions brought about a steady increase in population. In these circumstances it is hardly to be wondered at that the readjustment to a new way of life was not made without grave dislocation and great distress among that part of the rural population whose existence depended on the old conditions which were passing away.

From 1770 onwards a gradual exodus of population from the Highlands took place. Some drifted to the towns or the Lowlands, many emigrated to America, driven away by rising rents, by the enclosing of land for sheep farming or for the creation of larger and more economical farms. Some, like the small tenants of Glen Garry, went with the tacksmen whom the new conditions were driving from so many Highland estates and to whom they were bound by ties of sentiment, economic dependence or age-long custom.[4] By the end of the eighteenth century the depopulation of the Highlands had gone far to create the conditions which Telford had foreseen.

That the coming of sheep was partly to blame is certain. The sudden realisation of the possibilities of the new farming had induced a more commercial spirit in the outlook of the

[1] Anderson, *Account of the present state of the Hebrides*, 1785, 25–7
[2] Marshall, *General View of the Agriculture of the Central Highlands*, 1794, 52, 56
[3] Telford, op. cit.   [4] Hamilton, op. cit., 70

landlords towards their lands and their tenants. The urge was now to obtain with the minimum of trouble, obligation and capital outlay, the greatly increased rents which rising prices, due to the Continental Wars and the growth of commerce, enabled prospective tenants to offer. Economic pressure was great and in some cases eviction and emigration did without doubt follow directly as a result of the introduction of sheep ; but this was not the only cause. It is significant that the considerable emigration of 1770 took place before the growth of sheep farming had begun to have a wide-spread effect,[1] while even during the later period of emigration between 1783 and 1803 the Hebrides, which were little affected by the introduction of sheep, provided a large proportion of the emigrants, while Argyll which was much affected provided few.[2] The rise in population, the increased competition for farms and the gradual elimination of the tacksmen seem to have been more potent causes. Much has been written on the subject, and the determination of the part which sheep farming played has only incidental relevance to the present inquiry, but the evidence does appear to show that even if sheep farming had not come to the Highlands, emigration on a considerable scale would have taken place.

Despite the great development of sheep farming which took place at a time when the droving industry was at its height, the drove roads from the Highlands to the Lowlands remained for a great part of their existence primarily the routes of cattle. The earliest movement of stock in the Highlands was, as has been seen, largely the outcome of raiding expeditions, and sheep, as the old reivers knew, would not drive so easily, so quickly or so far as cattle. When more peaceful times came, cattle remained the chief droving stock, for the native sheep were little in demand for mutton, their chief value lying in their wool which, save perhaps in the case of the Aberdeenshire woollen trade, did little more than supply the needs of the local people, clad in the products of their own spinning-wheels and hand-looms. The demand for Scotland's livestock in the first half of the eighteenth century was largely a demand for meat to feed the growing towns of the South and to provision the trading and naval vessels of the English ports, and for this mutton was in less demand than beef. These were

---

[1] Adam, 'The Highland Emigration of 1770.' *Scot. Hist. Rev.*, Vol. XVI, 280
[2] Adam, 'The Causes of the Highland Emigration of 1783–1803.' *Scot. Hist. Rev.*, Vol. XVII, 73

conditions perhaps not unsuited to the character and inclination of the Highlander brought up in the tradition of his cattle-reiving ancestors. ' The Highlander, a child among flocks is a prince among herds,' wrote Scott of the eighteenth-century drover. ' His natural habits induce him to disdain the shepherd's slothful life so that he feels himself nowhere more at home than when following a gallant drove of his country's cattle in the character of their guardian.' [1] There was, too, another reason why up till the middle of the eighteenth century cattle took the road while sheep stayed at home. Before Wade built his roads, and indeed till well on in the second half of the eighteenth century, the roads of Scotland were primitive, and in much of the Highlands non-existent, and the rivers were almost all unbridged. While to the cattle drover these conditions presented little difficulty and were at times of positive advantage, it would have been very different for a drover of sheep. To drive a flock of sheep long distances day after day over rough, mountainous and open country would, in those circumstances, have been a slow and laborious task. Droving and shepherding the flocks by day and herding on the stance at night would alike present greater difficulty than in the case of cattle. The crossing of streams and rivers would have presented problems at times almost insoluble. Streams which even in moderate flood could be forded by cattle were for sheep formidable barriers, while rivers, narrow lochs and arms of the sea, which cattle could and did swim with ease, were for sheep impassable. In the last quarter of the eighteenth century when sheep traffic from the Highlands, stimulated by the growing demand for wool and mutton, was steadily increasing, considerable progress had already been made towards the improvement of the roads of the Highlands, and with the work of the Commissioners for Highland Roads and Bridges in the first part of last century, road and bridge construction in the Highlands made rapid strides. So the main growth of sheep farming came to Scotland at a time when conditions had made their droving possible.

The impression that sheep were unsuitable for droving appears to have persisted for some time after the improvement of Highland

---

[1] Scott, *The Two Drovers*, Chap. I

Scott was no doubt referring to shepherding in the Highlands at a time when the sheep population was still small in numbers, poor in quality and largely confined to the low-lying parts of the farms and the immediate neighbourhood of the farm buildings.

communications had begun. In 1794 Sir John Sinclair wrote of Lismore that cattle are the stock best suited to the island since ' they admit of being driven to distant markets,' while of the Island of Shuna he reports that ' the proprietor is thinking of abandoning sheep since they cannot be driven fat to market.' Another agricultural writer in the same year refers to the need of devising some method of getting sheep to market by water, dead or alive.[1] Sheep moreover could not be shod, and it may be that it was a general belief in the eighteenth century that their feet would not stand the long journey to the trysts. The history of the sheep trade in the nineteenth century shows, however, that none of these difficulties were in fact insurmountable, and it seems more probable that the explanation of the small part played by sheep in droving traffic during most of the eighteenth century is to be found in the small demand for mutton and the considerable local use of wool. A marked change took place towards the end of the century with the rapid growth of industrial population both in Scotland and England, and from that time on sheep formed an increasingly large part of the live-stock traffic to the trysts.

Throughout the first half of the nineteenth century the sheep traffic passing over the drove roads of Scotland showed a steady increase. Falkirk Tryst had displaced Crieff shortly after the introduction of large-scale sheep farming, and here the number of sheep brought to the Tryst as recorded in the local press of the day, shows clearly the rapid rise of the new stock farming. An agricultural report of 1812 estimated the number of sheep sold at Falkirk that year at 40,000,[2] and 150,000 sheep were reported to have been sold in 1818 at the newly established market at Inverness.[3] At the Falkirk Tryst of October 1836 the number sold there had grown to 75,000,[4] and before the middle of the century when the numbers at the September and October markets had almost reached 200,000, the trade in sheep is reported to have surpassed the trade in cattle.[5] From then onwards, though the increase in Highland sheep farming was to continue for another twenty-five years, the growth of the railways caused a gradual decline in the traffic on the drove roads.

[1] Robson, *General View of the Agriculture of Argyll and West Inverness-shire*, 1794, 20–1, 34
[2] Graham, *General View of the Agriculture of Stirlingshire*, 1812, 334
[3] Anderson, *State of Society and Knowledge in the Highlands of Scotland*, 1827, 127–8
[4] *Stirling Journal*, October 1836   [5] *Stirling Journal*, 1840–50, *passim*

But it was not for the trysts alone that sheep traffic passed along the old routes, and when in the second half of the nineteenth century a stricter view of land ownership and the growing importance of sporting rights gave rise to litigation, the testimony of the older witnesses in support of the traditional routes disclosed the existence of a widespread and cross-country traffic in sheep. Many indeed spoke of droving traffic to the trysts, but others told of sheep traffic caused by the movement of young stock between grazings widely separated or to the low ground and coastal farms for fattening or for wintering. Throughout the whole period of rather over a hundred years which elapsed between the beginning of large-scale sheep farming in the Highlands and the final decay of the droving industry in the seventies and eighties of last century, the routes used by the sheep traffic seem to have differed little if at all from those used by the cattle droves. The evidence of contemporary writers and Court witnesses and the recollection of the few shepherds and drovers who still recall those days, is of sheep on all the old established drove routes. On the road from Ullapool and Wester Ross to Muir of Ord and through Strath Glass to Fort Augustus ; on the Corrie-yairack Pass and on the road by Kingshouse and the Black Mount to Tyndrum ; on the hill tracks from Upper Donside to the Dee and in the passes leading to the Angus glens, sheep were on the move following the old routes marked out by the feet of the cattle whose place they had so largely taken.[1]

The growth and spread of sheep farming in Scotland continued throughout the greater part of the nineteenth century, reaching its peak about 1870. Then, from a variety of causes, a gradual decline in its prosperity set in, a decline which, with some fluctuations, has continued till very recent years. Many of the causes had been foreseen when sheep farming on a large scale first came to the Highlands. The enthusiasm with which the new farming was welcomed had induced many to stock their farms entirely with sheep, encouraged by their initial success on hill pasture enriched by the old system of cattle grazing. Little

[1] *McGregor & Others* v. *Breadalbane*, 1846, Court of Session Cases, 9 Dunlop's Reports, 210 ; 7 Bell's Appeal Cases, 43.
Mackenzie v. *Bankes*, 1868, Court of Session Cases, 6 Macpherson's Reports, 936
Scottish Rights of Way Society v. *Macpherson*, 1887, Court of Session Cases, 14 Rettie's Reports, 875
Winans and Chisholm v. *Tweedmouth*, 1888, Court of Session Cases, 15 Rettie's Reports, 540

thought was given to whether the hills so made over to sheep were indeed suited to them, or whether a mixture of sheep and cattle would, as more prudent men believed, be better. Heavy stocks of sheep, grazing the hills more constantly than cattle had done under the old system, ate steadily into the stored fertility of ground which received little or nothing in return, and it was not till about 1884 that serious attention was given to the advantages of a mixed stock, in which the less-searching grazing habits of the cattle would be complementary to the ' close inquisitive bite ' of the sheep.[1] By that time other factors had appeared which were to bring ruin to many of the sheep farmers. The demand for sheep to stock the new ground was dwindling and the low-ground farms were in active competition for the trade, while with foreign supplies the prices for wool and mutton were also declining.[2] The coming of sheep farming on a large scale had brought another change to the Highlands. Under the old system of cattle grazing on the hills, bracken appears not to have been a serious menace. The cattle on the hills no doubt trampled it down and kept it in check. The larger population of the Highlands at that time meant cultivation of much of the more fertile parts of the lower hill ground where the bracken thrives, and the cutting of such bracken as did grow to supply the cheapest and commonest form of thatch and bedding then available.[3] With the coming of sheep and the fall in population the bracken spread largely unchecked, to add one more to the list of problems of Highland resettlement, many of which date from the start of Scotland's eighteenth-century agricultural revolution, and some of which are still unsolved.

[1] *Napier Report* (Crofters' Commission) 1884, V, 45
[2] *Report of Committee on Hill Sheep Farming in Scotland*, 1943, 8
[3] While there appears to be general agreement that the spread of bracken on hill grazings was encouraged by the reduction in the number of cattle on the hills and the increase of sheep, the presence of bracken in seemingly large quantities is noted at least as early as 1808 when the growth of sheep farming was still in its early stages. Walker in 1808 refers to it as being particularly hurtful in sheep walks, and blames it for braxy among sheep. He classes it, however, as a valuable manure and considers that its destruction can best be achieved by cutting for use as manure or as thatch, or by burning. After three years cutting, he writes, it is reduced to negligible proportions. (Walker, *Economical History of the Hebrides and Highlands*, 1808, I, 158–60)

THE DECLINE OF THE DROVE ROADS

WERE the progress of the Scots droving trade after the Union of 1707 to be illustrated by means of a graph, it would be seen that the index line, after a relatively slow ascent in the first half of the eighteenth century, rose from the middle of the century with increasing steepness to reach its peak about 1835, and that its descent was short, sudden and complete. At the close of the eighteenth century the number of beasts—cattle and sheep—driven south from the Highlands and the grazing areas of south-western Scotland was increasing year by year. The growing industrial towns of North England and the Midlands meant a rising meat consumption ; the demand from London continued to expand, while the French War kept the needs of the Navy at a high level. In Scotland itself the demand for beef and mutton, though still relatively small, was steadily growing to meet the increasing needs of the towns of the Lowlands, where Glasgow's population alone had risen from 12,000 to 84,000 in the course of the century.[1] ' If a dry season lessen the demand from England,' says the Statistical Account of Crieff, ' the extensive pastures and vast consumpt in the south of Scotland suffers not the drovers to be disappointed of a sale.' [2]

Until the last years of the eighteenth century little in the shape of a comprehensive survey of Scotland's livestock had been attempted, and estimates based on the numbers sold at the various trysts are misleading, for the same animals might change hands at successive markets on the way, giving the impression

[1] As late as 1816 there were no butcher's shops even in Edinburgh, and in the rural districts meat was seldom seen unless a beast died or a ' mart ' was killed for salting in the autumn. In the northern counties, reported Sir John Sinclair in 1795, not five pounds of meat was consumed on a farm in a whole year and an egg was a luxury. ' We have seen in the summer season a haddock occasionally as a wonderful regalement.' Somerville reports that beef was seldom to be had except at fairs or on special occasions such as the land-setting at Hawick, when the beast was garlanded and led through the town by the town piper. George Robertson writing of Kincardine-shire in 1829 reported : ' Cheap as fish is here, there is but little of it used by the farm servants and still less of butcher meat.' (Croal, *Living Memories of an Octogenarian*, 16. Sinclair, *Agricultural Survey, Northern Counties* etc., 1795, 82. Somerville, *My Life and Times*, 1741–1814, 332–3. Robertson, *Rural Recollections*, 1829, 422–3)
[2] *O.S.A.*, Crieff, IX, 597

of a larger trade than in fact existed. The figures for the various parishes contained in the Statistical Account now for the first time gave some indication of the total cattle population in Scotland, and these figures, together with the County Agricultural Surveys, both of which we owe largely to the energy and initiative of Sir John Sinclair, make it possible to assess with some accuracy the volume of the droving traffic at the close of the eighteenth century. Writing in 1795, Sir John estimated the annual value of cattle sold from the Highlands at £200,000 to £300,000.[1] Taking the value per head at £4, which was the average price realised at Falkirk Tryst in 1794,[2] this would appear to represent a total of over 60,000 cattle, a figure which corresponds closely with contemporary estimates of the number sold at Falkirk. The droving trade from the south-western counties augmented by imports from Ireland had also reached large dimensions. Estimates in the last year of the eighteenth century of the number of cattle paying toll at the crossing of the Nith on the road to England place the total at over 20,000 per annum, and by the close of the century the total number of cattle driven from Scotland to England each year is believed to have reached 100,000.[3]

While the total volume of droving traffic was thus steadily rising towards its peak, a marked change had taken place in the sources from which it came. From Skye and the Hebrides came still a steady flow of beasts treading the well-worn paths from Lochaber, Rannoch and the Argyllshire coast. Writing in 1811, James Macdonald in his *General View of the Agriculture of the Hebrides*, estimated the total cattle population of the islands at 110,000, of which one-fifth were sold to the mainland each year, an estimate which accords well with Telford's estimate that 20,000 cattle each year would use the new drove road which he planned from Kyle Rhea by Rannoch to Killin and the South;[4] but these numbers showed no increase in any way proportionate to the increase which was taking place in the total volume of droving traffic to the South. The numbers reported in the Statistical Account as crossing Kyle Rhea from Skye in 1794[5] were in fact

---

[1] Sinclair, op. cit., 185   [2] *O.S.A.*, Falkirk, XIX, 83
[3] It may be noted, however, that even in 1813 a writer on the Agriculture of Inverness-shire refers to the difficulty in estimating, the size of the cattle trade being so great that no two people can be found to agree on the numbers brought from the Highlands each year. (Robertson, *General View of the Agriculture of Inverness-shire*, 1812, 303)
[4] See Appendix B (p. 227)   [5] *O.S.A.*, Glenelg, XVI, 270

considerably less than those noted by Pennant twenty years earlier, nor is any increase apparent in the numbers ferried from Mull or Jura.

The development in Scottish agriculture and the growing demands from the South had indeed affected very little the volume of the cattle traffic from the Islands and the west coast. Here from an early date the division of the land among many small tenants, each with his rights in a common grazing area, had already raised the numbers of stock up to, if not beyond, the capacity of the land. Disregard of the Winter Herding Act and the almost total absence of storage accommodation deterred tenants and sub-tenants from growing hay or turnips for winter food. The system of tenure and the temperament of the tenants were alike unfavourable to the adoption of the new methods which were fast transforming the stock farming of north-east Scotland, and it is in these north-eastern districts that the reasons must be sought for the expansion of droving traffic to its highest point in the second quarter of last century.

The rapid improvement in Scottish agriculture after 1760 resulted, as has been seen, in the restriction of the area given over to cattle grazing, and pushed that industry farther and farther north. The greatest effect of the change was felt in the north-eastern counties where a new mode of farming based on stock raising was tending to displace the traditional and cumbrous system of arable cultivation. All through the latter part of the eighteenth century the cattle trade of these north-eastern counties grew steadily. The demand from the South was growing for the better quality of cattle which the new farming was producing. By the end of the century the beasts driven south from Aikey Fair alone were in one year estimated at 6,000,[1] and the annual sales of one Aberdeenshire drover—Williamson of Fyvie—had reached 8,000.[2] From Morayshire too went a steady flow, while Kincardineshire and Angus added their quota, and each successive year saw more and still more beasts from the north-east bought at Falkirk for the grazings of Cumberland, Yorkshire and Norfolk.

Prices followed the rising demand. By 1811 the value of cattle sent southward each year from Aberdeenshire was estimated at £150,000.[3] Long before the French War ended, cattle were

[1] Alexander, *Northern Rural Life in the 18th Century*, 81
[2] Keith, *General View of the Agriculture of Aberdeenshire*, 1811, 466
[3] ibid.

being sold at Falkirk for as much as £25 a head,[1] while evidence given in the course of litigation in the Court of Session in 1800 disclosed dealings between one cattle dealer and an Angus farmer to the extent of £30,000 per annum.[2] Most of the cattle sold from the north-east counties were beasts locally bred, but some were brought to the richer grass from the Highlands, and the description of an Aberdeenshire cattle dealer's life in the early years of the century shows him buying as far afield as Caithness, Sutherland, Skye and the Western Isles.[3]

The peak of prosperity to which droving rose in the second quarter of last century was the Indian summer of the trade. Already certain adverse factors were at work, while others, more deadly still, were soon to emerge. From first to last the prosperity, the very existence, of the trade depended above all else on freedom of passage, freedom of wayside grazing and freedom of nightly stances. Each was essential, and the absence or severe restriction of any one would be fatal to the whole enterprise. As the years went on, increasing population, rising standards of knowledge and growing skill in the management and cultivation of land, encroached more and more on these essential freedoms, and by the end of the eighteenth century, despite the growing volume and value of the trade, it must have been increasingly clear to the more far-sighted among the drovers that the time was not far off when their trade must fight for its life. The first sign of changing times had indeed become apparent soon after the middle of the century when Crieff Tryst, hitherto the centre of the cattle trade in the Highlands, gave way before the growing importance of the Tryst at Falkirk. Falkirk was more accessible for buyers from the South, but the chief reason for the change, as reported by contemporary writers, lay in the importance to drovers of reaching the market from the North by the easiest and quickest routes. 'For a considerable time after the beginning of the century,' reported the writer of the Statistical Account for Crieff in 1794, 'the drovers from Argyll, Inverness, Ross-shire, etc., paid nothing for the pasturing of their cattle on the way to market ; but in the improved state of the country grass became more valuable, the roads more confined and the drovers were forced to enquire after the most convenient and cheap roads from

---

[1] Belsches, *General View of the Agriculture of Stirlingshire*, 1796, 45
[2] *Old Session Papers*, Signet Library, 1800, I, 410
[3] McCombie, *Cattle and Cattle Breeders*, 99

their several homes to the principal market place now at Falkirk, where the roads leading by the shortest course from every quarter of the Highlands towards England naturally unite ; and where the whole of the Argyll and near half of the Inverness-shire cattle can arrive some days' journey earlier than if they came by Crieff. Additional travel was no loss while the pasture cost nothing, but would now considerably affect their profits.' [1]

The reasons for the decline of Crieff Tryst were symptomatic of a widespread and permanent change which had set in affecting by degrees the whole of the country cultivated or capable of cultivation. In some parts this took the form of the enclosing of pasture and arable fields by the dry-stone dykes which had already caused serious rioting in Galloway as early as the beginning of the eighteenth century. In others the drovers' routes were themselves enclosed by dykes or turf walls to protect the arable ground through which they passed. Everywhere the drovers were coming to be more narrowly hedged in and deprived increasingly of the wayside grazing which had hitherto been their traditional and unchallenged right.

The early years of the nineteenth century brought more trouble to the drovers. When Wade built the first properly constructed roads in the Highlands, the routes he chose were selected with a view to military rather than civilian or commercial use. Some of these, like the route over the Pass of Corrieyairack, through Drumochter Pass and by Dalnacardoch to Crieff, were in fact routes long in use by the drovers, and one of the arguments used by those who resented Wade's work was that the new roads would wear the feet of the beasts. The argument had little substance, for at that time the droves were still free to wander almost at will on or off the road and, as has been seen, there is reason to think that where the roads were used by droving traffic, the resulting damage was to the roads and not to the beasts. The extension of the military road system which took place after Wade's time was for similar reasons probably not a serious matter for the drovers, but when early in the nineteenth century the Commissioners for Highland Roads and Bridges took over the old military roads and embarked on the work of road-building which the Scottish Highlands owe largely to Telford, a new situation arose. By now the new agriculture and the new outlook on land ownership had become a major factor. Many byways and

[1] *O.S.A.*, Crieff, IX, 596

cross-country routes were still open to the drovers, but more and more as time went on did they find themselves forced on to the made roads. Now, the grievances previously urged by Wade's opponents became more real, and from this time onwards the shoeing of cattle at intervals on certain parts of their journey to the South was a necessary part of the drover's work.[1] The new roads had for the drovers a further drawback. The old roads had followed closely the contours of the ground uphill and down dale, but as the technique of road-making improved, cuttings and embankments came into use, still further restricting the wayside grazing of the travelling beasts.[2]

Wade's roads and the system of military roads constructed after his time were made and kept up entirely by military labour, and up to the middle of the eighteenth century other roads in so far as they existed at all were in theory maintained by statute labour—a system by which proprietors and occupiers through whose land a road ran, were obliged either to pay a small sum based on the rental of their land or to give a certain number of days' work on the roads. The system proved highly unsatisfactory, but about 1750 increasing use began to be made of the system of turnpikes, and between 1750 and 1844 upwards of 350 Turnpike Road and Bridge Acts appear to have been passed in Scotland, setting up Turnpike Trusts empowered to levy tolls on traffic using bridges or sections of the road under their care.[3] Tolls on bridges at certain points had long been common in Scotland, but for the most part the drovers of these days could and did avoid the crossing of bridges, preferring to ford, ferry or swim the rivers. Scope for this was now becoming restricted, and tolls on roads and bridges became a material and growing item in the drovers' budget.[4]

[1] It must be admitted that it is not easy to reconcile this entirely with Telford's plan to construct a road specifically for drovers from Kintail to Killin. He clearly cannot have regarded a constructed road of this sort as unsuitable for droving traffic, nor does it appear that the opposition which led to the abandonment of the plan came from drovers who feared its effect on the feet of the stock using the road.

[2] The trend of subsequent legislation affecting the use of highways for the driving of stock may be judged by the inclusion in a recent Order of the following clause :

' The owner of any cattle or horses or any person for the time being in charge thereof who wilfully and habitually creates an avoidable nuisance by permitting the same to use any footway on the side of a public highway so that the said footway is damaged or littered with excremental matter shall be guilty of an offence and shall be liable on summary conviction to a penalty not exceeding Twenty Pounds.' (*Fife County Council Order Confirmation Act*, 1949, ch. lvii)

[3] *Report by Commissioners for Enquiring into matters relating to Public Roads in Scotland*, 1859, xvi   [4] See Appendix G (p. 242)

Freedom of passage had been challenged and freedom of wayside grazing restricted. Freedom of nightly resting-places for the droves was now to be attacked. When cross-country droving in Scotland on an appreciable scale first began, and for many a year thereafter, a great part of the Highland and upland areas of the country was common land, or at the least land which, while nominally owned by the local chieftain, was in fact unused and uncared for. In the earliest rentals for Islay and Kintyre, for example, the figures representing the total of the ' merk lands ' held by the tacksmen from the local chieftains do not amount to more than about one-third of the total extent of these areas as shown on modern maps. The rest was wasteland which was gradually merged into the tacksmen's holdings with the progress of agriculture.[1] The process by which this great unused area was absorbed into the holdings of the tacksmen or their sub-tenants was a gradual one, and not until sheep farming on a large scale became common in the Highlands were these upland areas put to fuller use than for the grazing of cattle from the sheilings in summer and early autumn. On the lower ground the position was more difficult for the drovers, and after the middle of the eighteenth century they found their old privileges of grazing their beasts at night increasingly challenged. The steady increase in droving traffic from now onwards aroused tenants and proprietors, particularly on the approaches to the trysts, to the opportunities of profiting by the demand which now existed for grazing on a scale which constituted a substantial burden on land, the increasing value of which had come to be recognised. So the old days of free grazing gave way to a new era in which stance rights had to be paid for on a scale which gradually increased from a nominal sum to the substantial payments which had become common before the droving industry came to an end. To avoid this burden some of the larger drovers started to rent grazings of their own at strategic points on the main routes to the trysts, and Cameron of Corriechoillie is said to have been able to pasture his beasts on grazing of his own all the way from Lochaber to Falkirk ; but operations on such a scale were possible only to a very few, and to the great mass of the drovers the increasing cost and difficulty of stance rights was a growing menace.

Despite the growing practice of demanding payments for

<hr>

[1] McKerral, ' The Tacksman and his Holding in the South-West Highlands.' *Scottish Historical Review*, Vol. XXVI, 10–25

Plate 16   The Kyle Rhea Crossing in Modern Times
(Photo by Robert M. Adam)

nightly grazing there still remained many areas of common land where the night's grazing of a passing drove was unchallenged, and probably in many cases free, but as time passed this privilege too was attacked. In 1695 an Act of the Scots Parliament had provided for the division of common lands with a view to avoiding the disputes to which common ownership so often gave rise.[1] For many years little use was made of the new legislation, but in the second half of the eighteenth century the division of common land became increasingly frequent. The procedure before the Sheriff or the Court of Session was complex and often long-drawn out, but some idea of the extent to which common lands were divided may be obtained from the fact that between 1750 and 1890 the number of Processes of Division of Commonty before the Court of Session alone, as recorded in H.M. Register House, Edinburgh, is over 450.[2] These included Hawick [3] and Gretna,[4] important stages on the drove route to England ; Sheriffmuir,[5] the last and most important resting-place for cattle from the Highlands bound for Falkirk, and the common land near Falkirk itself which was the original site of the Falkirk Tryst.[6]

While the rights of stance were thus becoming increasingly costly and circumscribed in the more cultivated districts and on the approaches to the trysts, they remained in the Highland districts for the most part unchallenged, and it was not until the middle of last century that the droving industry, already on the decline, was called on to meet an attack on rights vital to its continuance. It will be recalled that one of the main drove routes from Skye and Lochaber to the South ran from Fort William by Kinlochleven and the Devil's Staircase to the head of Glencoe, and so skirting the western edge of the Moor of Rannoch, by Inveroran, Bridge of Orchy and Tyndrum to Crieff and Falkirk. On this route, at intervals of approximately ten miles, were stances for the night—at Altnafeadh near Kingshouse, at Inveroran, at Tyndrum, at Luib in Glendochart and at Balquhidder. In 1844 Lord Breadalbane proposed to close the

---

[1] *A.P.S.*, IX, 462
[2] See Index to Processes of Division of Commonty, 1661/1890, H.M. Register House
[3] Hawick. *Currie Office* (Dalrymple), H. Bundle 4, 1768, H.M. Register House
[4] Gretna, *Mackenzie Decreets*, 9/8/1770, H.M. Register House
[5] Sheriffmuir, *Durie Decreets*, 2/12/1772, H.M. Register House
[6] Falkirk, *Durie Decreets*, 19/12/1807, H.M. Register House

stance ground at Inveroran, offering in its place another site at Clifton near Tyndrum. The new site was seventeen miles from Kingshouse and fourteen miles from the stance at Luib, distances too great for a drove of sheep or cattle to cover in a day, while it would make useless the existing site at Tyndrum. Faced with a change which threatened to make impossible for a drove the crossing of the Moor of Rannoch, the drovers were forced into a litigation [1] on the result of which depended the legal basis of stance rights enjoyed for generations.[2] The action was raised on behalf of drovers from Skye and the Outer Isles, from Knoydart and Lochaber, from Ardnamurchan, Morven and Ardgour, from Wester Ross, Sutherland and Inverness-shire and from south of the Border. The Court of Session favoured the claims of the drovers,[3] accepting their contention that, though in this case paid for, the right of stance was an essential part of the right of passage for livestock, which latter right was not then in dispute. The House of Lords thought otherwise, and on an appeal by Lord Breadalbane held that the drovers had failed to make out a relevant case and that the stance rights claimed had no legal foundation.[4] Consideration of the grounds on which the decision was based are beyond the scope of the present work, but it seems at least probable that a court of law today would endorse the view taken by the House of Lords in 1848 that the extensive but undefined stance and pasture rights then claimed, though based on the custom and unchallenged usage of centuries, constituted a

---

[1] *MacGregor and Others* v. *Breadalbane*, Court of Session Cases, 1846, 9 Dunlop's Reports, 210

[2] The importance of the route for these drovers is clear from a report of a committee appointed by them to inquire into the position, which showed that the route was used by 70,000 sheep and 8,000 to 10,000 cattle each year. (*Breadalbane Papers*, (*Roads*), Box 4, H.M. Register House)

[3] So did a portion of the contemporary press. After noting with approval John Stuart Mill's view that uncultivated land should be looked on as held in trust for the community, the *London Daily News* of 30 August 1848 commented thus on the position : ' Rights of road, especially footpaths and drift ways over enclosed land have been almost annihilated in England, and the Highland proprietors of Scotland seem to be rapidly effecting the same thing in the North. . . . There is too much reason to fear that the encroaching proprietor with an ultimate right of appeal to a Tribunal of his own class will be more than a match for the public. . . . Now this right [of stance] which has existed for centuries is not displaced to make way for cultivation or improvement of any kind but to foster the barbarous and puerile passion for artificial wild sports : and the feudal spirit of the House of Lords assists the purblind owners of Highland estates to push their proprietary right to this mischievous extreme.'

[4] *MacGregor and Others* v. *Breadalbane*. Court of Session Cases, 1848, H. L. 7 Bell's Appeals, 43

limitation on the ownership of land unknown to the law of Scotland.[1]

It might have been expected that the result of the Breadalbane litigation would have been a widespread closing of stances and so, in effect, of drove roads throughout the Highlands. There is little evidence that this took place on any large scale. The inevitable outcome of the House of Lords decision had it been fully and widely applied would have been the end of all droving, and it is doubtful whether public opinion would have supported a widespread attack on an ancient traffic the value of which was still considerable. The latter half of the nineteenth century did, however, see an increasing movement among the proprietors of Highland estates towards the closing of drove roads, the regular use of which was then fast diminishing. To combat this the drovers varied their routes where possible in an attempt to keep open to their traffic ways which otherwise would have been lost by disuse and lapse of time. Despite this device very many drove roads must have fallen into disuse, and, while it would be neither possible nor profitable to determine the routes so closed, it is beyond any doubt that those which still preserve the character of rights of way are but a remnant of the network which at one time covered the country.

Litigation of a major character took place on at least three occasions in the second half of the century, but in each case it was the right of way rather than the right of stance that was attacked. In 1868 the road up the Gruinard River used by the Lewis drovers from Aultbea and Gruinard in Wester Ross-shire was in dispute.[2] In 1887 an attempt was made to close the road through Glen Callater and Glen Doll to Kirriemuir,[3] while in the following year that from Strath Glass by Guisachan to Glen Moriston came under challenge.[4] In each case the right of way was upheld, the testimony of witnesses providing a wealth of

[1] The final outcome of the Inveroran litigation was that an alternative stance was provided at Bridge of Orchy, a mile farther south. Here the tenant of the farm of Achallader, on whose land the new stance was situated, is still bound by his lease to keep open the stance ground, ' having in return the right to levy the dues and charges which according to custom are now levied.'

[2] *Mackenzie* v. *Bankes*, Court of Session Cases, 1868, 6 Macpherson's Reports, 936. Notes of Evidence, *Session Papers*, Signet Library.

[3] *Scottish Rights of Way Society* v. *Macpherson*, Court of Session Cases, 1887, 14 Rettie's Reports, 875.

[4] *Winans and Chisholm* v. *Tweedmouth*, Court of Session Cases, 1888, 15 Rettie's Reports, 540

evidence as to the droving traffic of the districts concerned, stretching back to the early years of the century.

The increasing tendency to close to the drovers these cross-country routes was the outcome of a strict view of land ownership at odds with a trend to more liberal thought, a conflict which characterised the latter part of the nineteenth century. A new factor too in the shape of sporting interests was now emerging which added emphasis to the desire for the preservation of land. How early sporting rights became of material interest to Highland proprietors, either for their own use or as a source of profit, seems rather uncertain. Burt appears to have engaged in both shooting and fishing, if one can judge by the mention in his *Letters from the North of Scotland* that he did not shoot plover ' except to busk his flies for fishing.' Half a century later Colonel Thornton had great sport both shooting and fishing in Badenoch.[1] Grouse were being regularly shot there and in Ross-shire before 1815. The Marquis of Huntly's party killed ' 553 brace of muirfowl ' in the first week's shooting of 1816,[2] and a traveller of 1818 refers to the inn at Kirkmichael being much frequented during the grouse-shooting season.[3] Anderson's *Guide to Scotland* in 1834 states : ' it has now become a common practice for Highland proprietors to let the right of shooting over their grounds. Moors may be had at all prices from £50 to £500 for the season with accommodation varying according to circumstances.' [4] Of the year 1833 the Earl of Malmesbury wrote in his Memoirs : ' This was the first year that the Highlands became the rage and that deer forests were made and rented, but for prices not exceeding £300 a year. . . . I went later (1833) to the Isle of Skye and to Harris. I was harboured at the latter by Mr Stewart a gentleman farmer and breeder of cattle, and had the run of the Island which belonged then to Macleod, and the grouse, deer forest and fishing, all of which were first rate, were offered to me at £25 a year.' [5] From now on the possibilities of the Highlands to the sportsman became increasingly recognised. Deer stalking grew steadily in popularity all through the nineteenth century, and the conflict of interest between the proprietor of a Highland deer forest and a drover who sought to cross the hills with his beasts, and in the

[1] Thornton, *Sporting Tour*, 1804, Chap. 5
[2] *Inverness Courier*, 25 August 1816
[3] Larkin, *A Tour in the Highlands in 1818*, 36
[4] Barron, *The Northern Highlands in the 19th Century*, II, xxxvi
[5] Quoted by Barron op. cit., xxxvi–xxxvii

crossing to graze the corries at any time from June to October, needs little emphasis.

The great advance in agricultural knowledge which spread over Scotland after 1750 had, by the end of the century, gone far to transform Scottish farming methods, particularly in the east and north-eastern districts. At first the effects of the changes were almost wholly favourable to the droving industry. As late as 1779, Mr Andrew Wright, surveyor on the Annexed Estates, travelling through Aberdeenshire, had reported that 'he could observe no grass until he alighted and put on his spectacles '; but the practice of sowing artificial grass seeds and enclosing young grass and hay which became common in Aberdeenshire in the last quarter of the century, brought a steady improvement in the quality of the grazings. Stock breeding was still commoner than stock fattening, and the better grass in conjunction with steady demands from the South meant more and better cattle driven to the trysts, where prices rose to their peak as the French War approached its climax. But the new agriculture was based largely on a system of crop rotation made possible by the introduction of the turnip, and with its increasing cultivation came a fundamental change which was to prove in the end fatal to the drovers.

Turnips had been introduced into East Lothian shortly after the middle of the eighteenth century, but it is reported that as late as 1773 they were still regarded as such a rarity as to be served as a dessert on Edinburgh dinner tables.[1] A report of the Highland Society in 1812 mentions them as being tried by some tenants but not widely grown, and in the previous year a prize offered for the best acreage under the new crop was not awarded, no competitor of sufficient merit having come forward.[2] In Aberdeenshire itself where the new crop was to spread so rapidly, it is reported that until about 1820 few turnips were grown.[3] The next few years saw a rapid change, and by the date of the preparation of the New Statistical Account turnip growing in the main cattle-breeding districts of Scotland had become general. From parish after parish of Aberdeenshire came reports

[1] Topham, *Letters from Edinburgh*, 1776, 229
[2] *Transactions of Highland Society*, IV, 505, note
[3] McCombie, op. cit., 55
The value of turnips seems, however, to have been recognised before this date by some Aberdeenshire farmers. A description of the agriculture of the County in 1811 refers to the brothers Williamson of St John's Wells, near Fyvie having 200 acres of turnips. (Keith, *Agricultural Survey of Aberdeenshire*, 1811, 466)

of the great changes which it was bringing about. ' Nothing for many years back,' wrote the minister of the parish of Old Deer in Buchan, ' has contributed more to improve the farming interest in this part of the world than the discovery and general use of bone manure for the raising of turnips.' [1] His report was typical of many. From the parishes of Alford, Garioch and Ellon came similar reports,[2] while from Wigtownshire, Kirkcudbrightshire and Dumfriesshire the tale was the same.[3] The growing knowledge and new farming methods had moreover come at a time when the farmers of Scotland were at length in a position to take advantage of them. ' The improvements introduced by the landowners towards the conclusion of the last century,' wrote the minister of the Aberdeenshire parish of Tarves in 1840, ' were at first but slowly adopted by the tenantry. Depressed by bad seasons and deficient in capital, they had neither the courage nor the means to attempt expensive innovations. The rise however in the price of agricultural produce which succeeded the breaking-out of war between this country and revolutionary France, by increasing the capital of the farmers, enabled them to take advantage of the more decided and valuable improvements . . . and from this period the progress of improvements was extremely rapid.' [4] With turnip growing and the improvement of pasture came a change from stock breeding to stock fattening, and the same districts which reported the growing of the new crop reported also the keeping and feeding of cattle during the winter, now at last made possible.[5]

Had the changes in farming methods been unaccompanied by other great developments, the effect on the droving industry might have been little more than the increase in numbers, quality and price which was noticeable at the great trysts in the early part of last century. But now for the first time serious competitors to the drovers were entering the field. As the light failed on an October evening of 1786, a Highland drover resting

---

[1] *N.S.A.*, Old Deer, I, 154

[2] *N.S.A.*, Garioch and Ellon, XII, 575, 911–2

[3] *N.S.A.*, IV, Whithorn, Wigtown, Kirkcudbright, Kirkpatrick-Irongray, Sorbie, Crossmichael and Tongland.

[4] *N.S.A.*, XII. Tarves, 671

[5] The number of cattle which passed through the village of Tarves on their way south after Aikey Fair in 1836 was 2,200—little more than one-third of the number counted on the corresponding day about the beginning of the century. By 1876 the number sold at the fair was reported to be not more than 250. (Alexander, op. cit., 81)

beside the cattle which he had brought to the Falkirk Tryst, on its new site at Stenhousemuir, might have seen to the east- ward a glow in the sky, brightening as the twilight deepened. A quarter of a century earlier the first of the new furnaces had been blown in at Carron, a site chosen by Dr Roebuck and his col- leagues for its central position and its proximity to iron-stone and coal supplies, to replace the old fashioned 'bloomeries' in the West and North-west Highlands soon to decline with the exhaustion of the natural forests which had hitherto fed them.[1]

If the reflection of the Carron furnaces meant little to the Highland drover it was in fact full of significance for the future of his calling. The enterprise at Carron had been successful, and the furnaces now hard at work smelting iron for 'carronades' and shot for the British Navy and Army were soon to be yet busier helping to arm half the nations of a continent at war ; but Carron was the birthplace of other developments heralding a new age in which droving would have no place. Here, a few years before, had been constructed the first steam engine for winding coal and within the next few years Carron was to see the birth of the steamship. The first commercial steamship with engines made in the Carron works was launched on the Carron River in 1789, and soon ships of the Carron Company were regularly carrying goods and passengers between Carron and London.[2] The full effect of the new method of transport was not felt for another quarter of a century, but between 1820 and 1836 a marked change took place in the transport of cattle from the north-eastern districts. The new farming methods were now producing fat beasts not suited for droving, and farmers and buyers alike were becoming increasingly aware of the loss of weight and condition which the journeys by road entailed.[3]

[1] From the correspondence which passed between the promoters before the site at Carron was finally chosen, it appears that the availability of charcoal supplies was also taken into account. Indeed the Carron furnaces in their early years were operated entirely with charcoal, and at one time the Company purchased wood on the Glenmoriston Estate for this purpose at a cost of £900. The prospect of planting woods near Carron was also considered, but coal soon became the chief fuel used there. (Cadell, *The Story of the Forth*, 151, 152. Macadam, *Notes on the Ancient Iron Industry of Scotland*. Proc. Soc. Ant. Scot., 1886–87, IX, new series, 90)

[2] Cadell, op. cit., 184

[3] Arthur Young, discussing the loss of weight of the cattle on the road, quotes an instance of six bullocks of 50 stone each which, on a journey of 70 miles to Smithfield, lost 14 lb. each. Another writer of last century quotes an estimate that during the journey of a fortnight from Holkham in Norfolk to London the beasts dropped in value by as much as three guineas a head. (Unpublished MS. *The Elements and Practice of Agriculture*, Vol. 28, British Museum)

Already a small demand existed for transport of cattle from Aberdeen to Leith and London by sailing boat at a cost of £1 10s a head, and as the size and value of the beasts increased, graziers and dealers in Aberdeen, Banff and Wick took increasing advantage of the new steamship transport now becoming available, judging the chance of quicker passage to the South worth the risk to the beasts at sea and the freight charges of £2 10s to £3 a head.[1] ' The introduction of bone manure and the short-horned breed of cattle and the contemporaneous opening of the English markets for fat cattle by steamer,' wrote the minister of the Parish of Logie Buchan in 1840, ' have been productive of the greatest benefit to the agricultural interest,' a view which finds expression in page after page of the New Statistical Account of the parishes of north-east Scotland.

An account of the early development of cattle shipping from Aberdeen written by one who remembered it, makes it clear that the risks to the shippers and to the beasts were by no means small :

' Sometimes they made quick passage,' he writes, ' but this was uncertain and I have known them a month at sea. I have seen the same cargo of cattle driven back to Aberdeen two or three times. . . . Although the loss by deterioration in condition must have been great, it was astonishing how few deaths occurred in the sailing ships ; the proportion was greater in the steamers. A year seldom passes without the shippers having heavy losses. I was owner of a part of the cattle when every beast aboard the *Duke of Wellington* except three were either thrown overboard or smothered in the hold. . . . I have made enquiries of a cattleman as to the scene in the hold of a ship in a storm among the cattle. He says " I went once down to the hold among them but I was glad to get back with my life, and although you had given me the ship and all aboard her, I would not have gone back ".' [2]

In the cattle-breeding districts of the south-west the new sea transport was making similar inroads on the drovers' trade. By 1835 cattle were being transported regularly by steamship from Kirkcudbright to Liverpool, and others from Dumfries and Annan, while the running of steamers from Ireland to Liverpool

---

[1] McCombie, op. cit., 102   [2] McCombie, op. cit., 104

and Glasgow had so cut into the Irish cattle trade to Portpatrick that the traffic to the Wigtownshire coast, which in 1812 had reached the figure of 20,000 per annum, had fallen by 1837 to only 1,080. The writer of the New Statistical Account for the parish of Kirkpatrick-Irongray in Wigtownshire reported in 1842 that 'many of the farmers are beginning to adopt a different system, viz. to fatten their cattle at home and then send them south by steam to the market. This system, if fully acted upon, will put an end to droving which has proved of late years ruinous to all concerned.'

In the Hebrides the effect of the new methods of transport made itself felt more slowly, and until well on in the second half of last century the old sailing smacks remained in use for bringing cattle from the Outer Islands to the mainland. Shortly after the turn of the century, however, the newly formed shipping companies to the Islands began to introduce special facilities for loading cattle on to their steamers, and by about 1880 transport of cattle by steamer to the rail heads at Strome Ferry and Oban had almost entirely superseded the old methods.

The development of railways in Scotland was not at first unfavourable to the droving trade. The first railways to be built were largely for the transport of coal and iron. For many years the lines constructed were purely local with no kind of through connection, and not until 1848 did the Scottish Central Railway open a line giving access from the south of Scotland to Perth, the same year in which the North Eastern Railway Company completed a line to Aberdeen.[1] For some years after this the effect of the railways on the droving traffic as reflected in the numbers of beasts sold at Falkirk Tryst was negligible. Falkirk was now more accessible to buyers coming from the South, but the animal traffic by road from the Highlands suffered little reduction. As late as 1860 the local press commenting on the progress of Falkirk Tryst reported : ' It had been expected that after the introduction of railways the trysts would decline owing to facilities for buyers to go further north to buy, but this has not been the case. On the contrary, Falkirk tryst has continued to be the rallying point as being central.'[2] Shortly after this date, however, a rapid change set in. Buyers from the South started to go to the Highlands to buy direct from the graziers, and with the growing

---

[1] Hamilton, *The Industrial Revolution in Scotland,* 250
[2] *Stirling Journal,* 9 October 1860

practice of sending beasts south by rail from the Highlands and the grazing areas of the north-east, the railways came in the last quarter of the nineteenth century to constitute a major factor in the decline of the droving trade. In December 1888 the North British Railway carried 1,016 fat cattle from Aberdeen to London for the Christmas market, and in the same month of the following year the Caledonian Railway carried 1,048. During the year 1889 the Highland Railway transported 250,000 sheep to the South.[1]

Despite the growing use made of sea transport from 1820 onwards, Falkirk Tryst remained until past the middle of the century the centre of a great trade, and reports of the numbers of beasts sold there year by year as appearing in the local press of the time are a fair index of the fortunes of the industry. Here are recorded the total numbers of beasts at the trysts, the districts from which they came, and the prices realised with many a colourful description of the scenes on the tryst ground. By the closing years of the Napoleonic wars the numbers of stock sold each autumn at Falkirk had risen to about 50,000 cattle and nearly as many sheep, while the demand from the South had raised prices to such an extent that the total value of the stock sold in 1812 was estimated at nearly half a million pounds.[2] The end of the war though it ruined many an individual drover did not halt the upward trend in the total numbers of beasts sold, and contemporary reports show that at the two Falkirk Markets in September and October 1827 a total of 130,000 cattle and close on 200,000 sheep changed hands.[3] The extent of the cattle trade to England about this time may be gauged by the fact that in 1825 as much as £80,000 to £90,000 in Scots notes are believed to have been put into circulation at Carlisle each week during the main droving season.[4] The Aberdeenshire cattle breeder, William McCombie, writing of his experiences during the first half of the nineteenth century, has recorded having seen 1,500 cattle belonging to one breeder passing through Carlisle in a single drove bound for Norfolk,[5] and in 1844 the local press reported that at a recent Falkirk Tryst one bank alone had honoured bills to the extent of £150,000.[6]

[1] Acworth, *The Railways of Scotland*, 141 and 142
[2] Graham, *General View of the Agriculture of Stirlingshire*, 1812, 334
[3] *Stirling Journal*, 13 September and 11 October 1827
[4] Hamilton, op. cit.   [5] McCombie, op. cit., 71
[6] *Stirling Journal*, 27 September 1844

Though there were few indications that the Tryst was nearing its end, shortly after the turn of the century references to cattle salesmen, the forerunners of the auctioneers, began to appear.[1] At first the salesmen did their business at the trysts, but later they conducted their own sales in Edinburgh and Glasgow, and with the spread of railways to the North regular auctioneering businesses established themselves at Perth, Oban and Inverness. The sales at Falkirk in 1870 were said to be the smallest then on record, and five years later only 2,000 sheep appeared at the September Market.[2] The reason given was that buyers had gone north and were adopting the practice of buying year after year the stock of particular grazings over which they had obtained a right of pre-emption. As late as 1880, 15,000 cattle and 20,000 sheep were at the October Tryst,[3] but this seems to have been the last flicker of a dying flame. In the late eighties a few thousand cattle were still being driven each autumn from Oban and the West Highlands, but year by year the numbers dwindled, and before the century ended Falkirk Tryst had virtually passed from active life into the annals of Scottish Agriculture.

The closing years of the nineteenth century saw the last of the cattle and sheep droves passing over Wade's old road by the Corrieyairack Pass,[4] and about 1906 the last of the Skye droves crossed Kyle Rhea to the Glenelg shore where they were exposed for sale on the market stance near the ferry on the south side. Later they passed by Glenshiel into Glen Garry, taking for the last time Telford's route by Glen Ci-aig to Loch Arkaig and the crossing of the Spean.

The threads of living recollection which still link us with the droving days are slender, and each year sees the breaking one by one of the few that remain. There are still (1952) men living who have seen the cattle boats sailing into Loch Dunvegan with the Uist droves, or the ferry boats from Lagg bringing the Islay cattle across the Sound of Jura. Others tell how they helped in their youth to bring droves from Kintyre and Knapdale by Inveraray and Loch Lomond to Falkirk, or from Don-side across

---

[1] The risk of cattle disease or 'murrain' appears to have been an additional factor in the decline of the cattle trade, particularly to England. The local press for 1850 and 1865 reports that the September and October markets at Falkirk were largely spoiled by outbreaks of the disease. (*Stirling Journal*, 11 October 1850 and 9 October 1865)

[2] *Stirling Journal*, 17 September 1875

[3] *Stirling Journal*, 15 October 1880

[4] J. B. Salmond, *Wade in Scotland*, 250

the Dee to the Angus glens on the road to Perth. Their part in the last of the droving days is recalled with pride in an old and honourable trade ; with regret too for the passing of the peace of mind and the contemplative outlook of those less hurried days.

The brown sails of the cattle boats have gone from the Minch. On slipways and jetties from Skye to Kintyre thrift grows undisturbed in the crannies of stones once smooth and polished with the tread of hooves. The hills round Loch Ainort look down on lonely saltings where the Uist droves once grazed, while throughout the Highlands, in hill pass, moorland and upland valley, as in the minds of men, the passing years increasingly dim and obscure the mark and the memory of the men and the beasts that once travelled the drove roads of Scotland.

THE END

APPENDICES

APPENDIX A

(page 57)

THE SALTING OF BEEF IN SCOTLAND

SOME export of salted beef from Scotland, particularly to Flanders, appears to have existed in the sixteenth century while at the beginning of the eighteenth century Caithness, Orkney and Shetland were carrying on a similar trade with Leith ; but the quality of home produced Scots beef was not in general suitable for salting. William Mackintosh of Borlum, the great advocate of the enclosing of agricultural land, writing in 1729 forecast the improvement in the quality of stock which would result from enclosing. ' Our over-seas trading Merchants,' he wrote, ' who have occasion to send their ships far voyages will find in their own Mercats beef that will bear salt which our own half-fed beef heretofore would not do, and the ships were forced to call at some town in England or Ireland to have beef or pork to make a Mediterranean or American voyage or endanger the lives of their crew with the thin, lean, hard beef their own Mercats could afford.' (Mackintosh, *Essay on Enclosing*, 1729.)

A further reason for the lack of a successful salting industry in Scotland was the absence of suitable salt in Scotland for the purpose. The salt-pans on the Forth produced considerable quantities, and salt is mentioned by Fynes Moryson in 1598 as one of the exports of Scotland ; but though some was exported, the *import* of salt was being encouraged as early as 1535. The reason appears to have been that the home produced salt was not suitable for curing, and there are frequent references to the ill-effect of trying to cure with salt obtained from salt water. The development of the Scottish fishing industry made it necessary to import finer salt for curing and the recital to an Act of 1587 narrates that ' refynit salt utherwayes callit salt upone salt is verie necessar and proffittable for salting salmound, keilling, ling and utheris grite fisches, quhilk . . . now is accustumat to be maid and hes bene maid befoir within this realme.' This ' salt upone salt ' appears to have been obtained mainly from Spain or Brittany. Though the chief mention in contemporary records is of difficulty in salting fish, it seems probable that the difficulties in salting beef must have been at least as great (*A.P.S.* III, 494).

It appears that there are two chemical reasons why salt obtained from salt water is not suitable for curing. In the first place, the total saline matter in salt water—approximately 3·6 per cent—consists partly of magnesium sulphate and calcium sulphate. These give an unpleasant flavour which would be imparted to meat cured in this way. Further, these two chemicals produce in contact with the muscular tissues of the meat, hard and most unpalatable products, a result which would be particularly apparent in the case of lean meat

225

as Mackintosh of Borlum no doubt realised. For these reasons a high standard of purity in the salt used is required in the curing of meat today.

The establishment of a successful salting industry in Scotland up till the end of the eighteenth century was made still more difficult by the extremely complex Salt Laws regulating the use of imported salt. The writer of the *Statistical Account* for the Parish of Sorbie reported that, but for the Salt Laws, Scots cattle might be fattened, killed and salted at home for the use of the navy. (*O.S.A.*, Sorbie, I, 248.) Restrictions on the supply of salt appear to have had a further effect on the cattle trade. From the want of this article the farmers 'cannot even supply themselves in the proper season with butter and cheese and are therefore obliged very frequently to bring up more young cattle by means of the milk in summer than they can support in winter.' (Knox, *Tour through the Highlands*, cxlix.) These Salt Laws bore particularly hardly on the fishermen, and throughout the greater part of the eighteenth century bitter complaints of their adverse effects on the fishing industry came from Gigha, Lochalsh, Rum and many other parts of the west coast. 'With a view to secure this revenue' (from salt) wrote Knox, 'the fisheries have been laid under such restraints and subjected to such intricacies of the Custom-Houses that numbers abandoned the business and others were preparing to go to Ireland with their capitals, their vessels, and their experience where few or no impediments to fisheries exist.' (Knox, *op. cit.*, cxlvii.)

Attempts appear to have been made at various times to produce in Scotland a finer kind of salt more suitable for curing, and in 1696 the Scots Parliament had before it an Act in favour of Sir John Shaw of Greenock, John Haldan, Laird of Glenegies and others for making salt by a new process. The narrative of the Act, which was passed despite the opposition of the salt-masters, shows that Shaw and Haldan intended to set up a fishery and for that purpose 'project to make salt after a new fashion not formerly practiced within this Nation fit for curing of fishes without the help of any forraigne salt.' Their plans apparently included the purchase of land on the foreshore of the north side of the Forth 'betwixt the Toun Alloway and Crown Point below Culross . . .' (*A.P.S.*, X, 67 and 80.)

APPENDIX B

(*pages 78, 79, 80, 102, 194, 205*)

Report and Estimates by Thomas Telford relative to the Rannoch Road, included in the *Fifth report of the Commissioners for Highland Roads and Bridges—1811*

In improving the Highlands of Scotland, by means of Roads, Bridges, and Ferries, particular attention has been given :

1   To open communications between the hitherto remote and almost inaccessible Districts on the main land and Western Islands, and the more cultivated part of the Country, the principal Towns, Markets and Fairs :

2   To explore and establish general Lines of practicable communication, which as Drove Roads, might best accommodate those extensive tracts from whence Black Cattle and Sheep are sent to the markets in the southern parts of Scotland.

With a view to the immediate convenience of the Highland Proprietors, and all persons having occasion to travel in that country, the formation of those Roads which fall under the first description has naturally attracted the earliest attention.

Communications of the second description passing through the Estates of many different Proprietors, very remote from each other, though of material importance to the interest of every individual, are scarcely known to them as objects worthy of a combined effort. From this cause, the subject has hitherto undergone less investigation than it merits ; for it is of importance, even to the Public, that the most direct and commodious communications with the extensive Cattle-rearing Countries should be established.

It is well known that the produce of the whole of the Western parts of Scotland, northwest of the great Glen of The Caledonian Canal, and including the Isle of Skye, consists chiefly of Black Cattle and Sheep, and that they are sent to the markets in the south of Scotland held at Crieff, Callander, Falkirk, and Dumbarton, from whence they are driven into England. The Districts towards the Eastern side of Scotland being more arable than pasturage, do not furnish any great proportion of lean stock.

The chain of Lakes and Rivers which occupy the great Glen, and the unbroken mass of lofty mountains which extends along the Southern side of that valley between Inverness on the East and High-Bridge near Fort William on the West, have hitherto compelled the Drovers to take such directions as enable them to pass either by the Eastern or Western extremities of the great Glen, and of the ridge of mountains parallel to it.

APPENDIX B

The principal communication has hitherto been by the Western extremity, near Fort William, but previous to arriving at this point, the Highland drovers have hitherto passed through circuitous valleys, over rugged ridges of mountains, and dangerous and inconvenient ferries ; the delays, loss of Cattle, and general embarrassment thus arising from the want of convenient communication, are strongly felt by the Northern Sheep Farmers and the Cattle Dealers from the South who make purchases of them ; and although the personal inconvenience and toil are more immediately felt by these two classes of men, it is obvious that the pecuniary loss falls upon the Land Owners, and that the Public Markets are the less abundantly supplied.

Immediately to the South of Fort William the communication is difficult and circuitous ; for it is either by crossing steep ridges on the old Military Road by the top of Loch Leven and over the Devil's Staircase, or more to the Westward by crossing the Ferry of Ballachulish and proceeding up the rugged Pass of Glencoe to the King's House at the West side of the Moor of Rannoch.

From thence the communication continues, across the Black Mount to Tyndrum, and afterwards eastward down Glendochart toward Killin, at the head of Loch-Tay, three miles short of which it turns Southward to Callander and Crieff. Near Tyndrum, at Fillan, a Branch passes southward down the west side of Loch Lomond to Dumbarton.

The Northwest part of Scotland comprising the principal rearing Districts, Inverness is much too far eastward to answer for a general Drove Road, except for Sutherland and the eastern parts of Rossshire ; it is therefore to the Western extremity of the great Glen we must look for establishing a better communication between the rearing Countries in the Highlands and the Cattle Markets in the south.

It results from the general conformation of the Country, that the most important points upon this Line of Communications are High-Bridge near the Southwest end of Loch-Lochy, and Killin at the west end of Loch Tay. This is well known to all persons concerned in sending Sheep and Black Cattle in this direction to the Southward, and will appear evident from considering : 1. The nature and extent of the Communications from the N.W. Districts which may be concentrated at or near to High-Bridge ; 2. The comparative facility of proceeding from High-Bridge to Killin ; and 3. The nature of the Communications from thence to the Southern Cattle Markets.

---

1 Of the nature and extent of the Communications from the N.W. Districts which may be concentrated at High-Bridge : The great extent of the Isle of Skye will always render it an object well deserving attention. Although it appears probable that when the Loch Carron Road and the Ferries connected with it are completed, the intercourse between Skye and the East coast of Ross and Inverness will be carried on in that direction ; yet Kyle-Rhea, on account of the narrowness of

the Channel, will always remain the usual Ferry for the Black Cattle of Skye ; and this consideration, together with the importance of making a convenient outlet for the produce of the adjacent country of Glen-Elg, and accommodating at the same time the Districts of Loch-Alsh and Kintail, will necessarily require a good Road to be made from Kyle Rhea to the Southward.

This communication must either be through Glen-Elg by Loch Hourn-Head and part of the Glengarry Road, or by Glensheil and the Rhiebuie Road to a point on the Glengarry Road called Inch-Laggan ; the reason of uniting them at this point is, that from thence a direct and easy line may be carried Southward by the east end of Glen-Arkeg and the West end of Loch-Lochy to High-Bridge.

Glen-Elg consists chiefly of two valleys, the general direction of both running nearly between Kyle-Rhea and Loch Hourn-Head ; those valleys are included, excepting on the sea-side, by ridges of mountains, through which there is no Pass lower than that over Marn-Raatachan. At the south end of the two before-mentioned valleys there are Passes apparently of the same level as Raatachan, and about fourteen hundred feet perpendicular above the level of the sea. Of these two valleys which have been diligently explored, the Eastern one is most convenient for a Road, which would pass through the finest part of Glen-Elg with a uniform ascent for about twelve miles from Kyle-Rhea. Near the upper end of the valley the hills are steep, and much side-cutting would be required. From this summit to the head of Loch-Hourn, the country is rough and rocky and near to the Loch very precipitious. By preserving a uniform declivity from the summit to the termination at Loch-Hourn-Head, a distance of six miles, a commodious Road may be formed, but this would be accomplished at too great an expense as the rock-cutting, breast-works and parapets, would in many instances be an arduous task. The annexed Map shews, by single lines, in what direction these Glen-Elg Roads must pass, if ever attempted to be made. From Loch-Hourn-Head there is for about three miles a steep ascent on the Western part of the Glengarry Road ; afterwards that excellent Road may be considered as level.

But the most commodious line of Road from the Isle of Skye and Kyle-Rhea must pass through the northern part of Glen-Elg, and over Marn-Raatachan to Sheil-House (a distance of about twelve miles) by commencing the acclivity at a sufficient distance on each side of that pass, and this may be done at a comparatively moderate expense. From Sheil-House by the summit of Glen-Sheil to Rhiebuie the country is rugged, but not nearly so impracticable as the last six miles in Glen-Elg, towards Loch-Hourn-Head. From Rhiebuie to the Southward across Glen-Lyne to near Inch-Laggan (a distance of ten miles) a line sufficiently level may be formed.

By any Road through Glen-Elg to Loch-Hourn-Head, the Skye and Glen-Elg communications to the southward would be direct, but

Loch-Alsh and Kintail would be excluded from benefit, unless a Road was also made over Marn-Raatachan, and even then their journey would be circuitous ; but what is of still greater importance, the extensive tracts comprising the upper parts of Glenmorrison, Strath-Glass and of Loch-Carron, would remain without accommodation unless the Road between Rhiebuie and Inch-Laggan was made.

By Glen Sheil and Rhiebuie to Inch-Laggan, the summits to be passed over and the distance to be travelled even by the Skye and the Glen-Elg Cattle, would be more favourable than through Glen-Elg and by making a few miles of road between Sheil-House and Toteig-Ferry, the accommodation to all the other beforementioned Districts would be as perfect as the nature of the country admits.

The comparative distances are as follows :

BY LOCH-HOURN-HEAD

	Miles	Yards
From Kyle-Rhea to Loch-Hourn-Head	18	100
From Loch-Hourn-Head, by the Glengarry Road, to Inch-Laggan	17	1500
	35	1600

BY MARN-RAATACHAN AND RHIEBUIE

	Miles	Yards
From Kyle-Rhea to Sheil-House	11	840
From Sheil-House to Rhiebuie	11	1566
From Rhiebuie to Inch-Laggan	10	593
	33	1239
Difference in favour of the latter road	2	361

By these statements it is evident that for the general accommodation of the beforementioned extensive tracts of country, and still much farther along the Northwest coast, that a Road from Kyle-Rhea by Marn-Raatachan and Rhiebuie to Inch-Laggan in Glengarry, is unquestionably the most eligible.

To complete the communication on the north side of the great Glen, instead of passing from Inch-Laggan, ten miles along the Glengarry Road to Invergarry, and thence by the side of Loch-Oich and Loch-Lochy to High-Bridge (a further distance of about eighteen miles) making together twenty eight miles, a Road may be carried through a Pass of the Mountains immediately South from Inch-Laggan, which would cross the river Arkeg near its mouth, and passing by the Western end of Loch Lochy, would arrive at High-Bridge by a route about ten miles shorter than the former, and without crossing a single Ferry. The comparative distances are as follows :

	Miles
From Inch-Laggan to Invergarry	10
From Invergarry to High-Bridge	18
	28

	Miles	Yards	Miles	Yards
From Inch-Laggan to the foot of Loch Arkeg	10	950		
From the foot of Loch Arkeg to the Burn of Culross	4	—		
From the Burn of Culross to High-Bridge	3	224	17	1174
Difference in favour of the latter Road			10	586

This is nearly equal to a day's journey for a drove of Cattle or Sheep.

The Branch Road between Sheil House and Toteig Ferry mentioned in the preceding page as a useful auxiliary to the Main Road from Skye, has been estimated at £1,943. It is almost five miles in length, and is wholly in Rossshire.

The Expense of making a Road from Rhiebuie to the Upper Bridge of Morrison (to which the Glenmorrison Road, now under contract, extends) would be £3,210. Of this estimate £1,563 must be expended in Rossshire, and this has hitherto operated as an obstruction to the undertaking, the Road promising little benefit to that County.

In addition to the Districts which have here been already considered, the countries of Glen-Arkeg, Morer and Arassaig, will conveniently centre their communications at High-Bridge by means of the Loch-na-Gaul and Lochyside Roads and the Bridge which the Caledonian Canal Commissioners will construct upon the new River course intended at Mucomer, or otherwise by the Ferry of Lochy.

2 Of the Line from High Bridge to Killin.

Having stated the manner in which improved Drove Roads may be made to centre at High-Bridge, it is equally important to consider in what manner the communication can be rendered most perfect between that place and Killin, at the Western end of Loch Tay.

At present the Drovers travel Southward sometimes along the old Military Road from High-Bridge, by Fort William to the head of Loch-Leven, beyond which, from crossing sundry rugged and steep ridges, it is named the Devil's Staircase ; or in order to avoid this tedious and almost impassable piece of Road, pass from Fort Willlam down the side of Loch-eil and crossing Loch-Leven at Ballachulish Ferry, turn Eastward up Glencoe.

The Road up Glencoe, though preferable to the Devil's Staircase, is one of the most rugged in the Highlands ; the mountains on each side are extremely steep, and from the action of the frost and rain, sheets of rocky fragments are formed, which are successively precipitated to the bottom of the valley. In this direction it is impossible to avoid this dreadful Pass, because the country to the Southward is equally rugged, composed of similar materials and intersected by lakes which penetrate far inland.

From the junction of these two bad Roads at the top of Glencoe, Cattle pass on to The King's House, Eastward of which is an extensive open District, which in such a rugged country may be comparatively called a plain ; it is named the Moor of Rannoch. The Military Road passes by the Western extremity of this plain across the sloping skirt of a hill well known by the name of the Black Mount, at a height found by Mr. Nimmo to be six hundred feet above the level of the King's House, and thirteen or fourteen hundred above the level of the sea. From the Black Mount the Military Road goes to Tyndrum, and thence Eastward down Glen-Dochart, till it approaches Killin.

The objections to this Road are, its circuitous course, the danger and delay of the Ferry of Ballachulish, the difficult Pass of Glencoe and of the Black Mount, and subsequently the delay caused by passing Eastward from Tyndrum down Glen-Dochart to near Killin.

To remedy these very imperfect communications, a Line has been suggested to the Commissioners for Highland Roads and Bridges, and by their direction has been carefully examined and reported as not only practical but advisable. It commences near High-Bridge, and passes considerably to the East of Ben-Nevis by the side of Loch-Treag, and across the Moor of Rannoch direct to Killin. This line is not only very direct but from the following description it will appear to be particularly level and easy, considering the rugged character of the country.

From near High-Bridge, the Road would pass nearly on a level about seven miles along the Loch-Laggan Road to Tulloch, where it would cross the river Spean and ascend in an easy manner to the foot of Loch-Traig (sic), which is about seven hundred feet above the sea ; the Road should pass along the Eastern side of the Loch, from which, with few exceptions, the mountains rise with a regular slope, not much cut by torrents and protected by natural birch wood. The ascent to the summit, at the head of the lake, may be rendered one in fifty, this summit continues about eight miles nearly on the same level, and is about 1128 feet above the sea ; from hence the descent to the plain of the Moor of Rannoch is no more than a hundred feet.

Entering the Moor of Rannoch, the Line must pass near the East end of Loch-Lydoch and over a flat morassy tract, in nearly a straight direction, to the pass of Gual-Vearan, the head of which is the summit of this part of the country, from whence the water runs both to the

A

Eastward and Westward ; it is fourteen hundred feet above the level of the sea and is gained by an ascent of about one in a hundred. From thence to the head of Glen-Lyon the rate of descent may be about one in fifty, and a moderate rise carries the Line to the Pass called Larig-na-Loone, at the head of Glen-Lochy, down the north side of which the road may be carried along comparatively favourable ground and at a descent not exceeding one in thirty to Killin.

From High Bridge to Killin, along the present Road by Fort William, Ballachulish and Tyndrum, the distance is	68 miles
From High-Bridge to Killin, by the Rannoch Road	53
Difference in favour of the new line	15 miles

Thus it appears that the saving of distance in this District would be fifteen miles ; the ascents and descents much easier and no Ferry to be crossed. These advantages may be reckoned equal to two or perhaps three days journey for a drove of Cattle or Sheep.

3 From Killin to the Southern Cattle Markets.

From Killin, the communications after crossing by the Pass of Larig-Eilie and down Glen Ogle to the head of Loch-Earn, pass Eastward in a direct line by the north side of this Loch to Comrie and Crieff, or by a shorter route from Killin along the south side of Loch Tay for about six miles and by the new Road through Glen Lednaig to Comrie and from thence either Eastward to Crieff or Southward to Dunblain, Stirling and Falkirk. Southward from Loch-Earn-Head a Road passes down the east side of Loch-Lubnaig to Callander, Doune, Stirling and Falkirk, or from Callander to Dumbarton and Glasgow. From Killin, therefore, to the Southward, the communications are commodious and direct.

In addition to this direct communication between the northwest rearing Districts and the Southern Cattle Markets, this Road, by passing from High-Bridge through the interior of the country to Killin, affords many opportunities for collateral connexion ; part of Strathspey might be connected by means of the Loch-Laggan Road, and in another way by Loch Ericht. From the south side of the Moor of Rannoch a branch might conveniently unite with the present Military Road and pass by Tyndrum and Loch Lomond to Dumbarton and Glasgow, while another might be carried Eastward along Loch Rannoch and Loch Tummel to Dunkeld, Perth and Dundee.

Besides the Line from High-Bridge to Killin, which it has been considered most advisable to recommend, all the other Passes of the adjacent country have been examined ; but as they have been found more or less objectionable, it is unnecessary to incumber this Report with any account of them.

The advantages to be derived from thus lessening the distance, avoiding Ferries and acquiring regular and easy acclivities throughout this extensive Drove Road, are alone sufficient to demand the most serious attention of all the Landowners in the Northwest and interior parts of the Highlands of Scotland ; but besides this first and most important object, the proposed Line would also be the most direct and commodious communication for Travellers of all descriptions from the Southern parts of Scotland to the aforesaid extensive Districts.

The practicability of this important Line of Road having been ascertained, and its direction described as illustrated by the annexed Map, the following is an Estimate of the Expense at which the different portions of it may be completed :

ESTIMATES

of the expense of completing a Road from Kyle-Rhea in Invernessshire to Killin in Perthshire.

	Miles	Yards	£	s.	d.
From Kyle-Rhea to Shiel-House					
(Inverness £2056 8 0 ; Ross £2502 15 0)	11	840	4559	3	-
From Shiel-House to Rhiebuie					
(Ross £4802)	11	1566	4802	-	-
From Rhiebuie to Inch Laggan					
(Inverness £1102 10 ; Ross £2598 16 0)	10	593	3701	6	-
From Inch-Laggan to near Auchnacarrie					
(Inverness £5343 19 0)	10	950	5343	19	-
From near Auchnacarrie to High-Bridge					
(Of which remains to be done 2½ miles					
in Inverness £800)	7	224	800	-	-
From High-Bridge to Killin					
(Inverness £5760 ; Perth £9600)	53	—	15360	-	-
	104	653	£34566	8	-

A Moiety of the estimated Expense is £17283 4 -

The immediate advantage to be derived from this expenditure will result to the Breeders of Sheep and Black Cattle ; and has been estimated by Mr. Nimmo of Inverness on the supposition that 80,000 Sheep are annually driven in the direction of the proposed Road and that a saving of three or four days in Droving expenses, and the better condition of the animal at market, is equal at least to one shilling each, or £4000

And that a similar saving and augmentation of value will take place on 20,000 Black Cattle at eight shillings each to the amount to 8000

Estimated annual advantage Total £12000

(*Signed*) THOMAS TELFORD
May 1810.

APPENDIX C

CONTEMPORARY DESCRIPTIONS OF THE CATTLE OF THE HIGHLANDS

NUMEROUS descriptions of the cattle of the Scottish Highlands can be found in the writings of those who wrote of Scottish agriculture at the end of the eighteenth and in the early years of the nineteenth centuries, but the following description taken from James Macdonald's *General View of the Agriculture of the Hebrides*, 1811 (425 *et seq.*) is probably the most comprehensive :

A bull of the Kyloe breed should be of a middle size, capable of being fattened to fifty stone avoirdupois. His colour should be black (that being reckoned the hardiest and most durable species), or dark brown, or reddish brown, without any white or yellow spots. His head should be rather small, his muzzle fine, his eyes lively and prominent, his horns equable, not very thick, of a clear, green, and waxy tinge ; his neck should rise with a gentle curve from the shoulders, and should be small and fine where it joins the head ; his shoulders moderately broad at the top, joining full to his chine and chest backwards, and to the vane of his neck forwards. His bosom should be open, his breast broad, and projecting well before his legs ; his arms, or fore thighs, muscular, and tapering to his knee ; his legs straight, well covered with hair, and strong boned. His chine or chest should be so full as to leave no hollows behind his shoulders ; the plates strong, to keep his belly from sinking below the level of his breast. His back or loin should be broad, straight, and flat ; his ribs rising above one another in such a manner that the last rib should be rather the highest, leaving only a small space to the hips or hooks ; the whole forming a roundish, barrel-like carcase. His hips should be wide placed, rounded or globular, and a very little higher than the back. His quarters (from the hip to the rump) should be long and tapering gradually from the hips backwards, and the turls, or potbones, not in the least protuberant ; his rumps close to the tail ; his tail itself should be thick, bushy, well haired, long, and set on so high as to be in the same horizontal line with his back. His general appearance should combine agility, vivacity, and strength ; and his hair should be glossy, thick, and vigorous, indicating a sound constitution and perfect health.

For a bull of this description Mr Macneill of Collonsay lately refused 200 guineas ; and for one of an inferior sort he actually received L.170 Sterling. Mr Macdonald of Staffa bought one, nine years old, at 100 guineas.

It is unnecessary to enter in detail upon a description of a Kyloe, or West Highland, or Hebridian heifer, as the above, with some very obvious modifications, answers for animals of both sexes. Strangers, on visiting the Western Isles, cry out against the folly of the people in keeping cattle of a small breed ; when by changing it for the Irish, or the Lowland Scotch, they might greatly enlarge the carcases of their stock. But this is often a rash opinion. The great question in Hebridian grazing and rearing is, what breed will best answer the land and climate, and what size can be most easily and securely raised at the smallest expense ? Heavy cattle cannot seek their food in bogs and marshes, leap over ravines, rivers, and ditches, or scramble through rocks, and in the faces of cliffs and precipices, like the present breed, which is almost as active and nimble as a Chamois goat ; nor can the poor Hebridian tenant afford to breed any stock which is not proof against the inclemency of his rains and storms all the year round. It is infinitely safer for him, therefore, in the present imperfect state of his agriculture, and perhaps even at all times, and in all circumstances of his country to rear too small, than too large a breed of cattle ; and to improve his indigenous, hardy, excellent species, than to import from other districts such breeds as may be indeed profitable for their circumstances and climate, but, which would probably perish in the Hebrides, without more attention being paid to them than, in his situation, he can conveniently afford. A moderate size is accordingly preferred by all skilful graziers, i.e. bullocks or stots, which, fattened at the age of five, weigh 30–36 stone avoirdupois, and heifers which weigh, at the same age, 24–30 stone. This rule, no doubt, admits of considerable latitude of application ; and while the weight or size now specified answers extremely well for the common average of the best breeds used by gentlemen farmers in Islay, Mull, Coll, Tyree, and Skye, it may be deemed an under size on the lands occupied by the proprietors of Islay and Collonsay, and by some of their people, who have lately introduced green crops, and, by a skilful mode of managing their lands, can afford food and shelter for their cattle in abundance during the whole year. Those gentlemen may raise the native breed (still, however, preserving the same identical genus and species of cattle) to the weight, when fattened, of from 34 to 42 stone for their bullocks and heifers . . .

The following description of the cattle of Argyll is taken from John Smith's *General View of the Agriculture of the County of Argyll*, 1798 (235 et seq.) :

'The most profitable breed of cattle, and that which is found to be best suited for Argyllshire is the true West Highland breed. It was for some time considered as an improvement upon this breed to cross it with cattle brought from Sky. But from superior breeding, and greater attention in rearing, the native breed of Argyllshire is now of much greater size than that of Sky.

The form most wished for is, to get them short in the legs, round in the body, straight in the back, and long in the snout. They are of various colours, black, dun, branded and brown ; but the black is the most common, and the most run upon.

When in good condition, and from three to four years old, when they are commonly sold off, the carcase may weigh from 360 to 400 lb. avoirdupois. But such as are brought to better pasture as in England, may be brought to weigh 560 lb. or more. The price is generally according to the size and shape, but occasionally varies according to the demand.

They are not wrought, nor supposed to be well calculated for working, as they are too light for that purpose. . . .'

APPENDIX D

(*page 89*)

ROY'S SURVEY OF SCOTLAND, 1747–55

AFTER the Rebellion of 1745, those responsible for the patrolling of the Highlands found themselves greatly handicapped by the absence of a reliable survey of the country. In 1747 Colonel Watson, who was stationed at Fort Augustus, proposed to the Duke of Cumberland that a survey of the Highlands should be made, and through the Duke's influence sufficient additional men were added to the small staff of surveyors then available to make the work possible. Among those added to the survey staff was William Roy, who is believed to have been previously employed in the post office in Edinburgh. Roy's subsequent part in the work became so important that the survey which resulted is commonly known as General Roy's Survey, though, at the time of the work, he held only a very junior rank at a pay of 3s a day. The Survey, which was latterly extended to cover the Lowlands, appears to have been completed in 1754. It was never engraved and though a copy on a reduced scale of $2\frac{1}{2}$ miles to an inch was made, and apparently used, Roy's original survey itself remained practically unknown till the beginning of the nineteenth century. It may be that the outbreak of the Continental Wars in 1756 and the progressive settlement of the Highlands detracted from the interest in the work, besides removing some of those, including Colonel Watson, who were engaged on it.

In 1805 Arrowsmith undertook the construction of a map of Scotland which was published in June 1807. In the course of the work he obtained access to Roy's Survey which had hitherto remained practically unknown, in the King's Library where it had been deposited after Roy's death. In a Memoir, published in 1809, a copy of which is printed with the Reports of the Commissioners for Highland Roads and Bridges, Arrowsmith has described the discovery of the Survey and has given some detail about its construction, obtained from Sir David Dundas, who had himself been employed on part of the survey, and who was mainly responsible for making it available to Arrowsmith.

237

It appears from Arrowsmith's account that Colonel Watson had five junior surveyors under him, each of whom surveyed an allotted district, Roy being the principal organiser of the whole of the surveyors' work. Each of the surveyors was assisted by one N.C.O. and six men. One carried the theodolite, two measured with the chain, two marked the fore and back stations, and one acted as batman. The instruments used were plain theodolites of 7 in. diameter or $3\frac{1}{2}$ in. radius with common sights unfurnished with telescopes. The instruments were made by Cole of London, as were also the chains of 45–50 ft. As the party slept under canvas they were able to penetrate into the farthest parts of the Highlands. The summer months were spent in the field and the winter months at work on the survey in Edinburgh, the finished work being taken every year by Colonel Watson to London for inspection. The courses of all the rivers and streams were followed to their source and measured, while all the roads and the fresh and salt water lochs were surveyed. Each surveyor kept a field book and a sketch book in the latter of which he delineated the various stations and the face of the country which, says Arrowsmith, ' was then much less inclosed and woody than at present and favourably featured for a military sketch.'

The original survey is contained in 38 sheets on a scale of 1,000 yards to an inch. Though Roy himself described the survey as ' a magnificent military sketch rather than a very accurate map,' the work was evidently done with great care. Contours were, of course, not at that date in use, the hills being drawn in with skilful brush work which has the effect of making them stand out as if in relief. With its striking colouring the map, which is preserved in the map room of the British Museum, is a thing of considerable beauty.

Some doubt has been suggested as to the roads shown on Roy's map, and though these doubts do not appear to be supported by Sir David Dundas' account of the work, it may well be that many of the subsidiary routes marked as roads were, in fact, little more than tracks. However this may be, it would seem a fair assumption, in many cases supported by other evidence, that the routes shown by Roy indicate routes then in use by contemporary traffic, of which droving traffic formed at least a part.

Arrowsmith, *Memoir relative to the Construction of the Map of Scotland*, 1807

The Early Maps of Scotland, Royal Scottish Geographical Society and *Early Scottish Maps and Travel* (Moir), Royal Scottish Geographical Society

THE BRIDGE OF AWE

CURIOUSLY little information is available as to the date of the building of the old bridge of Awe, the three-arched stone bridge which stands a short way upstream from the modern bridge on the main road to Oban. In an article which appeared in Vol. X of the Proceedings of the New York State Historical Association written by the Secretary of the Association, the writer ascribes the building to Captain William Pitman, a friend of Major Duncan Campbell of Inverawe who was killed at Ticonderoga in 1758 and gives the date of the building of the bridge as 1756. In the Rev. John Smith's *General View of the Agriculture of the County of Argyll* published in 1798, however, the Author, after referring to the work of the late Captain Archibald Campbell of Glen Lyon in improving the roads of the County, adds the following passage :

' The same public-spirited gentleman was the means of throwing bridges over the two largest rivers in the county, Aw and Urchay, by obtaining liberal subscriptions from the Duke of Argyll, Lord Breadalbine, and other heritors. Both, under his management, were executed for £1,000, a sum which was long thought to be much less than was requisite for the first of them ; which shows that public money is capable of doing much more than is generally done with it. Indeed, these works would have been executed for still less money, if an unfortunate accident had not given the contractor a just claim for more than the sum agreed upon. The water of Aw, which discharges at one outlet all the collected streams of an extent of country near 50 miles in length and from 6 to 10 in breadth, is remarkably large and rapid, and subject to sudden rises. After the work was begun in a very dry season, it was carried on with all possible expedition, but just as the arches were locked, and before there was time for removing the timbers, a sudden flood swept timber and stone before it, and obliged the undertaker to recommence his labours. The second attempt succeeded ; and this useful bridge has since withstood every trial.'

APPENDIX F

(*page 141*)

FALKIRK TRYST IN 1849

'HAVING carried our readers to the Highlands we must, at the risk of being somewhat episodical, request that on their return south they will accompany us to Falkirk Moor on the second Monday or Tuesday in either September or October. They will there witness a scene to which certainly Great Britain, perhaps even the whole world, does not afford a parallel. We doubt whether we do not much under-rate the whole number of sheep collected at 100,000. Mr Paterson, Mr Sellers, Mr Kennedy and Mr Cameron of Corachoilie will each have several thousands on the ground. We have heard that this last patriarch has 50,000 head of cattle and sheep on his several farms. . . . No stranger accustomed to the bustle and the crowd, the handling and the haggling of an English fair, would suspect that transactions of a magnitude to which Barnet, St Faith's, and Wey Hill afford no parallel was on the eve of taking place. On a portion of the moor adjoining the sheep ground . . . a wooden pent-house about five feet square announces itself by exterior placard to be the ' Royal Bank of Scotland '; the British Linen Company, The Comercial Bank and every other banking company north of the Tweed appear there by similar wooden representatives. The purchasers come to the fair provided with Letters of Credit and stepping into the tabernacle to which they are accredited bring out in large notes the amount required. These are handed to the vendor in an adjoining booth and are probably in a very few minutes at his credit with the issuer or one of his rivals. . . . There are three trysts held every year—the first in August, the second in September and the last and largest in October. The cattle stand in a field in the parish of Larbert at a distance of nearly three miles from Falkirk, at a place called Stenhousemuir. The field on which they assemble contains above 200 acres, well-fenced and in every way adapted for the purpose. The scene, seen from horse-back, from a cart, or some erection, is particularly imposing. All is animation, bustle, business and activity ; servants running about shouting to the cattle, keeping them together in their particular lots and ever and anon cudgels are at work upon the horns and rumps of the restless animals that attempt to wander in search of grass or water.

The cattle dealers of all descriptions chiefly on horse-back, are scouring the field in search of the lots they require. The Scottish drovers are for the most part mounted on small, shaggy, spirited ponies that are obviously quite at home among the cattle ; and they carry their riders through the throngest groups with astonishing alacrity. The English dealers have, in general, large, stout horses, and they pace the ground with more caution, surveying every lot carefully as they go along. When they discover the cattle they want, they enquire the price. A good deal of riggling takes place, and when the parties come to an agreement, the purchaser claps a penny of arles into the hand of the stockholder, observing at the same time ' It's a bargain.' Tar dishes are then got, and the purchaser's mark being put upon the cattle, they are driven from the field. Besides numbers of shows, from 60 to 70 tents are erected along the field for selling spirits and provisions. The owners of these portable taverns pay 2s 6d for the ground they occupy on the first Tryst, and 4s 6d for each of the other two. . . . In one of these tents a few gentlemen attend from the Falkirk Bank to accommodate the dealers with the money they require. Many kindle fires at the end of their tents, over which cooking is briskly carried on. Broth is made in considerable quantities, and meets a ready sale. As most of the purchasers are paid in these tents, they are constantly filled and surrounded with a mixed multitude of cattle dealers, fishers, drovers, auctioneers, pedlars, jugglers, gamblers, itinerant fruit merchants, ballad singers and beggars. What an indescribable clamour prevails in most of these party-coloured abodes !

Far in the afternoon, when frequent calls have elevated the spirits and stimulated the colloquial powers of the visitors, a person hears the uncouth Cumberland jargon and the prevailing Gaelic, along with the innumerable provincial dialects, in their genuine purity, mingled in one astounding roar. All seem inclined to speak ; and raising their voices to command attention, the whole of the orators are obliged to bellow as loudly as they can possibly roar. When the cattle dealers are in the way of their business, their conversation is full of animation, and their technical phrases are generally appropriate and highly amusing.'

Gisborne, *Essays on Agriculture*, 1854, 15 et seq.

APPENDIX G

(*page 209*)

THE EFFECT OF TURNPIKES ON DROVING

THE serious view taken by the drovers of the establishment of tolls which they considered unwarranted encroachments on their ancient rights, may be judged from the proceedings of two meetings which took place in the year 1827. On 3rd September of that year a meeting of the Freeholders, Justices of the Peace and Commissioners of Supply of the County of Sutherland was held at Dornoch. This meeting ' having taken into consideration the present condition of the ancient drove-road leading from the most Northern parts of Scotland to the central Counties of England, and the great importance of preserving the same free from interruption,' came to the following resolutions :

1. That the servitude of driving Cattle and Sheep along the said drove road, has existed from beyond the memory of man, and still does exist without interruption, except in one or two instances of little importance.
2. That the Meeting, however, have seen with regret, that several attempts have been made of late years, to interrupt the right of passing this road, in different parts of Scotland, either by the imposition of heavy tolls, or by entirely shutting up the road itself, under the authority of local Acts of Parliament, which it is conceived it was not the intention of the Legislature should be applicable to this ancient and peculiar right of way, while the same remains free and uninterrupted throughout England.
3. That the preservation of this right of way is of the utmost importance to all the breeding district of the country.
4. That this Meeting therefore will use its best endeavours to preserve the said drove road, and those connected with it, from interruption during such a period of the year as shall be required for driving stock to market, whether the same shall be best effected by an application to Parliament or otherwise.

. . . . . .

(Copy Resolutions found among *Sutherland Estate Papers*)

On 11th September ' a numerous and respectable Meeting of the Breeders of Cattle and Sheep, in the Highlands and Lowlands of Scotland, and the Dealers and Feeders of Stock, who are in the practice of attending Falkirk Market ' was held at the Red Lion Inn, Falkirk, ' called in consequence of the great and increasing damage sustained by themselves personally, and by the public, by reason of the encroachments, which have, of late years, been made on the ancient droveways, leading from the different districts of Scotland, to the Falkirk Trysts, and from thence southward to the English Borders.' The following resolutions were unanimously adopted :

1st. That beyond all memory of man, the present Landholders and Farmers of Scotland, and their ancestors, have possessed a right of passage, for the stock bred in the pastoral district, to go to market, and to the feeder and consumer of such stock.

2nd. That this right of passage existed, for the most part, through sequestered parts of the country, where the stock had sufficient width of passage, and not meeting with the horses, carts, carriages, &c. which obstruct the common highways, the animals reached their destination in good health.

3rd. That, in the progress of improvement within the last forty years, almost every county in Scotland has obtained its private Act of Parliament, authorising parties interested in each particular district, to make turnpike roads suited to the convenience of that district, to confine all thoroughfares to these turnpikes, and to levy tolls for their maintenance.

4th. That in virtue of these powers, the ancient drove way was first begun to be encroached upon about twenty years ago, but, in so few instances, that for many years no serious injury was done ; and people submitted willingly to an inconvenience which they considered of little importance, compared to the public advantage derived from the turnpikes.

5th. That, of late years, however, measures have been used, in various places, along the ancient drove-way, to confine the cattle and sheep in their passage entirely to turnpike roads ; and the consequences which have already arisen from the exposure, during so long a journey, of animals, of their wild habits, to the concussion of horses, dogs, mail coaches, and carriages of all descriptions, are so serious, that, after impeding, by their numbers, the progress of all other travellers, who use the Turnpikes, they arrive at their destination in a diseased and foundered state, to the great injury of the owner, who is compelled to pay extravagantly for receiving damage and to the public who consume this diseased stock.

6th. That these effects have already followed from the partial measures which have been used in various places to prevent the stock from passing along its ancient drove-way, and confining them to Turnpikes. But if the measures of the Turnpike makers be completed, and the droves confined to Turnpikes during their whole passage, then, assuredly, it will be impossible for the breeders of cattle and sheep to bring them to market, worth to the purchaser the expense of their travelling, and the valuable supply of animal food now received by the consumer ; the profit derived by the farmer and feeder, and the rents paid to the landlord from the above species of stock, must, in a great measure, cease.

7th. That this Meeting feel satisfied that it is only necessary to point out to a British public the injustice and impolicy of the measures complained of, to induce a complete revisal of the various Turnpike Acts threatening so great an evil ; and an equitable arrangement calculated to enable the owners of cattle and sheep to bring them to market in a sound and healthy state ; they paying a fair remuneration, and no more, for whatever facilities shall be afforded them along their journey.

(Sutherland Estate Papers)

It is evident, however, that the troubles of the drovers from this source persisted, for in 1833 drovers from the North of Scotland, complaining of the effect of customs dues and tolls, particularly in Perthshire and Stirlingshire, on the traffic in cattle and sheep, urged the construction of a general drove road as recommended by Telford on which no tolls would be payable. Six years later a movement was on foot for the establishment of trysts at Spean Bridge in September and October. The reasons urged were the tolls on the roads, the heavy customs dues at the market, the exorbitant charges made by farmers for grazing in the neighbourhood of the existing Trysts and the damage caused to the stock by the long drive to Falkirk. It was then estimated that 50,000 sheep were driven from the Highlands and Western Isles for the September and October markets at Falkirk, 20,000 going by the western road through Lochaber and Rannoch and 30,000 by the eastern road through Badenoch and East Perthshire.

(Inverness Courier, 17th April 1833 and 17th July 1839)

BIBLIOGRAPHY

* *Of the sources listed in the Bibliography those which have proved most valuable are marked with an asterisk*

MANUSCRIPT SOURCES

RECORD OFFICE, H.M. REGISTER HOUSE, EDINBURGH

Bell, Thomas. *Manuscript letters (contained in Reid's Calendar of papers found at Dumfries).*

* *Breadalbane Papers.*
Papers in connection with Process of Division of Commonty
(a) of Sheriffmuir, (*Durie Decreets*, 2 Dec. 1772, and *Register of Decreets*, Vol. 586).
(b) of Falkirk (*Durie Decreets*, 19 Dec. 1807, and *Register of Decreets*, Vol. 835).
(c) of Gretna (*Mackenzie Decreets*, 9 Aug. 1700, and *Register of Decreets*, Vol. 612).
(d) of Reddingsrigg and Whitesiderigg (*Mackenzie Decreets*, 11 Mar. 1773, and *Register of Decreets*, Vol. 638).
Forfeited Estates Papers. Perth. Portfolio 21G., 21 Jan. 1771.
Records of Custom Dues collected at Kelso in 1683.
Sinclair of Mey (Caithness). *Manuscript letters.*

NATIONAL LIBRARY OF SCOTLAND, EDINBURGH

Balfour, Sir James of Denmylne. *The Chief Passages from the River Tay to the River Dee through the Mountains.* (Spalding Club Collection.) MS 33.2.27.

PUBLIC RECORD OFFICE, LONDON

Victualling Board Records (Admiralty).
Victualling Board Records (War Office).

BRITISH MUSEUM

Young, Arthur. *The Elements and Practice of Agriculture.* 44 Vols. (B.M. 34821 to 34864).

ROYAL BANK OF SCOTLAND

Minute Books.

BRITISH LINEN BANK

Minute Books.

CLERK OF THE PEACE, STIRLING

Justices of the Peace for the County of Stirling. *Minute Book of Quarter Sessions*, 6 Dec. 1819–

DUNROBIN CASTLE

Sutherland Estate Papers.

245

BONSER, KENNETH J., LEEDS

MS (unpublished) on *Scottish Drovers and Drove Routes in Yorkshire in the Mid-eighteenth Century.*

STEWART, JOHN, FALKIRK

MS (unpublished) *Falkirk Tryst.*

OFFICIAL PUBLICATIONS

Acts of the Lords of Council in Civil Causes, 1496–1501, Vol. 2, 1918.
* *Acts of the Parliament of Scotland* (Record Edition). 12 Vols., 1814–75
Border Papers 1560–1603. 2 Vols., 1894–6.
Exchequer Rolls of Scotland, 1264–1600. 23 Vols., 1878–1908.
Historical MSS Commission. *Mar & Kellie Papers,* 1904.
* Marwick, Sir J. D. *List of Fairs and Markets held in Scotland,* 1890.
Napier, Crofters' Commission. *Report on the Highlands.* 5 Vols., 1884.
Nautical Survey. New edition, 4 Dec. 1912. (Lochalsh and Kyle Rhea.)
* *Register of the Privy Council of Scotland,* 1st, 2nd and 3rd Series, 1545–1689. 1877–1933.
Report of Select Committee on Cultivation, etc. of Waste Lands, 1795.
Report of Select Committee on Finance (Vol. 13 of House of Commons Committees), June 1798.
* *Report of Select Committee on Promissory Notes in Scotland and Ireland,* 1826.
Report of Commissioners on Public Roads in Scotland, 1859.
* *Reports of Commissioners for Highland Roads and Bridges.* 3 Vols., 1803–60.
Report of Committee on Hill Sheep Farming in Scotland, 1943.
Report by George Brown on most important lines of Highland Roads, 1803, in 1st Report of Commissioners for Highland Roads and Bridges, Appendix C, pp. 23–9 *supra.*
Rotulae Scotiae. 2 Vols. (Record Commission), 1814–19.
Rymer, *Foedera.* (Record Commission), 1816–69.
State Papers. Domestic. Charles II, 1663–64.
Statutes of the Realm.
Survey and Reports of the Coasts and Central Highlands of Scotland in Autumn of 1802. Thomas Telford, 1803. (See Vol. I of *Reports of Commissioners for Highland Roads and Bridges, supra.*)

BOOKS

Acworth, William M. *Railways of Scotland,* 1890.
Aikin, Arthur. *Journal of a Tour through North Wales in 1787,* 1797.
* Alexander, William. *Notes and Sketches of Northern Rural Life in the 18th Century,* 1877.
Anderson, George and Peter. *Guide to the Highlands,* 1834, 1842 etc.
Anderson, James. *Account of the present state of the Hebrides, 1745,* 1785.
Anderson, John. *State of Society and Knowledge in the Highlands . . . at the period of the Rebellion, 1745,* 1827.
Arrowsmith, Aaron. *Memoir relative to Map of Scotland published . . . in year 1807.* Bound with 3rd Report of Commissioners for Highland Roads and Bridges.

BIBLIOGRAPHY

Bannatyne Club. 56. *Liber Sancte Marie de Melros*, 1837. 89. *Chartulary of Newbattle Abbey*, 1849. 100. *Black Book of Taymouth*, 1855.

Barron, James. *The Northern Highlands in the 19th Century*. 3 Vols., 1903–7.

Belsches, Robert. *General View of the Agriculture of the County of Stirling*, 1796.

Boswell, James. *Journal of a Tour to the Hebrides with Samuel Johnson.* Edited by F. A. Pottle, 1936 (Isham edn.).

Brand, John. *Brief Description of Orkney and Shetland*, 1701 (reprint 1883).

Brewer, E. Cobham. *The Historic Note-book*, 1891.

Brigg, John Jeremy. *The King's Highway in Craven : being notes on the history of the Yorkshire portion of the Keighley and Kendal turnpike Road*, 1927.

Brown, Peter Hume. *Early Travellers in Scotland*, 1891. *Scotland before 1700 from contemporary Documents*, 1893. *History of Scotland*. 3 Vols., 1899–1904. *Scotland in the time of Queen Mary*, 1904. *Legislative Union of Scotland and England*, 1914.

Buchanan, Rev. John Lane. *Travels in the Western Hebrides from 1782 to 1790*, 1793.

* Burt, Edward. *Letters from a Gentleman in the North of Scotland*, 5th ed., by R. Jamieson. 2 Vols., 1822.

Cadell, Henry Moubray. *Story of the Forth*, 1913.

Campbell, Alexander. *A Journey from Edinburgh through parts of North Britain.* 2 Vols., 1st ed., 1802.

Campbell, John. *Full description of the Highlands of Scotland*, 1752.

Chalmers, G. *Caledonia.* 8 Vols., 1887–1902.

Chambers, Robert. *Domestic annals of Scotland.* 3 Vols., 1858–1861.

Chambers, William. *History of Peeblesshire.* 3 Vols., 1864.

Cincinnatus Caledonius (John Gordon Barbour). *Lights and Shadows of Scottish Character and Scenery*, 2nd Series, 1825.

* Corrie, J. M. *The Droving Days in the southwest district of Scotland*, 1915.

Croal, George. *Living Memories of an Octogenarian*, 1894.

Culley, George. *Observations on Live Stock*, 1807.

Davidson, John, and Gray, Alexander. *The Scottish Staple at Veere*, 1909.

Defoe, Daniel. *A Tour thro' the whole Island of Great Britain in 1724 . . .,* 6th ed. 4 Vols., 1762.

De Quincey, Thomas. *Autobiographical sketches*, Vol. 14 of *Works* (edition of 1863).

Dixon, John H. *Gairloch in North-west Ross-shire ; its Records, Traditions, Inhabitants and Natural History*, 1886.

Don, William Gerard. *Archaeological Notes on Early Scotland relating more particularly to the Stracathro District of Strathmore in Angus* (Brechin 1896).

Donaldson, James. *General View of the Agriculture of Elgin or Moray*, 1794; *General View of the Agriculture of Kincardine or the Mearns*, 1795.

Donaldson, John E. *Caithness in the 18th Century*, 1938.

Donaldson, M. E. M. *Further Wanderings in Argyll*, 1926.

Fletcher, Joseph Smith. *The Making of Modern Yorkshire (1750–1914)*, 1918.

Forbes, Rev. Robert, Bishop. *Journal* (Rev. J. B. Craven's edition), 1886.

Forfeited Estates Papers, 1715–45. Scottish History Society, 1st Series, Vol. 57, 1909.

* Fraser, George Milne. *The Old Deeside Road*, 1921.

Fraser-Mackintosh, Charles. *Letters of two Centuries from 1616 to 1815.*

Gartmore MS. *An Inquiry into the Causes . . . of Rebellion . . . in the Highlands of Scotland*, 1747; printed as appendix in Jamieson's 5th edition of Burt's *Letters from a Gentleman in the North of Scotland*, Vol. 2, at p. 159, 1822.

Gilbey, Sir Walter. *Farm Stock 100 years ago*, 1910.

Gillespie, R. *Round about Falkirk*, 1879.

Gilpin, Rev. William. *Observations on several parts of the Counties of Cambridgeshire, Norfolk, etc.*, 1809.

Gisborne, Thomas. *Essays on Agriculture*, 2nd ed., 1854.

Graham, Henry Gray. *Social Life in Scotland in the 18th Century*, 1901.

Graham, Rev. Patrick. *General View of the Agriculture of Stirlingshire*, 1812.

Graham, R. B. Cunninghame. *A Hatchment*, 1913.

Grant, Mrs Anne, of Laggan. *Letters from the Mountains, 1773–1807*, 6th ed., 2 Vols., 1845.

Grant, Mrs Elizabeth, of Rothiemurchus. *Memoirs of a Highland Lady*, 1807, 1898.

Grant, I. F. *Economic History of Scotland*, 1934; *Social and Economic Development of Scotland before 1603*, 1930.

Hall, Rev. James. *Travels in Scotland*, 1807.

* Hamilton, Henry. *The Industrial Revolution in Scotland*, 1932.

Hardie, R. P. *The Roads of Medieval Lauderdale*, 1942.

Henderson, John. *General View of the Agriculture of Sutherland*, 1812.

Heron, Robert. *Journey through the Western Counties of Scotland in Autumn of 1792.* 2 Vols., 1799.

Highlands of Scotland in 1750. Edited by A. Lang, 1898.

Hodgson, John C. *History of Northumberland*, 1820–58.

Hogg, James. *A Tour in the Highlands in 1803*, 1888.

Hughes, P. Gwyn. *Wales and the Drovers*, 1943.

Hurtley, Thomas. *A concise account of some Natural Curiosities in the environs of Malham in Craven, Yorkshire*, 1834 (1st ed. 1786).

Innes, Cosmo. *Sketches of Early Scottish History*, 1861.

Institute of Historical Research. *Bulletin*, Vol. 3.

Iona Club, Vol. 1. Transactions of 1835 (*Collectania de Rebus Albanicis*). Edited by Donald Gregory and W. F. Skene, 1839.

Islay, The Book of. Edited by G. Gregory Smith, 1895.

Islay, The Stent Book of, 1718–1843. Edited by Mrs Lucy Ramsay of Kildalton, 1890.

Johnson, Samuel. *Journey to the Western Islands*, 1775.

Johnson, Walter. *Byways in British Archaeology*, 1912.

* Johnston, Rev. Bryce. *General View of the Agriculture of the County of Dumfries*, 1794.

Johnstoun, Alexander, of Kirkland. *Description of the Parish of Morvenside in Stirlingshire*, 1723 in Macfarlane's Geog. Collections, Vol. 1, p. 317 (Scot. Hist. Soc., 1st Series, 51, 1906).

* Keith, George Skene. *General View of the Agriculture of Aberdeenshire*, 1811.

Keith, Theodora. *Commercial Relations between England and Scotland 1603–1707*, 1910.

Keltie, J. S. *The Scottish Highlands.* 2 Vols., 1883.

Knox, John. *Tour through the Highlands of Scotland and the Hebride Isles in 1786*, 1787.

Larkin. *A Tour in the Highlands in 1818*, 1819.

Leslie, Rev. Wm. *General View of the Agriculture of Nairn and Moray*, 1811.

Lloyd, J. *Historical Memoranda of Breconshire*, 1903–4.

248

BIBLIOGRAPHY

Logan, James. *The Scottish Gael.* 2 Vols., 1831.
* McCombie, William. *Cattle and Cattle Breeders,* 1867.
Macculloch, John. *Highlands and Western Isles.* . . . 4 Vols., 1824.
McCulloch, John Ramsay. *Dictionary* . . . *of Commerce,* 1856.
MacDonald, Rev. Angus and Archibald. *The Clan Donald,* 1896–1904.
* MacDonald, James. *General View of the Agriculture of the Hebrides,* 1811.
McDowall, William. *History of the Burgh of Dumfries,* 1867.
MacFarlane's Geographical Collections. 3 Vols. Scot. Hist. Soc., 1st Series, 51–3, 1906–8.
MacGill, W. *Old Ross-shire and Scotland.* 2 Vols., 1909–11.
McIan, R. R., and Logan, James. *Highlanders at Home,* 1848.
MacIver, Evander. *Reminiscences.* Edited by Rev. George Henderson, 1905.
MacKenzie, Alexander. *History of the Munros,* 1898.
Mackenzie, Rev. William, and J. Nicholson. *History of Galloway.* 2 Vols., 1841 (published anon).
Mackenzie, W. *Old Skye Tales,* 1934.
Mackenzie, W. Mackay. *The Scottish Burghs,* 1949.
Macky, J. *Journey through Scotland,* 1723.
MacLeod, Rev. Norman. *Reminiscences of a Highland Parish,* 1871.
Macpherson, David. *Annals of Commerce.* 4 Vols., London 1805.
Marshall, Rev. Wm. *Historic Scenes in Perthshire,* 1880.
Marshall, Wm. *General View of the Agriculture of the Central Highlands,* 1794; *Rural economy of Norfolk,* 2nd ed., 2 Vols., 1795.
Martens, Georg Friedrich Von. *Recueil de Traités,* 1st Series, 2nd ed., tome 2.
Martin, Martin. *Description of the Western Isles of Scotland, circa* 1695, 1703, 1st ed. Edited by D. J. Macleod, 1934.
Mathieson, W. Law. *The Awakening of Scotland, 1747–97,* 1910.
Maxwell, Sir Herbert. *Memories of the Months,* 5th Series, 1909.
Millar, A. H. *History of Rob Roy,* 1883.
* Mitchell, Sir Arthur. *List of travels and tours in Scotland, 1296–1900* (Suppl.), 1902.
* Mitchell, Sir Arthur, and Cash, C. G. *Topography of Scotland.* 2 Vols., 1917 (Scot. Hist. Soc., 2nd Series, 14 and 15).
* Mitchell, Joseph. *Reminiscences of my life in the Highlands.* 2 Vols., 1883, 1884.
Munro, Neil. *History of the Royal Bank of Scotland, 1727–1927,* 1928.
Murray, David. *The York Buildings Company,* 1883.
Naismith, John. *Observations on the different breeds of sheep and the state of Sheep Farming in the Southern Counties of Scotland,* 1795.
New Spalding Club. *Historical Papers, 1699–1750.* 2 Vols., 1895, 1896.
* *New Statistical Account of Scotland.* 15 Vols., 1845.
Newte, Thomas. *Tour of England and Scotland in 1785,* 1791.
Nimmo, Wm. *History of Stirlingshire,* 1st ed., 1777.
Pease, Howard. *The Lord-Wardens of the Marches,* 1913.
Peebles. *Charters and Documents relating to Peebles, 1165–1710,* 1872. Scottish Burgh Records Society.
Pennant, Thomas. *A Tour in Scotland, 1769* ; and *A Tour in Scotland and Voyage to the Hebrides, 1772.* 3 Vols., 1790.
Pococke, Richard. *Tours in Scotland, 1747, 1750, 1760,* Scot. Hist. Soc., 1st Series, Vol. 1, 1887.

249

Porteous, Alexander. *History of Crieff*, 1912.

Postlethwayt, Malachy. *Britain's Commercial Interest Explained and Improved.* 2 Vols., 1757.

Ramsay, John. *Scotland and Scotsmen in the 18th Century.* Edited by Alexander Allardyce, 1888. 2 Vols.

Retail Meat Trade, Vol. 1, Gresham Publishing Co., 1929.

Ridpath, George. *The Border-History of England and Scotland*, 1776.

Robertson, Sir C. Grant. *England under the Hanoverians*, 1911 and 1939.

Robertson, George. *Rural recollections*, 1829.

* Robertson, James. *General View of the Agriculture of Inverness*, 1813.

Robson, James. *General View of the Agriculture of Argyll and West Inverness-shire*, 1794.

Roger, Rev. James. *General View of the Agriculture of Angus*, 1794.

Rogers, Rev. Chas. *Social Life in Scotland from early to recent times.* 3 Vols., 1884–6.

Royal Scottish Geographical Society. *The Early Maps of Scotland*, 1936.

Salmond, J. B. *Wade in Scotland*, 1938.

Savary Des Bruslons, Jacques. *Universal Dictionary of Trade and Commerce.* Translated by Malachy Postlethwayt. 2 Vols., 1751–5.

Scotland Described. . . . 3rd ed., Edinburgh 1806.

Scott, Sir Walter. *The Highland Clans with a particular account of Rob Roy and the Macgregors*, 1856 ; *The Two Drovers*.

* Sinclair, Sir John. *Statistical Account of Scotland.* 21 Vols., 1791–9 ; *Analysis of Statistical Account.* 2 parts, 1825, 1826 ; *General View of the Agriculture of the Northern Counties, including counties of Cromarty, Ross, Sutherland and Caithness, and islands of Orkney and Shetland*, 1795.

Singer, Rev. William. *Agricultural Survey of Dumfries*, 1812.

Smiles, Samuel. *Life of George Moore*, 1878 ; *Life of Telford*, 1867.

Smith, Adam. *Wealth of Nations*, 1887.

Smith, Alexander. *A Summer in Skye*, 1866.

Smith, James. *The Exact Dealer's Companion*, Edinburgh, 1727.

Smith, Rev. John. *General View of the Agriculture of the County of Argyll*, 1798

Smith, Samuel. *General View of the Agriculture of Galloway*, 1813.

Somerville, Rev. Thomas. *My own Life and Times, 1741–1814.* 1861.

Souter, David. *General View of the Agriculture of Banff*, 1812.

Spalding Club. *Collections for a history of the Shires of Aberdeen and Banff*, 1843.

Steuart, John. *Letter Book, 1715–52* (Scot. Hist. Soc., 2nd Series, Vol. 9, 1915).

Stevenson, Robert Louis. *St. Ives.*

Taylor, John (The Water-Poet). *Works*, 1630.

Third Spalding Club. *The Book of Glenbuchat*, 1942.

Thornton, Col. T. *Sporting Tour through Northern parts of England and . . . Highlands of Scotland*, 1804.

Topham, Edward. *Letters from Edinburgh*, 1776.

Tough, Douglas L. W. *The last years of a Frontier*, 1928.

Trevelyan, G. M. *English Social History*, 1944.

Tytler, Patrick Fraser. *History of Scotland*, 2nd ed., 1841–50.

Ure, Rev. David. *General View of the Agriculture of Dumbarton*, 1794.

BIBLIOGRAPHY

* Walker, Rev. John. *Economical History of the Hebrides and Highlands.* 2 Vols., 1808.
* Webster, James. *General View of the Agriculture of Galloway,* 1794.
Wight, Andrew. *Husbandry.* 6 Vols. 1778.
Wilson, James. *Annals of Hawick, 1214–1814,* 1850.
Wordsworth, Dorothy. *Journals, 1798–1828.* Edited by W. Knight, 1924.
* Youatt, W. *Cattle, their breeds, management and diseases,* 1834. (Library of Useful Knowledge.)

ARTICLES, PAMPHLETS, ETC.

Adam, M. I. *The Causes of the Highland Emigrations of 1783–1803.* Scot. Hist. Rev., Vol. 17, pp. 73–89, 1920; *The Highland Emigration of 1770.* Scot. Hist. Rev., Vol. 16, pp. 280–93, 1919.
Campbell, Duncan. *Highland Shielings in the Olden Times.* Transactions of Inverness Scientific Society, Vol. 5, pp. 62–90, 1896–9.
Celtic Magazine. Vol. VIII, p. 586.
Curle, James. *The Leg from a Roman Bronze Statue found at Milsington.* The History of the Berwickshire Naturalists' Club, xxix, p. 195.
Dumfries and Galloway Courier. *Notes and Queries,* 1913.
Farmers' Magazine, The, Edinburgh, 1804.
Fraser, G. M. *Highways and Bridges in Aberdeenshire in 1739.* Third Spalding Club Miscellany, Vol. 1, pp. 233–4, 1935; *An Old Drove Road over the Culblean.* Article in Aberdeen Free Press, 7th June 1921.
* Fussell and Goodman. *18th Century Traffic in Live Stock.* Economic History (Supplement to Economic Journal), Vol. 3, No. 11.
Highland Society *Transactions,* 1803, Vol. 2, pp. 169 and 204; 1816, Vol. 4, pp. 1–65 ; Vol. II, New Series, pp. 4–16.
Highland and Agricultural Society *Transactions,* Vol. 8, 4th Series, p. 147, 1876.
Inglis. *The Roads which led to Edinburgh.* Proceedings of Society of Antiquaries of Scotland, Vol. 50 (Vol. 2, 4th Series), pp. 18–49, 1915–16.
Jenkins, R. T. *A Drover's Account Book.* Caernarvonshire Hist. Soc. Trans., 1945.
Johnman, Rev. W. A. P. *Highways and Byeways.* Transactions of Hawick Archaeological Society, 1917.
Lloyd, J. *The Black Cattle Droves.* Historical Memoranda of Breconshire 1903.
MacAdam, Ivison. *Notes on the Ancient Iron Industry of Scotland.* Proceedings of Society of Antiquaries of Scotland, Vol. 9, New Series, pp. 89–131, 1886–7.
McGrouther, T. *The Cattle Trade with England.* Falkirk Arch. and Nat. Hist. Soc. Proceedings, Vol. 3, p. 45, 1938–9.
McIntire. *The Fords of the Solway.* Trans. Cumberland and Westmorland Ant. and Arch. Soc., Vol. 39, New Series, pp. 152–70, 1939,
MacIntosh, Wm. of Borlum. *Essay on Enclosing,* 1729. *A short scheme . . . by means of the Military Road made by General Wade . . . to stop depredation and theft so destructive to the Northern Counties of Scotland.* Edinburgh, 1742.
Mackenzie, Sir Kenneth S. *General Wade and his Roads.* Inverness Scientific

Society Transactions, Vol. 5, pp. 145–77 ; *Military Roads in the Highlands.* Inverness Scientific Society Transactions, Vol. 5, pp. 364–84.

McKerral, Andrew. *The Tacksman and his Holding in the south-west Highlands.* Scot. Hist. Rev., Vol. XXVI, pp. 10–25, 1947.

* Miller, Rev. Thos. *Origin of the Falkirk Trysts.* Proceedings of Falkirk Arch. and Nat. Hist. Soc., 1936.

Moir, D. G. *Early Scottish Maps.* Royal Scot. Geog. Soc.

Murray, Sir Patrick. *Memorial respecting the Road from Yetts of Muckhart through Glendevon and Gleneagles into Strathearn,* 1814. (In Patent Office Library, London.)

Reid, R. C. *Some Letters of Thomas Bell, Drover, 1746,* in Trans. Dumfriesshire and Galloway Nat. Hist. and Ant. Soc., Vol. XXII, 3rd Series,

Robertson, Rev. Archibald Aeneas. *Old Tracks, Cross-country Routes and ' Coffin Roads ' in the North West Highlands,* 1943.

Ross, Alexander. *Old Highland Roads.* Proceedings of Gaelic Society of Inverness, Vol. 14, pp. 172–93, 1887–8.

Simpson, W. Douglas. *Early Castles of Mar.* Proceedings of Society of Antiquaries of Scotland, Vol. 63 (Vol. 3, 6th Series), pp. 102–38, 1928–9.

* Skeel, Caroline. *The Cattle Trade between England and Wales from the 15th to the 19th centuries.* Royal Hist. Soc. Trans., Vol. 9, 4th Series, 1926.

Souvenir of the Highland Show, Dumfries, 1910.

* *Stirling Journal and Advertiser* (files in Stirling Public Library).

Thompson, William. *Cattle Droving between Scotland and England.* British Archaeological Assoc, Vol. 87, New Series, pp. 172–83, 1932.

LEGAL REPORTS, ETC.

Campbell v. *Campbell,* 1777. 5 Brown's Supplement to Morison's Dictionary of Decisions, p. 599.

* *McGregor* v. *Lord Breadalbane,* 1846. Court of Session Cases (9 Dunlop's Reports), p. 210.

McKenzie v. *Bankes,* 1868. Court of Session Cases (6 MacPherson's Reports), p. 936.

* Signet Library *Collection of Old Session Papers.*

Scottish Rights of Way Society v *Macpherson,* 1887. Court of Session Cases (14 Rettie's Reports), p. 875.

Torrie v. *Duke of Athol,* 1848. Court of Session Cases (12 Dunlop's Reports), p. 328.

Winans and Chisholm v. *Lord Tweedmouth,* 1888. Court of Session Cases (15 Rettie's Reports), p. 540.

MAPS

Armstrong, Mostyn J. *Map of Peeblesshire,* 1773.

Edgar, Wm. *Map of the River Forth,* 1745.

Elphinstone, John. *Map of North Britain,* 1745.

* Roy, William, General. *Survey of Scotland, 1747–55.* MS (British Museum).

Taylor, George, and Skinner, Andrew. *Survey of the Roads of Scotland,* 1839.

BIBLIOGRAPHY

Thomson, William.　*Atlas of Scotland*, 1832.
　　　　　　　　　Map of Selkirkshire, 1824.
　　　　　　　　　Map of Peeblesshire, 1821.
Ordnance Survey of Scotland, 6 in. to 1 mile.　1st edition 1863.

The Maps printed with the Reports of the Commissioners for Highland Roads and Bridges and in the Volumes of the New Statistical Account of Scotland have also been used.

INDEX

Aberdeen 39, 219 ; cattle shipped from 218 ; cattle sent by rail from 220 ; woollen industry in 188

Aberdeenshire, drove roads from 115–32 ; price of cattle in 59 ; turnips in 215 ; value of cattle from 206, 207 ; woollen trade 117, 120, 199

Aberfeldy 112 ; ferry 8–9

Aberfoyle 100

Abernethy (Inverness-shire) 29

Aboyne 126, 127 ; Castle 116

Accounts (drovers') not accurately kept 62

Achall, Glen 108n

Achallader, farm of 213n

Achnacarry 80

Achnasheen 107, 108

Add, River 97, 98

Age of cattle sold 59–60

Agriculture, crop cultivation 57 ; improvements in 6, 171, 190, 191, 192, 214, 215, 216, 218 ; infield and outfield 118 ; revolution in 3, 197 ; rotation of crops 215. *See also* Farming

Aikey Fair 29, 123, 146, 165 ; number of cattle at 206

Ainort, Loch 74

Aird of Lovat 109

Alford 216

Alloa 114

Allt-na-lairige 99

Alness 106

Altguish 108

Altnafeadh, a cattle stance 38n, 211 ; 80, 81

Alyth (Ellit, Elych, Elycht) 70, 116, 134

American War benefits droving 58

Amiens, Peace of, affects Scottish drovers 184

Amulree 81, 102, 112

An Sgarsoch, early cattle market at 128

Anderson, James, quoted 197–8

Anderson's *Guide to Scotland* 214

Angus 206 ; drove roads from 115–32 ; glens raided 8, 110, 202

Annan 31, 218 ; Annan to Gretna, drove road from 161, 166

Annandale, drove road through 158, 177 ; farmers introduce new breed of sheep into 192–3

Appin 87, 88

Applecross, number of cattle in 108

Arable farming 118 ; displaced by stock raising 206

Arbroath Abbey 188

Ardentinny 98

Ardeonaig 82

Ardgay 108n

Ardgour 87

Ardlui 99

Ardnamurchan 71, 87

Ardross 110

Argyll, cattle trade 14, 84 ; drove roads 84–103

Argyll, Earl of, and thieving of cattle 85 ; sheep increase in 193

Arisaig 33n, 71

Arkaig, Loch 80, 221

Armadale 75

Arms carried by drovers 25

Armstrong's map of Peeblesshire 153, 154

Army purchases of beef 177

Arnan, Glen 99

Arroch, Glen 75

Assynt 51, 105

Atholl 25 ; cattle trade 102

Auchendinny Bridge 14

Auchendrain 90

Auchterarder, drove road near 1

Auchterneed 108

Auctioneers, absence of 141 ; established 221

Augh-Chalada 81

Aultbea 108, 213

Aultnamain Inn 106

Avich, Loch 90

Aviemore 110

Awe, bridge of 88n, 89, 239

Awe, Loch 88, 89, 90, 94

Ayala 187

Ayton 18

Badenoch 25, 30, 102, 110

Badnogoach cattle stance 126

Bakewell, English cattle breeder 60 ; improves livestock 171

Bala 35n

Balfour, Sir James, of Denmylne 117, 118, 123, 129

Ballachulish 87

Ballater 126, 127

Balloch 100

Balquhidder 82, 83 ; stance at 38n, 211

Banchory Bridge 123

Band and Statutes of Icolmkill 41

Bane, Alexander, of Tulloch 70

Banff 218

Bank notes 49

Bank of Scotland, ceases payment 46, 70

Banking, early 47, 48, 49, 182–3 ; disaster in 49 ; Scottish banks at Crieff and Falkirk Trysts 137, 142

Bankrupt, drovers not allowed to become 62n

254

18

PRINTED IN GREAT BRITAIN AT
THE PRESS OF THE PUBLISHERS